THEORY OF
SIMPLE STRUCTURES

THEORY OF SIMPLE STRUCTURES

BY

THOMAS CLARK SHEDD, C.E.

Member of American Society of Civil Engineers;
Professor of Structural Engineering,
University of Illinois

AND

JAMISON VAWTER, C.E.

Member of American Society of Civil Engineers;
Professor of Civil Engineering,
University of Illinois

SECOND EDITION

NEW YORK

JOHN WILEY & SONS, INC.

LONDON: CHAPMAN & HALL, LIMITED

SECOND EDITION
Twelfth Printing, January, 1953

PRINTED IN U. S. A.

PREFACE TO SECOND EDITION

The rapid development in structural design during the present century has continued at an accelerated pace in the nearly ten years since the publication of the first edition of this book. The professional equipment of the civil engineer now must include a thorough working mastery not only of the laws of statics but also of the basic principles underlying the analysis of statically indeterminate structures.

To meet this need for their own students the authors have added two chapters to this book: Chapter X dealing with statically indeterminate structures composed of members acting primarily in flexure, and Chapter XI which extends the discussion to include statically indeterminate forms of trussed structures.

Advantage has been taken of the new edition necessitated by the additional chapters to make some minor changes, but in general the first nine chapters remain in substantially their original form and become Part One of the second edition.

In presenting Part Two the authors have followed their own teaching practice in centering the discussion on the changes in shape of the loaded structure, and the calculation of the magnitude of those changes by the geometry of small angle changes along the axes of the members. They regard the geometric approach to the analysis of statically indeterminate structures as fundamental, and have preferred to emphasize that procedure rather than to give a sketchy outline of numerous "methods" of analysis that are in reality only elaborations of the basic principles.

In the discussion of principles and in the illustrative examples formularization has been avoided as far as possible, as the authors heartily concur in the statement by Percival Lowell that: "Formulae are the anaesthetics of thought, not its stimulants. . . ." *
With that in mind no particular attempt has been made to attain complete uniformity in nomenclature.

* From the preface to "Mars and Its Canals," by Percival Lowell, p. ix.

At first the illustrative examples have been given in detail and the calculations carefully explained; later, as the background has become more fully developed, the illustrative calculations have been given in more condensed form and explanations gradually eliminated.

The authors wish to acknowledge that many years of close association with Professor Hardy Cross have greatly influenced their point of view. While they are glad to acknowledge that influence they must absolve Professor Cross of responsibility for any inadequacies that may be found in this book.

T. C. S.
J. V.

Urbana, Illinois
January, 1941

PREFACE TO FIRST EDITION

It is very important for the student beginning the study of the theory of structures to gain a clear and accurate understanding of the underlying principles of the subject. The tendency to try to memorize types of structures and procedures applicable to them, so evident in many students, influenced the authors to present this simple but thorough discussion of the application of the fundamental laws of statics in structural analysis.

An understanding of the principles underlying the analysis of indeterminate structures is unquestionably essential to the modern structural engineer, but the most important of these principles are the laws of statics, and the authors are emphatic in their belief that the study of indeterminate structures should follow a *thorough* course in determinate structures. As this text-book is intended for the student beginning the study of structural analysis, it therefore seemed best to devote it exclusively to a discussion of the essential fundamentals of the theory of simple structures.

Throughout the presentation of the material in this book the authors have endeavored, by constant and insistent emphasis on the laws of statics, to develop in the student's mind an appreciation of the importance of these fundamental principles, to show that the subject is in fact very simple, that there is no necessity for remembering standard classifications or cases or different methods for different structures, but that this single set of principles is directly applicable to every problem.

The text includes all the material essential for a thorough course in the analysis of simple structures and somewhat more than can be fully covered in the time usually devoted to the subject. In its preparation particular attention was given to a clear and careful presentation of reactions, shears, and moments, which the authors regard as the foundation stones of the subject. Influence lines are first discussed at the beginning of the study of moving loads and are freely used thereafter. It is believed that influence lines for simple structures are generally more useful qualitatively than quantitatively, but their use in calculation has been fully discussed, illustrated, and recommended when such use offers advantages. In all cases the authors have insisted on the construction of influence lines by the application of fundamental principles, and have not introduced any of the graphical or semi-graphical methods frequently presented, as they believe that these have a tendency to leave the student with the memory of a method of construction and only a vague notion of the principles involved. The discussion of moving concentrated loads is thorough, but special attention has been given to simplicity in presentation. In Chapter VII the authors have endeavored by constantly emphasizing the underlying principles of statics to impress on the student that graphic statics is not in any sense a separate method or science but merely a means of calculation which is sometimes more convenient than arithmetical methods in the solution of problems in statics.

It is important for the student to solve many problems in order to fix in his mind the principles discussed and to illustrate their application. For this purpose the authors have included an unusually large number of problems taken from among those they have prepared and used in their own teaching. These problems are grouped at the ends of the chapters in which the principles involved are discussed. Many of them do not represent common structures, but it has been found that a generous sprinkling of unusual exercises helps in keeping the student's mind focused on fundamental principles and in offsetting the tendency to memorize types and cases.

The order of presentation is that which the authors have found effective. Realizing, however, that the preparation of students varies, and that some teachers may prefer a different order, they have so arranged the book that Chapters V and VI may precede Chapter IV, and that Chapter VII, Graphic Statics, may be used as a separate course preceding or following the other material, or given concurrently, as some consider preferable.

In the preparation of the book the authors have had in mind technical school students, primarily. They believe, however, that the method of presentation should also make it especially adapted to the needs of men studying alone.

The authors wish particularly to acknowledge their indebtedness to Professor Hardy Cross, who has carefully read a major portion of the manuscript and made valuable suggestions. Acknowledgment is also made to Professor H. A. Rice for suggesting a convenient form of moment table, Tables III and IV being similar to one he has used in his classes for many years. Credit for photographs and some tabular matter has been given at appropriate points in the text.

T. C. S.
J. V.

Urbana, Illinois
June, 1931

CONTENTS

PART ONE—THEORY OF SIMPLE STRUCTURES

CHAPTER I

CHAPTER II

CHAPTER III

CHAPTER IV

CHAPTER V

CHAPTER VI

CHAPTER VII

CHAPTER VIII

CHAPTER IX

PART TWO—INTRODUCTION TO STATICALLY INDETERMINATE STRUCTURES

CHAPTER X

CHAPTER XI

PART ONE

THEORY OF SIMPLE STRUCTURES

CHAPTER I

INTRODUCTION

1. Relation of Analysis to Design.—The design of a structure or other engineering work consists, broadly speaking, of two stages. The first stage is the functional design, that is, the planning of the structure to perform in as efficient, reliable, enduring, and economical a manner as possible the service which it is intended to render. The second stage includes the arrangement of the various members or parts to meet properly the needs of the functional plan, and also the choice of material for, and proper proportioning of, each of these parts so that it will safely and economically fill its place in the completed project. In carrying out the second stage of the work the engineer is continually confronted with the necessity for calculating the **reactions, shears, bending moments,** and **stresses** produced in the structure by the loads which must be supported or resisted. The calculation of these reactions, shears, moments, and stresses is a necessary and important step in the design, but it is not its *object*, and the successful designer must have so thorough an understanding of the fundamental principles of structural analysis and such facility in their application that he makes these essential computations as a matter of course, leaving his mind free to focus on those aspects of his design in which technical skill, the application of the results of experience and engineering judgment, are all-important.

2. Importance of Fundamental Principles.—It is the purpose of this text to give a brief but thorough discussion of the fundamental principles of structural analysis necessary in the design of simple structures. Simple structures are those in which reactions, shears, moments, and stresses may be determined, or estimated with sufficient accuracy, by application of the **laws of statics.**

The rapid development in structural design in the last ten or fifteen years has made it practically imperative that the engineer specializing in the design of modern structures have training in the methods of analysis available for structures in which the application of the laws of statics is not sufficient. But the laws of statics are the structural engineer's fundamental tools and no others are so important. A working mastery of them will enable a satisfactory and economical solution of a majority of the problems in structural design, and without it an understanding and intelligent use of more advanced methods of analysis is impossible. It should be the purpose of every student of the theory of simple structures to gain such a thorough grounding in these fundamental principles that their correct use is a matter of second nature to him, so that his future study of advanced methods will rest on a secure foundation and be uninterrupted by the necessity for correcting weaknesses in fundamental training.

3. Fundamental Preparation.—In the preparation of this book the authors have had in mind technical-school students who have satisfactorily completed two years of college work, comprising the usual training in mathematics, physics, engineering drawing, and elementary mechanics. It should be possible, however, for a mature student who has not had these advantages, but who has a good understanding of arithmetic, the elements of algebra, the elements of mechanics, and especially the principles of plane geometry, to use the book successfully in private study. In their own teaching of the subject the authors expect students to have had, or to be pursuing concurrently, a fundamental course in the mechanics of materials.

It is presumed that in his study of elementary mechanics the student has learned the meaning of:

Force and its units of measure.
Equilibrium and the meaning of its fundamental laws.
Parallelogram of Forces, its meaning and use in the composition and resolution of forces.
Moment of Forces and Couples.

4. Equilibrium.—Too much emphasis cannot be placed on the importance of the student's having firmly fixed in his mind the statement and meaning of the fundamental laws of equilibrium, i.e.

$$\Sigma H = 0$$
$$\Sigma V = 0$$
$$\Sigma M = 0$$

It should be clearly understood that these laws are not susceptible to mathematical proof. They are based on the results of observation and were first advanced by Sir Isaac Newton in his statement of the laws of motion. They are merely a mathematical expression of Newton's law, which states that if a body is at rest (or in uniform motion) for every action upon it there is an equal and opposite reaction. In words, these expressions say that

$\Sigma H = 0$: The algebraic sum of all the horizontal forces acting on a body which is in equilibrium *must* equal zero.

$\Sigma V = 0$: The algebraic sum of all the vertical forces acting on a body which is in equilibrium *must* equal zero.

$\Sigma M = 0$: The algebraic sum of the moments of all the forces acting on a body which is in equilibrium, about any point in the plane of those forces, *must* equal zero.

The application of these laws is sufficient for a solution of every problem discussed in Part One (after making simplifying assumptions in some cases), and they must be satisfied for *every* structure in equilibrium whether or not they are sufficient for an analysis of its stresses.

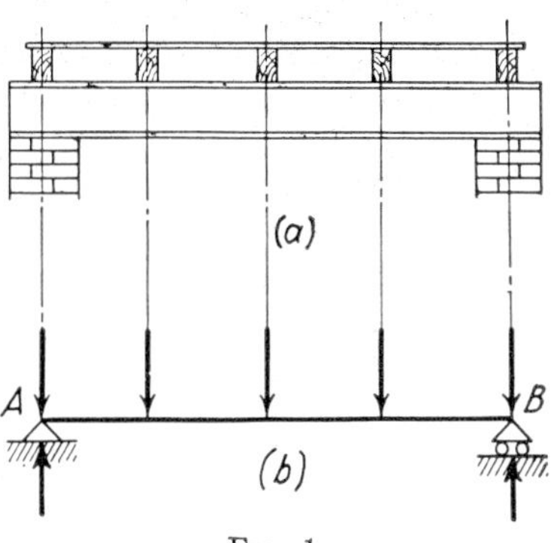

Fig. 1.

5. Practical and Ideal Structures.—In the analysis of structures it is usual to deal with an ideal structure, which may perhaps be roughly defined as a practical structure reduced to its center lines or simplest terms. For example, Fig. 1(*a*) represents a "practical" structure, i.e., an ordinary I beam resting on brick walls; (*b*) in the same figure represents the corresponding "ideal" structure. The practical structure has depth and width, rests on supports of considerable area, and supports timber beams of appreciable width which deliver loads to the I beam, these loads being distributed in some manner over the width of the timber beam. The ideal structure is represented as a line, is supposed to be supported at two points, A and B, located at the centers of the walls on which the practical beam rests, and supports loads which are in turn represented as applied at points which, as indicated by the arrows, are assumed at the centers of the timber beams.

There are similar differences between the practical and ideal forms of other types of structures. As another example, Fig. 2 shows the ideal form, used in analysis, of the practical truss of

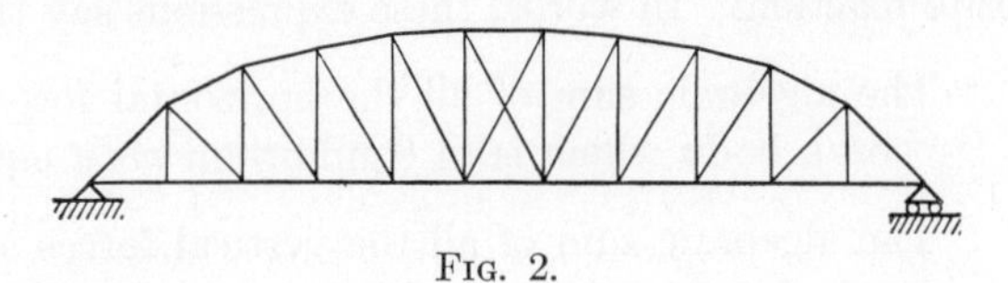

Fig. 2.

which a detail view is shown in Fig. 3. Here the ideal truss is composed of members represented as lines, assumed to be connected at their intersections by frictionless pins. The practical truss, on the other hand, consists of members of considerable width connected at their intersections by means of gusset plates of fairly large size. Sometimes the differences between the ideal and the practical forms introduce discrepancies into an analysis based on

Courtesy of Bruce Gilbert Johnston

Fig. 3.

the ideal form which are too large to be ignored, and more accurate studies are necessary. Such investigations are entirely beyond the scope of this text and will not be further discussed.

It is impracticable here to enter into an extended description of the differences between the line diagrams and the practical forms of the various structures which will be studied, but the student should be constantly on the alert to relate the ideal structure he is analyzing to its practical form which may be observed in or near most communities.

6. Symbols and Conventions.—In making sketches of the ideal structures which will be studied it will be convenient to make use of certain symbols and conventions in indicating the manner of support and construction of the framework under consideration. Those which will be most commonly employed are shown in Fig. 4. In this figure (*a*), (*b*), and (*c*) represent supports for beams or columns (the end of the beam or column is indicated by the line connecting at *A*) in which vertical or horizontal movement at the point of support, *A*, is prevented, but in which the beam or column is free to turn on the point of support *A*; (*d*), (*e*), (*f*), and (*g*) represent supports in which movement normal to the surface on

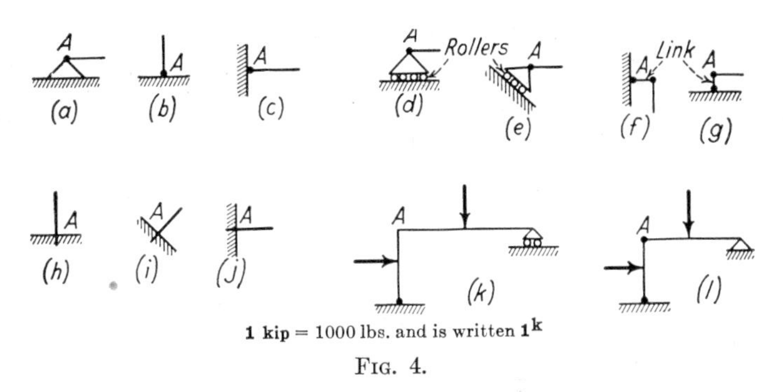

1 kip = 1000 lbs. and is written $\mathbf{1^k}$

FIG. 4.

which the rollers or links are supported is prevented, but in which rotation on the point of support and movement parallel to the surface of support are unimpeded; (*h*), (*i*), and (*j*) represent supports at which movement or rotation in any direction is absolutely prevented; (*k*) represents a structure composed of two members meeting at the corner *A* and so rigidly constructed that the angle between the members meeting at *A* cannot change regardless of the manner or magnitude of loading; (*l*) represents a structure which is similar to that shown in (*k*) but in which the construction is such that, although the members cannot separate, there is no resistance whatever to change in the angle between the members meeting at *A*. Although a dot has been used in Fig. 4 to represent a hinge a circle is sometimes used and both are used in what follows.

LOADS

7. Kinds of Loads.—The loads which a structure has to support may be divided into two general classes:

(1) **Dead Loads.**
(2) **Live Loads.**

8. Dead Loads.—Dead loads are loads which are always fixed in position, always acting, and of unchanging magnitude. The weight of the material of which a structure is composed, and the weight of permanent equipment such as gas or water pipes, or electric cables, etc., are loads of this character. Dead load always acts vertically.

9. Live Loads.—In the design of structures it is seldom that the engineer has to deal only with fixed or dead loads. In addition there are generally loads which are more or less temporary and which vary in magnitude, such as:

The goods stored on a warehouse floor.
The furniture, fixtures, and occupants of an office.
Snow on the roof of a building or deck of a bridge.
Cranes on the crane runways of a building.
Coal in the bunkers of a coaling station or power house.
Wind on any structure.
Trains or other vehicles on a bridge, etc.

Such loads are called "live loads." Live loads should be further divided into two classes:

(1) Live loads which *move*, such as trains, trucks, cranes, etc.
(2) Live loads which are *movable*, such as goods on a warehouse floor, furniture in an office, books in a library, etc.

Live loads of the first class often produce an effect greater than would be produced by loads of the same magnitude which were fixed in position. This additional effect is generally called **impact** and may be of considerable importance in the design of structures which must sustain moving loads.

10. Choice of Design Loads.—Sometimes the loads which a structure will be called upon to support or resist are very definite and easily determined, but more often the selection of the loads which should be used in the design is a matter requiring broad experience and an intimate knowledge of past development and present tendencies in the type of loads expected. For example, the engineer responsible for writing the load specification for the design of a railway bridge must have a thorough knowledge of the changes which have taken place in the rolling stock of his particular road over a long period of time, must be familiar with the current equipment and the policy of the road in regard to weight of trains regularly handled, and must in some way make an estimate or forecast of what developments are likely to take place during the probable life of the proposed structure. Hundreds of bridges have been replaced and hundreds of others are on current replacement programs because a forecast of future development in loads was not, or could not be, successfully made at the time of their construction. The authors have in mind a railroad which, because of radical changes in its rolling stock, found it necessary to carry out an extensive program of reinforcement for a series of bridges in less than ten years from the time they were originally built.

It is not possible or pertinent here to enter into a discussion of what loads should be used in design. Loads which are now in common use, however, will be briefly described and illustrated.

11. Weights of Structures.—The weight of a structure depends of course upon its size and the material from which it is built. For some kinds of structures there are quite reliable records of weights of many as actually built, and from these data the engineer may make an accurate estimate in advance of design. Data regarding many other kinds of structures are almost wholly lacking, and in such cases reliance must be placed on experience, and on preliminary estimates, which may require revision after a design has been prepared.

Useful data regarding the weights of steel bridges of all kinds may be found in "Bridge Engineering," by Dr. J. A. L. Waddell,[1] and in "Design of Steel Bridges," by F. C. Kunz.[2] Many texts on design give formulas for bridge weights. In general, such formulas are reliable, if at all, only for a given specification and live load, and these are often not stated. Nevertheless they may be helpful to the inexperienced engineer if used with discretion

[1] John Wiley & Sons.

[2] McGraw-Hill Book Co.

but the results should always be checked with estimates following design.

Buildings are so varied in type and character of construction, as well as in the loads to be expected, that few reliable records of their weights are available. Often the weight of the frame of a building is not a very important factor in comparison with the other loads supported, and it usually is comparatively easy to make a reasonable estimate of its magnitude. Formulas for roof truss weights are numerous, but are generally even less reliable than formulas for bridge weights, and most experienced designers prefer to make their own estimates.

In making estimates of weight from completed designs the data concerning regularly available structural forms given in manufacturers' handbooks and catalogs are essential. Useful information on the weights of various substances will be found in practically all engineer's handbooks. The weight of the material in a structure is a very definite quantity, and although it may be difficult to estimate reliably in advance of design, it is possible eventually to calculate it to any necessary degree of accuracy.

12. Movable and Moving Loads in General.—Generally speaking, the movable or moving loads to which a structure may be subjected are far less definite than the dead loads. The live load selected for use in design should simulate as accurately as possible, in effect, the actual loads which may be reasonably expected to come regularly upon the structure, and should be such that the resulting design will be safe, economical, and enduring under these conditions. It is necessary also that the structure be secure against failure under the action of the greatest load or combination of loads to which there is any reasonable possibility of its being subjected, but of course it is not necessary to make the design as though such an extraordinary load or combination of loads were to be of regular occurrence. Loads do not have the same effect on all parts of a structure and it may be wasteful to design an entire bridge or building for those loads which are necessary to secure safety and endurance in some one or two members. For example, an office floor may be subjected to very heavy loads over a relatively small area, such as would be caused by files and safes, and the floor framing must be so designed that the tenant may place equipment of this kind in any position he finds most convenient. However, so heavy a load over the entire area of the floor is impossible, and it would be ridiculous to design the frame as a whole for any such condition. Similar situations occur in bridge design.

It should be clear that in choosing a design load *probability* of occurrence, *frequency* of occurrence, and possible extent must all be considered, and that the working stress (i.e., "factor of safety") to be permitted under various conditions also enters into the problem. The problem is one requiring great technical skill and wide experience for a satisfactory solution and cannot be further discussed in this text. It is entirely appropriate, however, here to describe and illustrate loads which do actually occur, and to state what design loads are often used under typical conditions.

13. Movable and Moving Loads in Buildings.—The live loads to which buildings are subjected are more commonly movable than moving. The important loads in a warehouse, for example, are the goods stored therein. These goods must be handled of course, and during such handling, by hand or mechanically operated trucks, they are moving loads. Unless the handling equipment is very heavy, however, the effect on the structure as a whole is not likely to be as important as the great weight of the stored goods. Figure 5 shows five views in warehouses showing the storing and handling of various kinds of goods. Electric trucks of the kind shown in this view have fairly heavy wheel loads which may be important in the design of the flooring, but which are insignificant in the design of the frame as a whole.

It is necessary in the design of a warehouse to take into consideration the kind of material to be stored. Table I gives data on actual loads found to exist in warehouses of various kinds. It is impossible to say positively that a certain kind of material will be stored to a definite height over a given area, and, in choosing the design load, probable weight, probable height of piling, and probable area of storage must all be considered, as well as the fact that in design, loads will be taken over the entire area of a floor, whereas in fact passageways or aisles must be left between storage areas. Passageways, however, are not always in the same places and it is necessary that the design provide for storage over any area. Live loads often recommended for warehouse design are also recorded in Table I.[3]

[3] Taken by permission from A. I. S. C. "Handbook of Steel Construction."

TABLE I

Contents of Storage Warehouses

Material	Weights per cubic foot of space, pounds	Height of pile, feet	Weights per square foot of floor, pounds	Recommended live loads, pounds per square foot
Building Materials				
Asbestos	50	6	300	
Bricks, building	45	6	270	
Bricks, fire clay	75	6	450	
Cement, natural	59	6	354	300
Cement, Portland	73	6	438	to
Gypsum	50	6	300	400
Lime and plaster	53	5	265	
Tiles	50	6	300	
Woods, bulk	45	6	270	
Drugs, Paints, Oil, etc.				
Alum, pearl, in barrels	33	6	198	
Bleaching powder, in hogsheads	31	3½	102	
Blue vitriol, in barrels	45	5	226	
Glycerine, in cases	52	6	312	
Linseed oil, in barrels	36	6	216	
Linseed oil, in iron drums	45	4	180	
Logwood extract, in boxes	70	5	350	
Rosin, in barrels	48	6	288	200
Shellac, gum	38	6	228	to
Soaps	50	6	300	300
Soda ash, in hogsheads	62	2¾	167	
Soda, caustic, in iron drums	88	3⅜	294	
Soda, silicate, in barrels	53	6	318	
Sulphuric acid	60	1⅝	100	
Toilet articles	35	6	210	
Varnishes	55	6	330	
White lead paste, in cans	174	3½	610	
White lead, dry	86	4¾	408	
Red lead and litharge, dry	132	3¾	495	
Dry Goods, Cotton, Wool, etc.				
Burlap, in bales	43	6	258	
Carpets and rugs	30	6	180	
Coir yarn, in bales	33	8	264	
Cotton, in bales, American	30	8	240	
Cotton, in bales, Foreign	40	8	320	
Cotton bleached goods, in cases	28	8	224	
Cotton flannel, in cases	12	8	96	
Cotton sheeting, in cases	23	8	184	
Cotton yarn, in cases	25	8	200	200
Excelsior, compressed	19	8	152	to
Hemp, Italian, compressed	22	8	176	250
Hemp, Manila, compressed	30	8	240	
Jute, compressed	41	8	328	
Linen damask, in cases	50	5	250	
Linen goods, in cases	30	8	240	
Linen towels, in cases	40	6	240	
Silk and silk goods	45	8	360	
Sisal, compressed	21	8	168	
Tow, compressed	29	8	232	
Wool, in bales, compressed	48			
Wool, in bales, not compressed	13	8	104	
Wool, worsteds, in cases	27	8	216	

TABLE I—*Continued*

CONTENTS OF STORAGE WAREHOUSES

Material	Weights per cubic foot of space, pounds	Height of pile, feet	Weights per square foot of floor, pounds	Recommended live loads, pounds per square foot
GROCERIES, WINES, LIQUORS, ETC.				
Beans, in bags	40	8	320	
Beverages	40	8	320	
Canned goods, in cases	58	6	348	
Cereals	45	8	360	
Cocoa	35	8	280	
Coffee, roasted, in bags	33	8	264	
Coffee, green, in bags	39	8	312	
Dates, in cases	55	6	330	
Figs, in cases	74	5	370	
Flour, in barrels	40	5	200	
Fruits, fresh	35	8	280	250
Meat and meat products	45	6	270	to
Milk, condensed	50	6	300	300
Molasses, in barrels	48	5	240	
Rice, in bags	58	6	348	
Sal soda, in barrels	46	5	230	
Salt, in bags	70	5	350	
Soap powder, in cases	38	8	304	
Starch, in barrels	25	6	150	
Sugar, in barrels	43	5	215	
Sugar, in cases	51	6	306	
Tea, in chests	25	8	200	
Wines and liquors, in barrels	38	6	228	
HARDWARE, ETC.				
Automobile parts	40	8	320	
Chain	100	6	600	
Cutlery	45	8	360	
Door checks	45	6	270	
Electrical goods and machinery	40	8	320	
Hinges	64	6	384	
Locks, in cases, packed	31	6	186	
Machinery, light	20	8	160	300
Plumbing, fixtures	30	8	240	to
Plumbing, supplies	55	6	330	400
Sash fasteners	48	6	288	
Screws	101	6	606	
Shafting steel	125			
Sheet tin, in boxes	278	2	556	
Tools, small, metal	75	6	450	
Wire cables, on reels	....	....	425	
Wire, insulated copper, in coils	63	5	315	
Wire, galvanized iron, in coils	74	4½	333	
Wire, magnet, on spools	75	6	450	
MISCELLANEOUS				
Automobile tires	30	6	180	
Automobiles, uncrated	8	....	64	
Books (solidly packed)	65	6	390	
Furniture	20			
Glass and chinaware, in crates	40	8	320	
Hides and leather, in bales	20	8	160	
Hides, buffalo, in bundles	37	8	296	
Leather and leather goods	40	8	320	
Paper, newspaper, and strawboards	35	6	210	
Paper, writing and calendared	60	6	360	
Rope, in coils	32	6	192	
Rubber, crude	50	8	400	
Tobacco, bales	35	8	280	

The principal live load in private dwellings and office buildings consists of furniture, books, files, safes, and like equipment, and these are movable loads. Moving live loads in the form of con-

Courtesy of the Elwell–Parker Electric Co.

Fig. 5.

gested groups of people must also be taken into consideration, particularly in corridors or assembly rooms, and on stairways.

The load produced by a crowd of people has been the subject of much discussion and some experimentation. A very interesting study of possible loads from congested groups of people was made by Professor Louis Jerome Johnson of Harvard University and described by him in his discussion of C. C. Schneider's paper on "The Structural Design of Buildings."[4] Through the courtesy of Professor Johnson Fig. 6 is presented. This view shows a

Courtesy of Prof. L. J. Johnson

FIG. 6.

group of 40 students in a box 6 ft. by 6 ft. inside dimensions. These men averaged 163.2 lb. each in weight, giving an average load of 181.3 lb. per sq. ft. on the 36 sq. ft. loaded. The men were carefully selected with a view to producing as large a load as possible and of course do not in any sense represent what may be

[4] *Transactions, Am. Soc. C. E.*, Vol. 54, p. 441.

expected from a miscellaneous group. In order to illustrate the meaning of a live load of 100 lb. per sq. ft. from a group of people the authors have performed similar experiments in the classroom, and in connection therewith have obtained, without any attempt at selection or excessive crowding, loads exceeding 125 lb. per sq. ft.

The United States Department of Commerce Building Code Committee has made an exhaustive study of ordinary building loads. The results of this study were summarized in a report submitted Nov. 1, 1924, entitled " Minimum Live Loads Allowable for Use in Design of Buildings," which may be secured from the Superintendent of Documents, Government Printing Office, Washington, D. C. The following statement is quoted from the report:

MINIMUM LIVE LOADS ALLOWABLE FOR USE IN THE DESIGN OF BUILDINGS

As recommended by the
Building Code Committee of the Bureau of Standards,
United States Department of Commerce

1. Definitions.

1. *Dead Load.*—The dead load in a building includes the weight of walls, permanent partitions, framing, floors, roofs, and all other permanent stationary construction entering into a building.

2. *Live Load.*—The live load includes all loads except dead loads.

2. General.

Buildings and all parts thereof shall be of sufficient strength to support safely their imposed loads, live and dead, in addition to their own proper dead load; provided, however, that no building or part of a building shall be designed for live loads less than those specified in the following sections.

3. Human Occupancy.

1. For rooms of private dwellings, hospital rooms and wards, guest rooms in hotels, lodging and tenement houses, and for similar occupancies, the minimum live load shall be taken as 40 pounds per square foot uniformly distributed, except that where floors of one and two family dwellings are of monolithic type or of solid or ribbed slabs the live load may be taken as 30 pounds per square foot.

2. For floors for office purposes and for rooms with fixed seats, as in churches, school classrooms, reading rooms, museums, art galleries, and theaters, the minimum live load shall be taken as 50 pounds per square foot uniformly distributed. Provision shall

be made, however, in designing office floors for a load of 2,000 pounds placed upon any space 2½ feet square wherever this load upon an otherwise unloaded floor would produce stresses greater than the 50-pound distributed load.

3. For aisles, corridors, lobbies, public spaces in hotels and public buildings, banquet rooms, assembly halls without fixed seats, grandstands, theater stages, gymnasiums, stairways, fire escapes or exit passageways, and other spaces where crowds of people are likely to assemble, the minimum live load shall be taken as 100 pounds per square foot uniformly distributed. This requirement shall not apply, however, to such spaces in private dwellings, for which the minimum live load shall be taken as in paragraph 1 of this section.

4. Industrial or Commercial Occupancy.

In designing floors used for industrial or commercial purposes, or purposes other than previously mentioned, the live load shall be assumed as the maximum caused by the use which the building or part of the building is to serve. The following loads shall be taken as the minimum live loads permissible for the occupancies listed, and loads at least equal shall be assumed for uses similar in nature to those listed in this section.

Floors used for:	Minimum Live Load in lbs. per sq. ft.
Storage purposes (general)	250
Storage purposes (special)	100
Manufacturing (light)	75
Printing plants	100
Wholesale stores (light merchandise)	100
Retail salesrooms (light merchandise)	75
Stables	75
Garages	
All types of vehicles	100
Passenger cars only	80
Sidewalks—250 or 800 pounds concentrated, whichever gives the largest moment or shear.	

5. Roof Loads.

Roofs having a rise of 4 inches or less per foot of horizontal projection shall be proportioned for a vertical live load of 30 pounds per square foot of horizontal projection applied to any or all slopes. With a rise of more than 4 inches and not more than 12 inches per foot a vertical live load of 20 pounds on the horizontal projection shall be assumed. If the rise exceeds 12 inches per foot no vertical live load need be assumed, but provision shall be made for a wind force acting normal to the roof surface (on one slope at a time) of 20 pounds per square foot of such surface.

6. Allowance for Movable Partition Loads.

Floors in office and public buildings and in other buildings subject to shifting of partitions without reference to arrangement of floor beams or girders shall be designed to support, in addition to other loads, a single partition of the type used in the building, placed in any possible position.

7. Reductions in Live Loads.

Except in buildings for storage purposes the following reductions in assumed total floor live loads are permissible in designing all columns, piers or walls, foundations, trusses, and girders.

Reduction of total live loads carried

	Per cent
Carrying one floor	0
Carrying two floors	10
Carrying three floors	20
Carrying four floors	30
Carrying five floors	40
Carrying six floors	45
Carrying seven or more floors	50

For determining the area of footings the full dead loads plus the live loads, with reductions figured as permitted above, shall be taken; except that in buildings for human occupancy, listed in section 3, a further reduction of one-half the live load as permitted above may be used.

Industrial plants manufacturing metal products or other heavy articles are ordinarily provided with electric cranes of varying capacities for use in handling heavy pieces. Buildings housing such equipment are often subjected to extremely heavy loads. The maximum loads to be expected, however, are fairly definite in such cases, unless the cranes are severely overloaded, as sometimes happens. Figure 7 shows a 250-ton crane in a railroad shop handling part of a heavy freight locomotive. Figure 8 shows mono-rail hoists operating over storage bins of the Rainier Pulp and Paper Company, Shelton, Washington.

The structural engineer seldom has to deal with moving concentrated loads heavier than are produced by cranes of large capacity. As an example, the end trucks, with wheel loads and spacings, for 25-, 50-, 75-, and 100-ton cranes are shown diagrammatically in Fig. 9. The data were taken from "Crane Engineering," published by the Whiting Corporation.

14. Moving Loads on Highway Bridges.—The loads which highway bridges are called upon to carry have increased tremendously in recent years. Thirty years ago an occasional traction engine or a road roller was an exceptional load. Today large fleets of heavy motor trucks carry an enormous volume of local freight over the highways. These loads are not exceptional but usual, and may be observed at any time on through routes — in

Courtesy of the Harnischfeger Corporation

FIG. 7.

fact, on some routes between large cities they form probably a major portion of an almost uninterrupted stream of traffic. The exceptional load at present is usually some heavy piece of machinery or piece of contractor's equipment transported over the highway on a trailer of special construction. To illustrate loads of these types, Figs. 10 and 11 showing standard trucks and trailers, and Figs. 12 and 13 showing exceptional loads on specially constructed trailers are presented. In England trailers of the general type shown in Fig. 13, having a rated capacity of 100 tons, are in use, and in the United States a single load of 163 tons has been moved by highway on equipment of this sort.

In the design of a bridge it is of course impossible to investigate the stresses which may be produced by every possible truck or

Courtesy of the Harnischfeger Corporation

Fig. 8.

truck train which may at one time or another pass over the structure. In order to simplify the design procedure it is necessary to adopt a conventional load which will produce stresses as large as those which will be caused by the greatest loads to be regularly expected, and result in a structure capable of supporting (at a reduced margin of safety) the heaviest load ever likely to cross during its life.

The way in which recent design specifications have attempted to meet this necessity is illustrated in Figs. 14 and 15, taken from the report of a Conference Committee composed of representatives from the American Association of State Highway Officials and the American Railway Engineering Association. The data given are practically self-explanatory, but it may be noted that the uniform load shown with the electric car loading is to have a magnitude equal to that specified for the class load for which the bridge is designed; i.e., if the bridge is to carry H-20 loading a uniform load of 640 lb. per ft. of track is to precede *or* follow, or precede *and* follow the car loads.

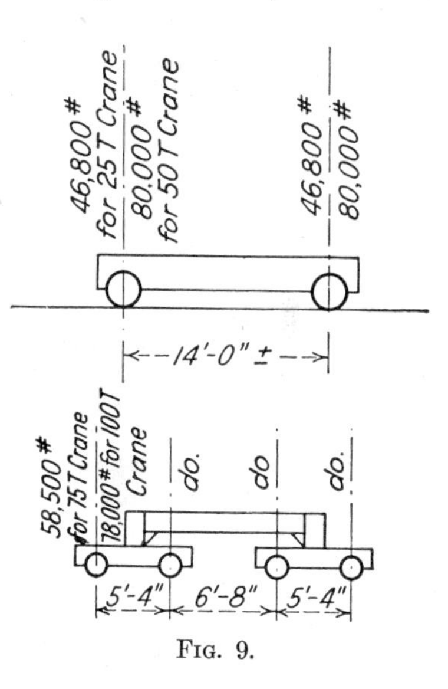

Fig. 9.

15. Moving Loads on Railroad Bridges.—There has been as marked a change in railroad bridge loads as in highway bridge loads, but in recent years the change has not been quite so rapid. In 1894 when Mr. Theodore Cooper, one of the best-known American bridge engineers, proposed a loading (to be mentioned later) intended to represent with reasonable accuracy the heaviest locomotives then in use, the 40,000-lb. axle loads which he suggested were thought to be sufficient. In 1903 Mr. Cooper raised the heaviest axle loads in his compromise locomotive to 50,000 lb., and stated that this should be "sufficient for future load requirements."[5] There are in use today locomotives with axle loads close to 80,000 lb., and probably most locomotives on major lines

[5] *Transactions, Am. Soc. C. E.*, Vol. 51, p. 105.

have axle loads of 60,000 lb. or more. A few years ago, 1931, the Pennsylvania Railroad Company began laying 152-lb. rails on por-

Courtesy of the Autocar Company

FIG. 10.

Courtesy of the White Company

FIG. 11.

tions of its main line, and these rails were designed to carry 100,000-lb. axle loads at 100 miles per hour.[6] About 25 years ago it was

[6] *Engineering News Record*, April 23, 1931, p. 693.

prophesied that the limit in axle loads had been reached, as the track structure and roadbed were thought to be unable to stand

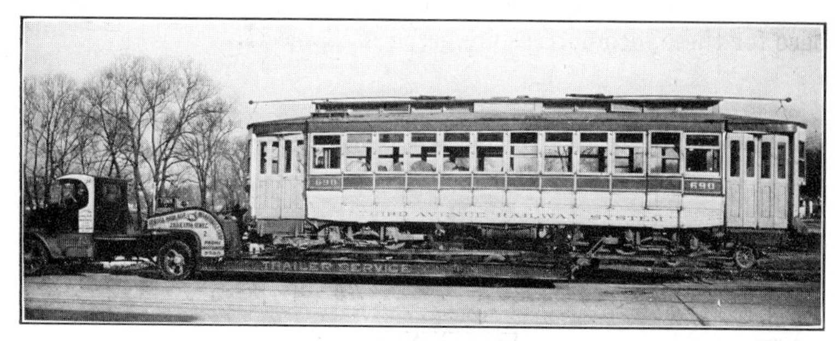

Courtesy of the Gerosa Haulage and Warehouse Corporation

Fig. 12.

Courtesy of the Rogers Tractor and Trailer Company

Fig. 13.

greater concentrations — at that time axle loads were little, if any, in excess of 65,000 lb. Figures 16 and 17 are presented to show examples of modern steam locomotives. Figure 16 shows passenger or fast freight locomotives and Fig. 17 heavy freight locomotives. Figure 18 shows a modern electric locomotive for heavy freight train service. Data regarding axle loads and wheel base for these locomotives are given in Table II.

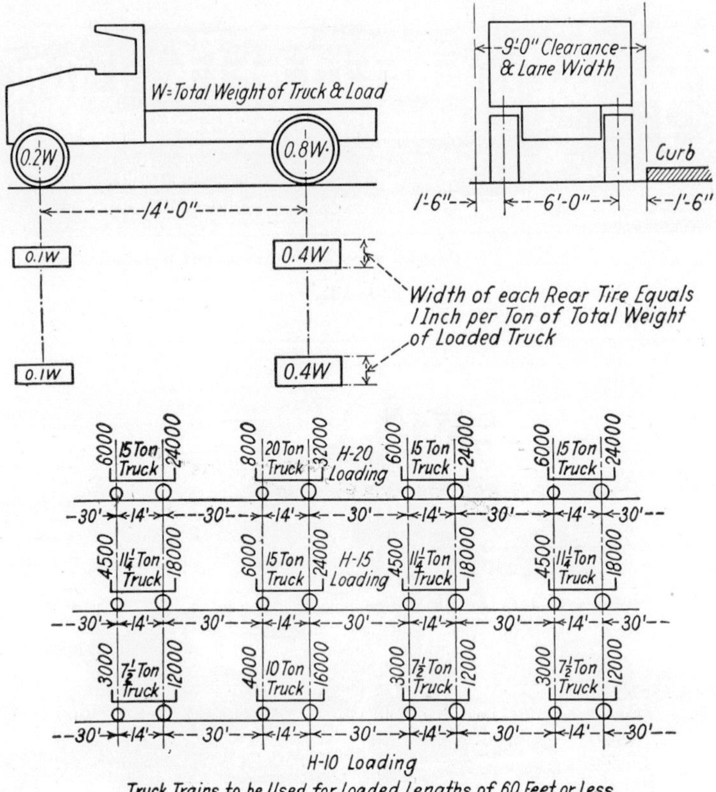

Fig. 14.

The train load is usually represented as a uniform load following or preceding, or following and preceding, the locomotives. When Mr. Cooper first suggested the loading which bears his name, 4000 lb. per ft. of track was thought to be ample. The train load now is generally taken as 7200 lb. per ft. of track, and ore trains operating on some roads are said to weigh 7500 lb. per ft. of track.

Occasionally special loads, such as heavy gun carriages or special well cars for transporting heavy machinery, may pass over

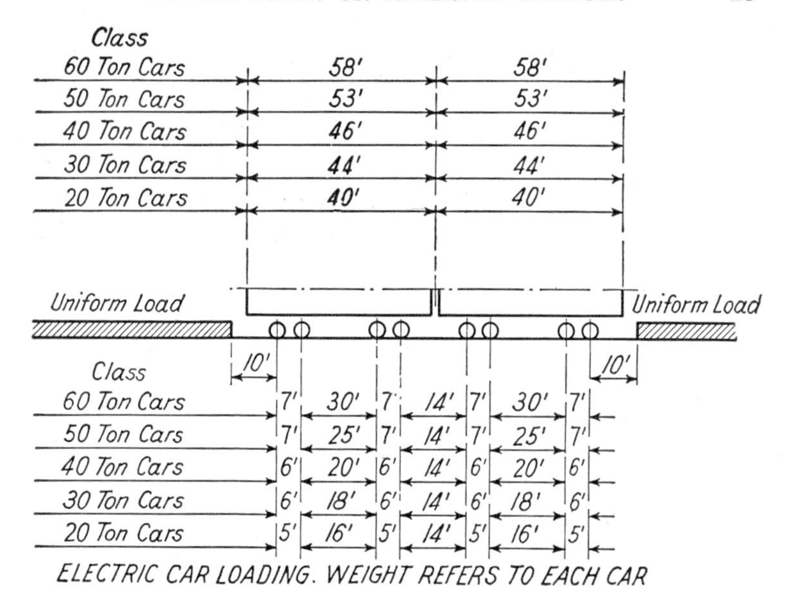

ELECTRIC CAR LOADING. WEIGHT REFERS TO EACH CAR

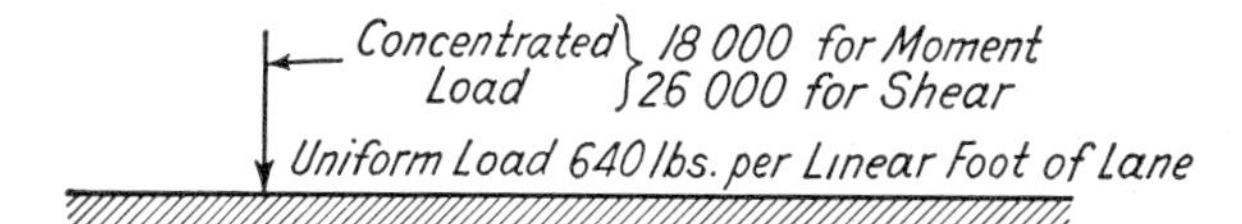

H 20 LOADING

Concentrated Load } 13 500 for Moment; 19 500 for Shear

Uniform Load 480 lbs. per Linear Foot of Lane

H 15 LOADING

Concentrated Load } 9 000 for Moment; 13 000 for Shear

Uniform Load 320 lbs. per Linear Foot of Lane

H 10 LOADING

EQUIVALENT LOADING FOR LOADED LENGTHS EXCEEDING 60 FEET

FIG. 15.

Courtesy of the American Locomotive Company and the Baldwin Locomotive Works

Fig. 16.

Courtesy of the Baldwin Locomotive Works

Fig. 17.

TABLE II

Railroad	Loco-motive No.	Type	Class	Weight in Working Order, Pounds					Wheel Base							
				On driving wheels	On truck		Total engine	Total engine and tender	Driving		Rigid		Total engine		Total engine and tender	
					Front	Rear			ft.	in.	ft.	in.	ft.	in.	ft.	in.
New York Central.....	5275	4–6–4	Pass. & Frt.	187,500	65,000	99,500	352,000	658,400	14	0	14	0	40	4	83	$7\frac{1}{2}$
Pennsylvania..........	6707	4–8–2	Pass. & Frt.	271,000	59,000	60,000	390,000	768,360	18	10	18	10	41	$9\frac{1}{2}$	96	$6\frac{3}{8}$
C. B. & Q............	6325	2–10–4	Freight	355,510	45,590	110,610	511,710	897,400	22	4	22	4	45	6	95	$11\frac{3}{4}$
Great Northern.......	2031	2–8–8–2	Freight	532,800	37,550	24,590	594,940	916,500	43	7	16	6	58	2	96	$3\frac{1}{2}$
Norfolk & Western....	2515	2–8–2–2–8–2	Freight	596,000*	58,000	58,000	828,000	....	62	0	16	6	83	0		

* On eight axles. Trucks 2 and 3 at 58,000 each not included.

railroads and may require examination of bridges which must be crossed. An example of extraordinarily heavy special equipment is shown in Fig. 19. This is one of three hot-metal cars used by

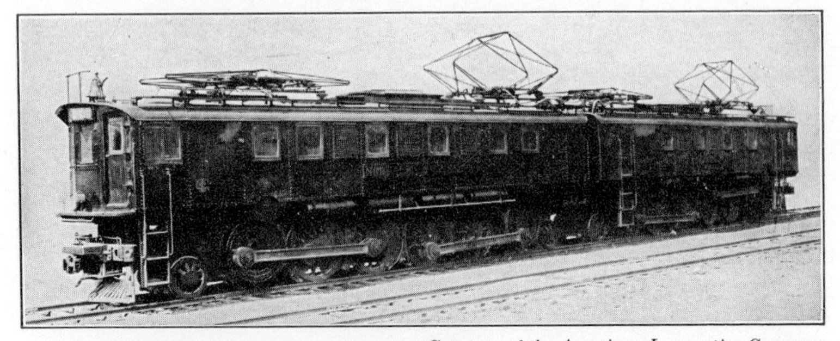

Courtesy of the American Locomotive Company

FIG. 18.

the American Rolling Mill Company to transport molten metal from its blast furnaces at Hamilton, Ohio, to the open-hearth department at Middletown, Ohio — a distance of about eleven miles. Figure 20 shows the axle loads and spacing for one car.

Courtesy of the American Rolling Mill Company

FIG. 19.

16. Conventional Loads for Railroad Bridges.—Locomotives have never been built to standardized designs and there is more or less variation in wheel spacing and axle loads. In the earlier days of railroad development it was customary to design the bridges for a particular road for the heaviest engines in use on that line. At that time most bridge designing was done by structural steel fabricators, and all bridge companies handling work of this kind had in their files dozens of engine diagrams representing the locomotives in use on different railroads. When so many different diagrams were used in design, no one diagram was used often enough to justify the preparation of elaborate tables giving shears and moments for various lengths and numbers of panels. The result was an enormous expenditure of time and effort in calculating the stresses needed for the preparation of designs. This led to many attempts to devise artificial engine diagrams which would represent with reasonable accuracy large numbers of locomotives. The system of this kind which received the widest acceptance was that devised by Mr. Theodore Cooper, mentioned previously. As a matter of fact, **Cooper's Loadings** became nearly a universal standard for railroad use. It is still the most common standard loading in spite of the fact that it is no longer an accurate representation of the heavy locomotives now in use.

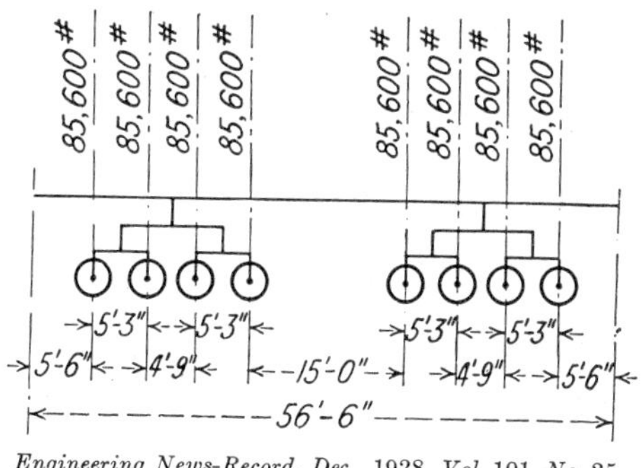

Engineering News-Record, Dec., 1928, Vol. 101, No. 25

FIG. 20.

Dr. D. B. Steinman in 1922 presented to the American Society of Civil Engineers a very elaborate paper entitled "Locomotive Loadings for Railway Bridges,"[7] which showed the great discrepancies between stresses produced by Cooper's loadings and those produced by the ten heaviest locomotives then in operation on American railroads. He also devised a new system, designated as M-loadings, which more accurately represents the effect of modern locomotives. The paper was widely discussed and received very general approval, except in railroad circles. It has not been very much used in design, although adopted as an alternative loading in the final report of an American Society of Civil Engineers

[7] *Transactions, Am. Soc. C. E.*, Vol. 86, p. 606.

Committee on "Specifications for Design and Construction of Steel Railway Bridge Superstructure." [8]

In 1929 a new system, designated as the A-64 loading, was proposed in "General Specifications for Steel Railway Bridges," [9] prepared by committees from the American Society of Civil Engineers and the American Railway Engineering Association.

Diagrams representing the three loadings just discussed are shown in Fig. 21. In the Cooper and Steinman series heavier or

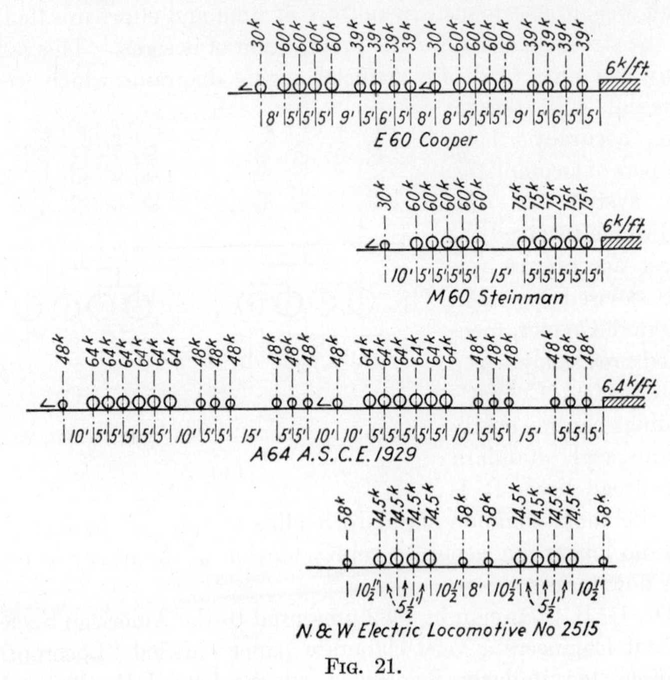

Fig. 21.

lighter loads are in direct ratio, i.e., an E-70 or M-70 loading is $\frac{70}{60}$ times the E-60 or M-60, and similarly an E-50 or M-50 is $\frac{50}{60}$ times the E-60 or M-60. The same relation presumably is to be used for loads heavier than A-64, and is so specified for lighter loads with a limit of $\frac{3}{4}$ the standard. A diagram of the axle loads and wheel spacing of the Norfolk & Western electric locomotive of Fig. 18 is also shown in Fig. 21 for comparison with the standard types.

[8] *Transactions, Am. Soc. C. E.*, Vol. 86, p. 471.

[9] *Proceedings, Am. Soc. C. E.*, December, 1929.

An approximate substitute for the A-64 loading is suggested in the Specifications mentioned above, which is as follows.[10]

For spans of less than 40 ft., a series of seven axle loads of 64,000 lb. each, spaced 5 ft. between centers. For spans of 40 ft. or more, a uniform load of 6400 lb. per ft. of track with a single load placed in the most effective position. For moments the single load shall be 128,000 lb.; for shears, the amount given by the formula:

$$E = 128 + \tfrac{1}{2}L$$

in which

E = the single load, in thousands of pounds;

and

L = the span length, in feet.

This formula for E leads to inconsistent stresses for certain bars in common trusses, and the authors doubt whether the formula as given will lead to the desired result.

17. Impact.—Loads moving along a structure tend to cause vibration if any of the loads are imperfectly balanced or if the track or roadway on which they move is not a perfectly smooth surface. This vibration results in stresses in the various parts of the structure which are larger than would be produced by the same loads at rest. The difference between the stresses caused by the moving loads and that which would result from the static loads is called **impact.** Impact has been the subject of considerable study and experimentation, but our knowledge is still insufficient to permit an entirely satisfactory treatment of the phenomenon. It is very generally agreed that some allowance should be made for impact, but there is some difference of opinion as to how much. Common allowances that have been used follow:

Buildings supporting traveling cranes:
25 per cent is added to the stresses produced by the cranes.

Highway bridges:

Floor I = 30 per cent

Trusses $I = \dfrac{50}{160 + L}$ Am. Soc. C. E., 1924.

$I = \dfrac{50}{125 + L}$ A.R.E.A. and A.A.S.H.O., 1929

[10] *Loc. cit.*

Railway bridges:

$$I = \frac{300}{300 + L} \quad \text{A.R.E.A., 1910.}$$

$$I = \frac{300}{300 + \dfrac{L^2}{100}} \quad \text{A.R.E.A., 1923.}$$

$$I = \frac{2000 - L}{1600 + 10L} \quad \text{Am. Soc. C. E., 1923.}$$

In all these formulas L is the length of roadway or track loaded (total length of track or roadway loaded in multiple-track railway or multiple-lane highway bridges) to produce the shear, moment, or stress to which the impact is to be added, and I is the percentage to be added.

Many other formulas have been proposed and used but these are sufficient to represent common practice.

18. Lateral Forces.—The most common lateral force is the pressure exerted by wind. Wind acts on all structures and in some localities is a very important factor. It has received a good deal of study in the past, and is now, because of the tremendous increase in building heights, being given further attention.

The reader is referred to a recent book, "Wind Stresses in Buildings," by Robins Fleming,[11] for an interesting discussion of the cause and effect of wind and a thorough summary of our present knowledge of the subject. The subject will not be further discussed here except to give the following data on common allowances for wind pressure.

Buildings: Wind pressures from 20 lb. per sq. ft. to 30 lb. per sq. ft. are given in design specifications. Forty pounds per square foot is often specified for buildings to be located in tropical countries. The sheltering effect of nearby buildings is frequently taken into consideration.

Bridges: The proper allowance for wind on bridges is nearly universally considered to be 30 lb. per sq. ft. on $1\frac{1}{2}$ times the projection on a vertical plane of the exposed area for the loaded structure, and 50 lb. per sq. ft. on the same area for the unloaded structure. Practically all design specifications set certain minimum amounts to be applied to the loaded and unloaded chords of the structure. Wind on the train is usually a

[11] John Wiley & Sons, 1930.

separate item and is most commonly taken as 300 lb. per ft. The wind load on a train is of course a moving load, and the other wind loads are nearly always required to be so treated. The recently proposed specifications of the American Society of Civil Engineers require that the projected area of all trusses be considered plus $1\frac{1}{2}$ times the projected area of the floor system.

An allowance is generally made for "side thrust" in buildings supporting traveling cranes. Side thrust results from lateral acceleration and deceleration of loads and from weaving or "nosing" of the crane. Very little is known as to its actual magnitude. It is generally assumed to be 20 per cent of the lifted load, which is almost certainly excessive but conservative and satisfactory pending more complete investigation.

An allowance for lateral "nosing" of locomotives is made in the design of bridges. In older specifications it was generally combined with an allowance for wind on the train. In the 1923 American Railway Engineering Association specifications an allowance of "5 per cent of the specified load on one track, but not more than 400 lb. per lin. ft." is required. Some writers have pointed out that it is impossible for the train to exert a lateral force in one direction throughout its length, but it seems not improbable that "nosing" may produce a lateral vibration which may produce stresses equivalent to a horizontal load acting in one direction throughout the length of the structure. The proposed 1929 specifications of the American Society of Civil Engineers provide that a single concentrated load of 20,000 lb. be used to represent the effect of side sway: this load to act in either horizontal direction at any point along the base of rail.

Centrifugal force is an important lateral force acting on bridges which support a curved track. It depends of course on the speed of the train and the curvature of the track. As the student should remember from his mechanics, its magnitude is given by:

$$C = \frac{W}{g}\frac{v^2}{R}$$

in which

C = horizontal centrifugal force;

W = the vertical load;

v = the velocity in feet per second;

R = the radius of curvature;

g = acceleration due to gravity = 32.2.

For use in connection with bridges this is usually reduced to

$$C = \frac{.067WV^2}{R}$$

in which

C, W, and R are as before;

V = speed in miles per hour, (usually assumed to be $60 - 2\frac{1}{2} \times$ degree of curvature);

W is generally taken to be the live load including impact.

19. Longitudinal Forces.—Longitudinal forces are produced by the starting and stopping of cranes on crane runways, and trains on bridges. The magnitude of this force on crane runways should generally be taken as about 20 per cent of the wheel loads. In older specifications for bridge design the longitudinal force was generally given as 20 per cent of the vertical load. More recent specifications have recognized that this is excessive and have required that 20 per cent of the driver loads plus 10 per cent — or in some cases 5 per cent — of the other loads be used, which is more reasonable.

20. Snow.—Snow load is an important load in the design of buildings. It is seldom considered in fixed bridges but may have importance in lift bridge design.

The amount of snow load to be used depends largely on the climate and on the slope of the roof. On flat roofs it is usually taken at 20 to 30 lb. per sq. ft., and on pitched roofs at decreased amounts depending on the slope. Roofs having slopes of 1 to 1 or greater are generally considered not to hold snow, but a sleet load of not less than 10 lb. per sq. ft. should be considered on all roofs, except where the climate is such that snow or sleet is impossible.

CHAPTER II

REACTIONS

21. General Principles.—If a body, subjected to forces acting in a plane, is at rest, there are three conditions of equilibrium which *must* be satisfied:

$$\Sigma H = 0$$

$$\Sigma V = 0$$

$$\Sigma M = 0$$

It follows that in determining the reactions acting on the body, the loads being known, not more than three unknown quantities can be found. There are three things which must be known about each force in order to have it fully determined: its *magnitude,* its *direction,* and its *point of application or line of action.* If a knowledge of all these concerning one reaction is lacking, then the magnitude, direction, and point of application or line of action of all other forces acting on the structure must be known. This reaction would then hold the body at rest against the action of the other forces.

In normal cases, when the loads are not parallel, there are two reactions; the direction of one reaction is known and a point on the line of action of each. The unknown quantities are the magnitude of each reaction and the direction of one. The beam shown in Fig. 22, for example, has reactions at A and B. The reaction at A must pass through the hinge at that point, but its magnitude and direction are unknown. The reaction at B must pass through the hinge at B and must be vertical since the bearing is on rollers (assumed to be frictionless) which rest on a horizontal plane; its magnitude, however, is unknown. This may be more briefly

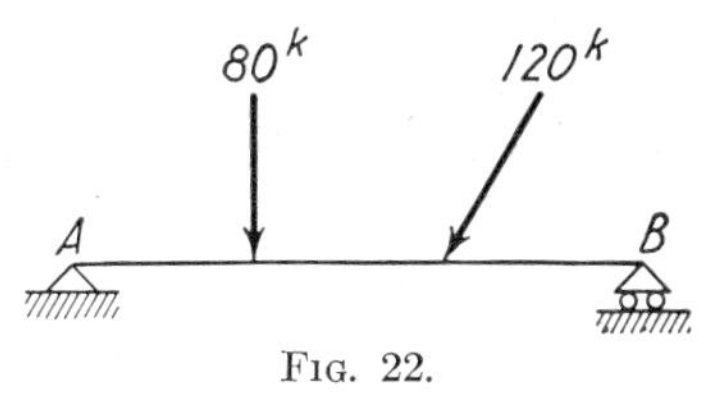

Fig. 22.

stated by saying that the three unknowns are horizontal and vertical reactions at A and a vertical reaction at B. It is practically always more convenient to deal with the horizontal and vertical components of reactions, and in what follows it is to be understood that it is these components which are to be found unless it is otherwise stated.

If the beam of Fig. 22 is supported as shown in Fig. 23, the statements made above are still correct except that the reaction at B must of course be normal to the plane on which the rollers are supported; i.e., it must act along the line $B - B'$. It is evident that there are still three unknowns: the magnitude and direction of the reaction at A and the magnitude of the reaction at B. If we state the unknowns in this case as the horizontal and vertical components of the reactions at A and B, it may seem at first that there are four reactions to be found. This is not the case, however, and a little study should make it clear that, since the direction of the reaction at B is fixed by the rollers, there is also a fixed relation between the horizontal and vertical components at this point. This relation is independent of the magnitude or position of the loads, and when one is determined the other is known at once. There is no fixed relation between the components at A; either may change independently of the other with changes in loading, and the determination of one does not fix the other.

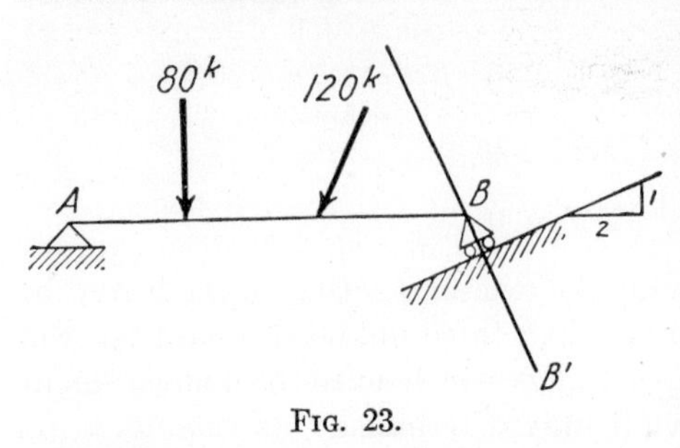

Fig. 23.

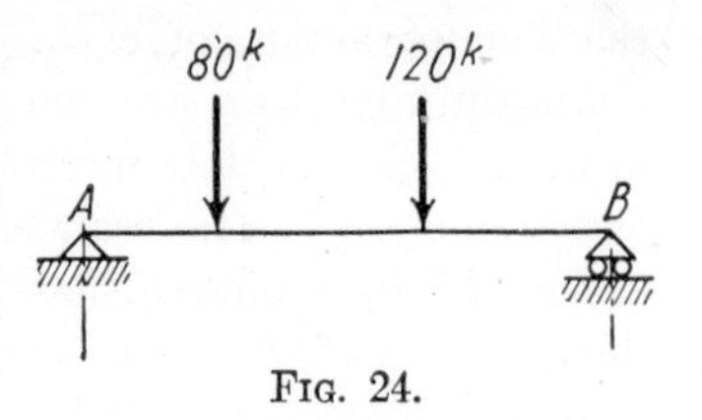

Fig. 24.

If the beam of Fig. 22 is subjected to vertical loads only, as shown in Fig. 24, it is clear without computation that there cannot be any horizontal reaction at A and that there are only two unknowns: the magnitude of the vertical reactions at A and at B. It is important to recognize, however, that in arriving at the conclusion of no horizontal reaction at A, the principle of $\Sigma H = 0$ has been used (consciously or unconsciously), and that only the two remaining equations of statics, $\Sigma V = 0$ and $\Sigma M = 0$, are available for calculating the magnitude of the vertical reactions at A and B.

It must be remembered that the number of unknowns which can be determined is fixed by the number of equations available, and it makes no difference whether they pertain to one reaction or to several reactions as long as the unknown quantities do not exceed in number the independent equations. As will be seen later, the conditions of support or construction of a structure may result in conditions of equilibrium in addition to those given by the laws of statics for the whole structure. It is possible in such cases to determine a greater number of unknowns than the laws of statics alone would permit without recourse to equations including the elastic properties of the structure. Obviously the number of unknowns which may be determined in addition to those given by the laws of statics will be equal to the number of conditions of equilibrium resulting from the method of support or construction.

22. Statical Indetermination.—When the number of unknown reactions exceeds the number of conditions of equilibrium, the structure is said to be **statically indeterminate**; that is, its reactions cannot be determined by the use of the laws of statics alone. Equations involving the elastic behavior of the structure will be involved to such an extent that the total number of independent equations from all sources will be equal to the number of unknown quantities. Structures may be somewhat arbitrarily classified as statically indeterminate externally, internally, or both. Externally statically indeterminate structures are those which are indeterminate with respect to their reactions as just stated. Internally statically indeterminate structures are those which are indeterminate with respect to the stresses in one or more of the members. Part One does not deal with the application to statically indeterminate structures of equations of equilibrium based on the elastic properties of the structure. It does deal, however, with the calculation of reactions, shears and moments, or stresses in such structures after enough unknowns have been determined so that the remainder may be computed by use of the laws of statics.

23. Examples for Classification.—It is important that the student be able to recognize whether or not a structure with which he has to deal is statically indeterminate. In Fig. 25 are represented a number of structures with varying conditions of support and construction. Each structure should be carefully studied to determine the number of unknowns and the number of conditions of equilibrium which are available for its analysis. The unknowns should be stated in terms of magnitude, direction, and point of application or line of action, as well as in terms of vertical and horizontal components.

24. Methods of Analysis.—A method of attack for such problems may be illustrated by considering the structure shown in Fig. 25 (*l*). This structure has reactions on the earth (which is the ultimate source of support for every structure) at *A* and *B*. Since hinges are shown at *A* and *C*, the reaction at *A* must pass

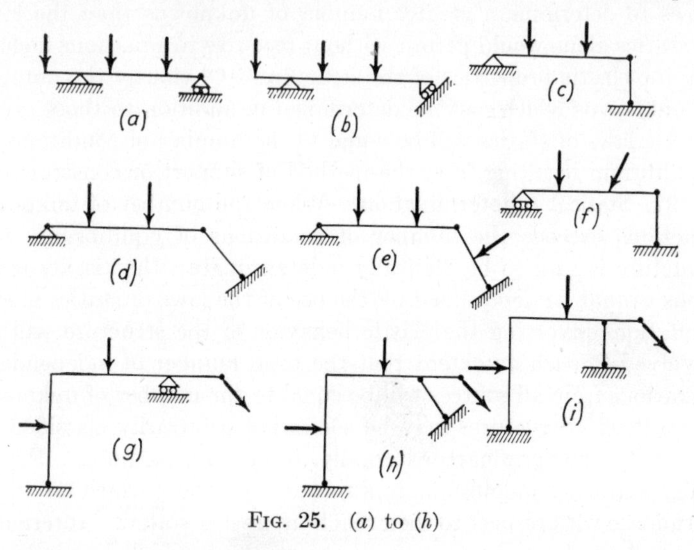

FIG. 25. (*a*) to (*h*)

through the hinge at *A* and act along the line *AC*. This reaction, therefore, is known in direction and line of action, and unknown in magnitude. The reaction at *B* is unknown in magnitude and direction, but the hinge at *D* makes it necessary for the reaction at *B* to pass through this point, and as a result a point on its line of action is known. There are therefore three unknowns: the magnitude of the reaction at *A* and the magnitude and direction of the reaction at *B*. As there are available three equations from the laws of statics the structure is statically determinate and its reactions may be calculated by applying these laws. The unknowns may be stated in terms of horizontal and vertical components. There are two components at A, one vertical and one horizontal, but the relation between them is fixed by the fact that their resultant must pass along AC. At B there are horizontal and vertical components and also a moment. There are then four unknown quantities: one at A

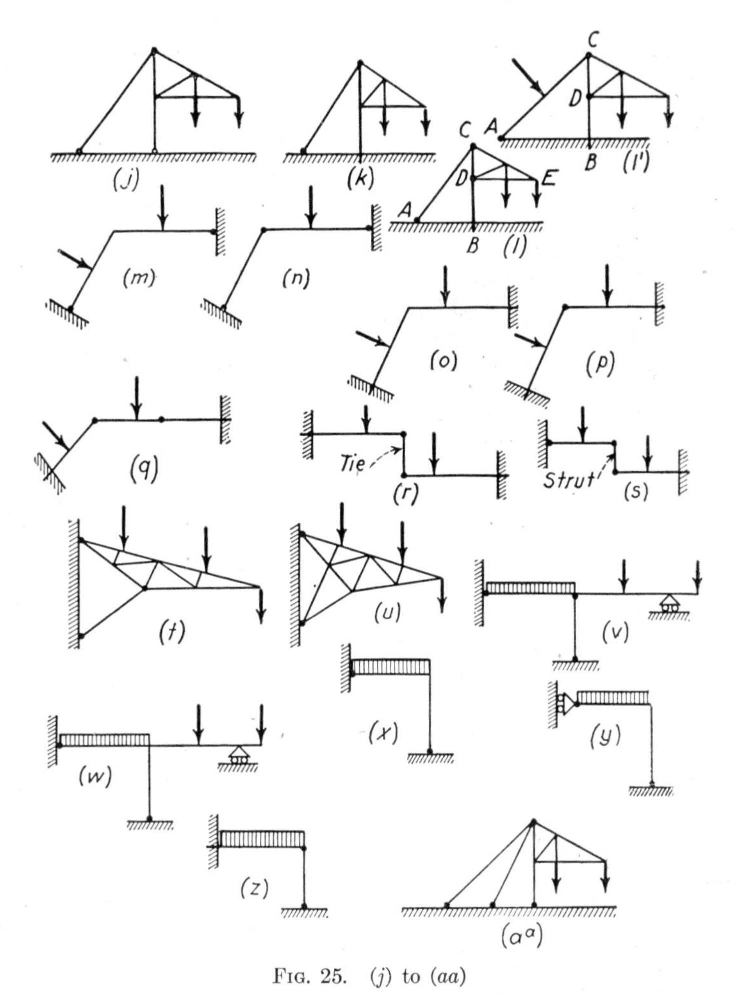

FIG. 25. (j) to (aa)

and three at B. But the fact that there can be no bending moment at D furnishes one condition of equilibrium in addition to the three laws of statics and, therefore, the structure is statically determinate.

Another method of attack which is often useful for problems of this kind is to break the structure up into two or more parts, each of which is a stable and determinate structure in itself; supported by, loaded by, or supported and loaded by other parts. In this

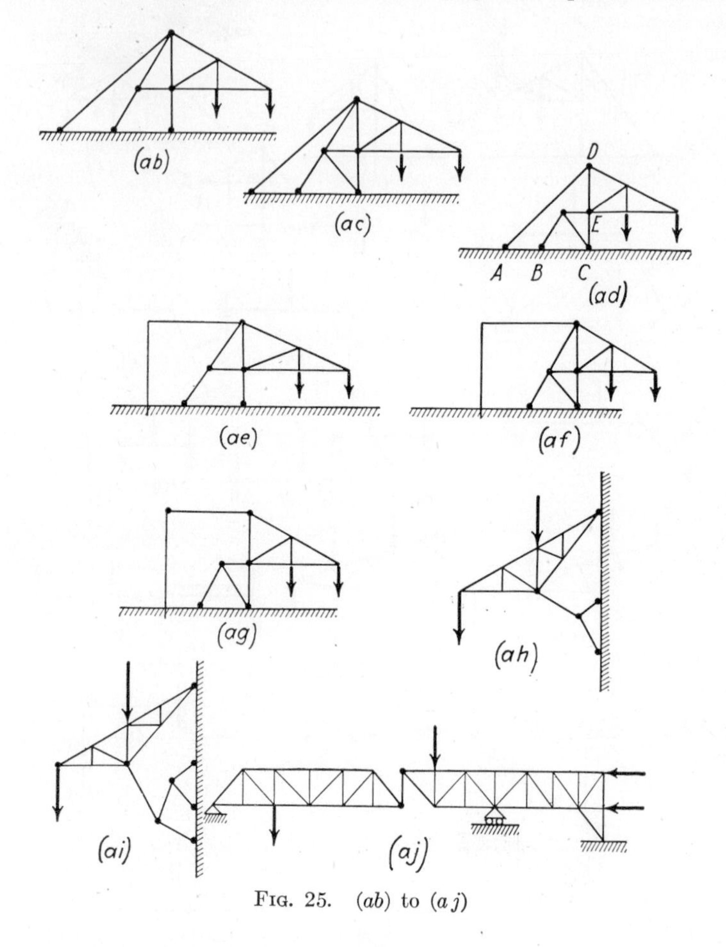

FIG. 25. (*ab*) to (*a j*)

particular problem, for example, the part CDE may be considered as a separate structure supported at C and D or at A and D; and the part DB as a separate cantilever beam loaded at D by the reaction of CDE upon it. Then, dealing with the separate structure CDE or $ACDE$, the reaction at C or at A is known in direction and line of action but unknown in magnitude, while the reaction at D is known to act at that point (that is, D is one point on the line of action of the reaction), but is unknown in magnitude and direction. These unknowns may be readily computed. The reaction at D may then be applied to the cantilever beam DB and the reactions at B (a horizontal component, a vertical component, and a moment) calculated directly.

25. Illustrative Examples.—The computation of reactions may now be illustrated by a few typical examples. Figure 26 shows a simple beam carrying vertical loads. It will be noted that, since an appreciable area of the beam is bearing at each end, the reactions

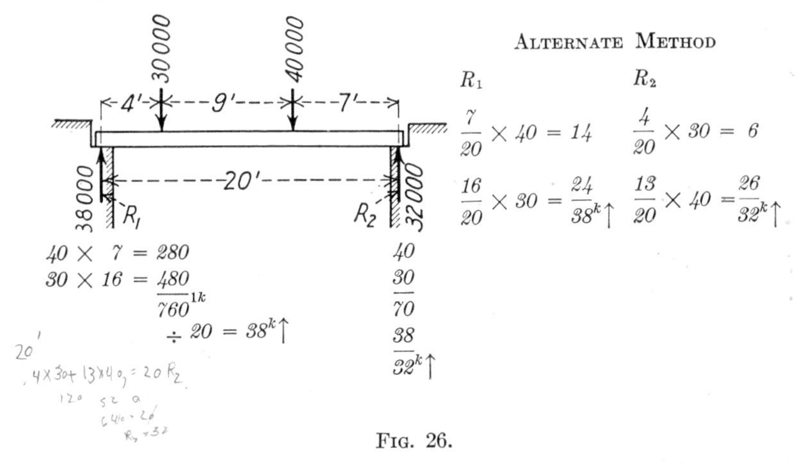

FIG. 26.

are not single forces, but are distributed loads acting upward on the ends of the beam over the support. As previously stated, it is customary to assume in such cases that the reaction is a concentrated force acting in the center of the support. Taking moments about the right reaction, the left reaction is found to be 38.0 kips. The right reaction is found to be 32.0 kips by taking moments about the left reaction or by application of $\Sigma V = 0$. The right reaction may be found by each of these methods if it seems desirable to have an arithmetical check. The calculations described above are shown on the figure. The alternate method of computation, shown to the right of the calculations described above, is frequently convenient. It evidently involves no new principle, but has the advantage that the effect of each load on the reaction is kept separate, and the individual calculations may often be made mentally.

26. In Fig. 27 is shown a simple beam with loads inclined to the vertical. The simplest way to determine the reactions is to resolve the inclined force into its horizontal and vertical components. The magnitudes of these components are shown as the dotted forces in the figure. By assuming the point of application at the beam, the horizontal component passes through the center of moments and the calculations may be made in the same manner as in the problem of Fig. 26. The necessary calculations are shown on the figure.

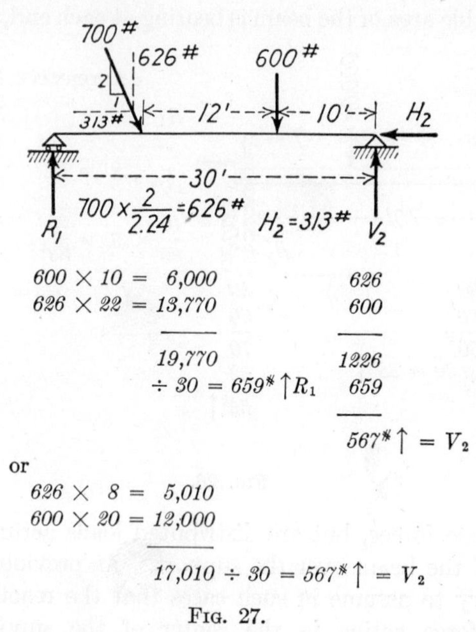

FIG. 27.

It should be noted in Fig. 27 that both reactions are hinged; one is supported on rollers and the other fixed to the masonry. The horizontal component at the fixed reaction must, of course, be equal to the algebraic sum of the horizontal components of all the forces acting on the beam. If both reactions were fixed against horizontal movement as well as hinged, the problem would be statically indeterminate since it would be impossible to determine how much of the horizontal component would be resisted by each reaction. If the reactions are both on rollers, the beam in Fig. 27 becomes unstable.

27. The beam shown in Fig. 28 has one end fixed in a wall and the other free. The beam is evidently statically determinate for the portion outside of the wall which supports it. We do not know how the forces which are acting on the portion of the beam inside the wall are distributed. The shear and moment at the face of the wall are taken as the reactions and are equal to the algebraic sum of all the forces acting on the portion of the beam which is outside the wall and the sum of the moments of these forces about the face of the wall. The calculations for these reactions are shown on the figure. A beam supported in this manner is commonly called a **cantilever** beam.

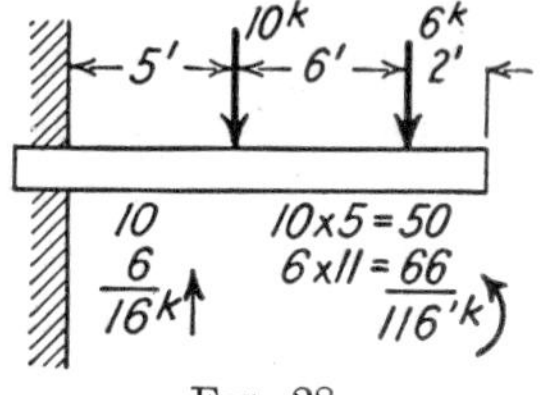

FIG. 28.

28. In Fig. 29 there is shown a beam with overhanging or

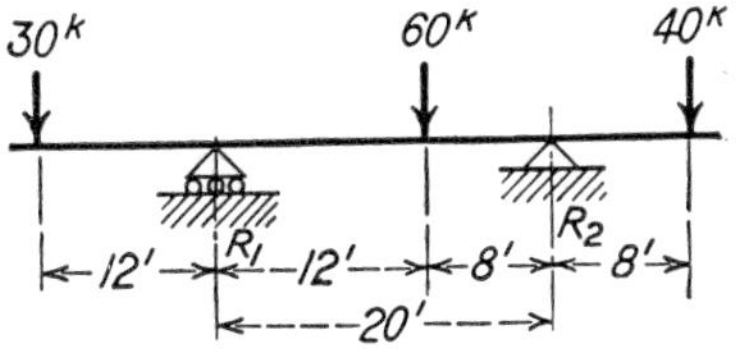

R_1 $60 \times 8 = 480$
$30 \times 32 = 960$
1440
$40 \times 8 = 320$
1120^{1k}
$\div 20 = 56^k \uparrow$

40
60
30
130
56
$R_2 = 74^k \uparrow$

ALTERNATE METHOD

R_1 $\frac{8}{20} \times 60 = 24$
$\frac{32}{20} \times 30 = \frac{48}{72}$
$\frac{8}{20} \times 40 = \frac{16}{56^k \uparrow}$

$\frac{12}{20} \times 60 = 36$
$\frac{28}{20} \times 40 = \frac{56}{92}$
$\frac{12}{20} \times 30 = \frac{18}{74^k \uparrow}$

FIG. 29.

cantilever ends. The reactions for such a beam may be determined in the same manner as for other simple beams. The calculations for the reactions in this case are shown on the figure.

29. The beam in Fig. 30 at first may appear to be statically indeterminate as it has four reactions (at A, B, E, and F) to be determined by only two equations of statics, as the condition that $\Sigma H = 0$ is not available since there are no horizontal forces. A little study, however, will make it clear that the two hinges placed in the middle span at C and D furnish two additional conditions of equilibrium and make the structure statically determinate. This furnishes another example of a structure which may be most conveniently analyzed by being broken up into several parts, each of which is a stable and determinate structure. In this case, for

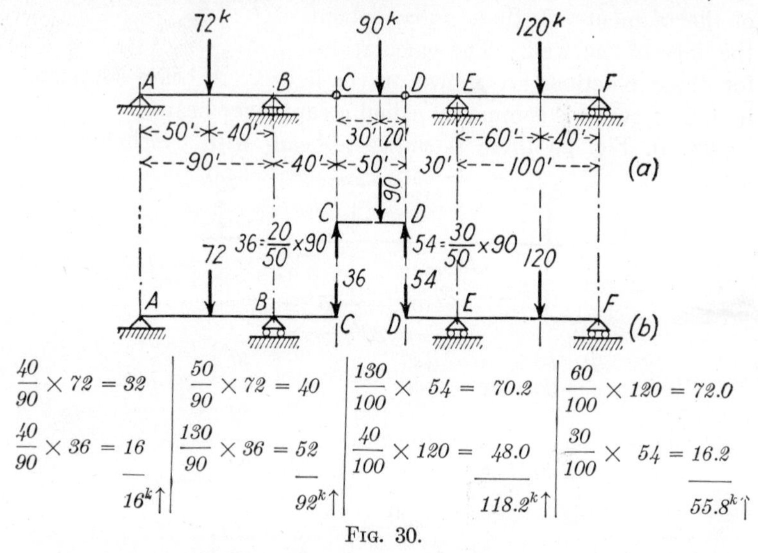

Fig. 30.

example, the portion CD may be considered as a simple beam supported at C and D; at C by the part ABC, which is, in itself, a stable and determinate structure; and at D by the part DEF, also a stable and determinate structure. The reactions at C and D may now be calculated easily and applied as loads on the separate portions ABC and DEF. The calculations for the reactions are shown on Fig. 30(b).

It should be noted in Fig. 30 that, although all the loads are vertical, it is necessary to have three reactions on rollers in order that the structure will be statically determinate for inclined loads. The horizontal reaction at A will equal the sum of all horizontal loads on the span.

30. A roof truss subjected to a wind load, assumed to be acting normal to the roof, is shown in Fig. 31, with rollers under the left support. The magnitude of each reaction is shown in parenthesis at its support. The student should check these values. The method of attack in finding the reactions is the same as has already been illustrated.

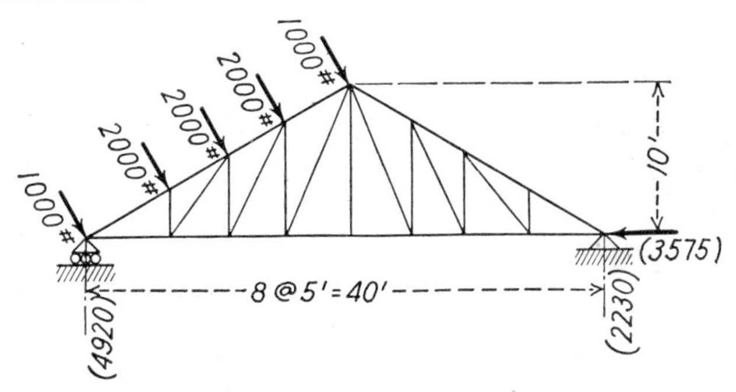

Fig. 31.

31. In Fig. 32 is shown a structure with reactions at different elevations. The direction of the right reaction is determined by the slope of the inclined post which is hinged at B and C. The magnitude of this reaction may be determined by taking moments about the point A. In taking moments the perpendicular distance from the line of action of the right reaction to the center of moments may be used, the right reaction may be resolved into two components, so taken that one component will pass through the center of moments, or the horizontal and vertical components may be expressed in terms of either and assumed as applied at B, or any other known point on the line BC. After one component is found the other may be found at once from the known relation between them: that is, if R_2 is the right reaction and H_2 and V_2 its horizontal and vertical components, the known slope of the line BC gives at once the relations:

$$H_2 = \frac{8}{12}V_2 \quad \text{and} \quad R_2 = \frac{14.4}{12}V_2 \quad \text{or} \quad \frac{14.4}{8}H_2$$

The left reaction may now be found from $\Sigma H = 0$ and $\Sigma V = 0$, or by taking moments at any convenient point. The calculations for the reactions are given on the figure. The student should apply a vertical load of 20 kips at the center of BC and recalculate the reactions.

32. One principle which it is convenient to keep in mind is that any three non-parallel forces which are in equilibrium must act in the *same* plane and must pass through a *common* point. If

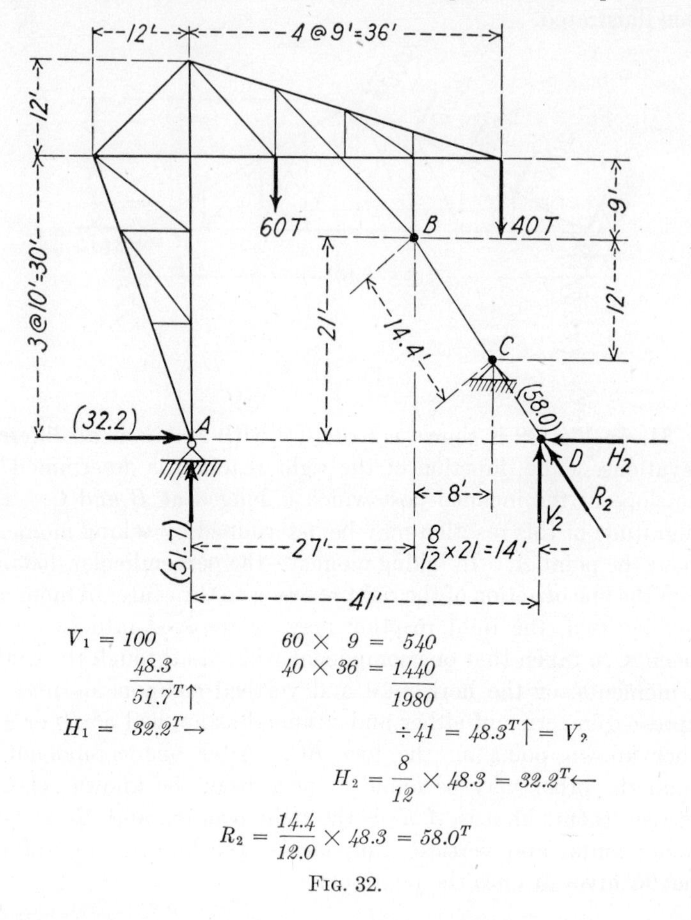

Fig. 32.

known loads are acting on a structure which has two reactions, the direction and line of action of one reaction being known and a point on the line of action of the other, then the second reaction *must* pass through the known point and the intersection of the first reaction with the resultant of the loads. Two points on the line of action of the second reaction now being known, its direction is determined. This principle is fundamental in **graphic statics,** but it also may be often used to advantage in analytic methods.

The structure shown in Fig. 33 may be used to illustrate this principle. As shown it is subjected to only horizontal external loads. The reaction at B must be vertical (because of the rollers) and must pass through the hinge at B. That is, it must act along the line BC. It is clear by inspection that the resultant of the external loads acts along the line FC. Since the reaction R_1 must pass through the hinge at A, application of the above principle at once fixes its line of action as AC. The necessary calculations

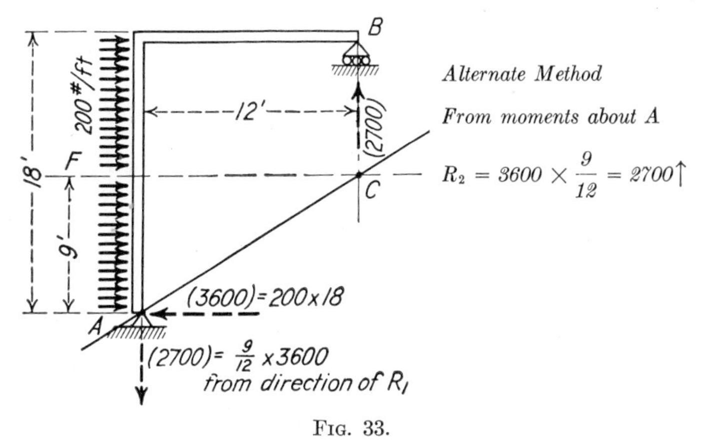

FIG. 33.

for the reactions using this principle are given on the figure. The calculations for the alternate method of taking moments about A are also given; it should be noted that the two methods involve identical computations.

33. In Fig. 34 is shown a structure having reactions at A and C fixed against horizontal or vertical movement, but free to turn about the hinges at these points. A point on the line of action of each reaction is known, but each is unknown in direction and in magnitude, or we may say that there are vertical and horizontal reactions at each support. There are, therefore, four unknown reactions, but the structure is made statically determinate by the addition of the hinge at B, the fact that there can be no bending moment at B furnishing an additional condition of equilibrium. (See Art. 36 for bending moment.) The calculations necessary in determining the reactions are shown on the figure. It should be noted that, although there are four unknowns, the calculations are no more difficult than in the case of an ordinary beam. The reactions at A and C being at the same level, taking moments about either A or C eliminates three of the four unknowns, since both horizontal reactions and one vertical reaction pass through the

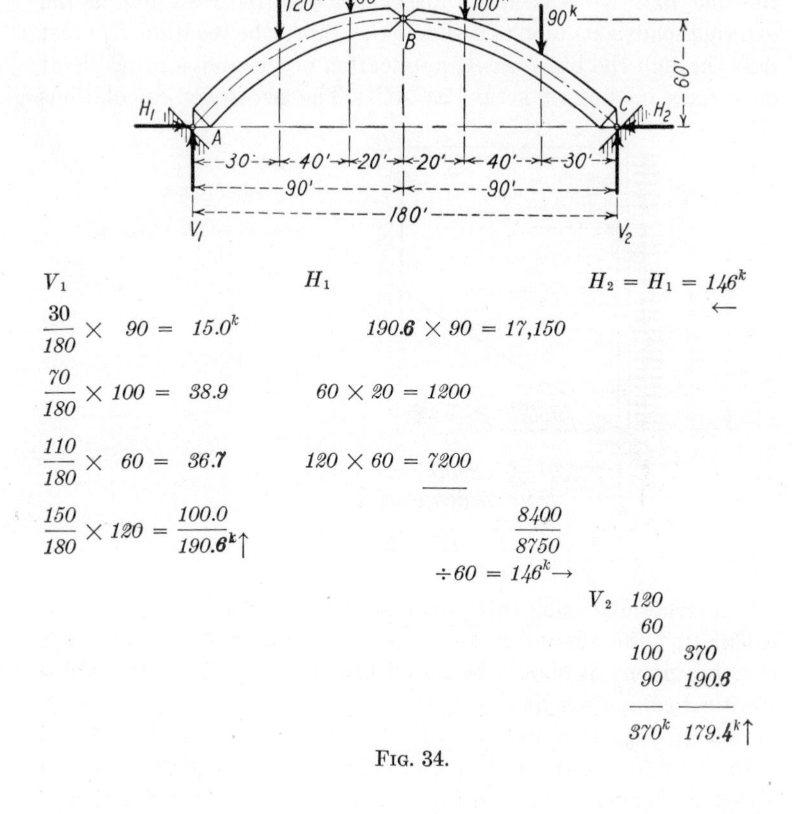

FIG. 34.

center of moments. The fourth unknown may then be found by direct calculation.

34. Arches.—The structure discussed in the preceding paragraph is known as a **three-hinged arch.** In general, arches are distinguished from other structures in having reactions fixed against horizontal movement. Arches may be *three-hinged, two-hinged, one-hinged,* or *hingeless.* Only those of the first-named type are statically determinate. The hingeless arch is very extensively used in modern concrete bridge construction. The one-hinged arch is rare. Two-hinged and three-hinged arches are widely used in large buildings such as armories, drill halls, and dirigible hangars, and for highway and railway bridges. The methods discussed in Part Two can be applied in the analysis of hingeless and two-hinged arches. In recent years there have been constructed many notable examples of arches of all types, except the one-hinged.

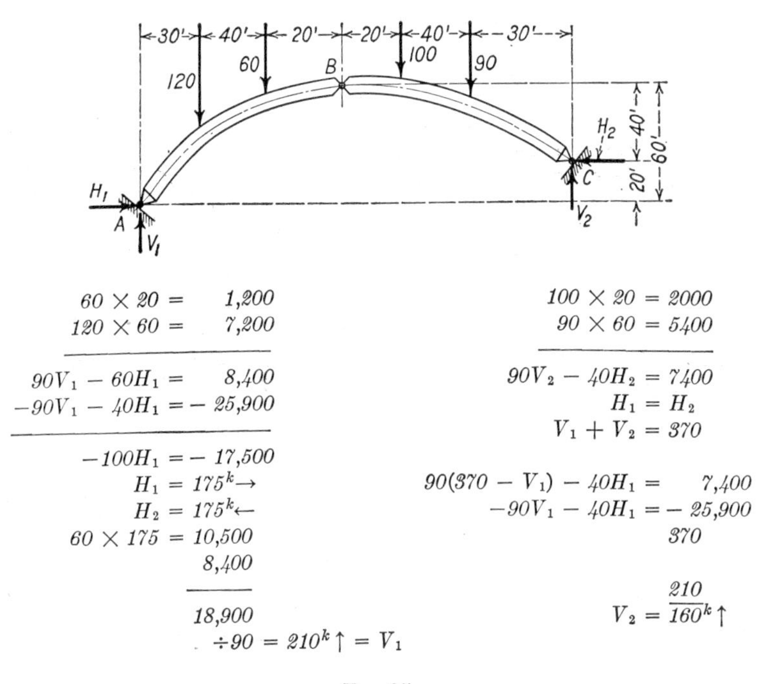

FIG. 35.

In Fig. 35 the arch of Fig. 34 is shown with reactions at different levels. The calculations in this case are more extensive but not more difficult. It is convenient in this case to obtain an equation involving H_1 and V_1 by taking moments about B of all forces on the left, and an equation involving H_2 and V_2 by taking moments about the same point of all the forces on the right. Then, from $\Sigma V = 0$ and $\Sigma H = 0$, the relation between V_1 and V_2 and between H_1 and H_2 may be found, which enables the two equations found by taking moments about B to be solved. The calculations are shown on the figure.

The reactions for the structure shown in Fig. 35 may also be found by resolving the reactions at A and C into vertical components and components parallel to a line passing through A

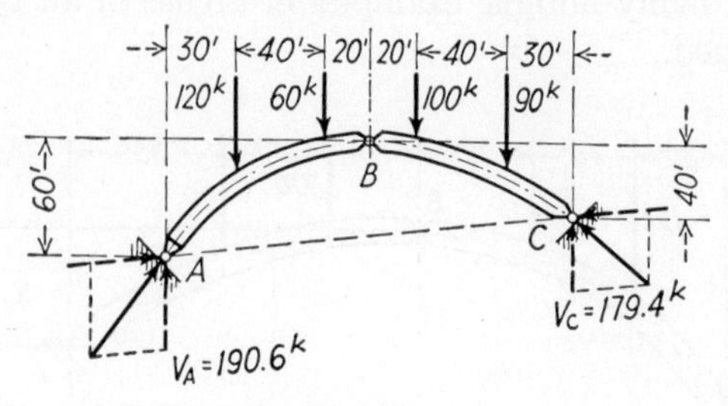

FIG. 36.

and C. The components of the reactions are then as shown in Fig. 36, and the computations for V_A and V_C are identical with those for V_1 and V_2 in Fig. 34. It should be understood that the vertical components thus found are not the true vertical reactions, that at A is more and that at C is less, owing to the vertical com-

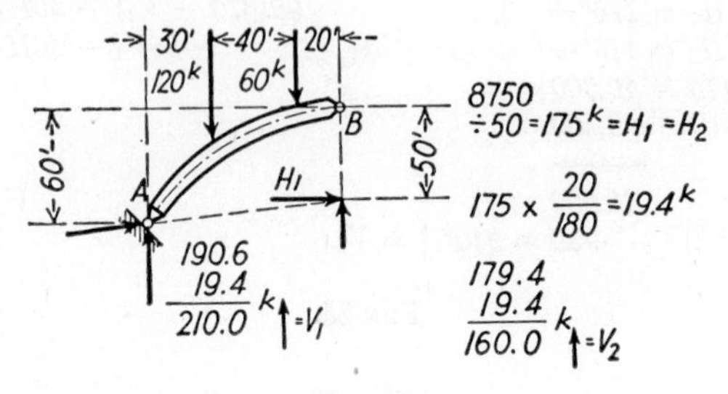

FIG. 37.

ponents of the inclined forces acting along the line through A and C. The calculations for this correction are shown in Fig. 37. The computations for the moment about B, 8750 ft.-kips, are the same as in Fig. 34, but, as shown in Fig. 37, the moment arm for computing H_1 is now 50 ft. The vertical components of the inclined reactions are obtained from the slope of the line through

A and C. Correcting V_A and V_C by this component gives the true values of V_1 and V_2. The student should note that the only changes in these computations, as compared with those for an arch such as in Fig. 34, are the substitution of the new moment arm for H_1 and adding and subtracting the corrections to V_A and V_C. This method has certain advantages in computing the reactions of an arch with supports at different levels.

PROBLEMS

In calculating reactions, compute the horizontal and vertical components only, unless otherwise instructed.

1. Find the reactions for the beam shown.

Ans. $V_1 = 105.6^k \uparrow$ $V_2 = 90^k \uparrow$
$H_2 = 43.2^k \rightarrow$

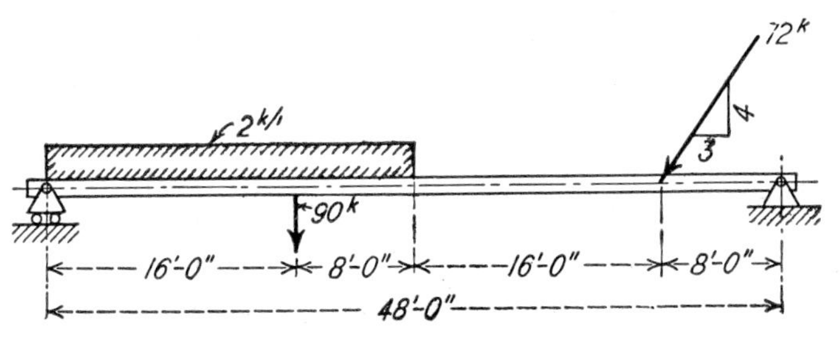

Prob. 1.

2. Find the reactions for this beam.

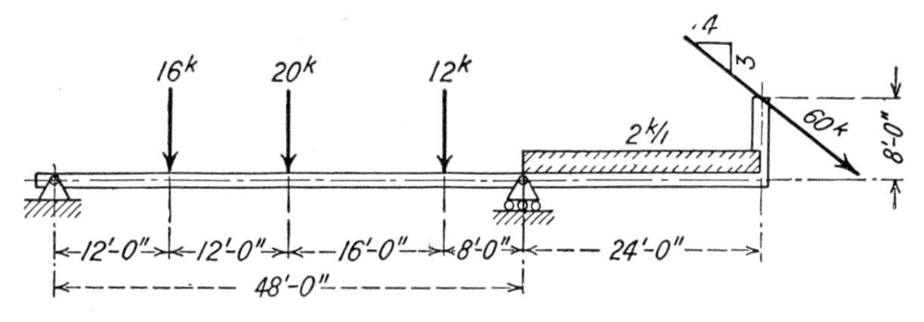

Prob. 2.

3. Compute the reactions for the structure shown.

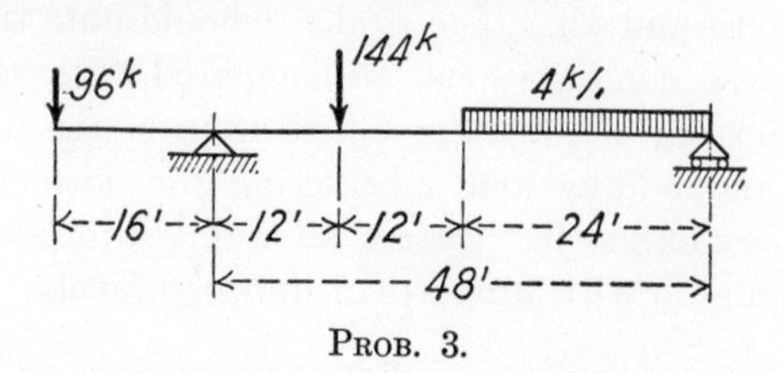

Prob. 3.

4. Compute the reactions for the structure shown.

Ans. $V_1 = 48^k\uparrow$ $V_2 = 106^k\uparrow$
$H_1 = 165^k\leftarrow$ $H_2 = 53^k\rightarrow$

Prob. 4.

5. Calculate the reactions on this structure.

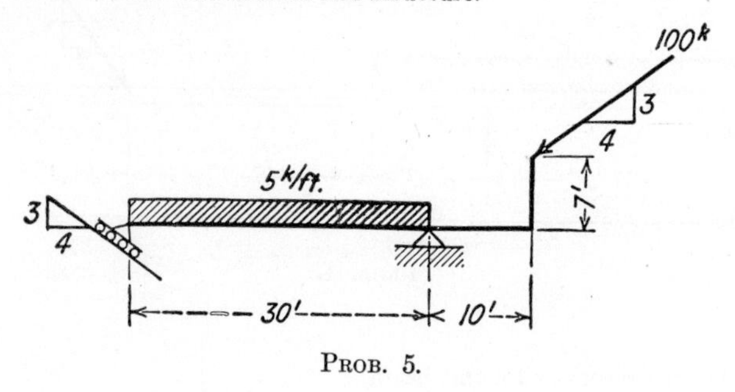

Prob. 5.

6. Calculate the reactions for the beam shown.

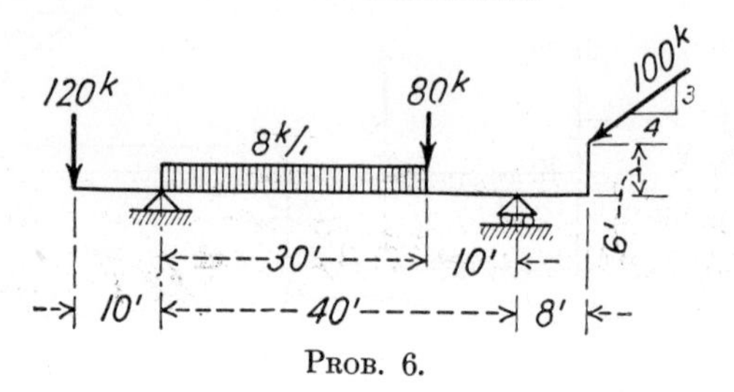

Prob. 6.

7. Calculate the reactions on the structure shown.

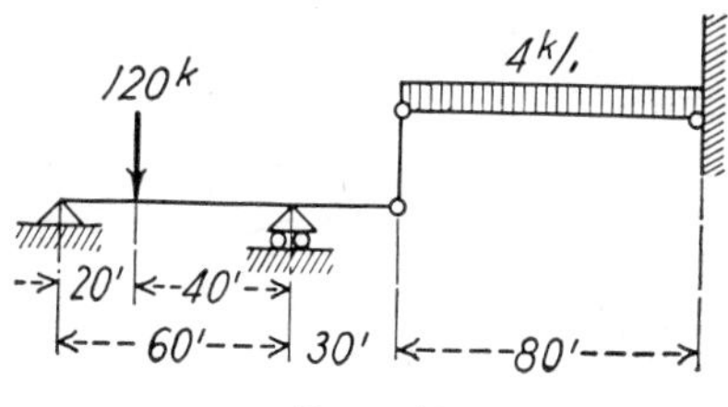

PROB. 7.

8. Calculate the reactions on the structure shown.

Ans. $V_1 = 282.9^k\uparrow$ $V_2 = 57.1^k\uparrow$
$M_1 = 9770'^k$

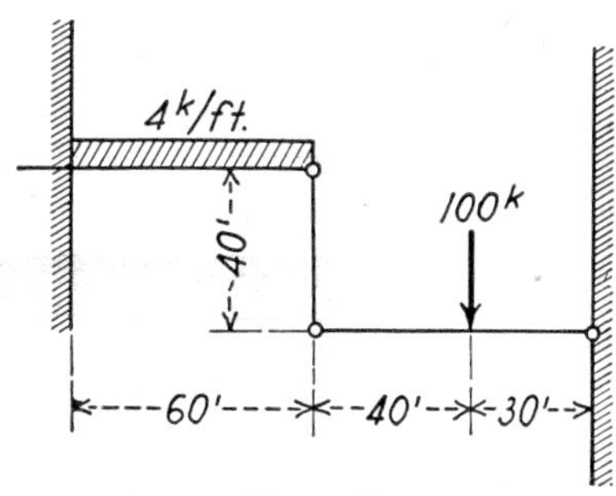

PROB. 8.

9. Calculate the reactions on the columns A, B, C, of the structure supporting the tank.

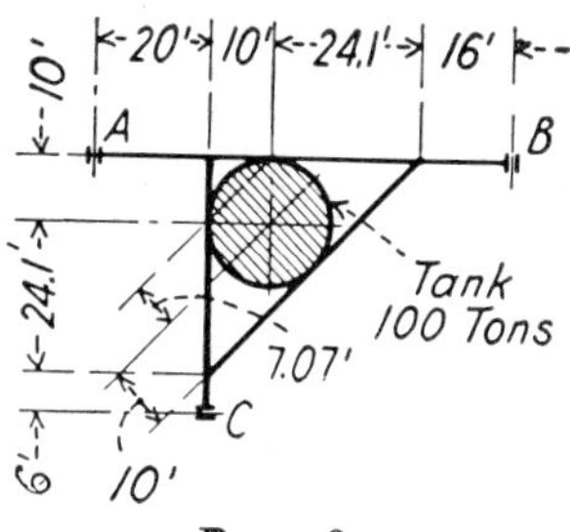

PROB. 9.

10. Calculate the reactions at A, B, and C.

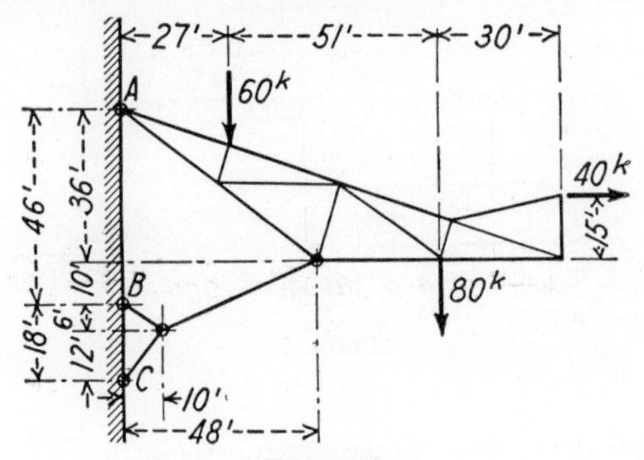

PROB. 10.

11. Calculate the reactions at A and B.

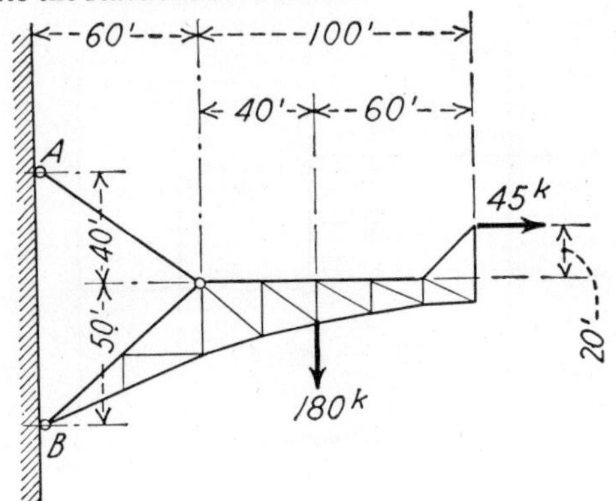

PROB. 11.

12. The wind pressure on the left side of the structure is horizontal and that on the truss is normal to the surface of the roof. Values as shown. Calculate the reactions.

Ans. $V_1 = 8.8^k\uparrow$
$H_1 = 29.2^k\leftarrow$

$V_2 = 13.7^k\uparrow$
$H_2 = 10.3^k\leftarrow$

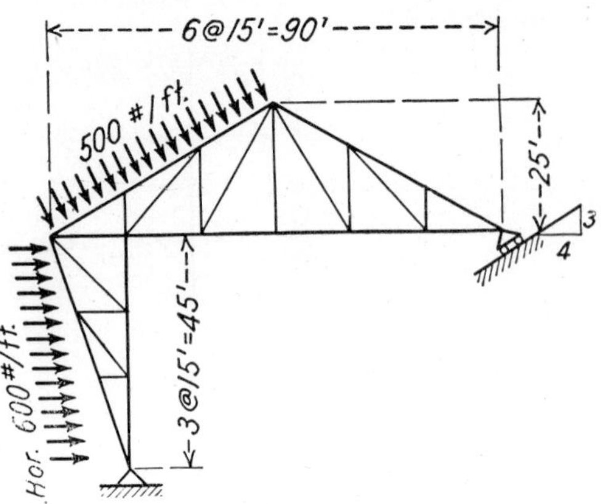

PROB. 12.

13. The loads shown are normal to the surfaces on which they act. Calculate the reactions.

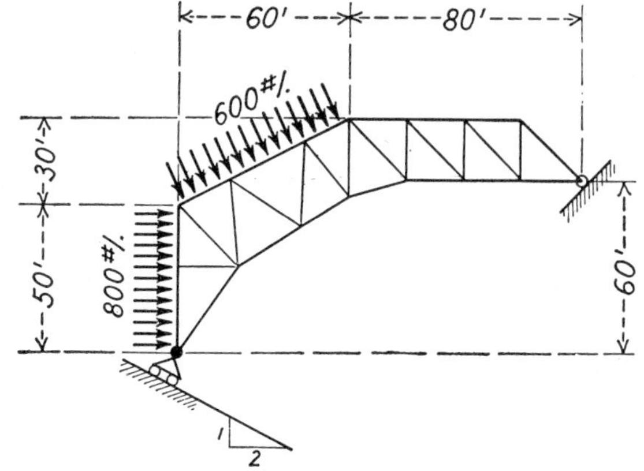

Prob. 13.

14. Compute the reactions for the structure shown.

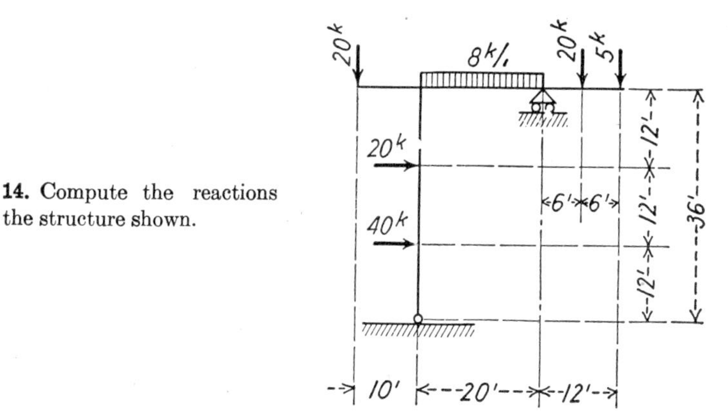

Prob. 14.

15. Calculate the reactions on the structure.

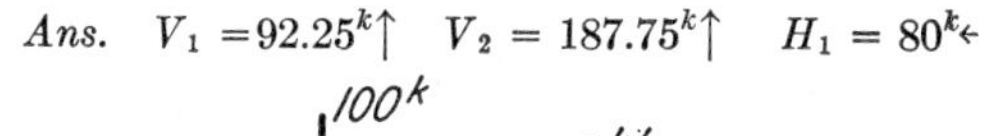
Ans. $V_1 = 92.25^k\uparrow$ $V_2 = 187.75^k\uparrow$ $H_1 = 80^k\leftarrow$

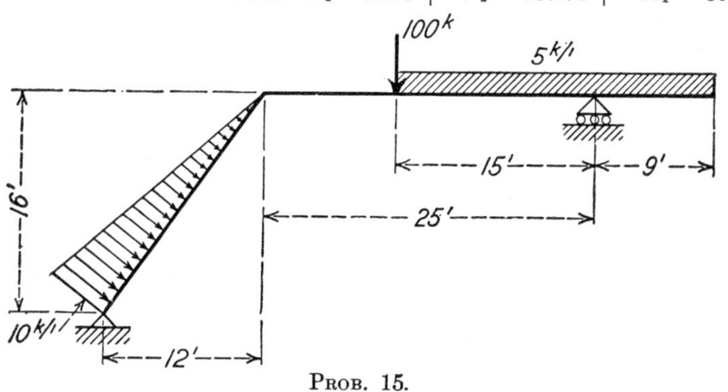

Prob. 15.

16. Calculate the reactions.

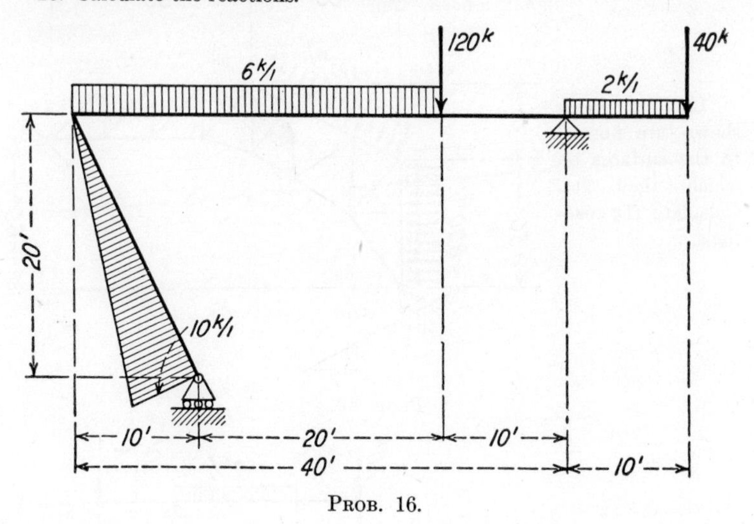

PROB. 16.

17. Compute the reactions for the structure.

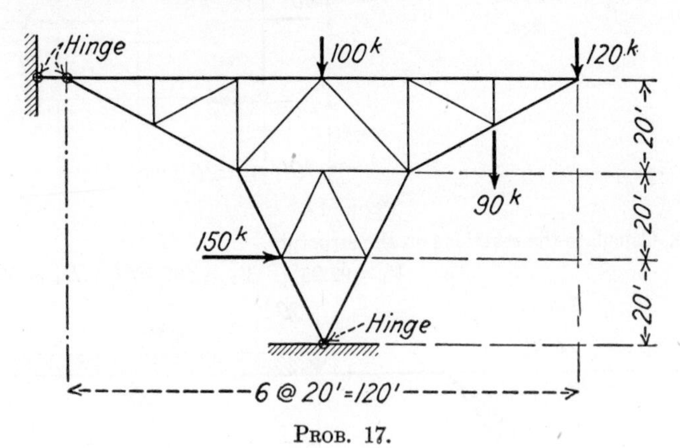

PROB. 17.

18. Find the reactions for the frame.

Ans. $V_1 = 93\frac{1}{3}^k\downarrow \quad V_2 = 213\frac{1}{3}^k\uparrow$
$H_1 = 56^k\leftarrow \quad H_2 = 56^k\rightarrow$

Tie Rod
Hinge
50'-0"
10'-0"
10'-0"
30'-0"
60^k
20^k
40^k
30'-0"
4 @ 10'-0" = 40'-0"

PROB. 18.

19. The normal pressures are to be taken as 20 lb. per sq. ft. for inclined surfaces and 30 lb. per sq. ft. for vertical surfaces. The truss shown is an intermediate truss in a series. Bents 20 ft. c. to c. (*a*) Compute the reactions with wind coming from the left. (*b*) Compute the reactions with wind coming from the right.

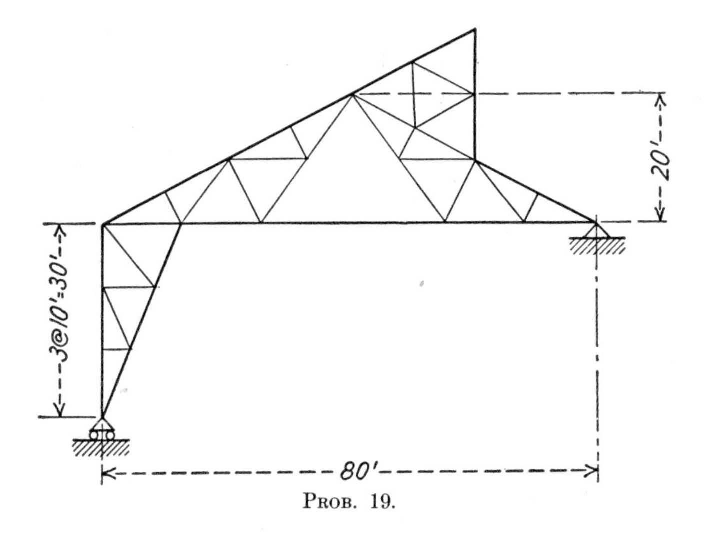

PROB. 19.

20. Find the reactions for the truss. The loads shown are normal to the surfaces.

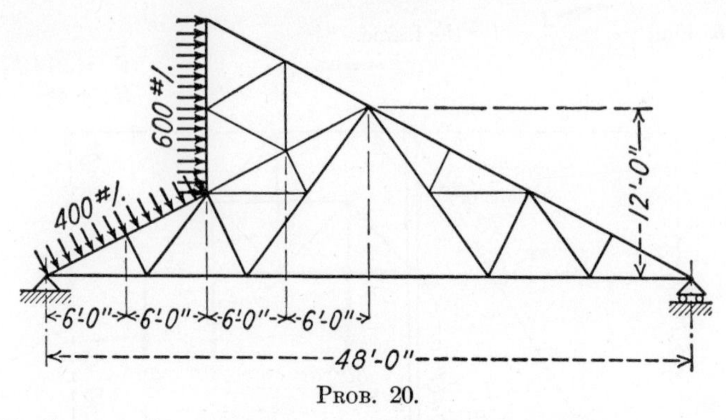

PROB. 20.

21. Compute the reactions for the structure.

Ans. $V_1 = 46.3^k\downarrow$ $V_2 = 103.3^k\uparrow$ $H_1 = 180^k\leftarrow$

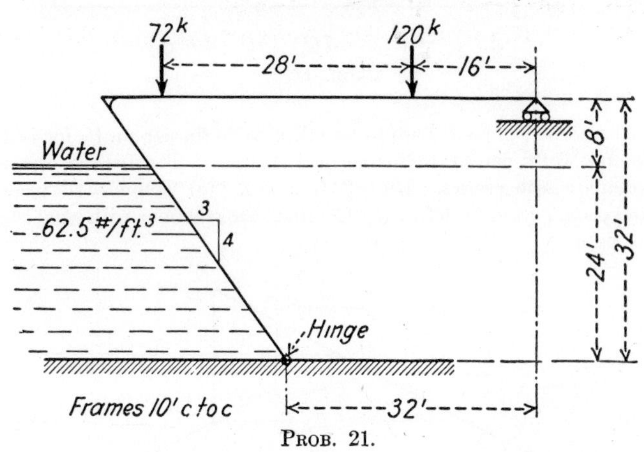

PROB. 21.

22. Find the reactions for the structure shown, given the following loads:

Car and load = 100^k

Hoisting engine = 50^k

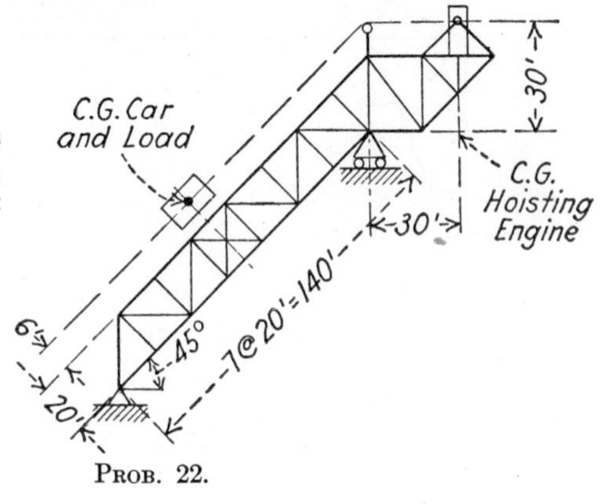

PROB. 22.

23. (*a*) Given that the weight of the bascule span is 450^k, compute the necessary weight of the counterweight for balance, neglecting friction.

(*b*) Compute the reactions at *A* and *B* due to the bascule and counterweight only: First when the span is closed, as shown, and second when it has opened 60°.

(*c*) Compute the reaction of the bascule on the pin at *B*; first when the span is closed as shown, and second when it has opened 60°.

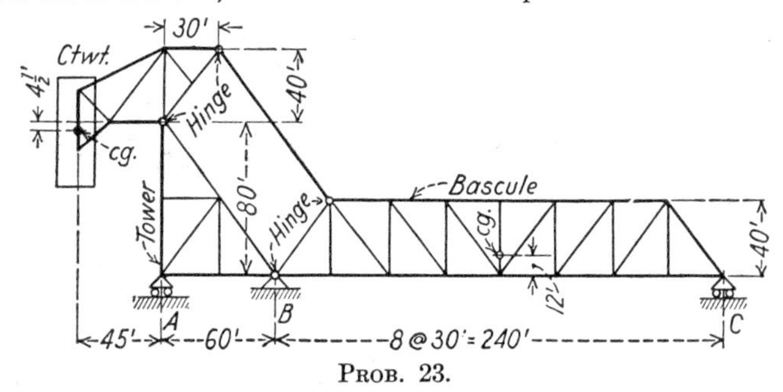

PROB. 23.

24. Is the structure shown (*a*) stable? (*b*) determinate? (*c*) If your answer to either (*a*) or (*b*) is no, why not? If your answer is yes to both (*a*) and (*b*), compute the reactions.

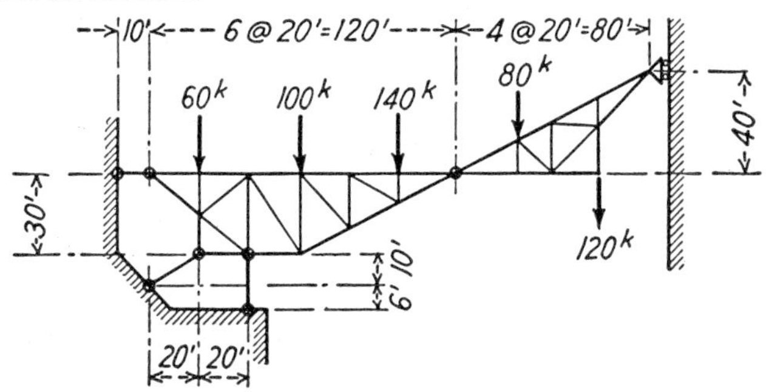

PROB. 24.

25. Find the reactions for the structure.

Ans. $V_1 = 89.8^k\uparrow$ $V_2 = 112.2^k\uparrow$
$H_1 = 12^k\leftarrow$

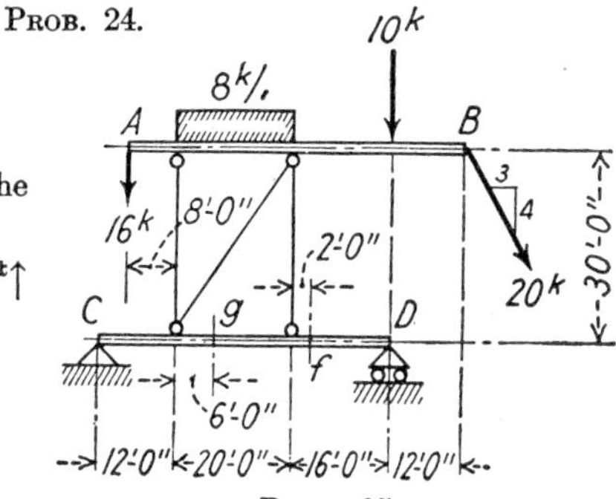

PROB. 25.

26. Find the reactions for the structure.

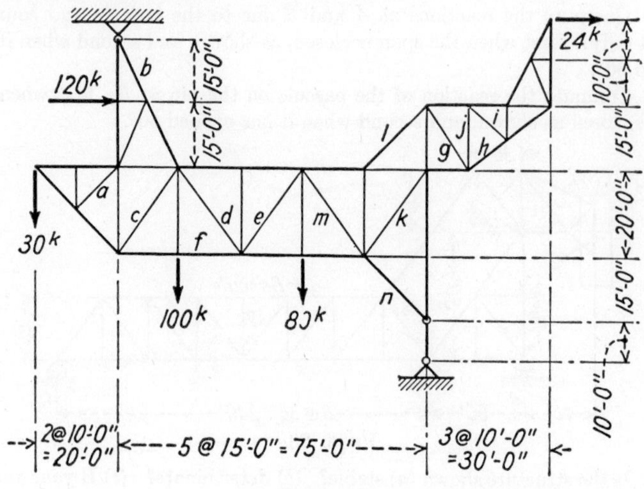

Prob. 26.

27. Find the reactions at A, B, and C for the structure shown.

Ans. $V_A = 147.8^k\uparrow$ $V_B = 178.1^k\uparrow$ $V_C = 14.1^k\uparrow$
$H_A = 443.3^k\leftarrow$ $H_B = 237.5^k\rightarrow$ $H_C = 205.8^k\rightarrow$

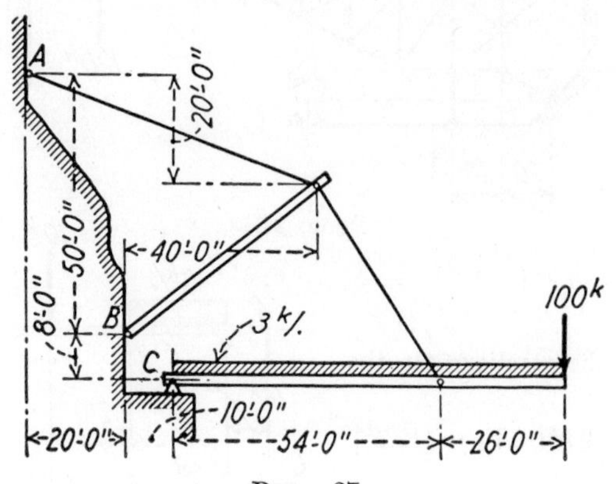

Prob. 27.

28. Find the reactions for the structure.

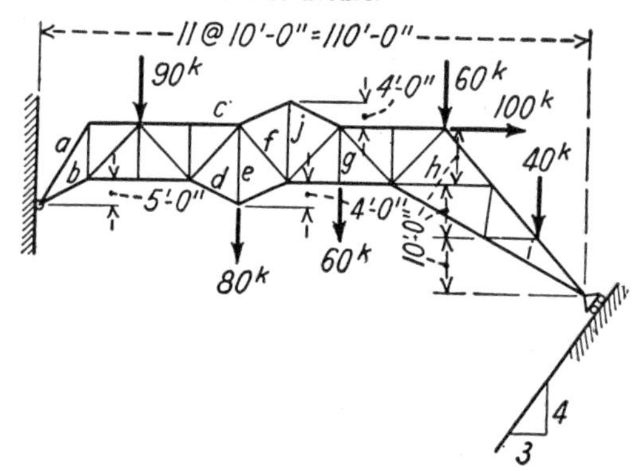

PROB. 28.

29. Calculate the reactions at *A*, *B*, *C*, *D*, and *E*.

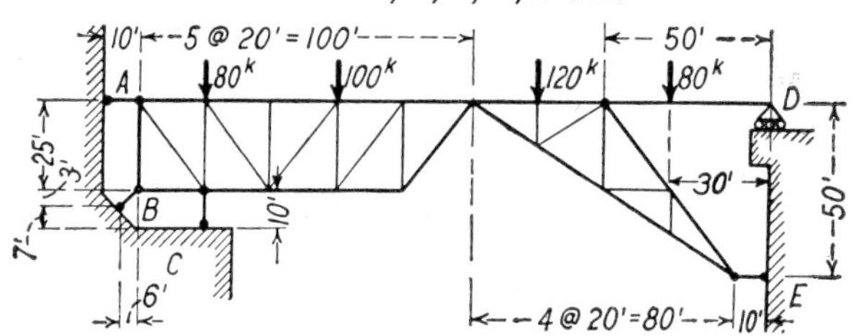

PROB. 29.

30. Calculate the reactions on the structure.

Ans. $V_1 = 0 \qquad V_2 = 425^k\uparrow$
$H_1 = 425^k\rightarrow \qquad H_2 = 425^k\leftarrow$

PROB. 30.

31. Calculate the reactions on the movable telpherage frame.

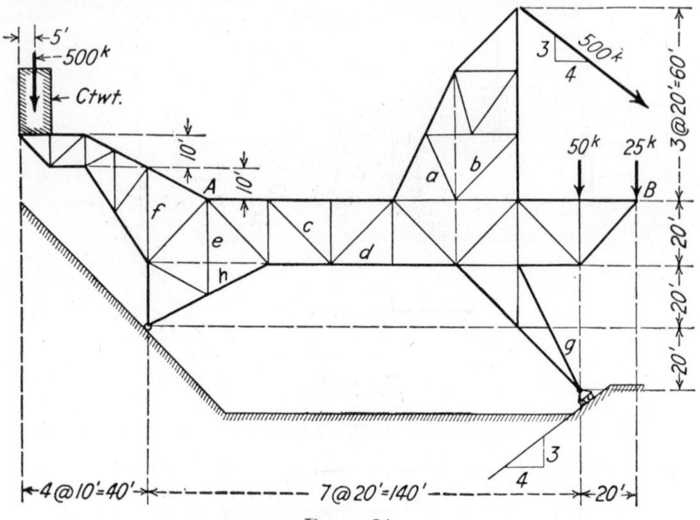

PROB. 31.

32. Calculate the reactions at A, B, and C.

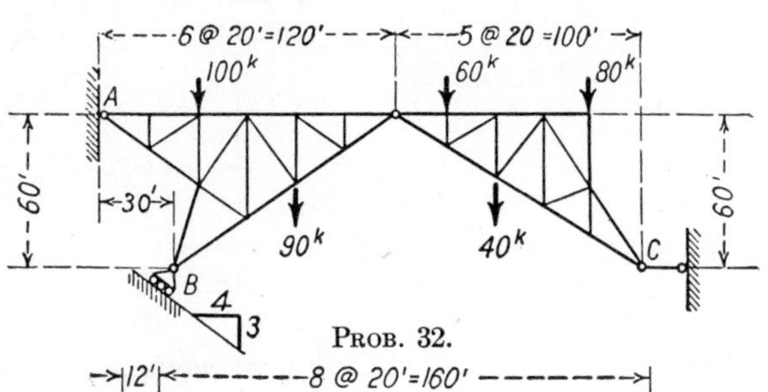

PROB. 32.

33. Calculate the reactions on the combined cargo hoist and gantry wharf crane.

Ans.

$V_1 = 235.4^k\downarrow$
$V_2 = 478.4^k\uparrow$
$H_1 = 313.9^k\leftarrow$
$H_2 = 77.9^k\rightarrow$

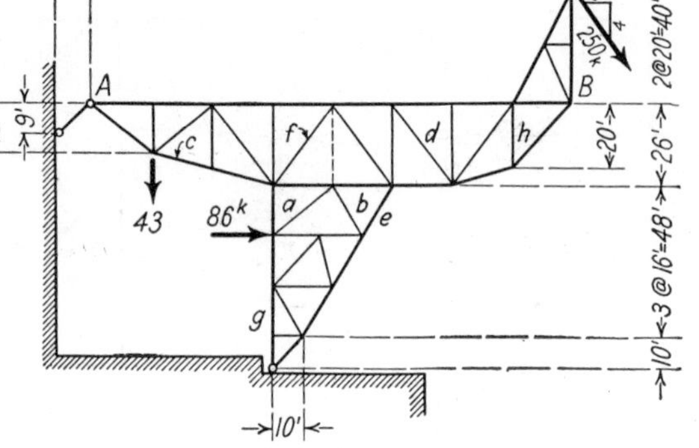

PROB. 33.

34. Calculate the reactions on the span.

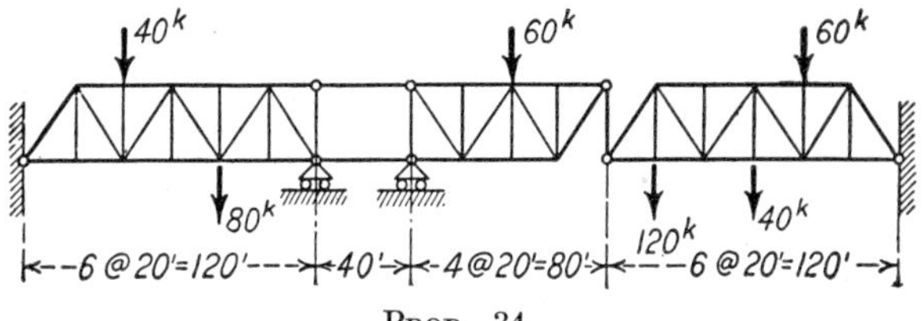

PROB. 34.

35. Calculate the reactions for the structure shown.

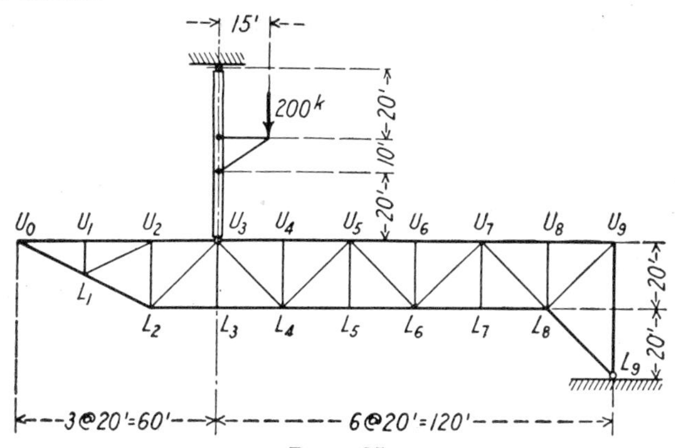

PROB. 35.

36. Calculate the reactions at *A* and *B* for the structure shown. The weight of the creeper and its load (applied at c. g.) is 80 kips, and the load of the structure itself may be taken as 54 kips at each bottom chord panel point.

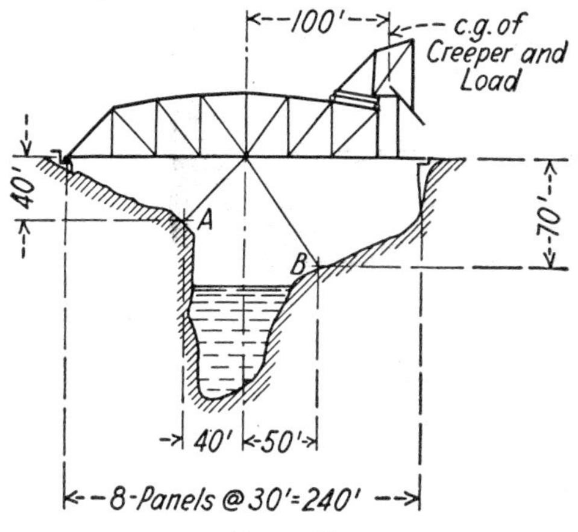

PROB. 36.

CHAPTER III

SHEARS AND MOMENTS — FIXED LOADS

35. In studying the internal stresses in a structure there is *one* and *only one* method of attack. The method is to pass an imaginary section cutting the structure into *two* parts, choose one of the parts, and apply the laws of statics to determine what *internal* forces must act on the cut section in order to hold the part under consideration in equilibrium against the known external forces.

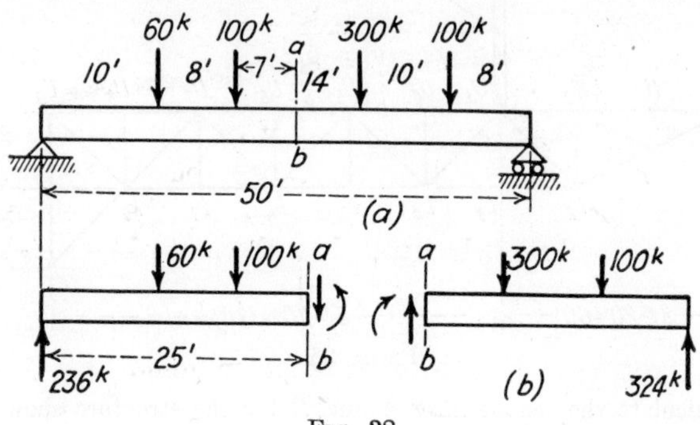

Fig. 38.

In making such an analysis two functions of the external loads are continually coming up. These functions are called the **shear** and the **bending moment.** For example, suppose that we wish to study the stresses at section *a–b* in the beam shown in Fig. 38 (*a*). Applying the method given above, pass an imaginary section at *a–b* cutting the beam into two parts, as shown in Fig. 38 (*b*), and consider the part on the left of the section. Adding up the external vertical forces at the left of the section, we find a resultant upward force of 76^k — this is the **shear** — and in order to satisfy the requirement $\Sigma V = 0$ there must be a vertical *internal* force of 76^k acting down on the section as shown in Fig. 38 (*b*). Taking the moments of the external forces to the left of the section about a point at the center of gravity of the section we obtain a resultant clockwise moment of 4300 ft.-kips — this is the **bending moment,** and in order to satisfy the requirement $\Sigma M = 0$ there must be an *internal* moment of 4300 ft.-kips acting on section a–b in a counter-clockwise direction. The internal moment is frequently called the **resisting moment** since it resists the effort of the external forces to bend the beam; i.e., it resists the bending moment of the external forces. As learned in mechanics of materials, the internal or resisting moment is a couple produced by the tensile and compressive stresses acting on the fibers of the beam. Since the uncut beam is in equilibrium these forces found by passing an imaginary plane at the section a–b must actually exist within the structure on this section, and must of course be exerted on the part of the beam to the left of the section by that part to the right. The same results will be obtained by considering the part of the beam to the right of the section a–b. There will be found necessary to hold the external forces on the right in equilibrium a vertical force of 76 k, but acting up instead of down, and a moment of 4300 ft.-kips, acting clockwise instead of counter-clockwise. As above, these forces must actually exist within the uncut structure at section a–b and must be exerted on the part of the beam to the right of the section by that part to the left.

36. Definitions.—We may now write definitions for shear and bending moment. It should be kept in mind that these are **definitions**; there is nothing to derive or prove, for they merely describe certain functions of the external loads which continually recur in the analysis of internal stresses and for which it is convenient to have a name.

SHEAR.—The shear at any section is *defined* as:

> **The algebraic sum of *all* the external forces acting parallel to the section on *either* side of the section.**

This definition should be carefully memorized and studied until it is thoroughly understood. It should be particularly impressed on the mind that *all* the external forces or components of external forces acting on the side considered which are *parallel* to the section must be included in the sum, but only those external forces on that side of the section. It is important also to understand clearly that external forces acting on *either* side may be used, and that that side which involves the smallest amount of work should be chosen; this will generally be that side on which the fewer external forces are acting. In general, sections are taken *normal to the axis of the beam.*

Moment.—Bending moment is *defined* as:

> **The algebraic sum of the moments of *all* the external forces acting on *either* side of the section taken about the center of gravity of the section.**

This definition also should be carefully memorized and studied until it is thoroughly understood. Again it is important to impress on the mind particularly that the moments of *all* the external forces acting on the side of the section considered must be included in the sum, but *only* those on that side. It is necessary to understand clearly that the moments of the external forces acting on *either* side of the section may be used, and that that side which involves the smallest amount of work should be chosen; this will generally be that side on which the fewer external forces are acting.

37. Signs.—The sign for shear is most conveniently determined by keeping in mind the beam shown in Fig. 39, on which a single concentrated load is shown acting. The reactions act as shown, and the shear on section *a–b* is taken as *positive.* The convention expressed by this figure may be stated in words by saying that when the external forces acting on the part of the beam to the *left* of the section tend to push that part *up,* the shear is positive, or when the external forces acting on the part of the beam to the *right* of the section tend to push that part *down* the shear is positive. Negative shear of course is the reverse.

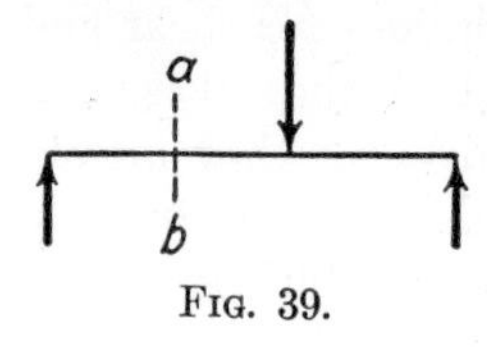

Fig. 39.

The most convenient convention for the sign of bending moments is that which calls moment producing **compression in the top fibers positive,** and **tension in the top fibers negative.** No other rule is necessary, and stating the convention in any other way tends to confusion rather than to clarity.

The same conventions should be used for vertical members, but in applying them in such cases the sheet should be turned so that the *right-hand side* becomes the *bottom.* For example, in Fig. 40 the signs of shear and moment at section *a–b* in the vertical member *BC* should be determined by turning the sheet around so that the right-hand side becomes the bottom. The end B is then the right-hand end. The part of the beam BC to the left of a–b then tends to move *up* and the shear is positive. The *top* fibers at a–b are in compression and the moment is positive.

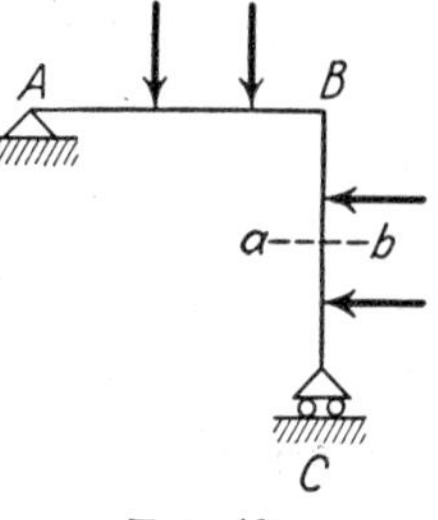

FIG. 40.

The sign conventions given above for columns are those adopted by Professor Hardy Cross in his treatment of statically indeterminate structures. They are convenient, automatic, and easy to remember, and errors in their application are nearly impossible.

38. Shear and Moment Diagrams.—It is frequently helpful in studying shears and moments to construct diagrams which show

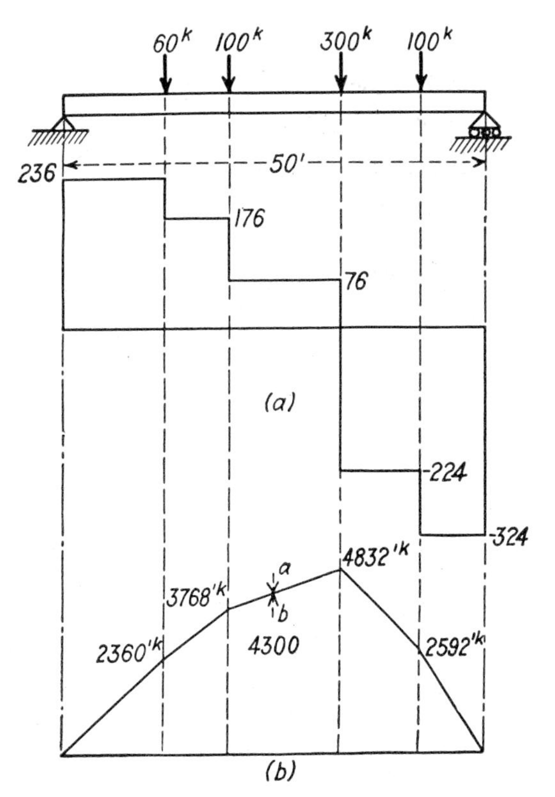

FIG. 41.

the variation in the shear, or in the moment, along the beam. This may be readily done by erecting at different points on the axis of the beam, or on a reference line of the same length, ordinates the length or height of which represent the magnitude of the shear, or of the moment, at the section where the ordinate is placed. A line, series of lines, or a curve connecting the tops of all the ordinates will then show the variation in the shear or moment across the beam. Positive shear and positive moment are generally plotted *above* the reference line. Reference lines for vertical members should be vertical, and positive shears and

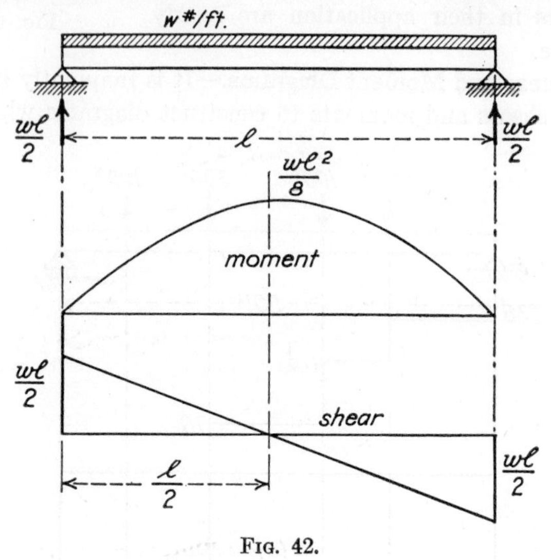

FIG. 42.

moments plotted *above* the line with reference to the right-hand side of the sheet as the bottom.

39. Examples.—There follow a number of examples showing shear and moment diagrams for beams under various conditions of loading. These should be carefully studied, keeping in mind the definitions and sign conventions given above. Figure 41 (*a*) and (*b*) shows the shear and moment diagrams for the beam of Fig. 38.

In Fig. 42 is shown a beam with a uniformly distributed load of w pounds per foot, the shear and moment diagrams being shown below the beam. As shown, the shear curve is a straight line and the moment curve is a parabola. The character of the shear or moment curve for any beam can be determined by writing the equation for shear or moment. Taking the origin at the left support, the equation for shear on this beam is

$$S = \frac{wl}{2} - wx$$

and the equation for moment,

$$M = \frac{wlx}{2} - \frac{wx^2}{2}$$

This may be written

$$M = \frac{w}{2} x (l - x)$$

or, if

$$x = a \text{ and } (l - x) = b$$

$$M = \tfrac{1}{2} wab$$

i.e., the bending moment at any section of a simple beam with a uniform load equals one-half the load per foot, times the product of the two segments into which the section divides the beam.

The shear will be a maximum when $x = 0$ or $x = l$ and will equal $\frac{wl}{2}$.

The moment will be a maximum when $x = \frac{l}{2}$ and will equal $\frac{wl^2}{8}$.

Care should be taken that only the uniform load to one side of the section is considered in calculating the shear or moment.

The expressions just given for bending moment on any section of a simple beam, ($M = \frac{1}{2}wab$) and at the center ($M = \frac{1}{8} wl^2$), should be remembered. In general it is objectionable to try to remember formulas for bending moment. However, it is so frequently necessary in practical work to calculate the bending moment at various points on a beam uniformly loaded, and at the load on a beam supporting a single concentrated load, that it is very convenient to keep in mind the expressions given above and those given below in Fig. 43.

Figure 43 (*a*) and (*b*) shows the shear and moment diagrams for beams supporting a single concentrated load. It should be noted that when a single concentrated load is applied at the center of the span the maximum bending moment is twice that on the same span with the same total load uniformly distributed.

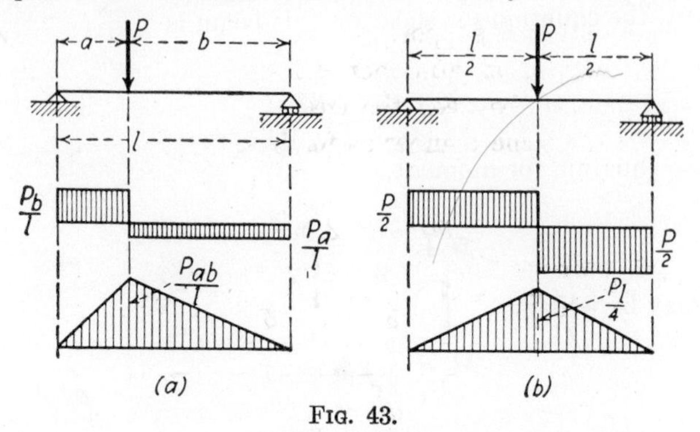

Fig. 43.

In Fig. 44 is shown a simple beam supporting several concentrated loads with its shear and moment diagrams below. It should be

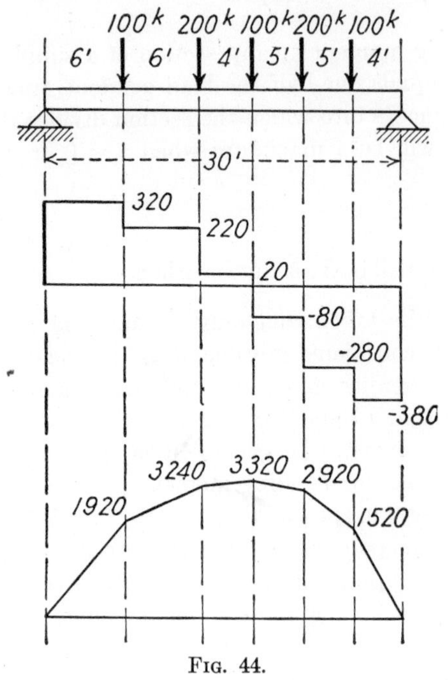

Fig. 44.

observed that the shear curve is a series of horizontal lines with a change in ordinate under each load equal to the load, while the moment curve is a series of straight lines, the equation changing at each load.

A cantilever beam supporting concentrated loads is shown in Fig. 45 with its shear and moment diagrams. The values of shear and moment between the free end and the fixed end are computed in the same manner as for beams simply supported at each end.

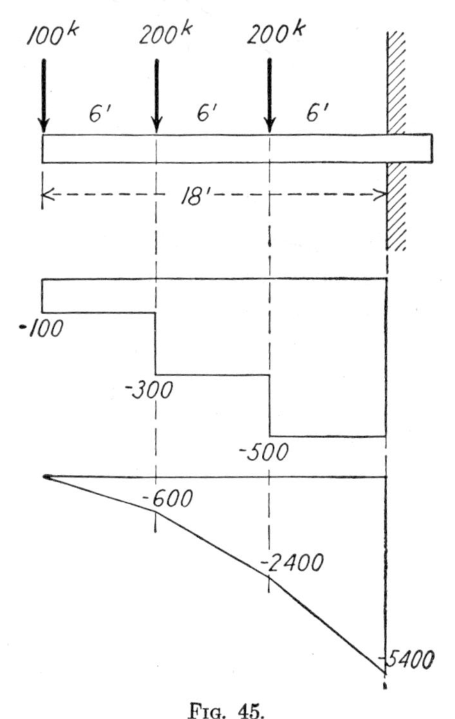

Fig. 45.

A very common form of loading is a uniform load (w pounds per foot) combined with several concentrated loads. The shear curve will be a series of straight lines having a slope equal to w pounds per foot and a change in ordinate under each concentrated load equal to the load; the moment curve will be a series of parabolic arcs, the equations changing at each concentrated load. Such a beam with its shear and moment diagrams is shown in Fig. 46.

A beam with a uniformly varying load is shown in Fig. 47 with its shear and moment diagrams and their respective equations.

The shear diagram is a parabola and the moment diagram a curve of the third degree.

It will be seldom that a structure is encountered the loading of which is not one of, or some combination of, the three types given,

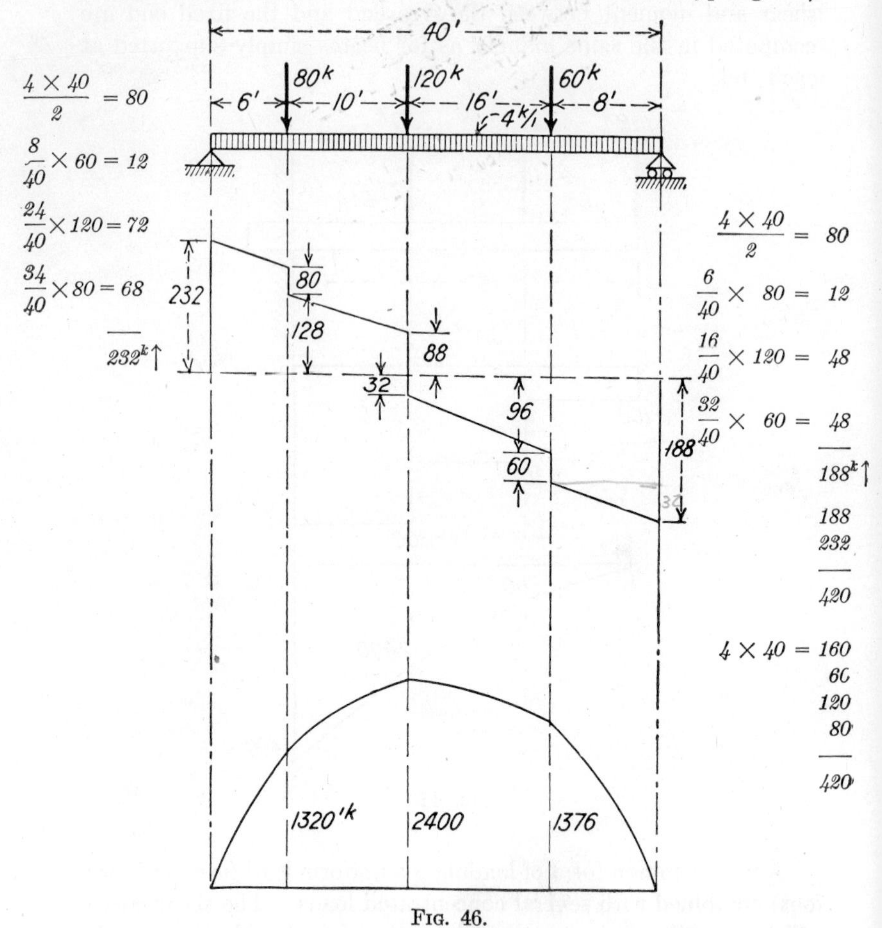

Fig. 46.

generally one, or a combination of the first two. In cases of complicated loading it may be found advantageous to calculate the shear or moment for each type of loading separately and add these values algebraically.

In Figs. 48 and 49 are shown beams having vertical as well as horizontal portions. The shear and moment diagrams should be very carefully studied with reference to the sign conventions adopted.

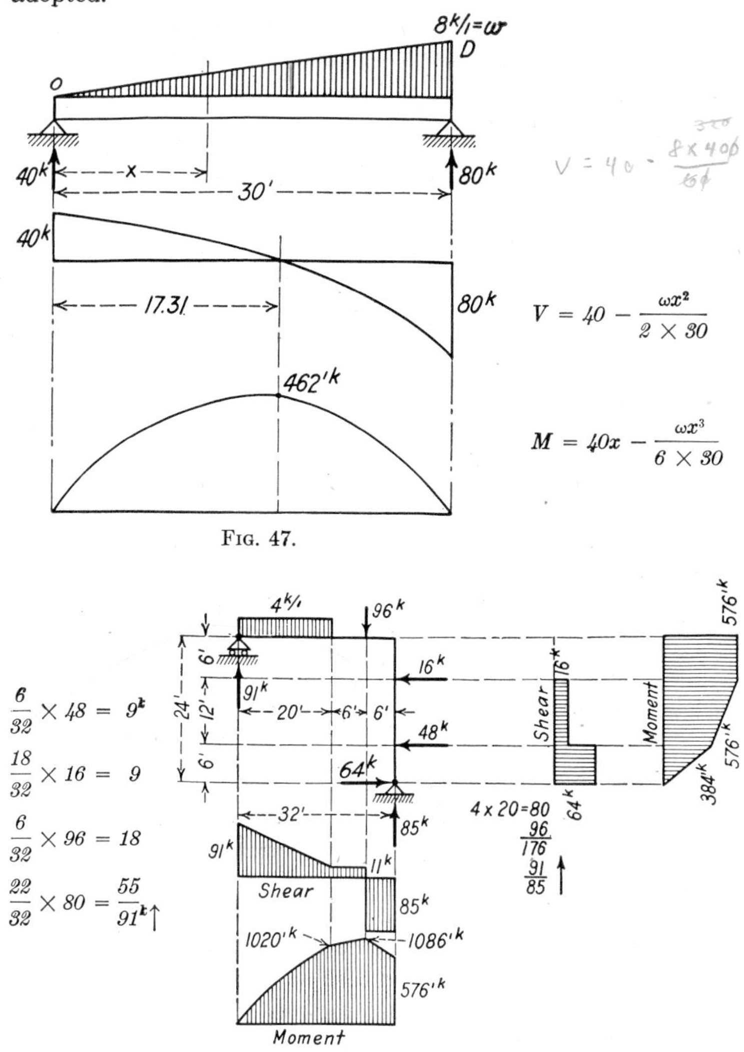

Fig. 47.

Fig. 48.

40. Relation between Loading and Shear.—The *definitions* of shear and moment given above fix certain relations between the loading and the shear and between the shear and the moment which are very useful. It is important to understand these relations clearly and to keep them in mind.

In Fig. 50 there is shown a beam subjected to miscellaneous loads and the resulting shear and moment diagrams.

Pass any section, as 1–1, and consider the part of the beam on the left. The shear is

$$V_{1-1} = R_1 - w_1 a - P_1 - P_2$$

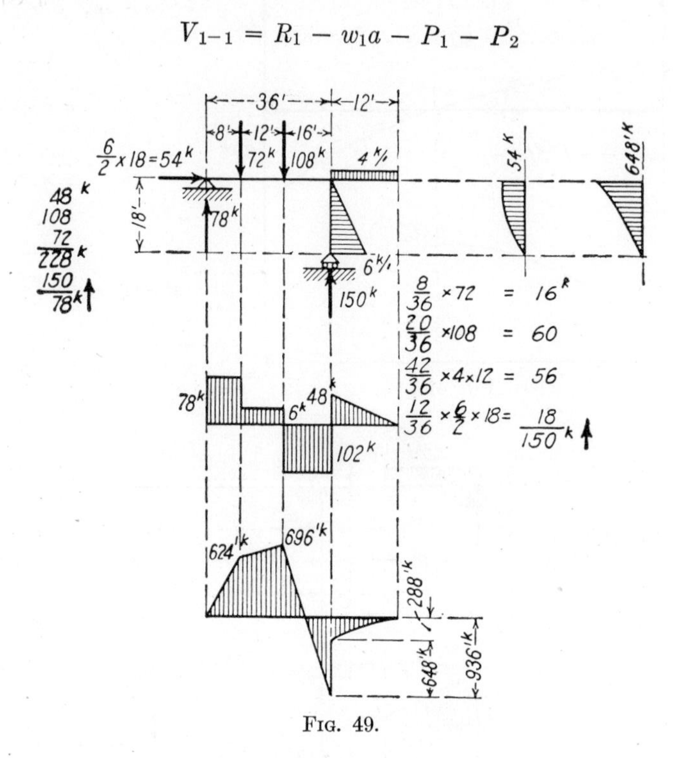

FIG. 49.

At a section a short distance dx farther along the beam, the shear is the same; i.e., there has been no change in shear between the sections, or we may say that the *rate of change* of the shear between the sections is zero. Evidently the shear line should be horizontal at this section. Pass another section as 2–2 and consider the part of the beam to the left. The distributed load through which the section 2–2 is passed is of varying magnitude and may be taken as p pounds per foot at any section, p being a variable. Calling the part of the distributed load between the section 2–2 and the left end of this load W, as shown in Fig. 50, the shear at 2–2 is

$$V_{2-2} = R_1 - w_1 a - P_1 - P_2 - W \tag{1}$$

If the *change* in shear between section 2–2 and a section a short distance dx farther along the beam is dV, evidently the shear at the latter section is

$$V_{2-2} + dV = R_1 - w_1 a - P_1 - P_2 - W - pdx \tag{2}$$

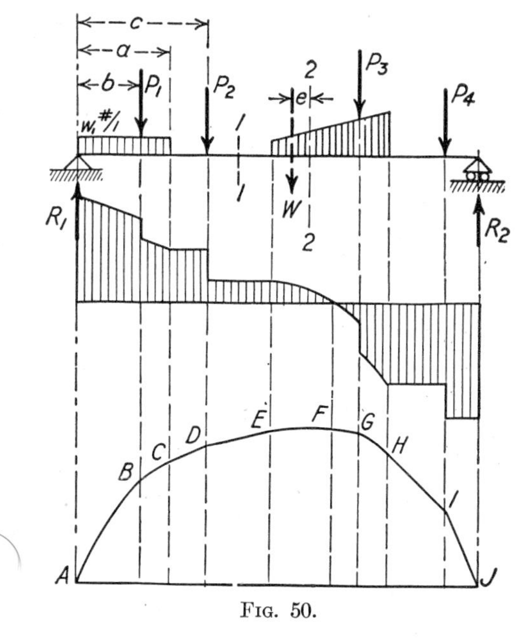

FIG. 50.

Subtracting (1) from (2)

$$dV = -\, pdx$$

and

$$\frac{dV}{dx} = -\, p$$

or **the rate of change of the shear at any section is the load per unit of length at that section.** The minus sign in front of p merely indicates that the shear is decreasing, as is clear from the shear diagram.

If a section is taken under a concentrated load, it should be clear that the *rate of change* of the shear is infinite, since we have a finite load divided by an infinitely short length. This means evidently that the slope of the shear diagram at a concentrated load is infinite: i.e., the tangent of the angle between the shear line and the reference line is infinite, or the angle is 90°, and at a concentrated load the shear line becomes vertical.

41. Relation between Shear and Bending Moment.—In Fig. 50 consider the bending moment at any section, such as 2–2 for example, and call the distance from the left reaction to this section, x. If e is the distance from the section 2–2 to the center of gravity of the portion of distributed load of weight W (see above) the bending moment at section 2–2 evidently is

$$M_{2-2} = R_1x - P_1(x - b) - P_2(x - c) - w_1a\left(x - \frac{a}{2}\right) - We \tag{3}$$

If dM is the *change* in bending moment between section 2–2 and a section a short distance dx farther along the beam, the bending moment at the latter section is

$$M_{2-2} + dM = R_1(x + dx) - P_1(x + dx - b) - P_2(x + dx - c) - w_1a\left(x + dx - \frac{a}{2}\right) - W(e + dx) - pdx\cdot\frac{dx}{2} \tag{4}$$

where p, as above, is the magnitude of the variable distributed load at the section under consideration. Subtracting (3) from (4), and neglecting $pdx\cdot\frac{dx}{2}$ as a quantity too small to be conceived

$$dM = R_1dx - P_1dx - P_2dx - w_1adx - Wdx$$

and

$$\frac{dM}{dx} = R_1 - P_1 - P_2 - w_1a - W = V_{2-2}$$

or **the rate of change of the bending moment at any section is the shear at that section.**

If a section is taken at a concentrated load, there is a sudden change in shear and, therefore, a sudden change in the rate of change of the bending moment: in other words, there must be a sudden change in the direction of the moment curve at a concentrated load.

It is convenient to deal with some loads as concentrated loads, but it should be clearly understood that a load concentrated at a mathematical point is a physical impossibility. It is physically impossible to have a shear line which has a vertical portion at a load or a moment curve which suddenly "breaks" or changes from one direction to another. In Fig. 51, for example, is a beam

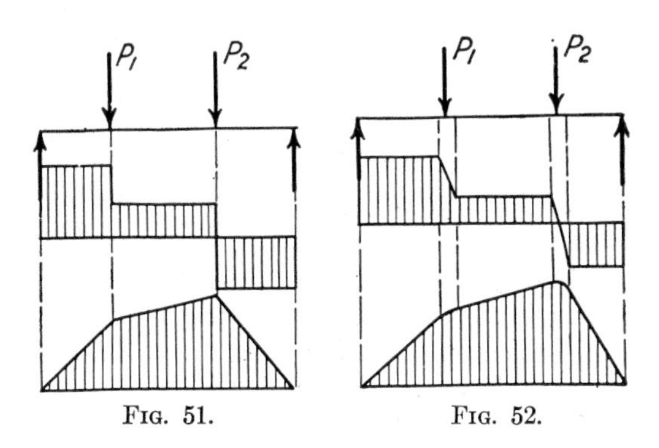

Fig. 51. Fig. 52.

with two concentrated loads. It is usual and convenient to deal with this beam as shown in Fig. 51 and to consider that its shear and moment diagrams are as shown there. The physical facts are, however, that the loads P_1 and P_2 are actually distributed over *some* length, however small, and the true shear and moment diagrams are as shown in Fig. 52.

The relations between load and shear and between shear and moment discussed above are very important. They should be carefully studied.

42. In making the calculations for bending moment diagrams two very important corollaries of the relation between shear and bending moment are often very convenient.

(1) From the fact that the rate of change of the bending moment is the shear, it follows directly that the bending moment passes through a maximum or a minimum value wherever the shear passes through zero. Having constructed the shear diagram,

application of this principle fixes at once the location of the high and low points on the bending moment diagram.

(2) Since the *rate* of change of the bending moment is the shear, it is evident that the *total* change in bending moment between two sections separated a distance dx is Vdx. That is,

$$dM = Vdx$$

and

$$M_{1-2} = \int_1^2 Vdx = \text{area under shear diagram between sections 1 and 2}$$

where

M_{1-2} = the *change* in bending moment between sections 1 and 2.

The application of the second of these principles is often quite convenient in computing the value of moments by the area of the shear diagram. The student should check the values of moment shown in Figs. 41 to 49 by making use of both of these principles and should note that, since the moment at the reaction of a simply supported beam is zero, the moment at any point in such a beam will be equal to the area under the shear diagram between the end and that point, taking proper account of algebraic signs.

The shape of the moment diagram may be quite easily determined from the fact that the shear is the rate of change of the bending moment. Where the shear diagram is horizontal the change in moment is constant and the moment diagram will therefore be a straight line, and will have a positive or negative slope according to whether the shear is positive or negative. Where the positive value of the shear is decreasing or the negative value increasing (summing from the left), the moment diagram will be a curve and will be concave downward. The converse necessarily follows.

43. Application of Statics to Continuous Structures.—Continuous structures are statically indeterminate: i.e., it is impossible to determine their reactions, shears, moments, or internal stresses by the laws of statics alone. In the analysis of such structures it is necessary, as previously pointed out, to establish conditions of equilibrium based on the elastic properties of the structure in addition to the conditions furnished by the laws of statics. The number of conditions thus established in any case must be such that the number of independent equations, including those furnished by the laws of statics, is equal to the number of unknowns to be determined. The complete solution of such problems is, of course, out of place in a text treating statics alone. However, after the number of unknowns has been reduced to that which may be determined by the laws of statics, the problem may well be discussed as an exercise in the application of these laws.

In Fig. 53, for example, is shown a structure having eight unknown reactions: two at A, one at C, two at E and three at F. There are available the three laws of statics and the additional fact that there can be no moment at D between the horizontal continuous beam $BCDF$ and the vertical member DE. The hinge at D is located at the center of gravity of the continuous beam

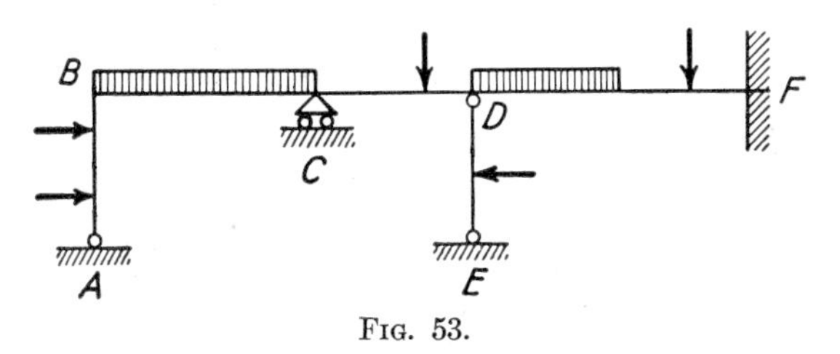

FIG. 53.

$BCDF$ but is shown below the line of the beam in Fig. 53 for clearness and to indicate that the beam is continuous around the hinge. It is necessary, therefore, to determine four unknowns from the elastic properties of the structure. The normal procedure would be to calculate by some appropriate method the bending moments at B, C, D, and F in the horizontal beam. These bending moments having been determined, the remainder of the problem, calculation of the reactions, shears and moments, is one in the application of the laws of statics. In Fig. 54 values are assigned for bending moments at B, C, D, and F, the reactions calculated, and the shear and moment diagrams constructed. Problems of this kind furnish excellent training in the application of the laws of statics, and the solution given in Fig. 54 should be carefully studied.

The bending moments which exist in the continuous beam at B, C, D, and F have been calculated and are given in the figure. The knowledge of these four bending moments and the fact that because of the hinge at D there can be no moment between the vertical member DE and the horizontal member $BCDF$, furnish five conditions of equilibrium in addition to the three laws of statics, thus making it possible to determine the eight reactions on the structure. One of these, the moment at the wall at F, is known at once, of course, since it is the indeterminate moment in the beam at F, and this was given by the same operation used to calculate the moment at B, C, and D.

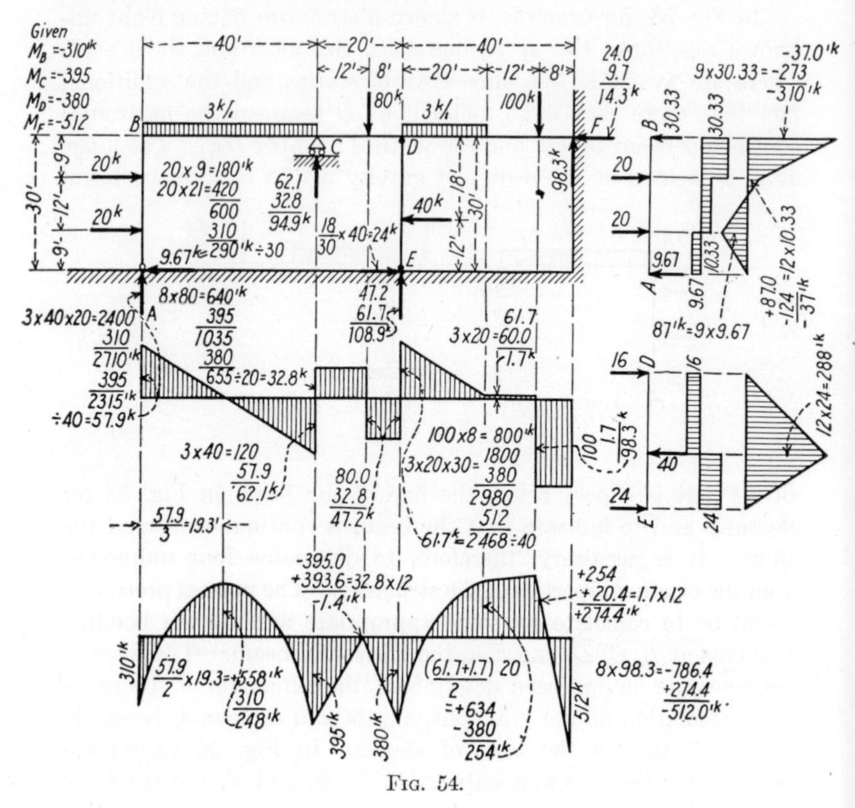

FIG. 54.

The calculations shown in Fig. 54 are brief but complete, and the following explanation of the method of attack should remove any difficulty in understanding them.

The calculation of the reactions and the construction of the shear diagram have been combined into a single operation in this problem — or a more accurate statement would be that the reactions have been determined by calculating the shears on each side of each reaction, and these shears have furnished the data necessary for the construction of the shear diagram as well as determining the reactions.

The horizontal reaction at A is found by considering the vertical portion BA cut away from the rest of the structure by an imaginary plane an infinitesimal distance to the right of B, and taking moments about B of all forces between A and B. The unknown shear at B passes through the center of moments, as does the vertical reaction at A. Since the bending moment at B is known, the only unknown entering into the sum of the moments about B is the horizontal reaction at A. The calculations for determining this reaction are shown at the right of the hinge at A in Fig. 54.

The shear just to the right of B and the shear just to the left of C are next calculated by considering the part of the beam between these sections cut away from the rest of the structure. The part considered and the forces acting on the cut ends are shown in Fig. 55. Taking moments about C:

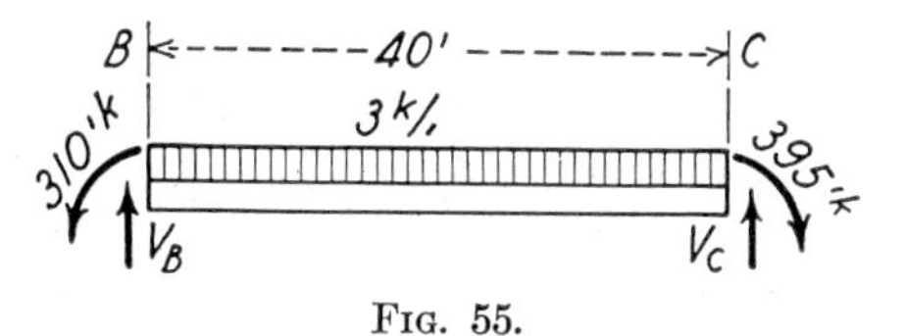

FIG. 55.

i.e., the right-hand end, the shear V_B is directly determined by the calculations given at the left-hand end of the shear diagram in Fig. 54. The shear V_C then follows at once from the principle $\Sigma V = 0$. The calculations are given adjacent to the corresponding ordinate in the shear diagram in Fig. 54. These data determine the vertical reaction at A and fix the shear diagram between AB and BC.

Proceeding in the same manner, sections are passed an infinitesimal distance to the right of C and to the left of D. Considering the portion of the beam cut away from the structure by these sections enables the determination of the shear just to the right of C, as shown by the calculations adjacent to this ordinate in the shear diagram in Fig. 54. The shear just to the left of D follows directly from application of the principle $\Sigma V = 0$. Knowing the shear just to the left and just to the right of C, enables us to determine that the reaction here is $62.1 + 32.8 = 94.9^k$ acting up as shown.

The calculations necessary to determine the remaining reactions and finish the construction of the shear diagram follow the same procedure and need no further explanation.

Application of the first of the principles given in Art. 42 fixes the point of maximum bending moment in the span BC, and appli-

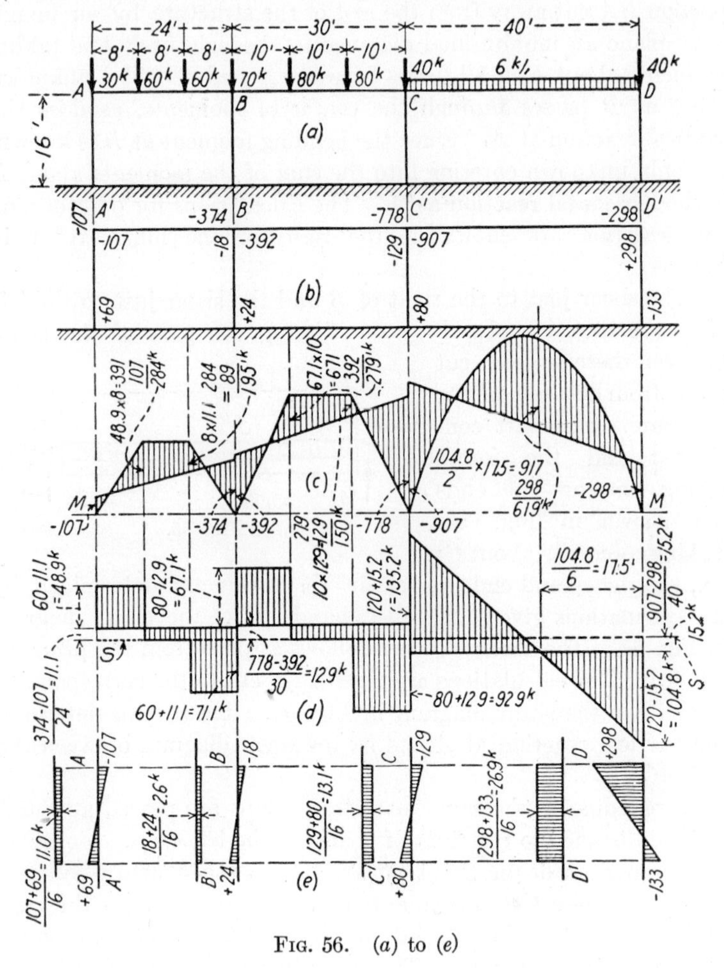

FIG. 56. (a) to (e)

cation of the second gives very simply the magnitude of this bending moment as shown by the calculations adjacent to this ordinate in the bending moment diagram in Fig. 54. The same principles are used in calculations for the remainder of the moment diagram.

44. In Fig. 56 (a) is shown a structure similar to that in Fig.

54. In Fig. 56 (*b*) there are given the bending moments at the ends of each column and each girder, these moments having been

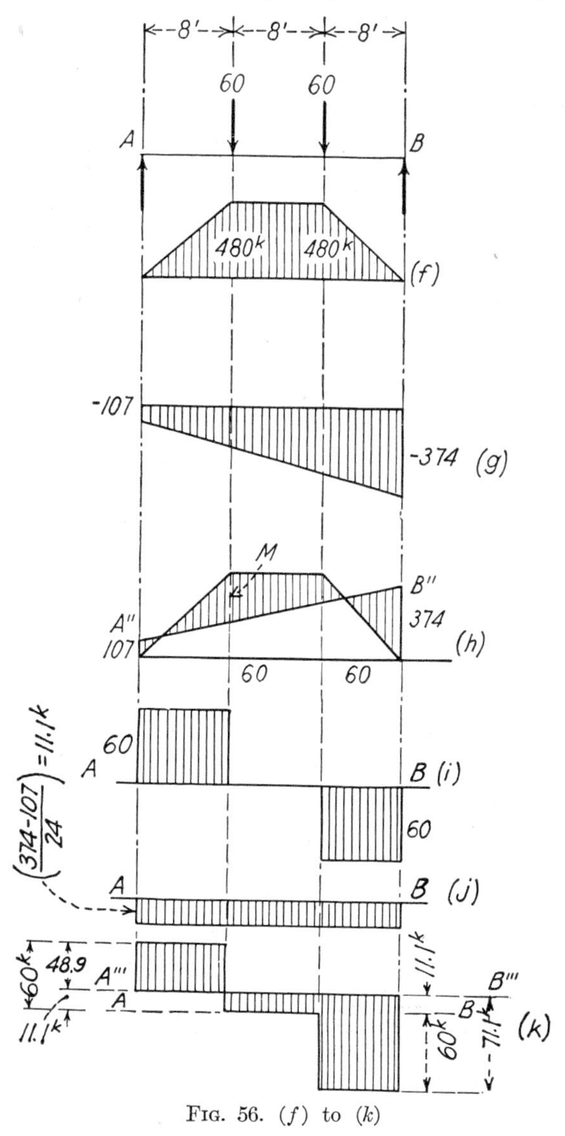

FIG. 56. (*f*) to (*k*)

calculated by methods applicable to indeterminate structures. The remainder of the problem, the construction of shear and moment diagrams and the calculation of the reactions, requires only the application of the laws of statics. The methods presented in connection with the problem in Fig. 54 are adequate in any such problem, but in order to illustrate a somewhat different procedure a complete solution is given.

In constructing the moment diagram the procedure is to draw a bending moment diagram for each span as a simple beam, i.e., the portion of the beam *A–B* is considered as a simple beam supporting the loads between these points, as is done also for the portions *B–C* and *C–D*. From this simple beam moment diagram there is then subtracted (or added algebraically) the moment diagram due to the end moments. For the portion *A–B*, for example, the simple beam moment diagram is as shown in Fig. 56 (*f*). The moment diagram for the end moments given in Fig. 56 (*b*) would evidently be as shown in Fig. 56 (*g*). It should be clear that we may subtract the moment diagram in Fig. 56 (*g*) from that given in Fig. 56 (*f*) by simply plotting the former on the latter but *above* the reference line. The resulting diagram is as shown in Fig. 56 (*h*). The shaded portion then represents the true moment diagram for the part of the beam *AB*. The bending moment at any section is measured vertically from the reference line $A'' B''$ — thus the moment under the first load from the left end is represented by the vertical ordinate M. Proceeding in the same manner with the other spans results in the moment diagram shown in Fig. 56 (*c*).

The shear diagram is drawn in a similar manner. The simple beam shear diagram is drawn as shown in Fig. 56 (*i*), and from this is subtracted the shear diagram resulting from the end moments at A and B, the latter shear diagram being shown in Fig. 56 (*j*). As in the moment diagram this is simply done by plotting the diagram in (*j*) on that in (*i*), but *above* the line. The resulting diagram is as shown in (*k*) and the ordinates are measured from the new reference line $A''' B'''$. Treating the other spans in the same manner results in the shear diagram shown in Fig. 56 (*d*).

The shear and moment diagrams for the columns are shown in Fig. 56 (*e*). The reactions at A', B', C' and D' are easily computed from the data given in Fig. 56, (*a*) to (*e*) inclusive, given also that the columns are 16 ft. high.

45. Spans with Floorbeams.—Very often the loads to which a beam or girder is subjected are not applied to it directly but to a secondary framing system which is supported by the beam or girder. For example, in Fig. 57 (*a*) there is shown in plan and sectional elevation a bridge in which the roadway is supported on longitudinal beams marked S in the figure, and generally called *stringers* or *joists.* These stringers are supported by the transverse beams marked F in the figure, and generally called *floorbeams.* The floorbeams in turn are connected to the main bridge girders marked G. Consequently, any loads which are applied to the roadway are transmitted to the main girders at certain fixed points, the points at which the floorbeams are connected. Similarly in Fig. 57 (*b*) is shown in plan and sectional elevation the framing for a typical floor panel in a building. In this case the

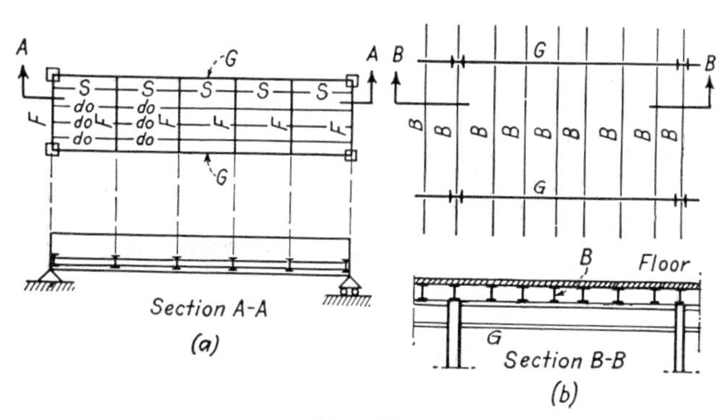

FIG. 57.

floor is supported on beams marked B, generally called floorbeams or joists. These beams or joists are supported by the girders marked G. Here, as in the bridge, the load is applied to the girder at certain fixed points. The joists, B, are generally framed into the girders, G, with their tops in about the same planes, but in Fig. 57 (*b*) they are shown resting on top of the girders to show more clearly how the floor loads are delivered to the girders. Although the entire floor panel may be covered with a uniformly distributed load, the girders, G, are subjected to a series of concentrated loads acting at the points where the joists rest.

46. Bending Moment in Spans with Floorbeams.—In Fig. 58, (*a*) and (*b*), are shown two girders having the same length and each loaded with a uniformly distributed load of 4000 lb. per ft. which is applied to the girders through joists as shown. In Fig.

58 (*a*) the spacing of the joists is regular, and in Fig. 58 (*b*) it is irregular. Under each beam is shown in dotted lines the parabolic bending moment diagram which would result if the load were applied directly to the girders instead of through the joists. It should be observed that under each concentrated load the magnitude of the bending moment is shown as exactly the same whether the load is applied directly to the girder or through the joists indicated in the figure. The student should show that this is necessarily correct for a uniformly distributed load, whether the joist spacing is regular or irregular. In Fig. 58, (*a*) and (*b*), the load is shown as uniformly distributed, but the statement that

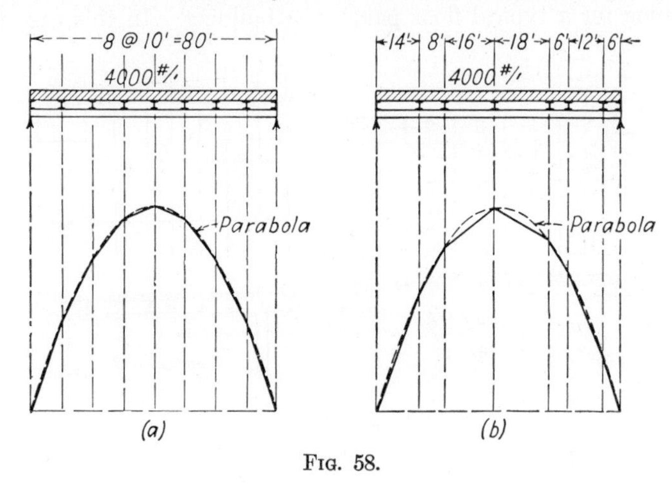

FIG. 58.

the bending moment is the same at the joist points (or panel points) as though the loads were applied directly to the beam is true whether the load is a uniformly distributed load, a variable distributed load, or any combination of distributed and concentrated loads.

47. Importance of Shears and Moments.—A thorough understanding of shears and moments is a fundamental requirement in structural engineering. This is as true in the analysis of frames as in beams and girders. The constantly widening use of continuous construction in all materials and forms, and the growing necessity for better and more accurate design of such constructions, have resulted in the development of powerful modern methods of analysis. These methods in general depend on the calculation of statically indeterminate moments at controlling points and have increased the importance of a comprehensive knowledge, and facility in the use, of shears and moments. There is no portion of the theory of structures which will better repay careful study. This is true whether the student intends to follow his course in statics with one in statically indeterminate structures (which has become a necessity for the modern structural engineer), or to pursue only the usual undergraduate work.

PROBLEMS

In all problems involving shear or moment diagrams, plot positive values above horizontal base lines and to the left of vertical base lines. Compute the controlling ordinates (i.e., maximum and minimum, and values occurring at loads or supports) and mark them on the diagram.

37. Draw the shear and moment diagrams for the beam shown.

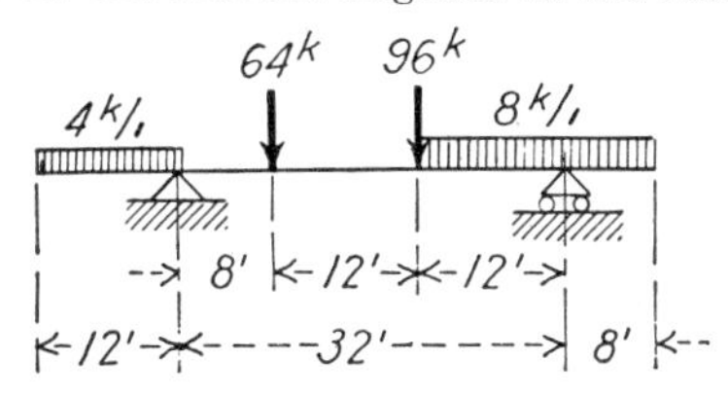

PROB. 37.

38. Draw the shear and moment diagrams for the beam shown.

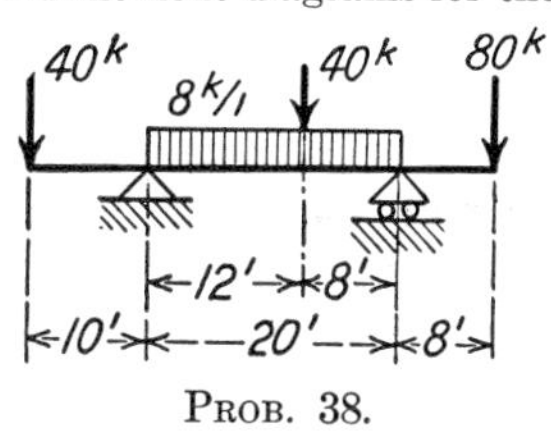

PROB. 38.

39. Draw the shear and moment diagrams for the beam shown.

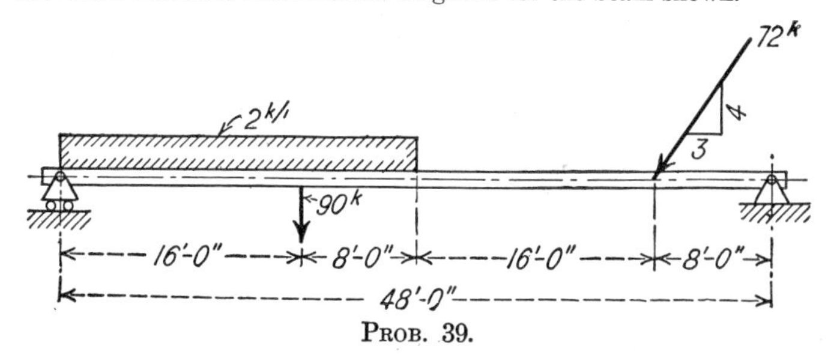

PROB. 39.

40. Draw the shear and moment diagrams for the beam shown.

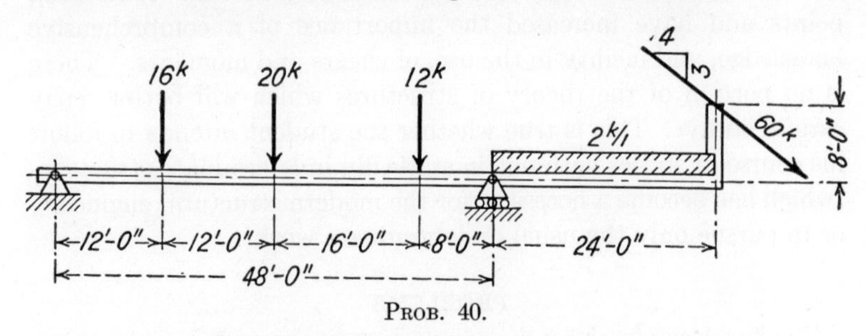

PROB. 40.

41. Draw the shear and moment diagrams for the structure shown.

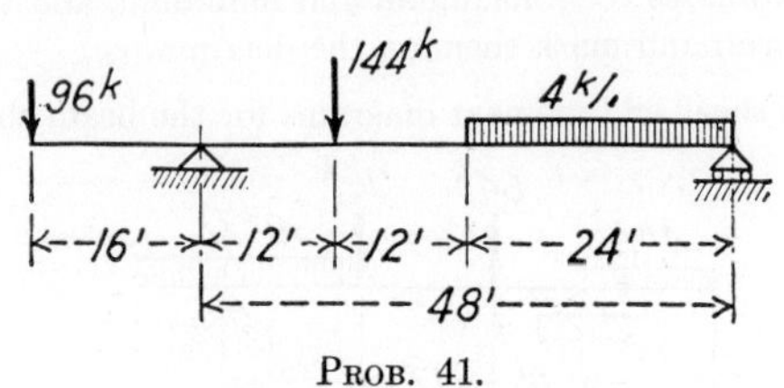

PROB. 41.

42. Draw the shear and moment diagrams for the structure shown.

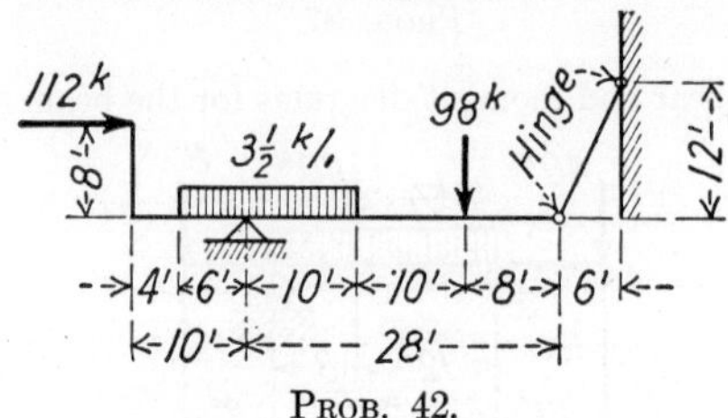

PROB. 42.

43. Draw the shear and moment diagrams for the structure shown.

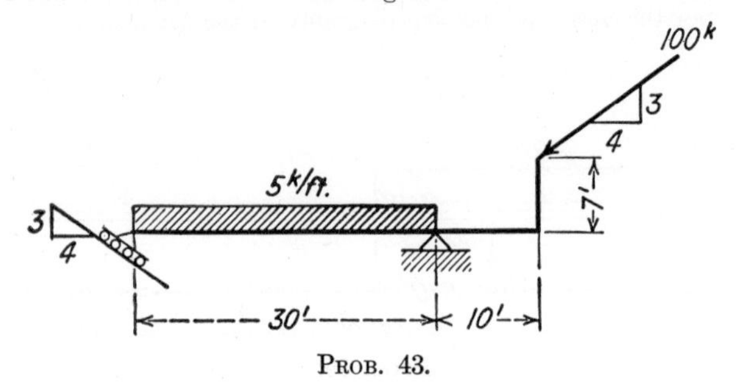

PROB. 43.

44. Draw the shear and moment diagrams for the structure shown.

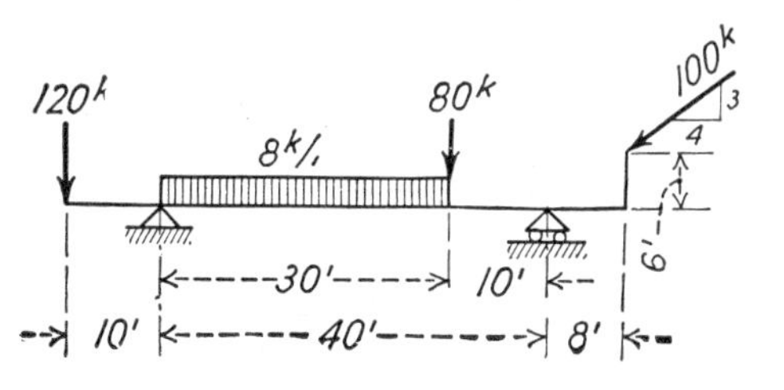

PROB. 44.

45. Draw the shear and moment diagrams for the structure shown.

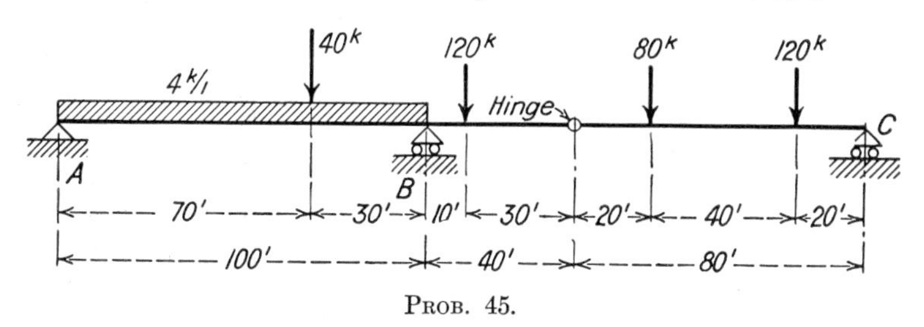

PROB. 45.

46. Draw the shear and moment diagrams for the structure shown. Consider a strip 1 ft. in length perpendicular to the page.

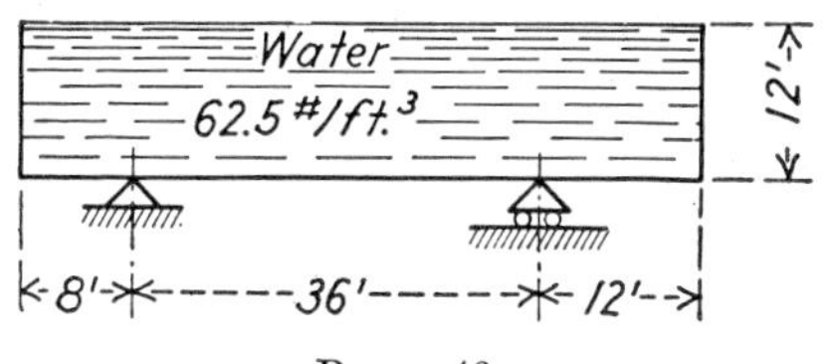

PROB. 46.

47. Draw the shear and moment diagrams for the structure shown. Consider a strip 1 ft. in length perpendicular to the page.

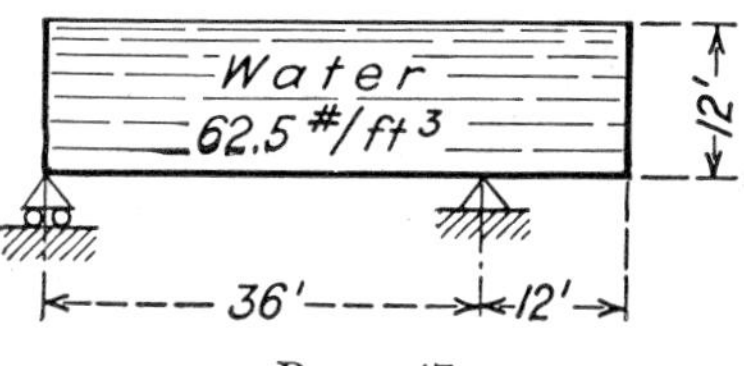

PROB. 47.

48. Draw the shear and moment diagrams for the structure shown.

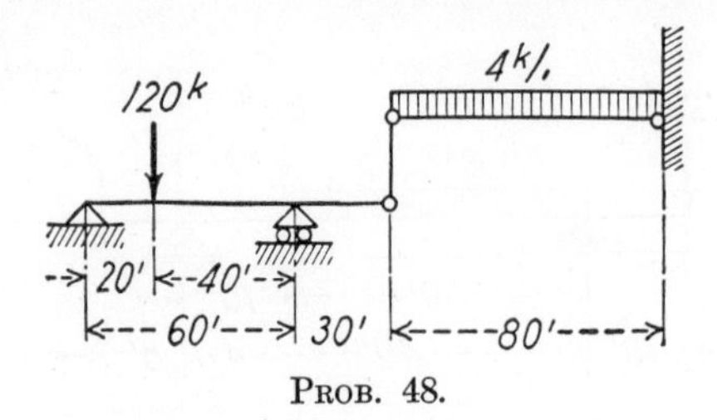

PROB. 48.

49. Draw the shear and moment diagrams for the structure shown.

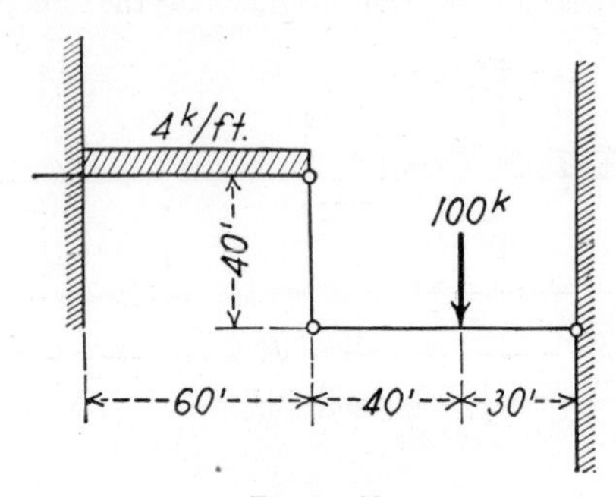

PROB. 49.

50. Draw the shear and moment diagrams for the structure shown.

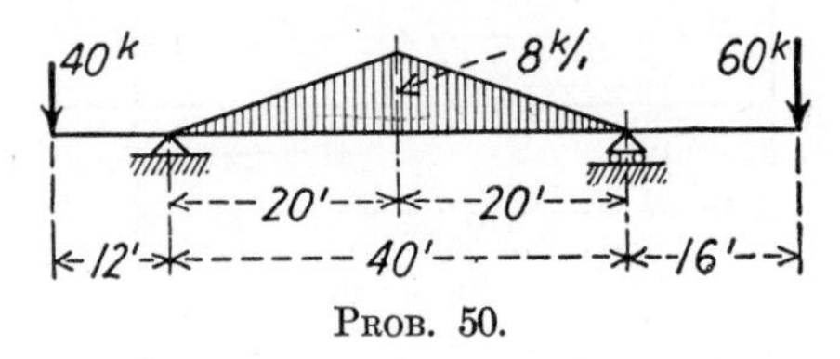

PROB. 50.

51. Draw the shear and moment diagrams for the structure shown.

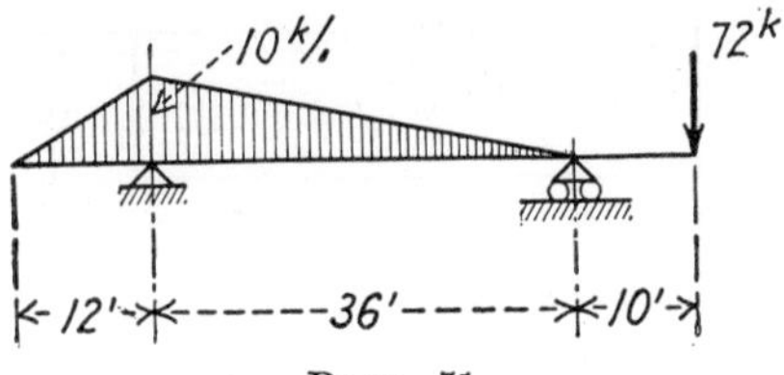

PROB. 51.

52. Draw the shear and moment diagrams for the structure shown. (Beam continuous through center support.)

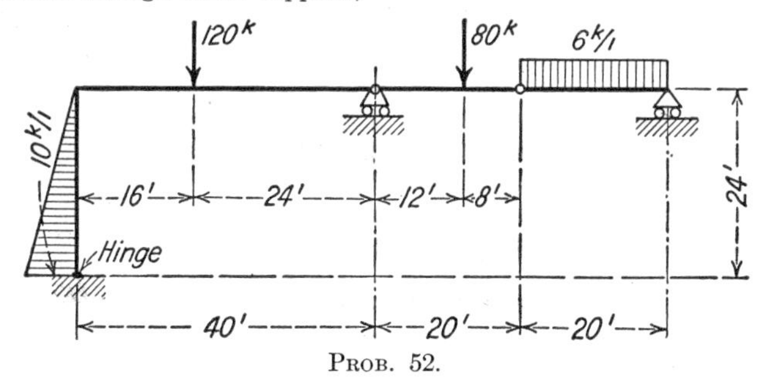

PROB. 52.

53. Draw the shear and moment diagrams for the structure shown.

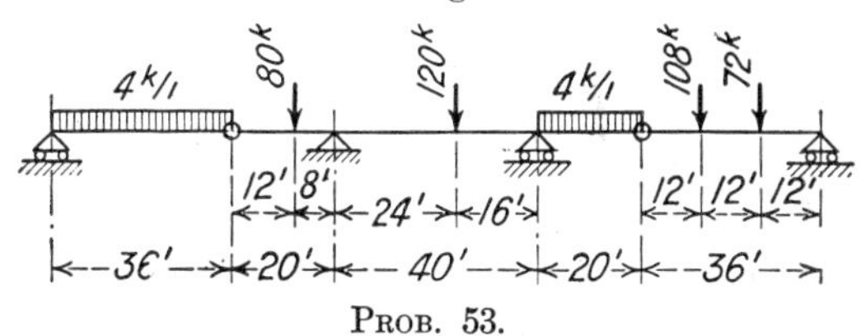

PROB. 53.

54. Draw the shear and moment diagrams for the beam AB.

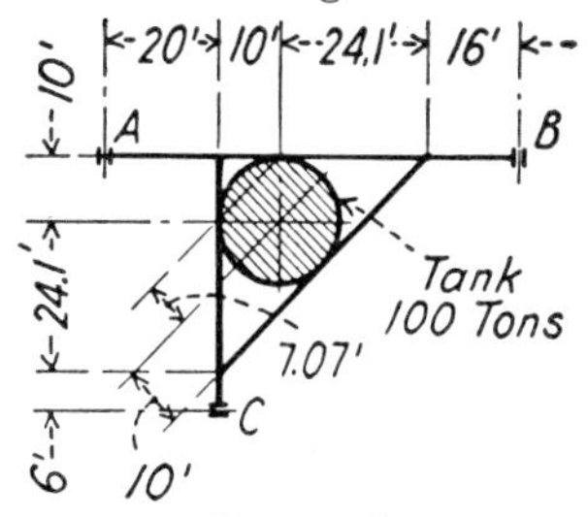

PROB. 54.

55. This shows diagrammatically a barge to be used in connection with a bridge erection by floating. The 400^k load applied to the barge is to be taken as distributed uniformly over the 5-ft. base. Draw the shear and moment diagrams for the barge as a whole.

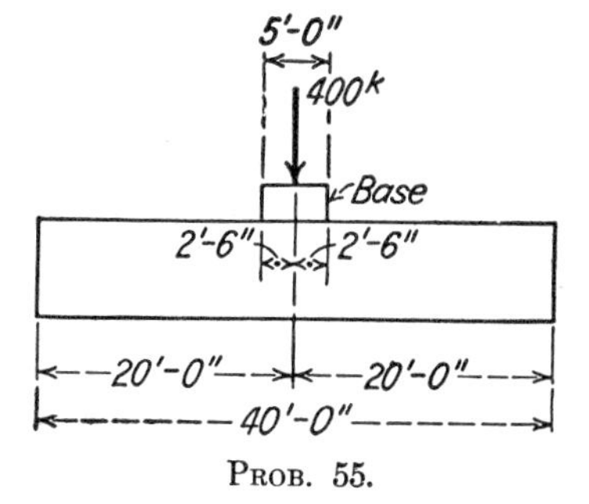

PROB. 55.

56. Draw the shear and moment diagrams for the structure shown.

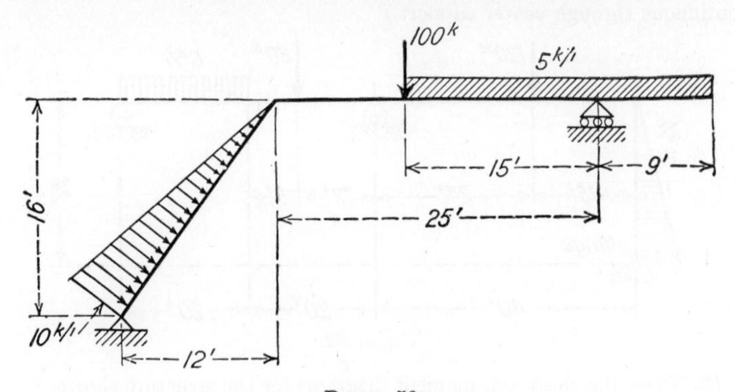

PROB. 56.

57. Draw the shear and moment diagrams for the structure shown.

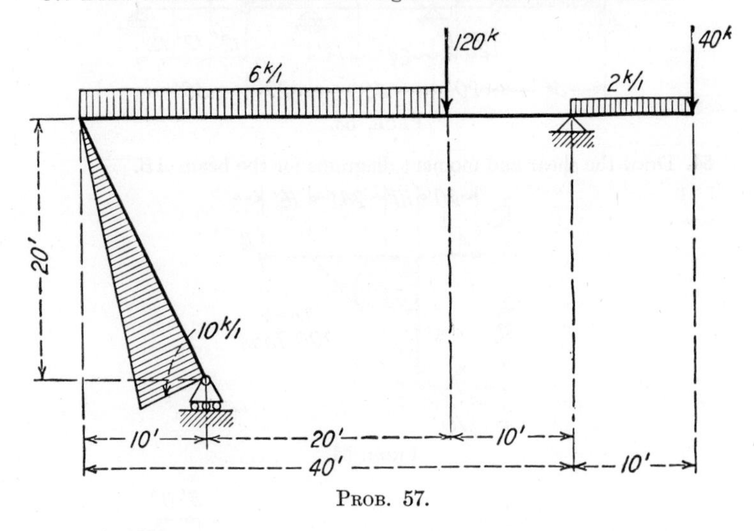

PROB. 57.

58. Draw the shear and moment diagrams for the beam shown. Give controlling ordinates and locate points of zero shear and moment.

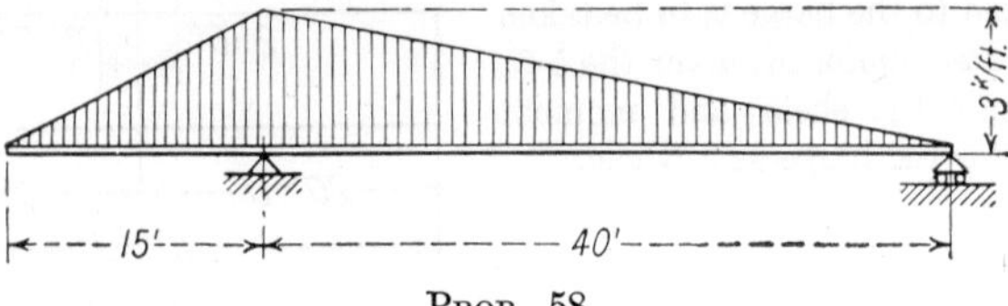

PROB. 58.

59. (*a*) Draw the shear and moment diagrams for the beam A–B in the frame shown.

(*b*) Draw the shear and moment diagrams for the beam C–D in the same frame.

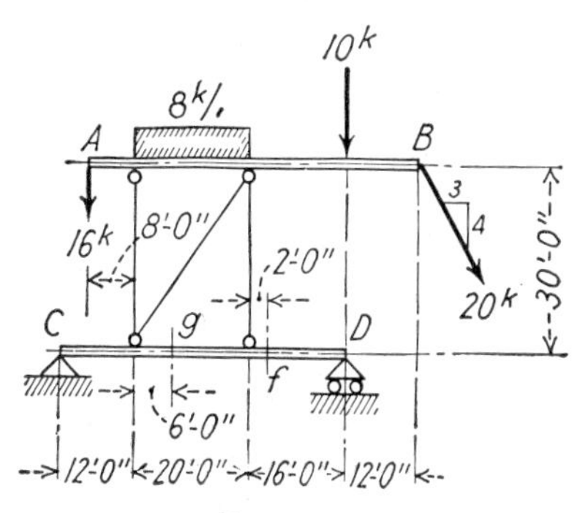

PROB. 59.

60. A combined caisson foundation for two columns in a large office building is shown. For this problem the column loads are to be assumed as distributed uniformly along the 16-in. and 24-in. widths shown, and the caisson loads are to be assumed as uniformly distributed along the 5-ft. 0-in. and 10-ft. 0-in. dimensions shown. Determine the distance A in accordance with these assumptions and draw the shear and moment diagrams for the girder. Do not consider any loads other than the column loads given.

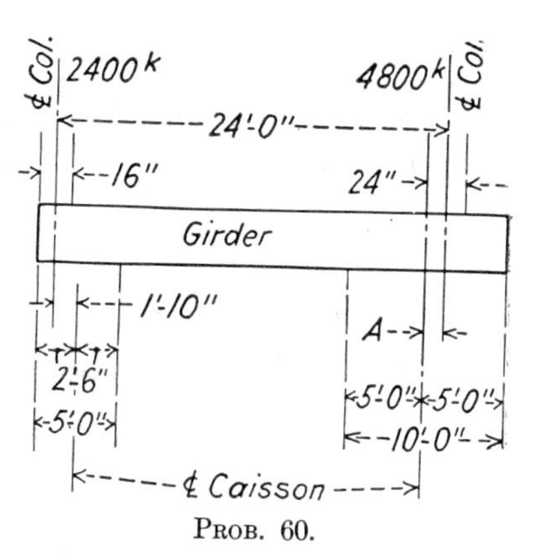

PROB. 60.

61. The beam shown is floating in water. Determine what the distance x must be to make the upward reaction of the water uniform across the beam, and draw the shear and moment diagrams for the beam.

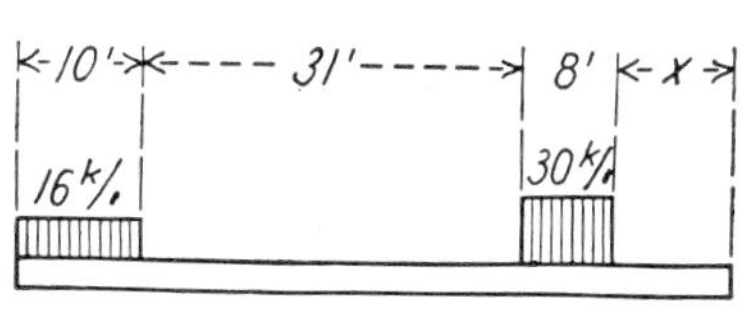

PROB. 61.

62. A spread footing to carry two column loads is shown diagrammatically. Assume that each column load is concentrated at its center line and that the earth pressure is uniform along the girder. Calculate the dimension C and draw the shear and moment diagrams for the girder. *Ans.* $C = 8$ ft.

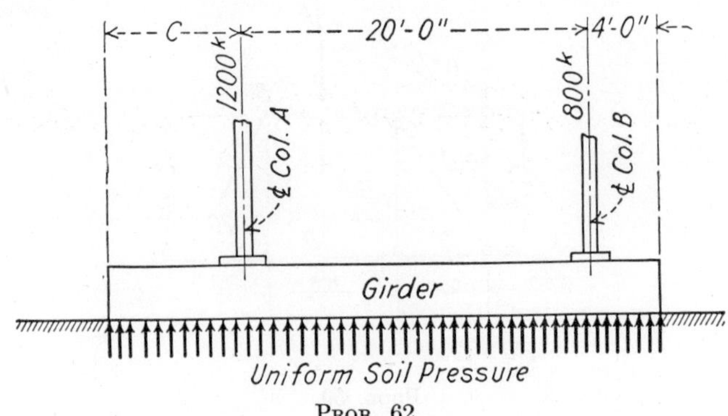

PROB. 62.

63. The figure shows a plan and section of a steel ore barge. With ore loaded as shown, draw the shear and moment diagrams for the *vertical* loads acting on the barge as a whole. The barge is floating in smooth water. The dimensions of the loaded volume are to be taken to the center lines for the problem.

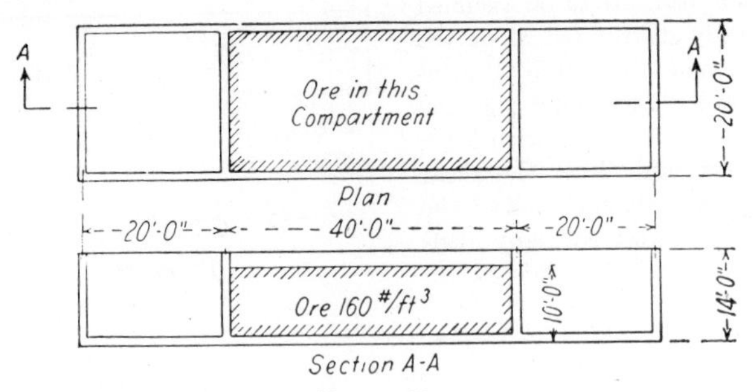

PROB. 63.

64. Draw the shear and moment diagrams for the columns shown in Figs. (*a*) and (*b*) in Problem 142 on p. 195.

65. Draw the shear and moment diagrams for the mast above U_3 in the structure shown.

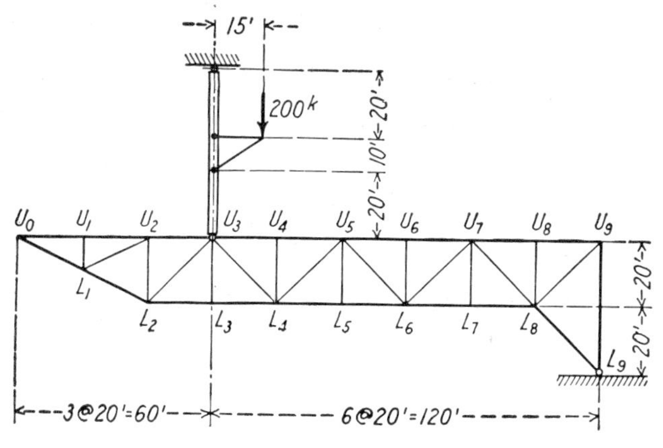

PROB. 65.

66. The figure shows a strip having a dimension of 1 ft. perpendicular to the page cut from an electrolytic tank. The vertical sides of the tank are made rigidly a part of the horizontal beam. Draw the shear and moment diagrams for the beam and also the vertical portions.

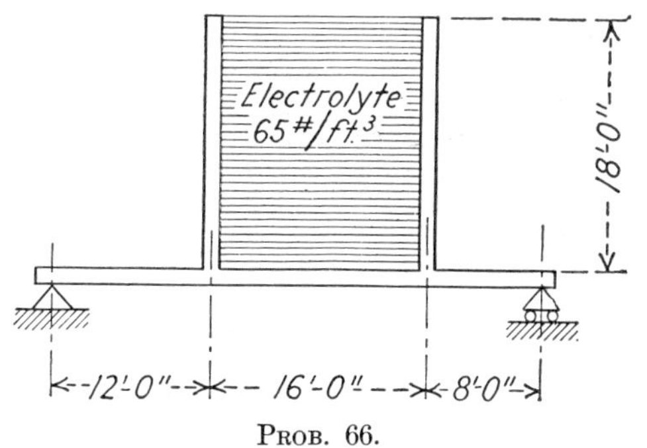

PROB. 66.

67. Draw the shear and moment diagrams for the structure shown.

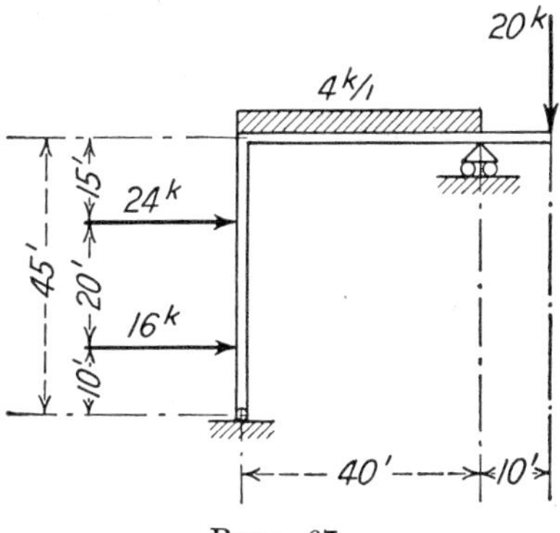

PROB. 67.

68. Draw the shear and moment diagrams for the structure shown.

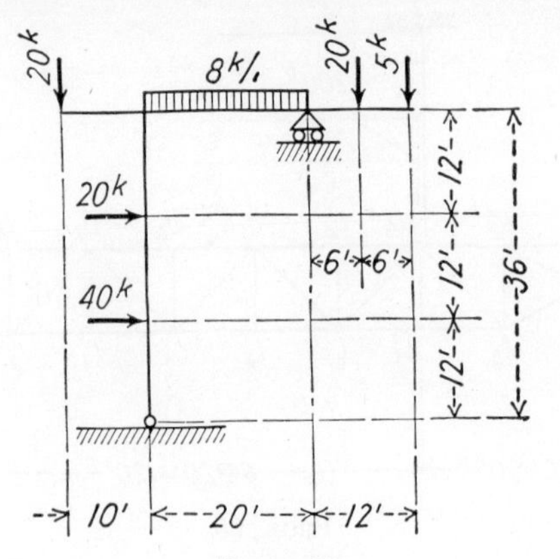

PROB. 68.

69. Draw the shear and moment diagrams for the structure shown.

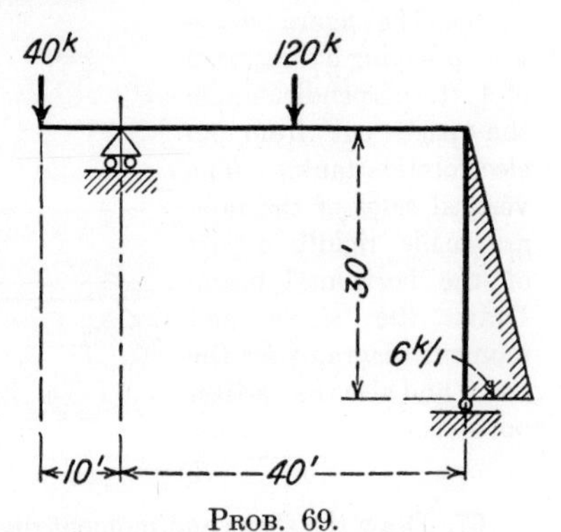

PROB. 69.

70. Draw the shear and moment diagrams for the stucture shown.

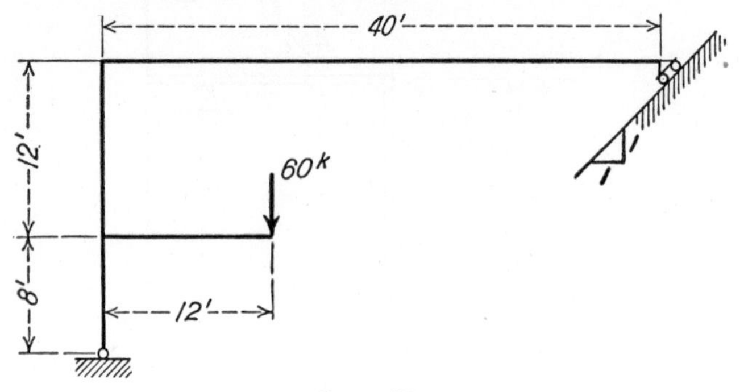

PROB. 70.

71. Draw the shear and moment diagrams for the structure shown.

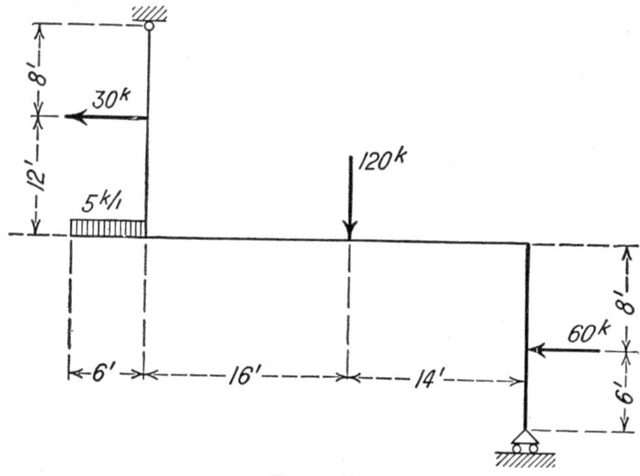

PROB. 71.

72. (*a*) Draw the shear and moment diagrams for the beam.
(*b*) Draw the shear and moment diagrams for the vertical mast.
(*c*) Draw the shear and moment diagrams for the cantilever projection of the mast.

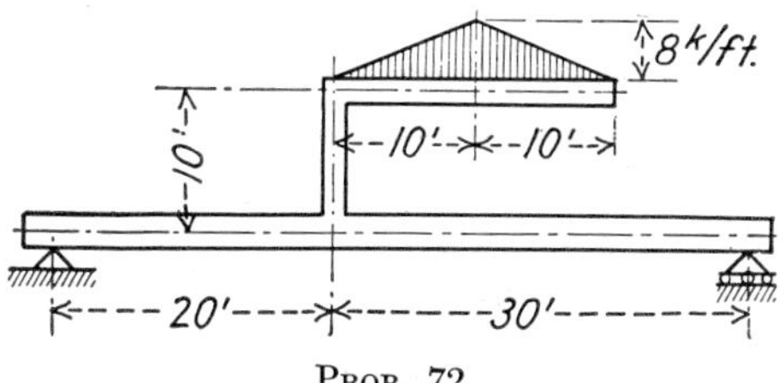

PROB. 72.

73. Draw the shear and moment diagrams for the structure shown. Give ordinates. The moment at $A = -800$ ft.-kips and the reaction at $C = 170^k$ upward.

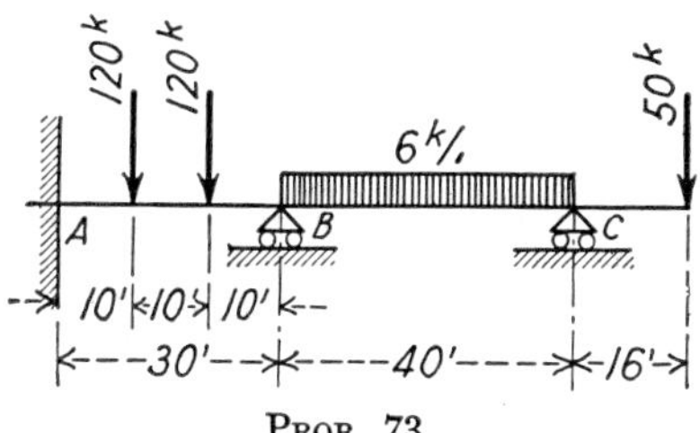

PROB. 73.

74. The girder A, B, C is continuous over the support B and the moment at that point is -2100 ft.-kips. Calculate the reactions and draw the shear and moment diagrams, giving ordinates.

Ans. $A = 48^k\uparrow$
$B = 193^k\uparrow$
$C = 79^k\uparrow$

150k 90k 80k
20' 30' 40' 40' 20'
A B C

PROB. 74.

75. Draw the shear and moment diagrams for the beam shown, given that the shear at $B = +13^k$ and the moment at $A = +165$ ft.-kips.

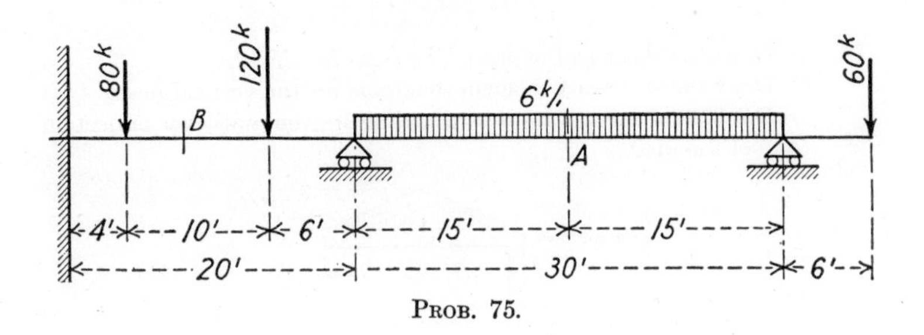

PROB. 75.

76. Draw the shear and moment diagrams for the structure, given the bending moments shown.

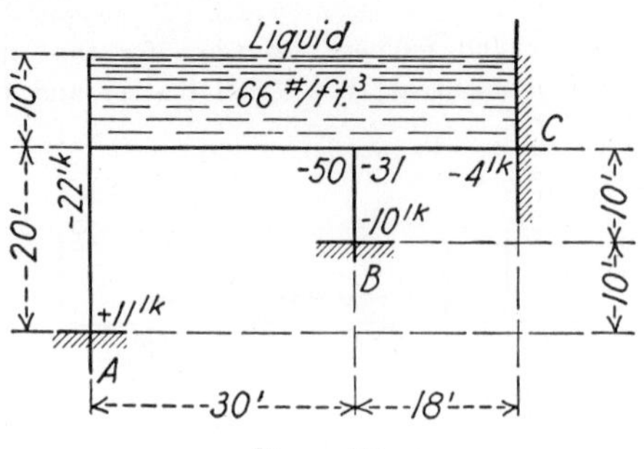

PROB. 76.

77. Draw the shear and moment diagrams for the structure, given that the shear at $E = -16^k$.

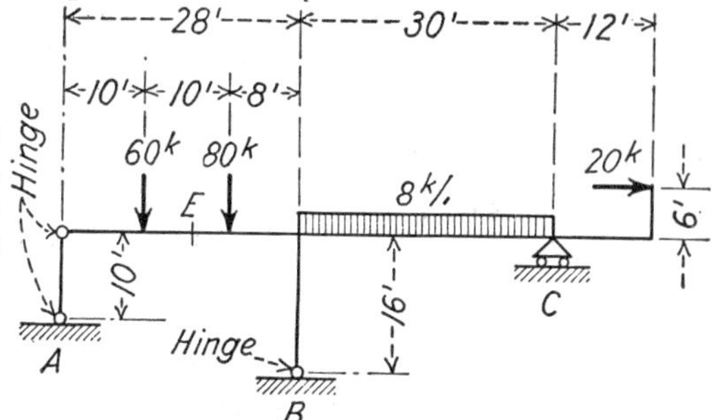

PROB. 77.

78. Draw the shear and moment diagrams for the structure, given that:

Moment at $A = -300$ ft.-kips.
Shear at $D = +\ 8^k$.
Moment at $C = -500$ ft.-kips.

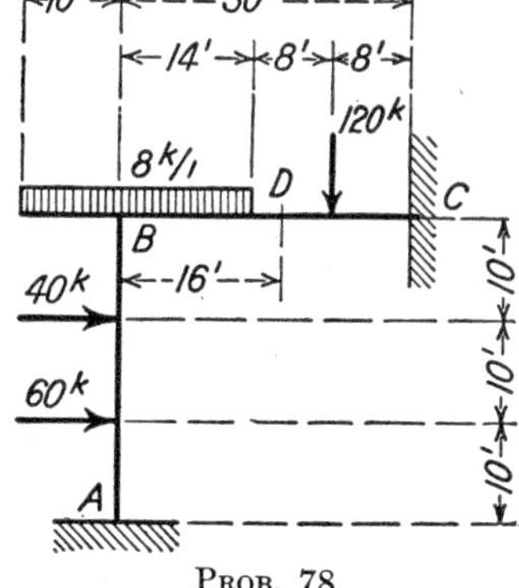

PROB. 78.

79. Calculate the reactions and draw the shear and moment diagrams, giving controlling ordinates for the structure, given the following bending moments:

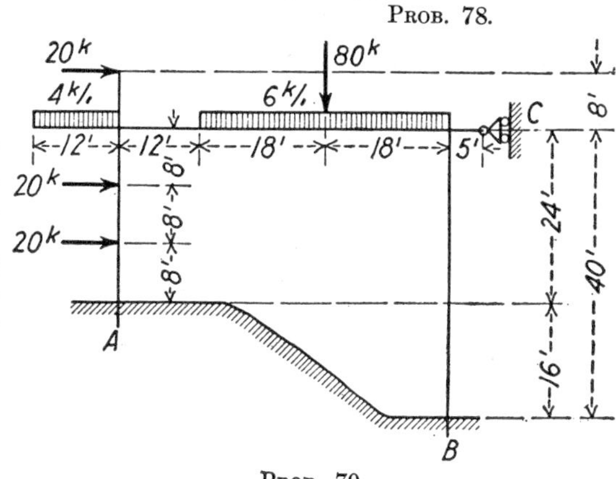

PROB. 79.

Top of Col. $A = -870$ ft.-kips. Top of Col. $B = +1170$ ft.-kips.
Bottom of Col. $A = +280$ ft.-kips. Bottom of Col. $B = -585$ ft.-kips.

Ans. $V_A = 155.4^k\uparrow$ $V_B = 188.6^k\uparrow$ $H_C = 44.0^k\leftarrow$
$H_A = 27.9^k\rightarrow$ $H_B = 43.9^k\leftarrow$

80. The following bending moments have been determined for the structure shown.

$BD = +\ 140$ ft.-kips.	$EB = -\ 650$ ft.-kips.	$CB = -\ 45$ ft.-kips.
$BC = -\ 310$ ft.-kips.	$EG = +\ 180$ ft.-kips.	$GE = -\ 90$ ft.-kips.
$BE = -\ 650$ ft.-kips.	$EF = -\ 470$ ft.-kips.	$FE = -\ 66$ ft.-kips.

Draw the shear and moment diagrams by *both* of the methods discussed in this chapter.

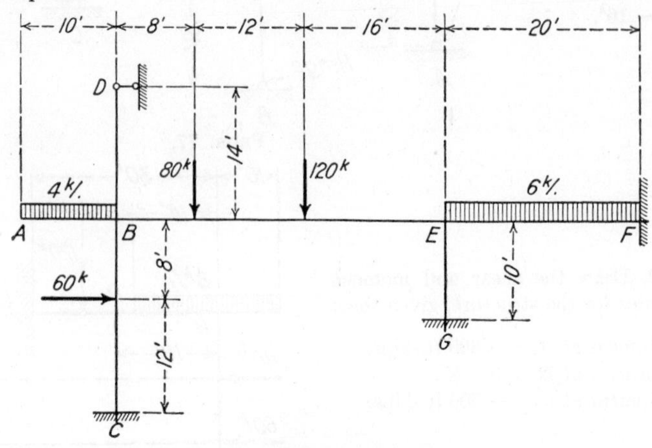

PROB. 80.

81. The following bending moments have been determined for the structure shown.

$BC = -\ 188$ ft.-kips.	$CD = -\ 460$ ft.-kips.	$AB = +\ 90$ ft.-kips.
$CF = +\ 115$ ft.-kips.	$CG = -\ 100$ ft.-kips.	$GC = -\ 400$ ft.-kips.
	$DE = +\ 10$ ft.-kips.	

Draw the shear and moment diagrams by *both* of the methods discussed in this chapter.

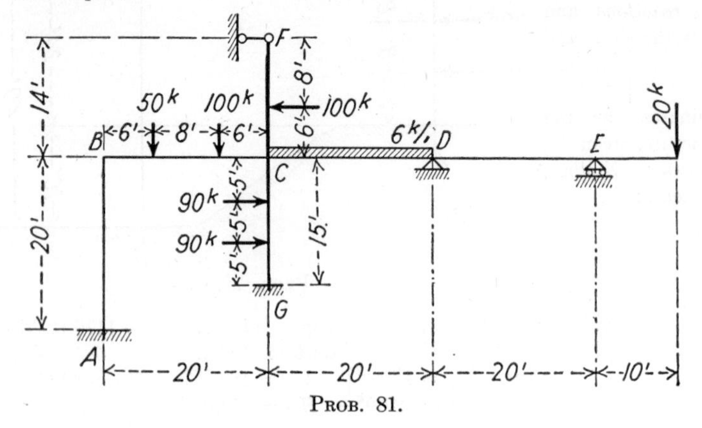

PROB. 81.

82. Draw the shear and moment diagrams for the beam. Give controlling ordinates and locate points of zero moment and shear.

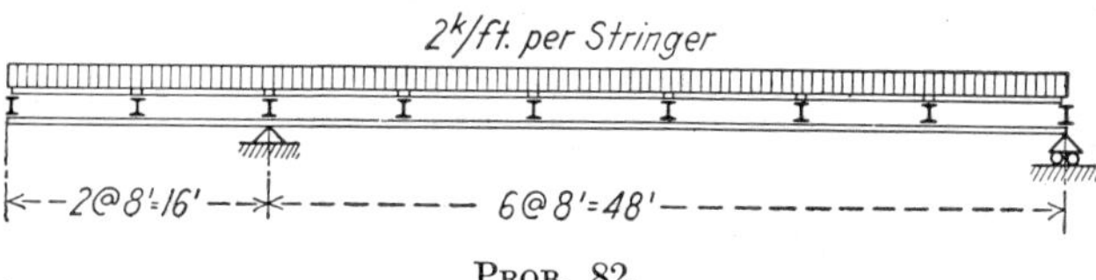

PROB. 82.

83. (*a*) Draw the shear and moment diagrams for the beam shown in (*a*).

(*b*) Draw the shear and moment diagrams for the beam shown in (*b*) and compare the controlling ordinates with the corresponding ordinates to the diagrams drawn for the beam in (*a*).

(*c*) Draw the shear and moment diagrams for the beam shown in (*c*) and compare the controlling ordinates with the corresponding ordinates to the diagrams drawn for the beam in (*a*).

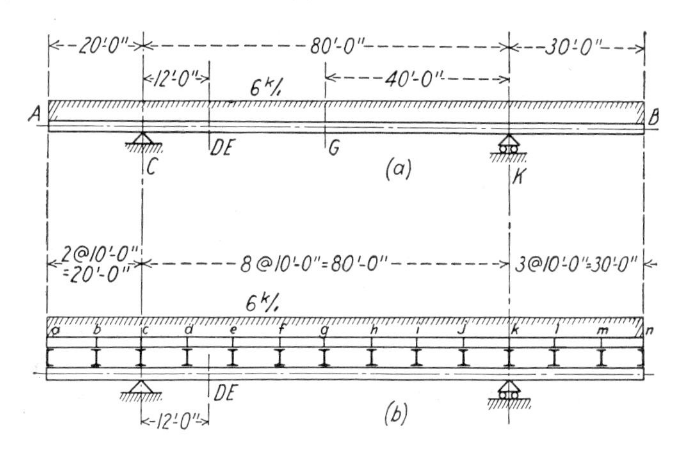

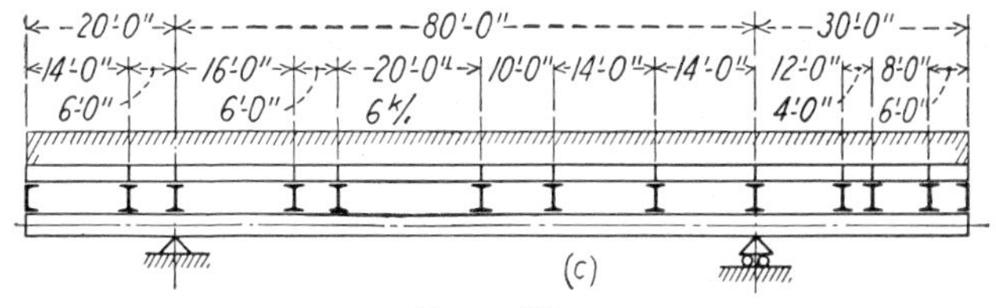

PROB. 83.

84. Draw the shear and moment diagrams for the structure shown.

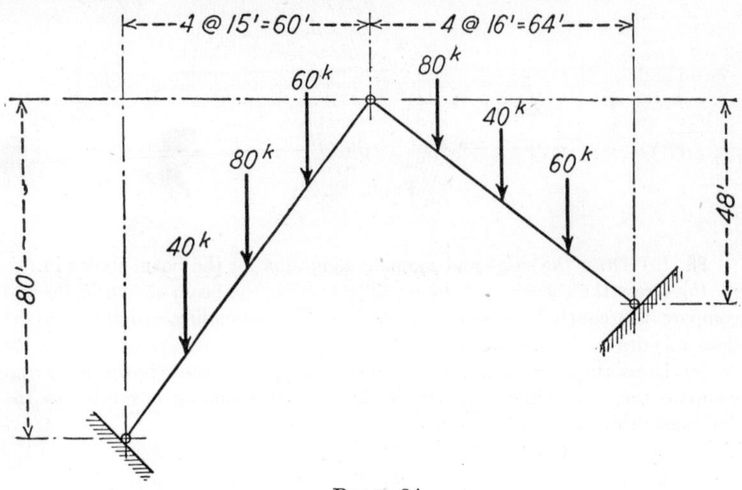

PROB. 84.

85. Draw the shear and moment diagrams for the structure shown:

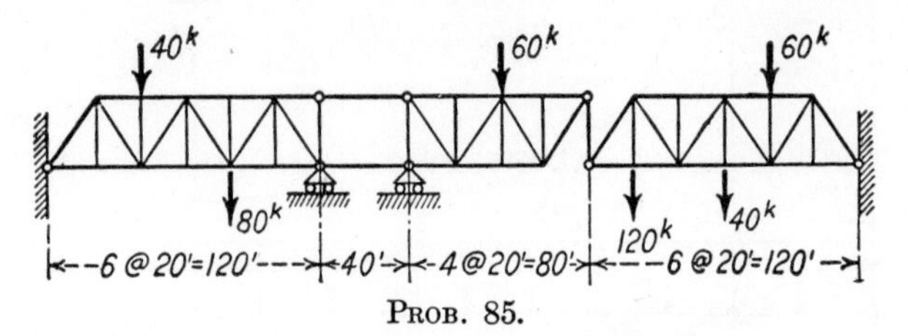

PROB. 85.

CHAPTER IV

REACTIONS, SHEARS AND MOMENTS — MOVING LOADS

48. Live Loads.—Live loads, either moving or movable, produce varying effects in a structure, depending on the location of the part being considered, the function being considered, i.e., reaction, shear, bending moment, etc., and the position of the loads which are producing the effect. It is necessary to determine the position of the adopted system of loading which will produce the greatest reaction, shear, or bending moment, and, having found this position, to calculate the resulting effect on the part under consideration.

The purpose of this chapter is to study the effect of moving or movable loads on reactions, shears, and moments; to determine the position of a given system of loads which produces the greatest values of these functions; and to present methods of calculating these maximum values.

49. Influence Lines.—In studying the effect of a system of loads moving across a structure, the use of diagrams called **influence lines** is often helpful. An influence line is a diagram showing the variation in the shear, moment, stress in a member, reaction, or other direct function, due to a unit load moving across the structure. An influence line is constructed by plotting directly under the point where the unit load is placed an ordinate the height of which represents to some scale the value of the particular function being studied when the load is in that position. This definition and statement of the method of construction is complete and furnishes all the information necessary for the construction of any influence line. This text, however, will discuss only those influence lines commonly useful in the design or analysis of statically determinate structures.

Many interesting and ingenious methods of constructing influence lines have been developed, some semi-graphical and others wholly so. The writers are firmly convinced that these methods, however interesting, should be avoided by beginners. After the student thoroughly understands the principles involved and is able to construct influence lines readily by studying the effect of successive positions of the unit load on the function being considered, the methods mentioned above may be used if they offer advantages in any case. The majority of such methods depend on scale drawings, and generally the information furnished by the influence line can be most easily obtained by calculating directly two or three controlling points.

50. Methods of Construction.—The following examples illustrate the construction of a few simple influence lines. If the definition of an influence line given above and the constructions below are clearly understood, there should be no difficulty in extending these methods to the construction of any influence line for any statically determinate structure.

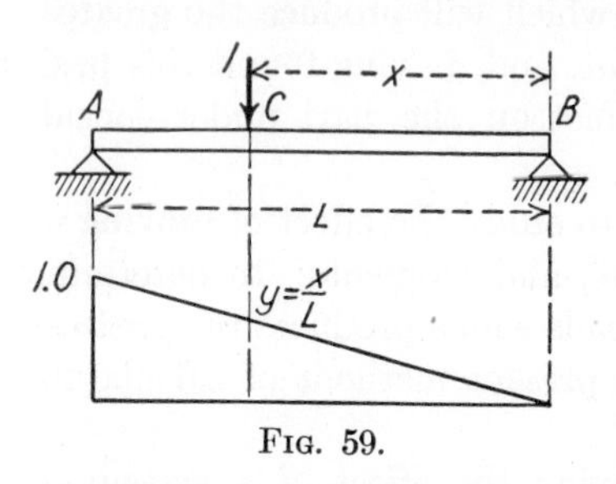

Fig. 59.

In Fig. 59 is shown a simple beam and the influence line for its left reaction. Keeping in mind that this influence line should show the variation in the left reaction as a unit load moves across the span, the student should reason as follows. When the load is at B the reaction at A is zero and the ordinate to the influence line at B is zero. As the load moves from B towards A the reaction at A increases, and as this reaction is

$$R_A = \frac{x}{L}$$

when the unit load is at any point, C, x feet to the left of B, it must be increasing at a uniform rate and the influence line must be a straight line as shown, the ordinate at A being 1, since that will be the reaction at A when the load is at that point.

In drawing influence lines, positive values of the function being considered are generally plotted above the reference line. Reactions which act upward are considered as positive, and the signs for shear and moment are as previously defined.

51. In Fig. 60 is shown a simple structure and the influence line for the reaction at D as a unit load moves from A to B.

When the unit load is at A the reaction at D is $\frac{3}{10}$, and since it acts downward the ordinate to the influence line at A must be $-\frac{3}{10}$ as shown. As the load moves to the right the reaction at D decreases numerically, evidently at a uniform rate, and when it is directly over the support at C the reaction at D is zero. As the unit load moves to the right toward B the reaction at D increases at a uniform rate until the load reaches B. When the unit load is at B the reaction at D is $1\frac{1}{2}$ and the influence line must be as shown.

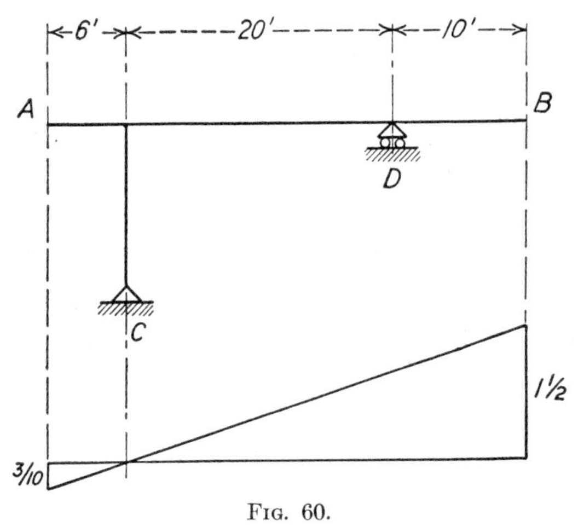

FIG. 60.

52. In Fig. 61 is shown a simple beam with the influence lines for shear and for bending moment at C. In studying the influence line for shear at C, as the unit load moves from B towards A, pass a section at C and consider the part of the beam on the left of the section. As long as the unit load is between B and C the only force acting on the part of the beam to the left is the reaction at A, and evidently between B and C the influence line for shear at C must be the same as the influence line for reaction at A. After the load passes C it is more convenient to consider the part of the beam on the right of the section at C since the only force acting on this part is the reaction at B. The shear at C varies as the reaction at B when the unit load is between C and A, and this variation is as shown. Although the reaction at B acts upward the shear at C is negative in accordance with the definition previously given, and is so shown in the figure.

In drawing the influence line for bending moment at C the same method of attack is used. When the unit load is between B and C the bending moment at C is the left reaction multiplied by the distance from this reaction to C. This is the product of a reaction which is changing at a uniform rate and a constant distance, and the bending moment, therefore, is changing at a uniform rate. When the unit load is between A and C the bending moment at C is the right reaction multiplied by the distance

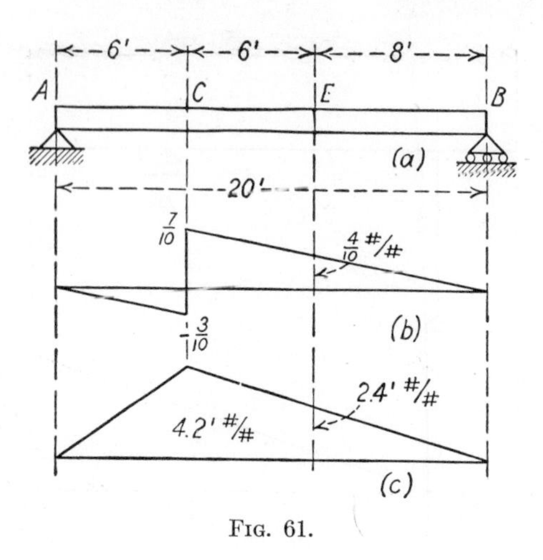

Fig. 61.

from B to C, and obviously changes at a uniform rate as shown in the figure.

53. Influence Lines for Spans with Floorbeams.—In Fig. 62 (*a*) is shown diagrammatically a bridge girder loaded through a floor system in the manner shown in Fig. 57 (*a*). In drawing influence lines for such girders it is usual to deal with a unit reaction from the floor system; that is, the load applied to the floor system is assumed to be of such magnitude and so located that when it is over a floorbeam the reaction of that floorbeam on the girder will be one unit.

The influence line for bending moment at *panel point* 3, shown in Fig. 62 (*c*), needs no explanation; the method of attack is the same as that used in drawing the influence line for bending moment in Fig. 61 (*c*). The influence line for shear shown in Fig. 62 (*b*), however, differs from that shown in Fig. 61 (*b*) in that the former is an influence line for shear at any section within a panel whereas the latter is an influence line for shear at a specific section. Since the load can be applied to the girder in Fig. 62 (*a*) only at the panel points, the shear between panel points must be constant, and an influence line for shear at any section within a panel is an influence line for shear at all sections in that panel. In studying the influence line for shear in panel 2–3, which is shown in Fig. 62 (*b*), the same method may be used as before except that it is only when the unit load is between 3 and *B* or between 2 and *A* that the reaction is the only force acting on the part of the structure being considered.

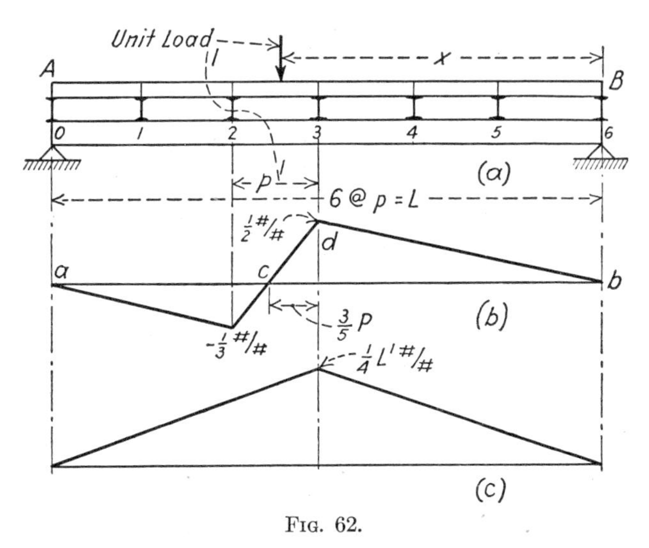

FIG. 62.

The portion of the influence line drawn for the unit load between the points just mentioned is of course similar to that drawn for shear at *C* in Fig. 61, but when the unit load is between points 2 and 3, an additional force acts on the part of the beam under consideration. For example, pass the section 1–1 shown in Fig. 62 (*a*) and consider the part on the left of this section. As long as the unit load is between 3 and *B* the reaction at *A* is the only force acting on the part of the structure under consideration, and the construction of this portion of the influence line for shear in the panel is very simple. As soon as the unit load passes point 3 moving towards *A* there begins to be a downward force at point 2 on the part of the beam on the left of the section.

This downward force at point 2 increases uniformly as the unit load moves from 3 to 2, and at the same time the reaction at A is increasing at a uniform rate. Since the shear in panel 2–3 is the reaction at A minus the downward force, or floorbeam reaction, at point 2, it is evident that it also is changing at a uniform rate and the influence line for shear in the panel may be completed by connecting the ordinates at points 2 and 3 by a straight line as shown. If this statement does not seem clear it is easy to write an equation for this portion of the influence line in terms of x, the length of span L, and the panel length p. The student may do this to satisfy himself that the equation is that of a straight line connecting the ordinates to the influence line at points 2 and 3.

54. Importance of Fundamental Method.—It may seem that unnecessarily detailed attention has been given to the construction of these very simple influence lines. The writers believe, however, that much of the confusion regarding influence lines often existing in the student's mind is the result of attempting to remember the shape of the simple forms first encountered in studying the subject instead of carefully building them up, step by step, from the fundamental definition.

55. Units.—Attention should be called to the units of measure for the ordinates of influence lines. In the influence line shown in Fig. 59 the ordinate at A is given as 1, which means that the reaction at A will be 1 *lb. per lb.* of load at A. Similarly at a section E, 8 ft. to the left of B in Fig. 61, the ordinate to the influence line for shear at C is $\frac{4}{10}$-lb. per lb.; i.e., for each pound of load placed at E there will be a shear at C of $\frac{4}{10}$ lb. The influence line for bending moment at C has at E an ordinate of 2.4 *ft.-lb. per lb.*, or there will be a bending moment at C of 2.4 ft.-lb. for each pound of load placed at E. Evidently the unit load instead of being 1 lb. may be 1 kip, 1 ton, 1 kilogram, or one unit of weight in any system we wish to use, without affecting in any way the construction of the influence line.

56. Use in Computation.—Since an influence line is constructed to show the effect of a *unit* load, it is clear that we may determine from it the effect of a load of any magnitude in any position by multiplying the ordinate at the load by the magnitude of the load. Thus in Fig. 61 at point E the ordinate to the influence line for shear at C is $\frac{4}{10}$ lb. *per* lb. of load at E, and the ordinate to the influence line for bending moment at C is 2.4 ft.-lb. per lb. of load at E. Consequently, if a load of 10,000 lb. is placed at E, we have due to this load:

$$\text{Shear at } C = \tfrac{4}{10} \text{ lb. per lb.} \times 10{,}000 \text{ lb.} = 4000 \text{ lb.}$$

$$\text{Bending moment at } C = 2.4 \text{ ft.-lb. per lb.} \times 10{,}000 \text{ lb.} = 24{,}000 \text{ ft.-lb.}$$

Also it should be clear that if we place a uniformly distributed load of w lb. per ft. anywhere on the beam, the effect of this load on any function may be found from the influence line for that function. Considering a short length dx, the load on it is wdx, and if the ordinate to the influence line at the point where dx is taken is y, the effect of this load is $wydx$ and the total effect is

$$w \int ydx = w \times \text{area under influence line between limits of distributed load.}$$

For example, if a uniformly distributed load of 4000 lb. per ft. is placed on the beam in Fig. 61 extending from E to C, we have:

$$\text{Shear at } C = (\tfrac{7}{10} \text{ lb. per lb.} + \tfrac{4}{10} \text{ lb. per lb.})\tfrac{1}{2} \times 6 \text{ ft.} \times 4000 \text{ lb. per ft.} = 13{,}200 \text{ lb.}$$

$$\text{Bending moment at } C = (4.2 \text{ ft.-lb. per lb.} + 2.4 \text{ ft.-lb. per lb.})\tfrac{1}{2} \times 6 \text{ ft.} \times 4000 \text{ lb. per ft.} = 79{,}200 \text{ ft.-lb.}$$

Although influence lines may be used in the calculation of shears and bending moments as indicated above, it is only in a few cases that their use in this manner offers any advantage over ordinary methods. They are very useful in the calculation of stresses in the diagonals and verticals of trusses with non-parallel chords subjected to moving uniform loads, or moving uniform loads combined with a single concentrated load, and they are also useful in the calculation of maximum shear in the various panels of a girder loaded through a floor system and subjected to a moving or movable uniform load. Except in these and some other instances, their greatest usefulness is not in the actual calculation of shears, moments, or stresses, but in indicating where a distributed load should be placed to produce the greatest effect in a given case. They may also be used in determining the position in which a series of concentrated loads should be placed to secure the greatest shear, moment, stress, etc.

57. Maximum Effect from Moving Uniform Loads.—The position of a moving or movable uniform load which is necessary to produce maximum reaction on a beam or girder or to produce maximum shear or bending moment at some point along the beam or girder is easily determined from an inspection of the influence line for the function under consideration. In many cases the proper position of the uniform load is obvious without reference to an influence line. For example, it is clear that a load anywhere between A and B on the beam in Fig. 59 will contribute to the reaction at A and that a uniform load should cover the entire span to produce maximum reaction at A. Similarly it is obvious that a load anywhere between A and B on the beam in Fig. 61 will produce

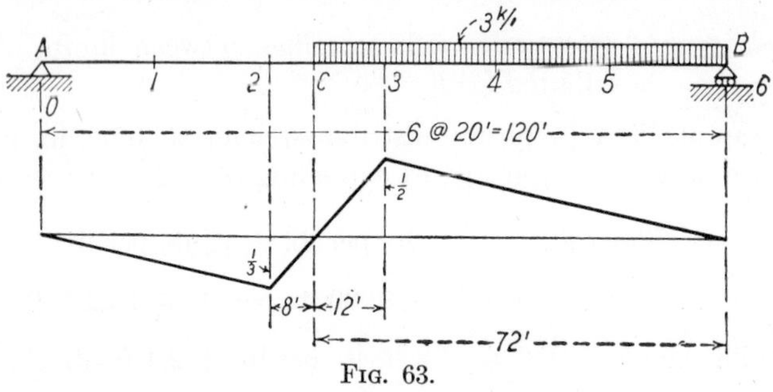

FIG. 63.

positive bending moment at C (or at any other point between A and B), and that for maximum bending moment at C (or at any other point between A and B) a uniform load should cover the entire span. Also it is clear that a load anywhere between C and B on the beam in Fig. 61 will produce positive shear at section C, and for maximum positive shear at C a uniform load should extend from C to B. Reference to the influence lines drawn in these figures confirms these conclusions, but is not necessary for their statement.

The position of a uniform load to produce maximum positive shear in panel 2–3 of the beam shown in Fig. 62, however, is not obvious, and in this case the influence line is helpful, showing at once that the load should extend from c to b. In this case also the calculation of the shear may be conveniently made from the influence line as explained above, or directly.

As an example, a girder span having a floor system is shown diagrammatically in Fig. 63, together with the influence line for shear in panel 2–3. The dimensions are as shown in the figure, and the girder is to be subjected to a moving uniform load of 3 kips per ft. The influence line shows at once that to produce maximum positive shear in the panel the load should extend from C to B as shown. The calculation of this shear from the influence line is as follows:

$$\text{Area} = \tfrac{1}{2} \times \tfrac{1}{2} \times 72 = 18$$

$$\text{Shear} = 3 \times 18 = 54^k$$

Knowing the position of the load which produces maximum positive shear in the panel, the shear may be calculated directly.

$$3 \times 72 \times \frac{36}{120} = 64.8 \quad \text{reaction at } A$$

$$3 \times 12 \times \frac{6}{20} = 10.8 \quad \text{panel reaction at 2}$$

$$54.0^k \quad \text{shear in panel}$$

58. Maximum Shear by Conventional Full Panel Load Method. —An approximate method of calculating maximum shear in a girder span having a floor system and subjected to a moving uniform load is of some interest at this point. Referring again to Fig. 63 we may see at once that, with the uniform load in the position shown, the panel loads are as follows:

At 4 and 5, full panel loads $= 60^k$ each

At 3, $3 \times 12 \times \dfrac{14}{20} + \dfrac{3 \times 20}{2} = 55.2^k$

At 2, $3 \times 12 \times \dfrac{6}{20} = 10.8^k$

The conventional full panel load method of calculation assumes that the panel load at 3 is 60^k instead of 55.2^k and neglects entirely the partial panel load of 10.8^k at 2. That is, if using this conventional approximation, we should place full panel loads at 3, 4, and 5 for maximum shear in panel 2–3; at panels 2, 3, 4, and 5 for maximum shear in panel 1–2, and so on. This is evidently equivalent to extending uniform load from panel point 2 back to B and neglecting the half panel load at 2, when calculating shear in panel 2–3; and extending uniform load from panel point 1 back to B and neglecting the half panel load at 1, when calculating shear in 1–2. The calculation of the shear using this approximation is very simple since it evidently must be equal to the reaction ahead of the panel loads. For panel 2–3 this method gives a shear of:

$$3 \times 60 \times \tfrac{2}{6} = 60^k$$

This is larger than the true maximum shear, and it should be clear that this conventional approximation must always result in a shear greater than the true value, except in the end panel in which it gives the maximum shear correctly.

The conventional approximation lends itself to a systematized procedure in calculation, based on the fact that the shear in any panel must always be equal to the reaction *ahead* of the loads, i.e.,

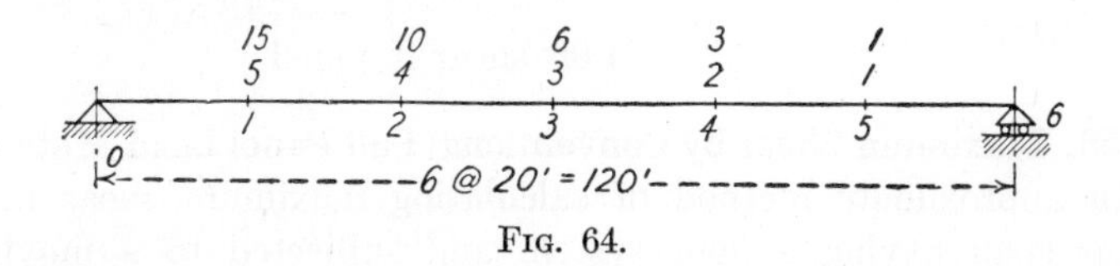

Fig. 64.

it must be equal to the reaction to the left of the panel when the loads are on the right of the panel. Referring to Fig. 64 it is clear that if a load, P, is placed at panel point 5, the reaction at A is $\frac{1}{6}P$. If a load, P, is placed at panel point 4 the reaction at A due to this load is $\frac{2}{6}P$, and if loads are at 4 and 5 simultaneously the reaction at A is $(\frac{2}{6} + \frac{1}{6})P = \frac{3}{6}P$. Similarly, if there are loads at panel points 3, 4, and 5 (as there must be for maximum shear in panel 2–3 by the approximate method) the reaction at A, and therefore the shear in panel 2–3, must be:

$$(\tfrac{1}{6} + \tfrac{2}{6} + \tfrac{3}{6})P = \tfrac{6}{6}P$$

Evidently, then, if the panel points are numbered from right to left starting with 0 at the right reaction and these numbers summed up, as shown above the beam in the figure, the sum may be used to calculate quickly the conventional maximum shear in any panel. Using the sums shown in the figure, the maximum shears for panel 0–1, 1–2, and 2–3 will be as follows, for a uniform load of 3^k per foot which gives a panel load of 60^k.

$$\text{Panel } 0\text{–}1 \quad \tfrac{15}{6} \times 60 = 150^k$$

$$\text{Panel } 1\text{–}2 \quad \tfrac{10}{6} \times 60 = 100^k$$

$$\text{Panel } 2\text{–}3 \quad \tfrac{6}{6} \times 60 = 60^k$$

Accurate results are so easily obtained from influence lines that the conventional approximation is not used so much as formerly in determining live load stresses. It is still used in the calculation of stresses in lateral trusses — as will be seen in Chapter IX — because the uncertain character of most lateral forces

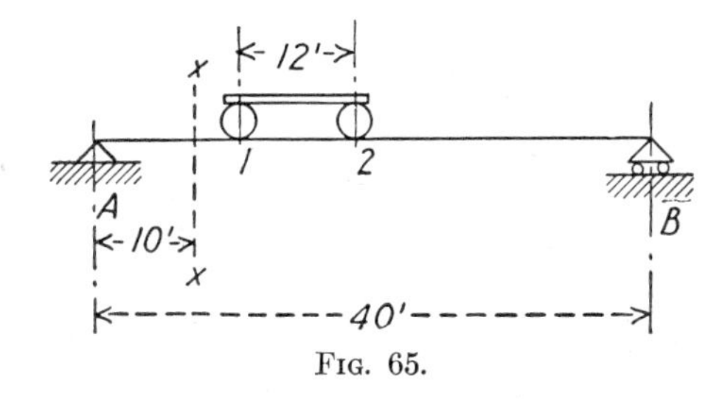

Fig. 65.

renders more accurate computations unnecessary if not misleading.

59. Moving Concentrated Loads.—In dealing with many of the simpler forms of concentrated loads, such as cranes, trucks, road rollers, interurban cars, etc., the position of a given loading to produce maximum reaction, shear at a section, or moment at a certain point is often easily determined by inspection. Suppose, for example, that the beam in Fig. 65 supports one end of a four-wheel electric crane. If the wheel loads are equal, it is evident by inspection that the maximum reaction at A will occur when wheel 1 is directly over the end A with wheel 2 on the span. Similarly it should be clear by inspection that, to produce maximum positive shear at section X–X, the wheels should be on the right of the section with the first wheel as close to the section as possible. Also, it should be clear that when one of the wheels is at the center, the position of the other being fixed by the frame connecting them, the greatest moment possible at that point will result.

More complicated systems of loads such as steam or electric locomotives followed by trains, trucks followed by a series of trailers, etc., are not so easily dealt with, and the position of such loads which produces the maximum reaction, shear, or moment must be determined by trial or by application of methods described below.

60. Reactions Due to Moving Concentrated Loads.—In Fig. 66 (*a*) is shown a girder 60 ft. long between centers of bearings, and in Fig. 66 (*b*) a series of concentrated loads representing a steam locomotive. The figures just above the wheels are the loads in thousands of pounds, and the figures below, the distances between them in feet.

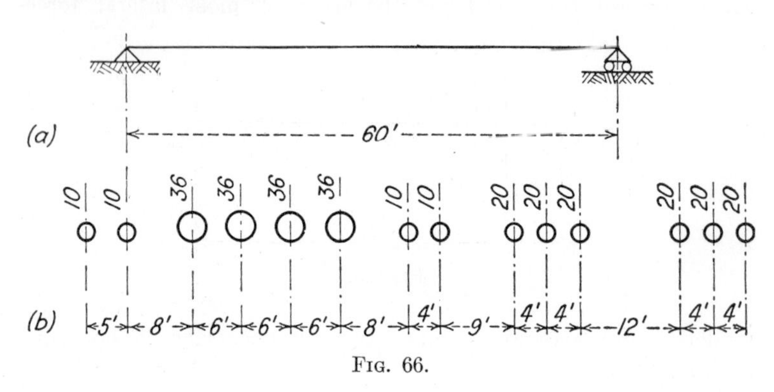

Fig. 66.

Considering the left reaction and bringing the locomotive on from the right, it is easy to see that there will begin to be a reaction at A as soon as the first wheel comes on the span. This reaction will evidently increase as the locomotive moves toward the left and until the first wheel is directly over the bearing at A. Any further movement to the left will cause wheel 1 to move off the span, and as this occurs there will be a sudden decrease in the reaction at A, the amount of this decrease being equal to the load on wheel 1. However, if movement to the left continues, the reaction will increase at once and will continue to increase until wheel 2 is directly above the bearing at A. Further movement to the left, causing wheel 2 to move off the span, will again result in a sudden decrease in the reaction, a decrease equal in amount to the weight on wheel 2. As before, the reaction after this sudden decrease will increase again with continued movement to the left, and keep on increasing until wheel 3 is directly above the bearing at A. Evidently this cycle will be repeated for each wheel in the group, the reaction reaching a maximum value each time a load comes directly over it and decreasing suddenly as that load passes off the span. Since the reaction has *a* maximum value each time a load comes directly over the bearing, it would be possible to obtain the greatest reaction by trial, calculating the reaction for each wheel over the bearing. This would be tedious even though it would be necessary to try only the first two or three wheels. It is much easier to study the *change* in the reaction as successive wheels move over the end of the span.

Since, as shown in Fig. 59, the value of the reaction for a load P located x feet from the other end of the span is $\frac{Px}{L}$; if the load

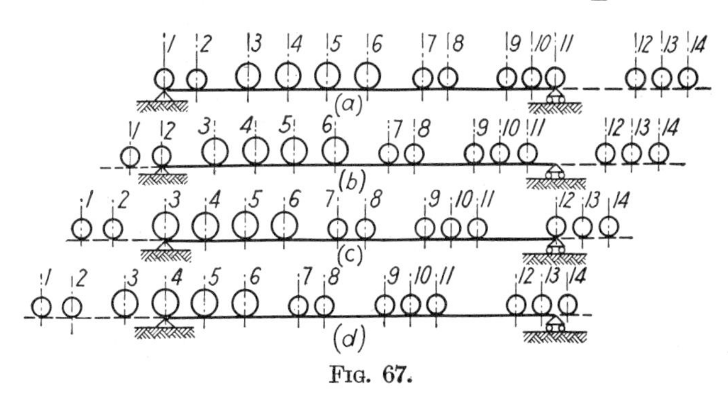

FIG. 67.

moves a distance d the reaction becomes $\frac{P(x+d)}{L}$, and the change is $\frac{Pd}{L}$. If a number of loads make the same movement the increase will be the sum of the loads times $\frac{d}{L}$. This is also equal to the loads times the slope of the influence line $\left(\frac{1}{L}\text{ in this case}\right)$ times the distance moved.

In Fig. 67 (a) the loads and girder of Fig. 66 are shown with wheel 1 just over the bearing at A. As explained above, on further movement to the left, wheel 1 will pass off the span causing a sudden decrease in the end reaction, but as movement to the left continues the reaction will increase from this reduced amount owing to the effect of wheels 2 to 11 inclusive moving to the position shown in Fig. 67 (*b*). It should be clear that, if the increase in the reaction at A due to wheels 2 to 11 inclusive moving from the position shown in Fig. 67 (*a*) to that in Fig. 67 (*b*) is greater than the load on wheel 1, the *total* change in the reaction due to the movement has been an increase. If the *change* in the reaction at A due to this movement of the loads proves to be an *increase*, the loads may be moved again, to the position shown in Fig. 67 (*c*), and the *change* for this second movement calculated. As long as moving the loads to the left causes an increase in the reaction at A, the movement should continue, but it should cease as soon as moving from one load over A to the next causes a decrease in the reaction. This simple relation may be expressed in mathematical form as follows:

ΔR = *change* in reaction due to moving from one load over the reaction to the next.

P_1 = the load which was over the reaction and is moved off the span.

d_1 = the distance between P_1 and the following wheel.

L = the length of the span.

ΣP = the sum of all the loads which are on the span and *stay* on during the movement.

$$\Delta R = \frac{\Sigma P d_1}{L} - P_1$$

If a load which is not on the span at the beginning of any movement comes on during the movement, it is clear that it will add a small amount to the increase in the reaction under consideration. It is easy to take account of such a load, although it is seldom that the result will be appreciably affected. The expression above may be modified to include the effect of a load coming on as follows:

P' = a load which comes on during movement.
e = the distance which P' comes on the span.

$$\Delta R = \frac{\Sigma P d_1}{L} + \frac{P'e}{L} - P_1$$

61. Illustrative Example.—The use of this relation may be illustrated by applying it to the beam shown in Figs. 66 and 67. With the loads in the position shown in Fig. 67 (*a*) move to the left until position shown in Fig. 67 (*b*) is reached. Then:

$$\Delta R = 234 \times \frac{5}{60} - 10 = \text{an } \textit{increase.}$$

Move to the left from the position shown in Fig. 67 (*b*) to that in Fig. 67 (*c*).

$$\Delta R = 224 \times \frac{8}{60} + 20 \times \frac{1}{60} - 10 = \text{an } \textit{increase.}$$

Move from the position shown in Fig. 67 (*c*) to that in Fig. 67 (*d*).

$$\Delta R = 208 \times \frac{6}{60} + 20 \times \frac{3}{60} - 36 = \text{a } \textit{decrease.}$$

Since the reaction was *decreased* by moving from the position shown in Fig. 67 (*c*) to that shown in Fig. 67 (*d*), the movement should not be made and the former position of the wheels is the one producing maximum reaction at A. The treatment of wheels 12 and 13 which come on the span during movements should be noted as well as the fact that neglecting them would not have affected the conclusion regarding the position for maximum reaction. Occasionally a wheel or wheels coming on the span during a movement will cause a shift of one wheel in the critical position, i.e., if neglecting the wheel or wheels coming on results in the conclusion that a particular wheel, say wheel 3, at the section produces maximum value of the function under consideration, taking account of the loads which come on may show that wheel 4 at the section is really the critical position. In such cases the actual value of the function will generally be practically the same for either wheel at the section.

62. Shear.—The position of a group of wheel loads which will produce maximum shear at a given section may be found by the method of attack used in finding the position to produce the greatest reaction. Detail differences in application of the method may be cleared up by considering a general case.

In Fig. 68 (*a*) is shown the beam of Fig. 66; in Fig. 68 (*b*) is shown the influence line for shear at the section shown; and in

Figs. 68 (*c*) to (*f*) are shown the loads in successive positions on the beam. It should be clear from inspection of the influence line that to produce positive shear at the section loads must be placed on the beam between *C* and *B*. It should also be clear that with loads on the beam as shown in Fig. 68 (*b*) the shear at the section will be increased by moving the loads to the left, the increase continuing until wheel 1 reaches the section and the loads are in the position shown in Fig. 68 (*c*). Any further move-

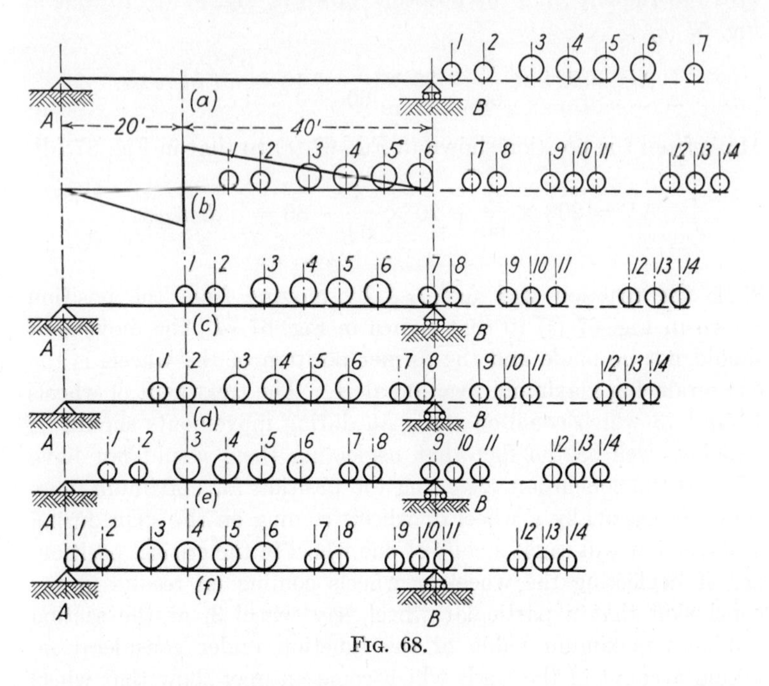

FIG. 68.

ment to the left will cause wheel 1 to pass to the left of the section and produce a sudden decrease in the shear at the section, the amount of the decrease being the magnitude of the load on wheel 1. If movement to the left continues, the shear will start to increase again and continue to increase until wheel 2 reaches the section. Evidently the same cycle will be gone through as each wheel comes up to the section, the shear increasing until the wheel reaches the section and suddenly decreasing as it passes. Since the shear passes through *a* maximum value each time a load comes up to the section, it evidently would be possible to determine the greatest shear obtainable by trial, by calculating the shear for successive wheels at the section, but, as in the case of the reaction, this would be tedious, and it is easier to study the *change* in the shear as the loads move to the left.

When the loads are in the position shown in Fig. 68 (*c*), the shear is equal to the left reaction, and when the loads are as shown in Fig. 68 (*d*) the shear is the left reaction minus wheel 1. Evidently the *change* in shear occurring during passage of the wheels from the first position to the second is the *change* in the reaction minus wheel 1. The change in the reaction is due to the change in position of the loads which are on the span and *stay* on, plus the effect of any which come on during movement. The relation between change in shear and reaction may be expressed in mathematical form.

ΔV = *change* in shear due to moving from one wheel at the section to the following wheel at the section.

Other symbols as in Art. 60.

$$\Delta V = \frac{\Sigma P d_1}{L} - P_1 \quad \text{when no loads come on during movement.}$$

and

$$\Delta V = \frac{\Sigma P d_1}{L} + \frac{P'e}{L} - P_1 \quad \text{when a load } P' \text{ comes on during movement.}$$

When P_1 is less than the other term or terms on the right-hand side of the equation, the shear was increased by the change in the position of the loads and movement should continue until the load which passes the section is greater than the increase in the reaction.

63. Illustrative Example.—The application of the method developed in the preceding article may be shown in connection with Fig. 68. The magnitudes of the wheel loads and the distances between them are as in Fig. 66.

Wheel 1 at section to wheel 2 at section:

$$\Delta V = 174 \times \frac{5}{60} + 10 \times \frac{2}{60} - 10 = \text{an } \textit{increase}.$$

Wheel 2 at section to wheel 3 at section:

$$\Delta V = 184 \times \frac{8}{60} + 20 \times \frac{1}{60} - 10 = \text{an } \textit{increase.}$$

Wheel 3 at section to wheel 4 at section:

$$\Delta V = 204 \times \frac{6}{60} + 20 \times \frac{3}{60} - 36 = \text{a } \textit{decrease.}$$

Therefore, wheel 3 should be at the section for maximum positive shear.

In each of the three lines of calculations above, the second term on the right-hand side of the equation shows the effect of a wheel which was not on the span at the start of the movement but came on during it. In each case it should be observed that the omission of the effect of the wheel which came on would not have affected the conclusion.

64. Loads Moving Off the Span.—If a load which is between the section and the left end of the beam at the start of a movement moves off the span during the movement, it of course should not be included in the sum of the loads which are on the span at the start and stay on. A load between the section and the left end produces negative shear at the section and its removal from the span will therefore *increase* the positive shear. Evidently, if a load moves off the span during movement, the negative shear which it produced at the section before movement started should be *added* to the change in shear. This procedure may be illustrated by determining the position of the loads to produce maximum shear at a section 10 ft. from the left end of the beam in Fig. 68.

Wheel 1 at section to wheel 2 at section:

$$\Delta V = 184 \times \frac{5}{60} + 20 \times \frac{3}{60} - 10 = \text{an } \textit{increase.}$$

Wheel 2 at section to wheel 3 at section:

$$\Delta V = 194 \times \frac{8}{60} + 40 \times \frac{5}{60} + 10 \times \frac{5}{60} - 10 = \text{an } \textit{increase.}$$

Wheel 3 at the section to wheel 4 at the section:

$$\Delta V = 224 \times \frac{6}{60} + 10 \times \frac{2}{60} - 36 = \text{a } \textit{decrease.}$$

Therefore wheel 3 should be at the section.

In the second line of the calculations above, the quantity $10 \times \frac{5}{60}$ is the effect of wheel 1 passing off the span as wheel 3 moves up to the section, and in the third line the quantity $10 \times \frac{2}{60}$ is the effect of wheel 2 passing off the span as wheel 4 moves up to the section.

65. Moment.—It is frequently necessary to know the position of a group of moving concentrated loads which will produce maxi-

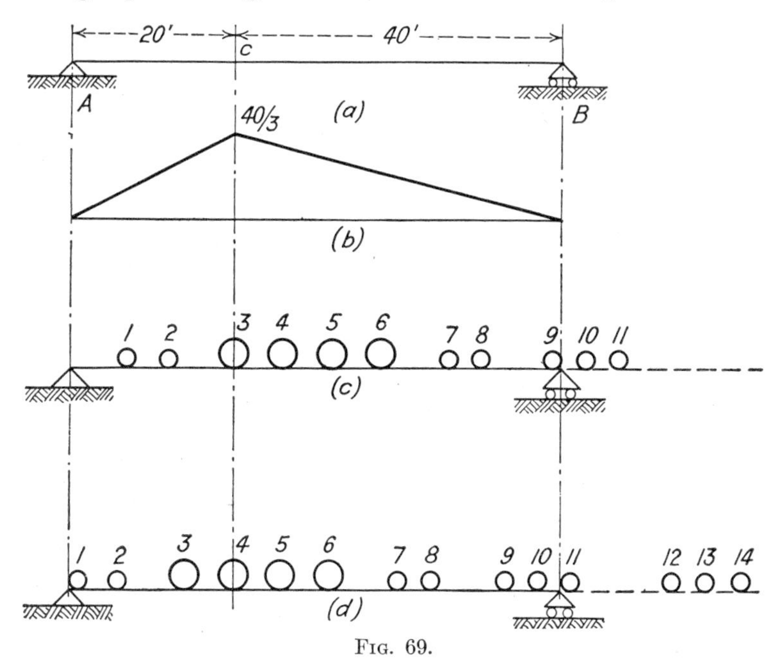

Fig. 69.

mum bending moment at a given point in a beam. The position may be found by trial, of course, but the work would be tedious, and as in the case of reaction and shear it may be done very simply by studying the *change* in moment. In Fig. 69 (*a*) is shown again the beam of Fig. 66, and immediately below in Fig. 69 (*b*) is shown the influence line for bending moment at the point C. The group of loads shown in Fig. 66 (*b*) will be used, and the position to produce maximum moment at the point C will be discussed in general and as a specific problem.

It is clear that a load at any point on the beam between the bearings at A and B will produce bending moment at the point C. Inspection of the influence line confirms the statement and shows further, as would be expected, that the closer the loads can be placed to C the greater will be the bending moment at that point. Also it is evident that as loads come on the span from the right the bending moment at C due to them increases as they move to the left until they reach C, and as soon as they pass this point the bending moment due to them begins to decrease. It follows that if the loads on the span are moved to the left, the bending moment at C will be increased owing to the movement of those loads on the *right* of C and decreased owing to the movement of those on the *left.* It should be clear that the *change in moment* will be the *increase* due to those loads on the right of C minus the *decrease* due to those loads on the left. This may be expressed in mathematical form as follows:

ΔM = the *change* in bending moment due to moving all loads to the left.

I = the increase in bending moment at the section due to the movement of those loads on the right of the section.

D = the decrease in bending moment due to the movement of those loads on the left of the section.

$$\Delta M = I - D$$

The bending moment at C is increased by the movement of the loads toward the left if I is greater than D. If they are equal, the moment does not change, and if I is less than D, the moment decreases. Inspection of the influence line in Fig. 69 (*b*) shows that, if the loads move to the left, the bending moment at C will increase at a uniform rate owing to the movement of any load on the right of C, and decrease at a uniform rate owing to the movement of any load on the left. It follows from this fact that if I is greater than D at the start of the movement to the left, the bending moment at C is an increasing function and cannot change to a decreasing function unless a load passes from the right-hand side of C to the left.

To make the relation discussed above usable, I and D must be expressed in terms of the loads. In Fig. 70 is shown the influence line of Fig. 69 (*b*) with the loads of Fig. 66 (*b*) on it and moving to the left. For a unit movement to the left evidently the *increase* in bending moment at C due to the loads on the right is the slope of the influence line B–O times the sum of the loads on the right, and the *decrease* in the bending moment at C due to the loads on the left is the slope of the influence line A–O times the sum of the loads on the left. Or

$$I = W_2 \times \frac{i}{b}$$

$$D = W_1 \times \frac{i}{a}$$

and

$$\Delta M = W_2 \times \frac{i}{b} - W_1 \times \frac{i}{a}$$

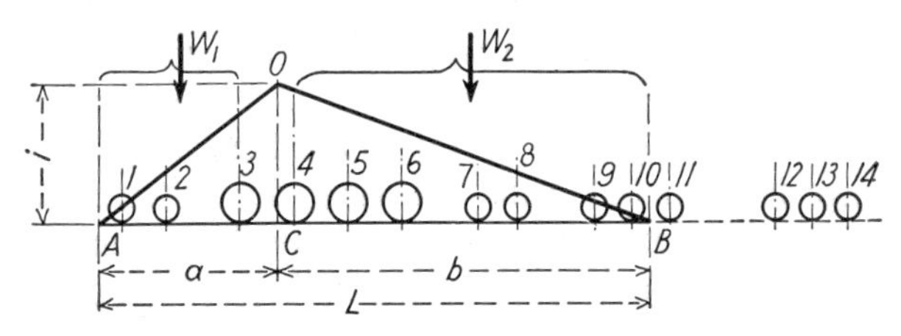

FIG. 70.

This form of the relation between I and D should make clear the statement above that the bending moment at C cannot change from an increasing to a decreasing function unless a load passes from the right of C to the left. In other words, for ΔM to change from a positive quantity to a negative quantity W_2 must become smaller or W_1 larger.

In order to pass through a maximum value, the bending moment must change from an increasing to a decreasing function, and for this to happen the *change* in moment must become equal to zero, i.e., for a maximum

$$\Delta M = 0$$

and

$$W_1 \times \frac{i}{a} = W_2 \times \frac{i}{b}$$

or

$$\frac{W_1}{a} = \frac{W_2}{b}$$

In words this expression says that for a maximum bending moment at any section C, the average load on the left of the section must equal the average load on the right.

If

$$\frac{W_1}{a} = \frac{W_2}{b}$$

$$\frac{W_1}{a} = \frac{W_1 + W_2}{a + b} = \frac{W}{L}$$

where

W = the total load on the span;

L = the length of the span.

This is the form in which the criterion is most commonly stated and used, and in words the statement is: The moment is a maximum when the average load on the left of the section is equal to the average load on the span. In using this criterion in either form it should be remembered that for the bending moment to pass from an increasing to a decreasing function it is necessary for a load to pass from the right-hand side of the section to the left, and that when the moment has a maximum value a load will be at the section. A particular load satisfies the criterion if the average load on the span (or on the right of the section) is greater than the average load on the left of the section with this load an infinitesimal distance to the right of the section, and less than the average load on the left of the section with the same load an infinitesimal distance to the left of the section. More than one load in a series may satisfy the criterion, but this can occur only when loads pass off the span at the left or come on the span from the right. If successive wheels satisfy the criterion, the difference between the bending moment which occurs for one at the section will be very little different from that which occurs when the others are at the section. If wheels which are in the same group, but widely separated, satisfy the criterion, it is generally possible to eliminate one or more by inspection.

66. Illustrative Examples.—The principles discussed above may be illustrated by applying them quantitatively to the problem given in Fig. 69. The loads and spacing are as shown in Fig. 66 (*b*). The problem is to determine what position of the wheels will give maximum bending moment at section C. Since for a maximum moment there should be as much load as possible on the span it is hardly worth while to try any wheel before wheel 3 at the section. Wheels 3, 4, and 5 will be tried and the loads on the span for the first two cases are shown in Fig. 69 (c) and (d).

Wheel 3:

To right $\frac{204}{60} > \frac{20}{20}$

To left $\frac{204}{60} > \frac{56}{20}$ Wheel 3 does *not* satisfy criterion.

Wheel 4:

To right $\frac{224}{60} > \frac{56}{20}$

To left $\frac{224}{60} < \frac{92}{20}$ Wheel 4 *does* satisfy criterion.

Wheel 5:

To right $\frac{224}{60} > \frac{72}{20}$

To left $\frac{224}{60} < \frac{108}{20}$ Wheel 5 *also* satisfies criterion.

The student will find that wheel 6 does not satisfy the criterion but that as the loads continue moving to the left wheel 10 at the section will do so. It is easy to see by inspection that loads on the span when wheel 10 is at the section will not produce as large a bending moment as will the loads on the span when either wheel 4 or wheel 5 is at the section, but it is impossible to be sure by inspection whether wheel 4 or wheel 5 at the section will result in greatest bending moment possible at C. It is not difficult to write an expression for the *change* in moment at C as the loads move from wheel 4 at the section to wheel 5 at the section, and this would of course tell which wheel at the section results in the larger moment, but it is sometimes about as easy to compute both moments and thus determine the larger. Both methods will be given as illustrations.

Wheel 4 at section:

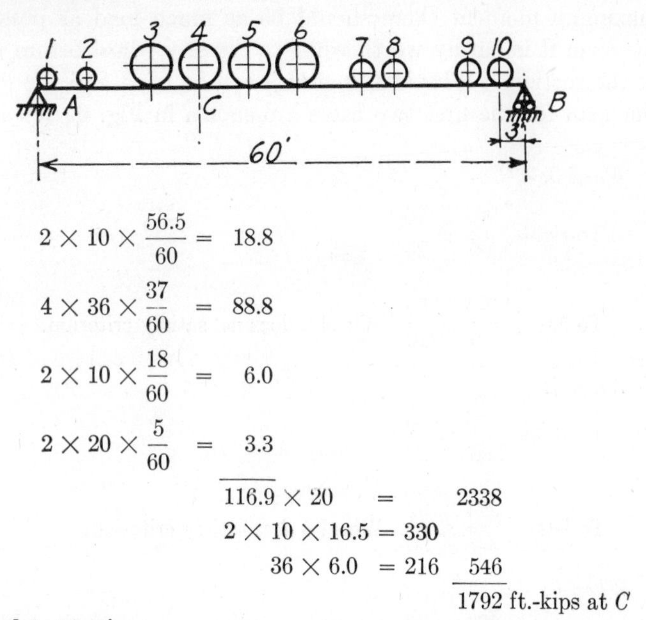

$$2 \times 10 \times \frac{56.5}{60} = 18.8$$

$$4 \times 36 \times \frac{37}{60} = 88.8$$

$$2 \times 10 \times \frac{18}{60} = 6.0$$

$$2 \times 20 \times \frac{5}{60} = 3.3$$

$$116.9 \times 20 = 2338$$

$$2 \times 10 \times 16.5 = 330$$

$$36 \times 6.0 = 216 \quad 546$$

1792 ft.-kips at C

Wheel 5 at section:

$$4 \times 36 \times \frac{43}{60} = 103.2$$

$$2 \times 10 \times \frac{24}{60} = 8.0$$

$$3 \times 20 \times \frac{9}{60} = 9.0$$

$$120.2 \times 20 = 2404$$

$$2 \times 36 \times 9 = 648$$

1756 ft.-kips at C

The calculations just given show that wheel 4 at the section gives the larger moment. As stated above, it is also possible to reach this conclusion by calculating the *change* in moment at C

as the loads move from wheel 4 at the section to wheel 5 at the section.

Change in b.m. at C as wheels move from 4 to 5 at section

$$204 \times \frac{6}{60} \times 20 + 20 \times \frac{5}{60} \times 20 - 72 \times 6 - 20 \times \frac{3.5}{60} \times 40$$

$$408 + 33.3 - 432 - 46.7 = -\ 37.4 \text{ ft.-kips}$$

which shows that moving from wheel 4 at the section to wheel 5 at the section reduces the bending moment 37.4 ft.-kips. The actual calculation of the moments gives a reduction of 36 ft.-kips, the difference being due to not carrying the reaction calculations to more than one decimal.

In the above expression for change in moment the term $204 \times \frac{6}{60} \times 20$ is the increase in moment due to wheels 3 to 10, inclusive, moving to the left 6 ft., the term $20 \times \frac{5}{60} \times 20$ is the increase in moment due to wheel 11 coming on the span 5 ft., the term 72×6 the decrease in moment due to wheels 3 and 4 moving 6 ft. further to the left of the section, and the term $20 \times \frac{3.5}{60} \times 40$ is the decrease in moment due to wheels 1 and 2 moving off the span.

67. Point of Greatest Moment.—The criterion developed in Art. 65 gives the position of a group of moving concentrated loads which will produce maximum moment at a given point. It is often necessary to know *where* the maximum moment will occur and its value; the maximum moment at the center is generally not the absolute maximum moment, and in a short beam the difference becomes appreciable.

In Fig. 71 let W represent the sum of all of the loads on the beam, and x the distance from the center of gravity of these loads to the right support. Let P represent one of the loads on the beam and a its distance from the center of gravity of all the loads. Let W_1 represent the sum of all the loads to the left of P, and b the distance from the center of gravity of these loads to P. It is desired to find the position of the loads which will make the moment under P a maximum. The expression for bending moment at the load P is

$$M = R_1(L - a - x) - W_1 b$$

in which

$$R_1 = \frac{Wx}{L}$$

Then

$$M = \frac{W}{L}(Lx - ax - x^2) - W_1b$$

Differentiating this and equating to zero we find that for maximum moment,

$$x = \frac{L}{2} - \frac{a}{2}$$

That is, the maximum moment under any load will occur when that load and the center of gravity of all the loads on the beam are equidistant from the center of the beam.

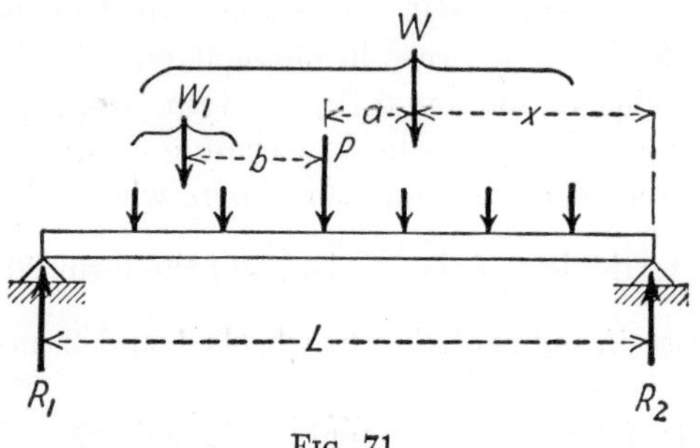

FIG. 71.

The load nearest the center of gravity of all the loads on the beam generally will be the one which will produce the maximum possible moment. This may not be true if this load is much smaller than other loads which are near the center of gravity. It may sometimes be necessary to try several loads in order to find the one which gives the greatest moment. If the criterion of Art. 65 is used to find the load which will cause maximum bending moment at the center of the beam, it generally will not be necessary to try more than this load and the two adjacent ones.

As an aid in selecting the wheel which will produce the maximum possible moment, it should be kept in mind that after the wheel is placed in accordance with the criterion above it must also satisfy the criterion for maximum moment at that point (i.e., the average load to the left should equal the average on the span); if it does not it can be dropped from further consideration.

MOVING CONCENTRATED LOADS ON SPANS WITH FLOORBEAMS

68. Moment.—As previously pointed out, the bending moments at the panel points of a girder with floorbeams are exactly the same as at the corresponding points in a girder without a floor system, whether the loads are uniformly distributed or concentrated, and whether the panel lengths are equal or unequal. Consequently, to determine the position of a group of concentrated loads which will produce maximum moment at a given panel point, or to calculate the moment, having found the position of the loads. we may

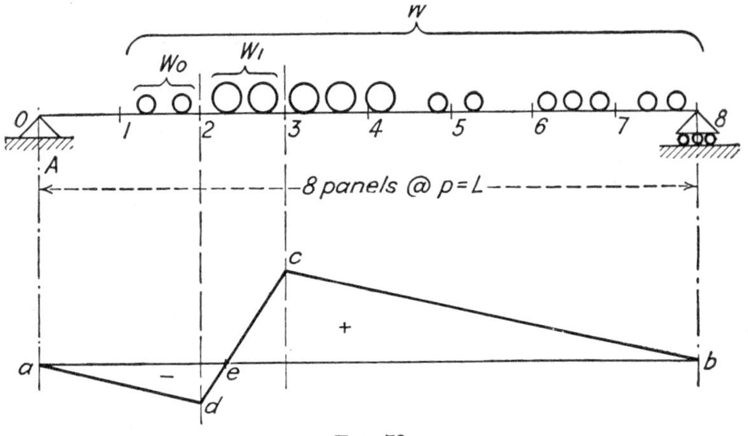

FIG. 72.

proceed exactly as though the girder did not have a floor system. It is sometimes necessary to find the position of a group of moving concentrated loads which will produce maximum moment at some point between the panel points. The case is relatively rare, but will be treated later in connection with stresses in truss members due to moving concentrated loads.

69. Shear.—In Fig. 72 there is shown diagrammatically a girder with a floor system, the points 0, 1, 2, 3, etc., representing the panel points at which floorbeams frame into the girder. Immediately below the girder is shown the influence line for shear in panel 2–3. The method of determining the position of a group of moving concentrated loads to produce maximum shear in a given panel will be developed by discussing the problem in connection with this panel.

Inspection of the influence line shows that there should be as many loads as possible between e and b and that no loads should pass e unless the *increase* in shear in the panel due to loads coming on the span or moving to the left between e and b is greater than the decrease in shear due to the loads passing the point e moving to the left. The maximum shear in a panel generally occurs when there are loads in the panel and between the panel and the right-hand end (for positive shear). Occasionally there may be loads beyond the panel to the left, and in order to deal with a perfectly general case, loads are shown on the span in Fig. 72 to the left of the panel as well as in the panel and to the right of it. As shown in the figure

W_0 = the sum of all loads to the left of the panel;
W_1 = the sum of all loads in the panel;
W = the sum of all loads on the span.

The shear in the panel is evidently the left reaction minus the loads W_0 and minus the reaction at panel point 2 due to the loads W_1 in the panel. If the loads move to the left so short a distance that no loads pass out of the panel, pass off the span to the left, or come on the span from the right, it is evident that the *change* in shear due to this movement will be the increase in the left reaction due to all the loads on the span moving to the left minus the increase in the reaction at panel point 2 due to the loads in the panel 2–3 moving to the left. If the distance moved is dx, we may write

$$\Delta V = W\frac{dx}{L} - W_1\frac{dx}{p}$$

where

ΔV = the *change* in shear in the panel due to the movement dx,

and the other symbols are as shown and noted.

It should be clear that when movement to the left causes an *increase* in shear in the panel, the increase must continue until a load passes from the right into the panel; i.e., the shear in the panel cannot change from an *increasing* to a *decreasing* function unless W_1 in the above expression becomes larger or W becomes smaller. The latter is practically impossible, so we may say that for the shear to change from an increasing to a decreasing function a load must pass from the right into the panel 2–3. Evidently the shear passes through a maximum value as the *change* in shear becomes zero or as

$$W\frac{dx}{L} = W_1\frac{dx}{p}$$

$$\frac{W}{L} = \frac{W_1}{p}$$

This expression states that the shear in a panel is a maximum when the average load in the panel is equal to the average load

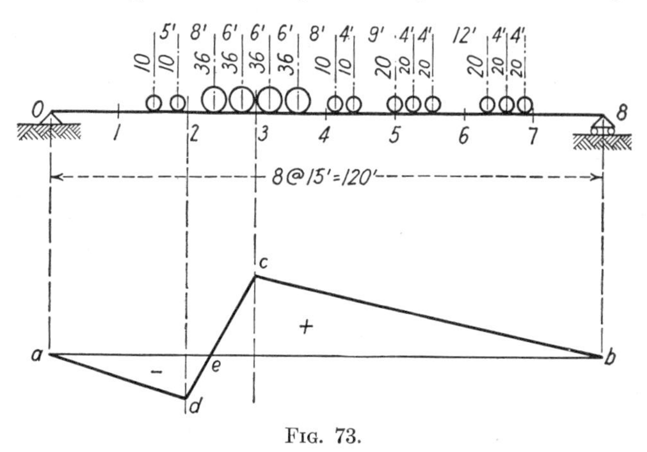

FIG. 73.

on the span. It should be clear from the discussion above that this can occur only as a load passes from an infinitesimal distance to the right of the panel point 3 to an infinitesimal distance to the left of the point, or in other words, can occur only when a load is at the panel point.

70. Illustrative Example.—To show the application of the principle, assume that the girder of Fig. 72 has 8 panels of 15 ft. as shown in Fig. 73, and determine the position of the loads of Fig. 66 (*b*) to produce maximum shear in the panel 2–3.

Wheel 1:

To right of p. p. 3 $\quad \frac{264}{120} > \frac{0}{15}$

To left of p. p. 3 $\quad \frac{264}{120} > \frac{10}{15}$ Wheel 1 does not satisfy criterion.

Wheel 2:

To right of p. p. 3 $\frac{284}{120} > \frac{10}{15}$

To left of p. p. 3 $\frac{284}{120} > \frac{20}{15}$ Wheel 2 does not satisfy criterion.

Wheel 3:

To right of p. p. 3 $\frac{304}{120} > \frac{20}{15}$

To left of p. p. 3 $\frac{304}{120} < \frac{56}{15}$ Wheel 3 does satisfy criterion.

When the panels have equal lengths, as is usual, it is evidently correct and more convenient to use the panel length as one and the number of panels as the span length.

The criterion can then be conveniently applied as follows:

Wheel 1:

To right of p. p. 3 / To left of p. p. 3 $\left.\begin{matrix} 0 \\ 10 \end{matrix}\right\} \frac{264}{8} = 33$ Does not satisfy.

Wheel 2:

$\left.\begin{matrix} 10 \\ 20 \end{matrix}\right\} \frac{284}{8} = 35.5$ Does not satisfy.

Wheel 3:

$\left.\begin{matrix} 20 \\ 56 \end{matrix}\right\} \frac{304}{8} = 38$ Satisfies.

71. Loads Pass Out of the Panel.—When panels are short, loads may pass out of the panel to the left as the group is moved from one wheel at the right end of the panel to the next wheel at this point. When this occurs more than one wheel may satisfy the criterion for maximum shear in the panel. For example, consider the span shown in Fig. 74 with the loads of Fig. 66 (*b*) except that wheels 9 to 14, inclusive, are now 25^k each. Determine the position of these loads for maximum shear in panel 1–2.

Wheel 1:

Right / Left $\left.\begin{matrix} 0 \\ 10 \end{matrix}\right\} \frac{234}{8} = 29\frac{1}{4}$

Wheel 2:

$$\left.\begin{array}{ll}\text{Right} & 10\\ \text{Left} & 20\end{array}\right\}\frac{259}{8} = 32\tfrac{3}{8}$$

Wheel 3:

$$\left.\begin{array}{ll}\text{Right} & 10\\ \text{Left} & 46\end{array}\right\}\frac{284}{8} = 35\tfrac{1}{2} \quad \text{Satisfies.}$$

Wheel 4:

$$\left.\begin{array}{ll}\text{Right} & 36\\ \text{Left} & 72\end{array}\right\}\frac{309}{8} = 38\tfrac{5}{8} \quad \text{Also satisfies.}$$

It is easy to determine which wheel at panel point 2 gives the greater shear by calculating the shear for each position, but it is

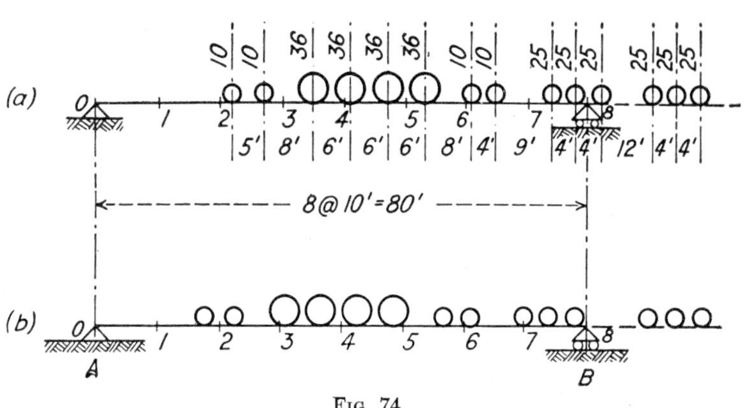

FIG. 74.

possible here as in the case of moment to write an expression for the change in shear resulting from moving from wheel 3 at panel point 2 to wheel 4 at panel point 2. The student should calculate the shear for each position and also write an expression for the change and compare the two methods.

Also he should note that in order to determine which wheel gives the greater shear it is not necessary to evaluate the change in shear but merely to determine whether the change is an increase or a decrease.

When loads move onto the span as the group is moved from one wheel at the right end of the panel to the next wheel at this point, more than one wheel may also satisfy the criterion for maximum shear in the panel. When this occurs the procedure will be similar to that above and an illustrative example is not necessary.

72. Maximum Floorbeam Reaction.—In the design of a floorbeam it is necessary to know the greatest load which can come on it from the stringers which it supports. For a uniform load the sum of the two stringer reactions, or the floorbeam reaction, will be a maximum when both panels are fully loaded. For a system of concentrated loads it is necessary to find the position which will produce the maximum floorbeam reaction. In Fig. 75 are shown two panels having lengths of p_1 and p_2, and also the influ-

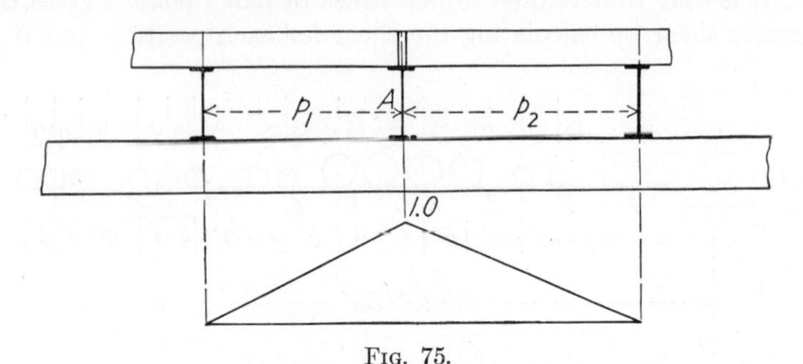

FIG. 75.

ence line for the reaction of the stringers in these panels on the floorbeam A. It should be noted that the shape of this influence line is the same as that of the influence line for moment at the point A in a simple span having a length of p_1 plus p_2. The position of the loads which will produce maximum floorbeam reaction therefore must be the same as that which will produce maximum moment at A in a simple span having a length p_1 plus p_2, and the criterion previously developed may be used. In making trial placements the heaviest loads of the system should be placed in the two panels.

To show the use of the criterion in such cases the position of the loads of Fig. 66 (*b*) to produce maximum floorbeam reaction at panel point 3 of the girder span of Art. 70 will be found.

The left half of the girder is shown in Fig. 76 with the influence line for the floorbeam reaction at panel point 3. The loads are shown on the span with wheel 4 at panel point 3. Bring the loads on from the right and first try wheel 3 at panel point 3.

Wheel 3 at p. p. 3:

Right $\frac{128}{2} > \frac{20}{1}$

Left $\frac{128}{2} > \frac{56}{1}$ Wheel 3 does not satisfy criterion.

Wheel 4 at p. p. 3:

Right $\frac{154}{2} > \frac{46}{1}$

Left $\frac{154}{2} < \frac{82}{1}$ Wheel 4 does satisfy criterion.

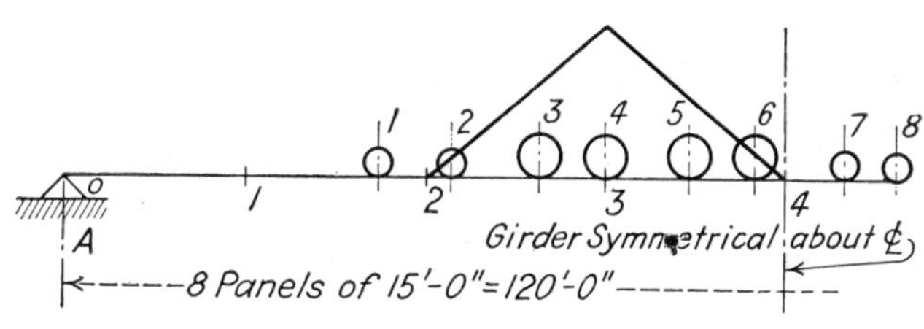

FIG. 76.

The student should observe that wheel 5 also satisfies the criterion, but that inspection shows wheel 4 or 5 to produce the same reaction on the floorbeam.

73. Moment Tables.—The calculation of maximum shears and moments, and particularly of truss stresses, resulting from a series of concentrated loads, involves a large amount of very tedious labor. To shorten the work as much as possible elaborate moment tables have been prepared for certain standard loadings. Two such tables are shown as Tables III and IV. Table III is a moment table for the standard loading known as Cooper's E–60, and Table IV a moment table for the standard loading known as Steinman's M–60.

These tables give the moments of all wheels to the left or right of any wheel about that wheel (or the moment of any number of adjacent wheels). Using the E–60 table as an example, the figure above each wheel gives the axle load in kips, the wheels are numbered from 1 to 18, and immediately below is given the spacing in feet. The first line of figures in each horizontal row (shown in plain type) represents total distances, the second line (shown in *italics*) represents total loads, and the third line (shown in **bold-faced** type) represents moments. The moment of any adjacent group of wheels about wheel 11 will be given in the column of figures under 11. For example, using the figures in the first row under the wheel, wheel 11 is 64 ft. from wheel 1, the weight of wheels 1 to 11 inclusive is 516 kips, and the moment of all wheels to the left about 11 is 17,544 ft.-kips. Using the figures in row 3 under the same wheel, the distance from 3 to 11 is 51 ft., the weight of wheels 3 to 11 inclusive is 426 kips, and the moment of wheels 3 to 11 about 11 is 12,264 ft.-kips. Using row 16 under wheel 11, the distance from wheel 16 to wheel 11 is 29 ft., the weight of wheels 16 to 11 inclusive is 318 kips, and the moment of wheels 16 to 11 about 11 is 3867 ft.-kips. It will therefore be observed that figures above the heavy zigzag line represent total distances, weights, and moments for wheels to the left of the wheel above the column of figures, and figures below the zigzag line represent distances, weights, and moments for wheels to the right. The right-hand column of values gives distances, weights, and moments for wheels to the left of the head of the uniform load. The M–60 table is constructed in a similar manner and will be used the same as outlined above.

The use of these tables may be illustrated by calculating the maximum bending moment due to Cooper's E–60 at a point C, 20 ft. from the left end of a 60-ft. girder.

The calculations are shown to the right of Fig. 77. The quantity 10,488 is the moment of wheels 1 to 9, inclusive, about wheel 9, and is taken from the table at the top of the column under wheel 9. The quantity $426^k \times 5$ ft. added to 10,488 gives the moment of these loads about the right support, 426^k being the sum of loads 1 to 9, inclusive (taken from the table), and 5 ft. the distance from wheel 9 to the right support. This moment divided by 60, the span length in feet, gives the left reaction which, multiplied by 20, is its moment about point C. It is then necessary to subtract the moment of wheels 1 and 2 about C and this, which is 690 ft.-kips, is taken from the table below wheel 3.

These tables are based on axle loads, and to obtain the bending moment on one girder the result found above should be divided by 2. Other Cooper loadings E–40, E–50, E–70, etc., are directly proportional to the E–60, and their effects may be found by direct proportion from the results obtained from the E–60 table. The same statements are true with regard to the M–60 table and other M loadings.

The scale shown above the wheels in the tables may be conveniently used in connection with the table. If the span under

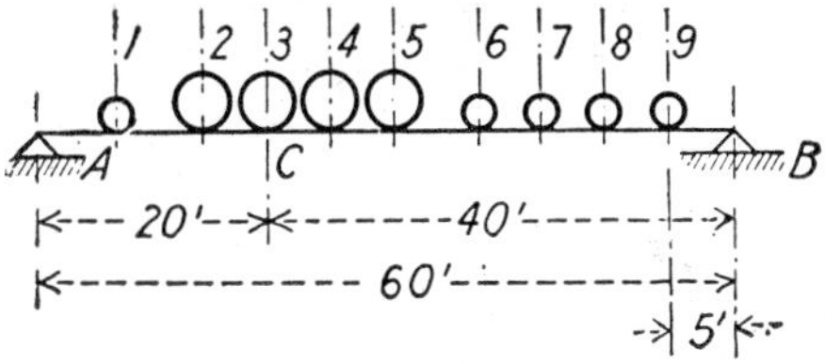

Wheel 3 $\left.\begin{array}{l}\frac{90}{20} < \\ \frac{150}{20} > \end{array}\right\} \frac{426}{60}$ *Satisfies*

Wheel 4 $\left.\begin{array}{l}\frac{150}{20} < \\ \frac{210}{20} > \end{array}\right\} \frac{456}{60}$ *Satisfies*

Wheel 3 gives max.

$$\begin{array}{r} 10{,}488 \\ 2{,}130 = 426 \times 5 \\ \hline 12{,}618 \end{array}$$

$$\div 60 = 210.3^{k}$$

$$\times 20 = 4206'^{k}$$

$$\begin{array}{r} 690 \\ \hline 3516'^{k} \end{array}$$

FIG. 77.

consideration is laid off according to this scale and the point in question is placed under a particular wheel, it is possible to see at a glance the position and number of wheels on the span. To try another wheel the span may be moved so that the point in question is under the new wheel being tried.

Courtesy of the Phoenix Bridge Company

Through plate girder span passing under two-hinged arch. Cottage Farm Bridge, Metropolitan District Commission, Massachusetts.

TABLE III.—E-6

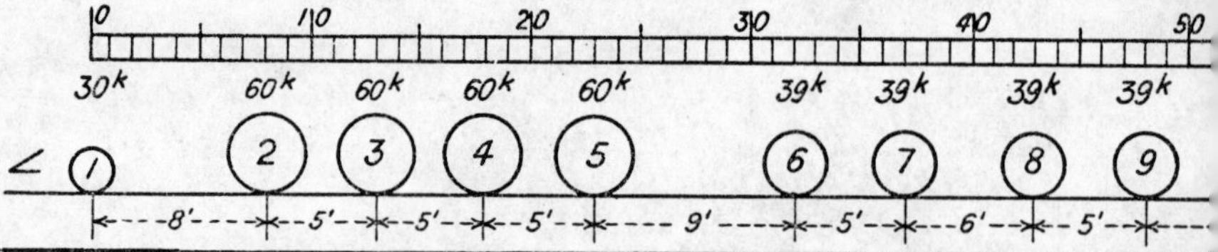

	1	2	3	4	5	6	7	8	9
1	0 *30* **0**	8 *90* **240**	13 *150* **690**	18 *210* **1440**	23 *270* **2490**	32 *309* **4920**	37 *348* **6465**	43 *387* **8553**	48 *426* **10,488**
2	8 *90* **480**	0 *60* **0**	5 *120* **300**	10 *180* **900**	15 *240* **1800**	24 *279* **3960**	29 *318* **5355**	35 *357* **7263**	40 *396* **9048**
3	13 *150* **1260**	5 *120* **300**	0 *60* **0**	5 *120* **300**	10 *180* **900**	19 *219* **2520**	24 *258* **3615**	30 *297* **5163**	35 *336* **6648**
4	18 *210* **2340**	10 *180* **900**	5 *120* **300**	0 *60* **0**	5 *120* **300**	14 *159* **1380**	19 *198* **2175**	25 *237* **3363**	30 *276* **4548**
5	23 *270* **3720**	15 *240* **1800**	10 *180* **900**	5 *120* **300**	0 *60* **0**	9 *99* **540**	14 *138* **1035**	20 *177* **1863**	25 *216* **2748**
6	32 *309* **4968**	24 *279* **2736**	19 *219* **1641**	14 *159* **846**	9 *99* **351**	0 *39* **0**	5 *78* **195**	11 *117* **663**	16 *156* **1248**
7	37 *348* **6411**	29 *318* **3867**	24 *258* **2577**	19 *198* **1587**	14 *138* **897**	5 *78* **195**	0 *39* **0**	6 *78* **234**	11 *117* **624**
8	43 *387* **8088**	35 *357* **5232**	30 *297* **3747**	25 *237* **2562**	20 *177* **1677**	11 *117* **624**	6 *78* **234**	0 *39* **0**	5 *78* **195**
9	48 *426* **9960**	40 *396* **6792**	35 *336* **5112**	30 *276* **3732**	25 *216* **2652**	16 *156* **1248**	11 *117* **663**	5 *78* **195**	0 *39* **0**
10	56 *456* **11,640**	48 *426* **8232**	43 *366* **6402**	38 *306* **4872**	33 *246* **3642**	24 *186* **1968**	19 *147* **1233**	13 *108* **585**	8 *69* **240**
11	64 *516* **15,480**	56 *486* **11,592**	51 *426* **9462**	46 *366* **7632**	41 *306* **6102**	32 *246* **3888**	27 *207* **2853**	21 *168* **1845**	16 *129* **1200**
12	69 *576* **19,620**	61 *546* **15,252**	56 *486* **12,822**	51 *426* **10,692**	46 *366* **8862**	37 *306* **6108**	32 *267* **4773**	26 *228* **3405**	21 *189* **2460**
13	74 *636* **24,060**	66 *606* **19,212**	61 *546* **16482**	56 *486* **14,052**	51 *426* **11,922**	42 *366* **8628**	37 *327* **6993**	31 *288* **5265**	26 *249* **4020**
14	79 *696* **28,800**	71 *666* **23,472**	66 *606* **20,442**	61 *546* **17,712**	56 *486* **15,282**	47 *426* **11,448**	42 *387* **9513**	36 *348* **7425**	31 *309* **5880**
15	88 *735* **32,232**	80 *705* **26,592**	75 *645* **23,367**	70 *585* **20,442**	65 *525* **17,817**	56 *465* **13,632**	51 *426* **11,502**	45 *387* **9180**	40 *348* **7440**
16	93 *774* **35,859**	85 *744* **29,907**	80 *684* **26,487**	75 *624* **23,367**	70 *564* **20,547**	61 *504* **16,011**	56 *465* **13,686**	50 *426* **11,130**	45 *387* **9195**
17	99 *813* **39,720**	91 *783* **33,456**	86 *723* **29,841**	81 *663* **26,526**	76 *603* **23,511**	67 *543* **18,624**	62 *504* **16,104**	56 *465* **13,314**	51 *426* **11,184**
18	104 *852* **43,776**	96 *822* **37,200**	91 *762* **33,890**	86 *702* **29,880**	81 *642* **26,670**	72 *582* **21,432**	67 *543* **18,717**	61 *504* **15,693**	56 *465* **13,368**

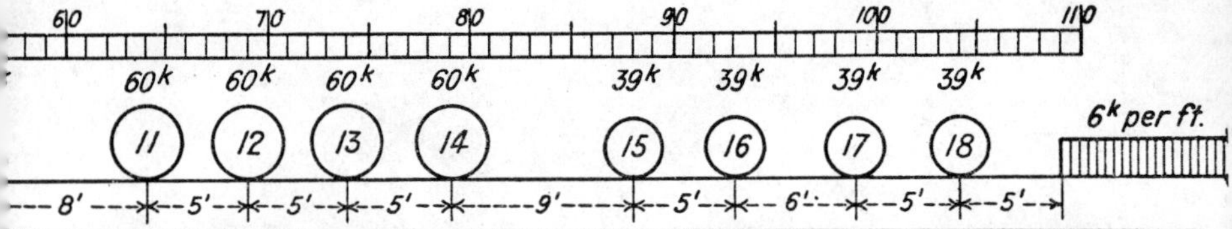

60 70 80 90 100 110

	60^k	60^k	60^k	60^k	39^k	39^k	39^k	39^k	6^k per ft.	
Wheel	11	12	13	14	15	16	17	18		
Spacing	8'	5'	5'	5'	9'	5'	6'	5'	5'	
	64 *516* **17,544**	69 *576* **20,124**	74 *636* **23,004**	79 *696* **26,184**	88 *735* **32,448**	93 *774* **36,123**	99 *813* **40,767**	104 *852* **44,832**	109 *852* **49,092**	**1**
	56 *486* **15,624**	61 *546* **18,054**	66 *606* **20,784**	71 *666* **23,814**	80 *705* **29,808**	85 *744* **33,333**	91 *783* **37,797**	96 *822* **41,712**	101 *822* **45,822**	**2**
	51 *426* **12,264**	56 *486* **14,394**	61 *546* **16,824**	66 *606* **19,554**	75 *645* **25,008**	80 *684* **28,233**	86 *723* **32,337**	91 *762* **35,952**	96 *762* **39,762**	**3**
	46 *366* **9204**	51 *426* **11,034**	56 *486* **13,164**	61 *546* **15,594**	70 *585* **20,508**	75 *624* **23,433**	81 *663* **27,177**	86 *702* **30,492**	91 *702* **34,002**	**4**
	41 *306* **6444**	46 *366* **7974**	51 *426* **9804**	56 *486* **11,934**	65 *525* **16,308**	70 *564* **18,933**	76 *603* **22,317**	81 *642* **25,332**	86 *642* **28,542**	**5**
	32 *246* **3984**	37 *306* **5214**	42 *366* **6744**	47 *426* **8574**	56 *465* **12,408**	61 *504* **14,733**	67 *543* **17,757**	72 *582* **20,472**	77 *582* **23,382**	**6**
	27 *207* **2736**	32 *267* **3771**	37 *327* **5106**	42 *387* **6741**	51 *426* **10,224**	56 *465* **12,354**	62 *504* **15,144**	67 *543* **17,664**	72 *543* **20,379**	**7**
	21 *168* **1683**	26 *228* **2523**	31 *288* **3663**	36 *348* **5103**	45 *387* **8235**	50 *426* **10,170**	56 *465* **12,726**	61 *504* **15,051**	66 *504* **17,571**	**8**
	16 *129* **864**	21 *189* **1509**	26 *249* **2454**	31 *309* **3699**	40 *348* **6480**	45 *387* **8220**	51 *426* **10,542**	56 *465* **12,672**	61 *465* **14,997**	**9**
	8 *90* **240**	13 *150* **690**	18 *210* **1440**	23 *270* **2490**	32 *309* **4920**	37 *348* **6465**	43 *387* **8553**	48 *426* **10,488**	53 *426* **12,618**	**10**
	0 *60* **0**	5 *120* **300**	10 *180* **900**	15 *240* **1800**	24 *279* **3960**	29 *318* **5355**	35 *357* **7263**	40 *396* **9048**	45 *396* **11,028**	**11**
	5 *120* **300**	0 *60* **0**	5 *120* **300**	10 *180* **900**	19 *219* **2520**	24 *258* **3615**	30 *297* **5163**	35 *336* **6648**	40 *336* **8328**	**12**
	10 *180* **900**	5 *120* **300**	0 *60* **0**	5 *120* **300**	14 *159* **1380**	19 *198* **2175**	25 *237* **3363**	30 *276* **4548**	35 *276* **5928**	**13**
	15 *240* **1800**	10 *180* **900**	5 *120* **300**	0 *60* **0**	9 *99* **540**	14 *138* **1035**	20 *177* **1863**	25 *216* **2748**	30 *216* **3828**	**14**
	24 *279* **2736**	19 *219* **1641**	14 *159* **846**	9 *99* **351**	0 *39* **0**	5 *78* **195**	11 *117* **663**	16 *156* **1248**	21 *156* **2028**	**15**
	29 *318* **3867**	24 *258* **2577**	19 *198* **1587**	14 *138* **897**	5 *78* **195**	0 *39* **0**	6 *78* **234**	11 *117* **624**	16 *117* **1209**	**16**
	35 *357* **5232**	30 *297* **3747**	25 *237* **2562**	20 *177* **1677**	11 *117* **624**	6 *78* **234**	0 *39* **0**	5 *78* **195**	10 *78* **585**	**17**
	40 *396* **6792**	35 *336* **5112**	30 *276* **3732**	25 *216* **2652**	16 *156* **1248**	11 *117* **663**	5 *78* **195**	0 *39* **0**	5 *39* **195**	**18**

	30^k (1)	60^k (2)	60^k (3)	60^k (4)	60^k (5)	60^k (6)	75^k (7)	75^k (8)	75^k (9)	75^k (10)	75^k (11)	6^k per ft.	
	10′	5′	5′	5′	5′	15′	5′	5′	5′	5′	5′		
1	0 *30* **0**	10 *90* **300**	15 *150* **750**	20 *210* **1500**	25 *270* **2550**	30 *330* **3900**	45 *405* **8850**	50 *480* **10,875**	55 *555* **13,275**	60 *630* **16,050**	65 *705* **19,200**	70 *705* **22,725**	**1**
2	10 *90* **600**	0 *60* **0**	5 *120* **300**	10 *180* **900**	15 *240* **1800**	20 *300* **3000**	35 *375* **7500**	40 *450* **9375**	45 *525* **11,625**	50 *600* **14,250**	55 *675* **17,250**	60 *675* **20,625**	**2**
3	15 *150* **1500**	5 *120* **300**	0 *60* **0**	5 *120* **300**	10 *180* **900**	15 *240* **1800**	30 *315* **5400**	35 *390* **6975**	40 *465* **8925**	45 *540* **11,250**	50 *615* **13,950**	55 *615* **17,025**	**3**
4	20 *210* **2700**	10 *180* **900**	5 *120* **300**	0 *60* **0**	5 *120* **300**	10 *180* **900**	25 *255* **3600**	30 *330* **4875**	35 *405* **6525**	40 *480* **8550**	45 *555* **10,950**	50 *555* **13,725**	**4**
5	25 *270* **4200**	15 *240* **1800**	10 *180* **900**	5 *120* **300**	0 *60* **0**	5 *120* **300**	20 *195* **2100**	25 *270* **3075**	30 *345* **4425**	35 *420* **6150**	40 *495* **8250**	45 *495* **10,725**	**5**
6	30 *330* **6000**	20 *300* **3000**	15 *240* **1800**	10 *180* **900**	5 *120* **300**	0 *60* **0**	15 *135* **900**	20 *210* **1575**	25 *285* **2625**	30 *360* **4050**	35 *435* **5850**	40 *435* **8025**	**6**
7	45 *405* **9375**	35 *375* **5625**	30 *315* **4050**	25 *255* **2775**	20 *195* **1800**	15 *135* **1125**	0 *75* **0**	5 *150* **375**	10 *225* **1125**	15 *300* **2250**	20 *375* **3750**	25 *375* **5625**	**7**
8	50 *480* **13,125**	40 *450* **8625**	35 *390* **6675**	30 *330* **5025**	25 *270* **3675**	20 *210* **2625**	5 *150* **375**	0 *75* **0**	5 *150* **375**	10 *225* **1125**	15 *300* **2250**	20 *300* **3750**	**8**
9	55 *555* **17,250**	45 *525* **12,000**	40 *465* **9675**	35 *405* **7650**	30 *345* **5925**	25 *285* **4500**	10 *225* **1125**	5 *150* **375**	0 *75* **0**	5 *150* **375**	10 *225* **1125**	15 *225* **2250**	**9**
10	60 *630* **21,750**	50 *600* **15,750**	45 *540* **13,050**	40 *480* **10,650**	35 *420* **8550**	30 *360* **6750**	15 *300* **2250**	10 *225* **1125**	5 *150* **375**	0 *75* **0**	5 *150* **375**	10 *150* **1125**	**10**
11	65 *705* **26,625**	55 *675* **19,875**	50 *615* **16,800**	45 *555* **14,025**	40 *495* **11,550**	35 *435* **9375**	20 *375* **3750**	15 *300* **2250**	10 *225* **1125**	5 *150* **375**	0 *75* **0**	5 *75* **375**	**11**

PROBLEMS

An influence line is not complete unless the values are shown at all controlling points.

86. (*a*) Draw the influence line for the left reaction of the structure shown, as a unit load moves along the upper chord.

(*b*) Draw the influence line for the *vertical* component of the right reaction for the same structure.

(*c*) Draw the influence line for the *horizontal* component of the right reaction for the same structure.

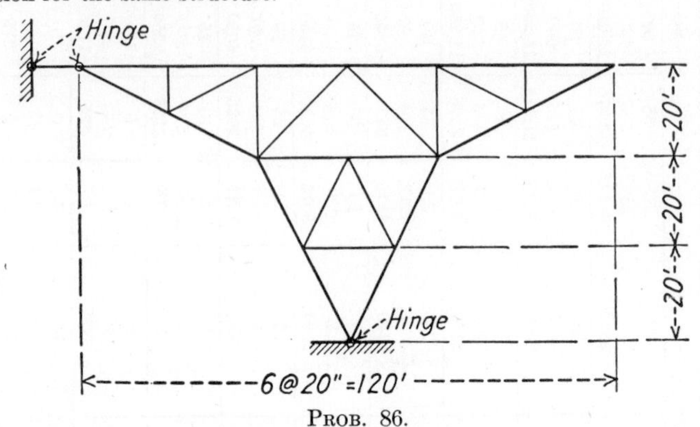

PROB. 86.

87. Draw the influence lines for the reactions at *A*, *C*, *D*, and *E* for the structure shown. The unit load moves from *A* to *D*.

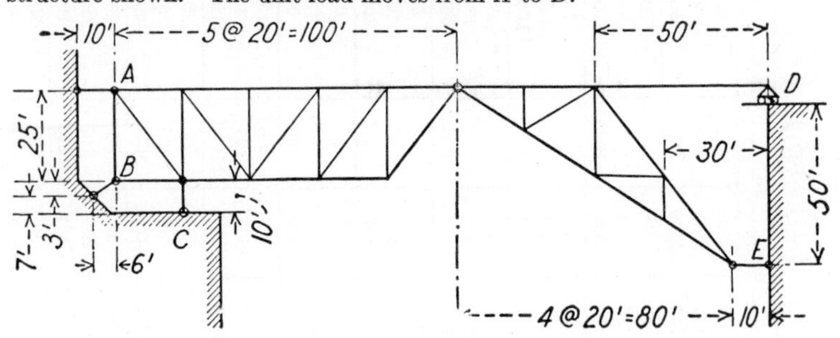

PROB. 87.

88. Draw the influence lines for shear and the influence lines for moment at *A*, *B*, and *C* in the beam. *B* is just to the right of the left support.

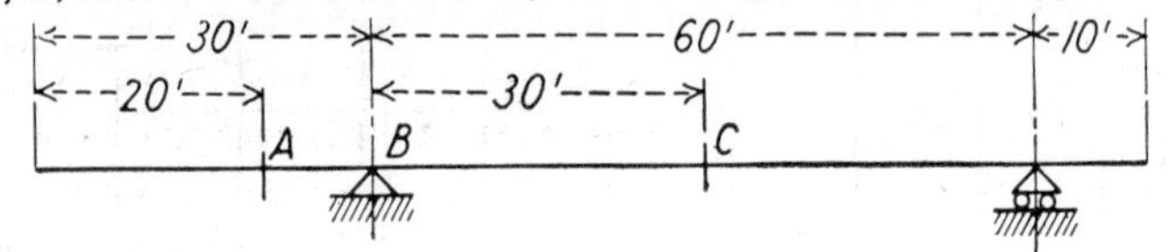

PROB. 88.

89. (*a*) Draw the influence lines for shear at sections *a*, *b*, and *c*; *a* and *c* are to be taken an infinitesimal distance to the left of the supports.

(*b*) Draw the influence lines for moment at *a*, *b*, and *c*.

(*c*) Draw the influence lines for shear at *a* and *c* when they are an infinitesimal distance to the right of the supports.

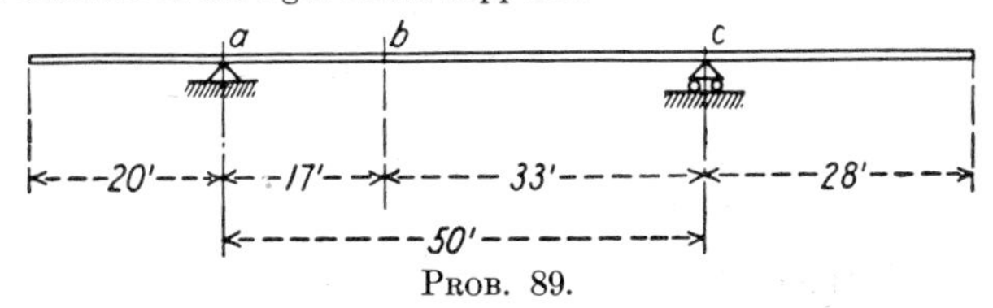

PROB. 89.

90. (*a*) Draw the influence line for vertical component of the tie rod reaction as a unit load moves from *A* to *B*.

(*b*) Draw the influence line for moment in the mast at *B* as a unit load moves from *A* to *B*.

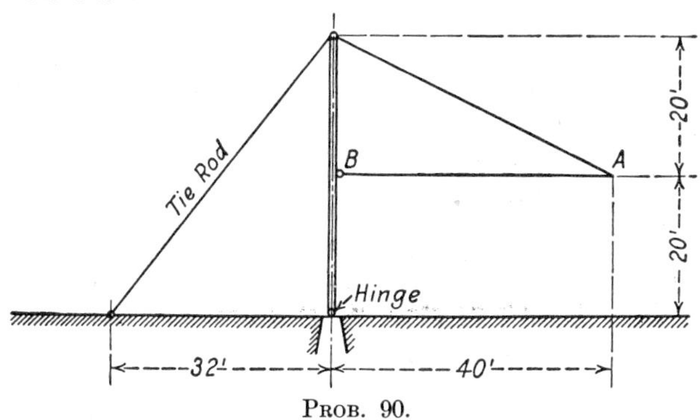

PROB. 90.

91. Draw the following influence lines for the structure shown. In all cases the unit load moves between *B* and *C*.

(*a*) Vertical component of the reaction at *A*.

(*b*) Shear and moment at *b*.

(*c*) Shear and moment at *c*.

(*d*) Shear and moment at *d*.

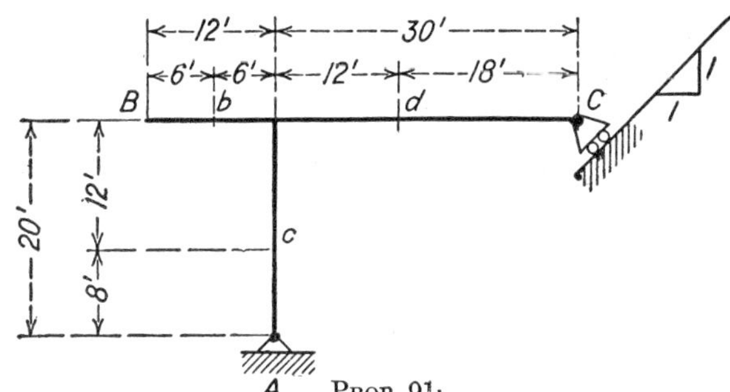

PROB. 91.

92. Draw the influence lines for shear and moment at C and D in the beam shown, as a unit load moves from A to B.

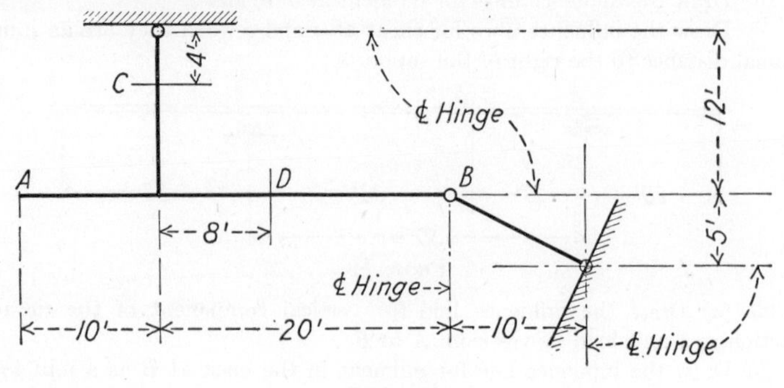

PROB. 92.

93. Draw the following influence lines for the structure shown. In all cases the load moves from B to D.

(*a*) Reaction at C.
(*b*) Shear and moment at 1.
(*c*) Shear and moment at 2.
(*d*) Shear and moment at 3.

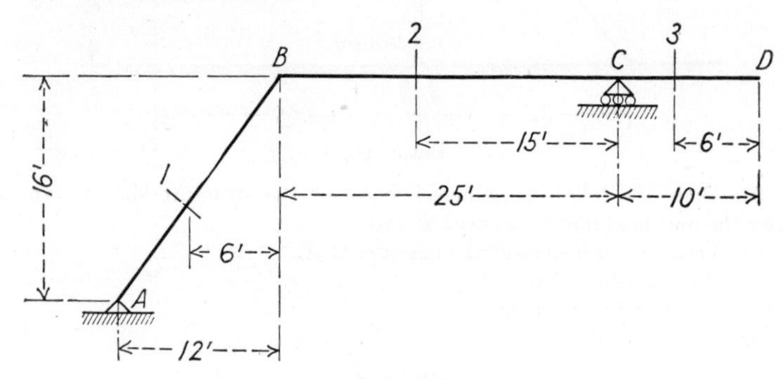

PROB. 93.

94. (*a*) Draw the influence line for the reaction at K, for the beam shown in (*a*), as a unit load moves from A to B.

(*b*) Draw the influence line for shear at DE, in the same beam, as a unit load moves from A to B.

(*c*) Draw the influence line for shear at DE, in the beam shown in (*b*), as a unit load moves from a to n.

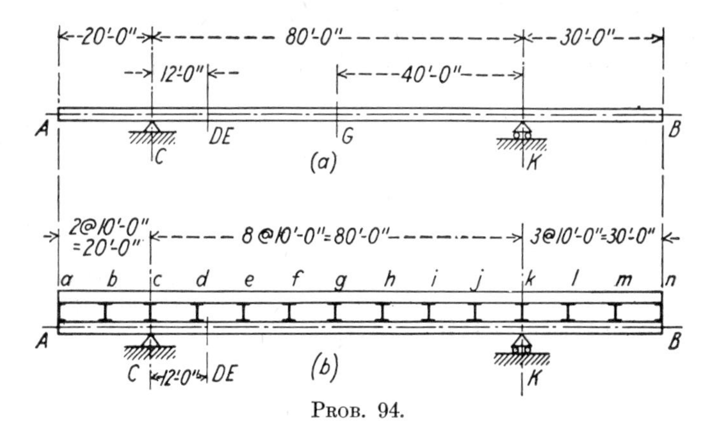

PROB. 94.

95. (*a*) Draw the influence line for moment at *DE*, in the beam shown in Problem 94 (*a*), as a unit load moves from *A* to *B*.

(*b*) Draw the influence line for moment at *DE*, in the beam shown in Problem 94 (*b*), as a unit load moves from *a* to *n*.

(*c*) Draw the influence line for moment at *G*, in the beam shown in Problem 94 (*a*), as a unit load moves from *A* to *B*.

(*d*) Draw the influence line for moment at panel point *g*, in the beam shown in Problem 94 (*b*), as a unit load moves from *a* to *n*.

96. As a unit load moves from *A* to *D*, draw influence lines for:

(*a*) Shear and moment at 1–1.

(*b*) Shear and moment at 2–2.

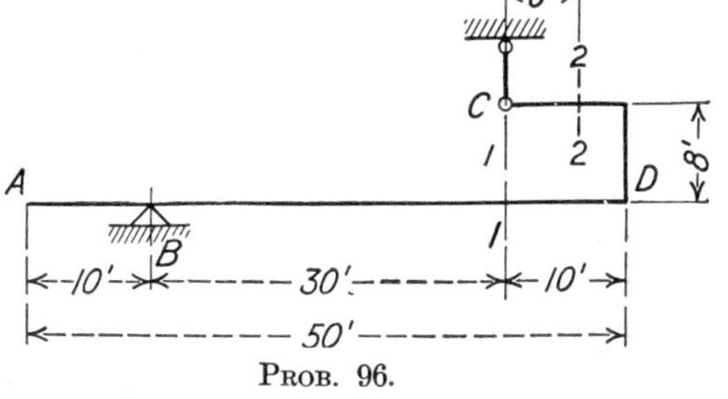

PROB. 96.

97. (*a*) Draw the influence lines for shear and moment at *f*, in the beam *CD* of the frame shown, as a unit load moves from *A* to *B*.

(*b*) Draw the influence lines for shear and moment at *g* in the same beam for the same movement of the unit load.

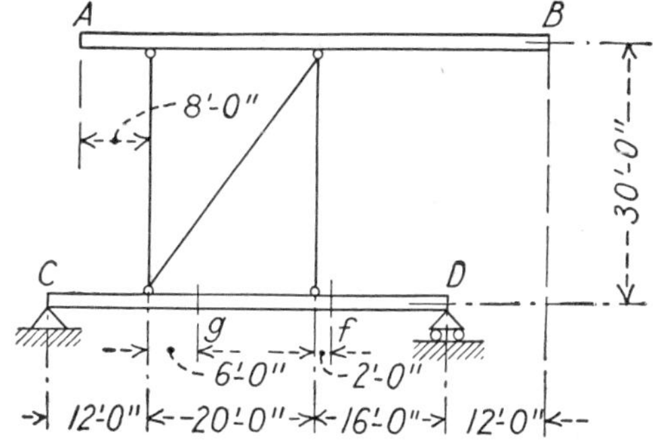

PROB. 97.

98. (*a*) Draw the influence line for shear in panels 0–1, 1–2, and 2–3.
(*b*) Draw the influence line for moment at panel points 1, 2, and 3.

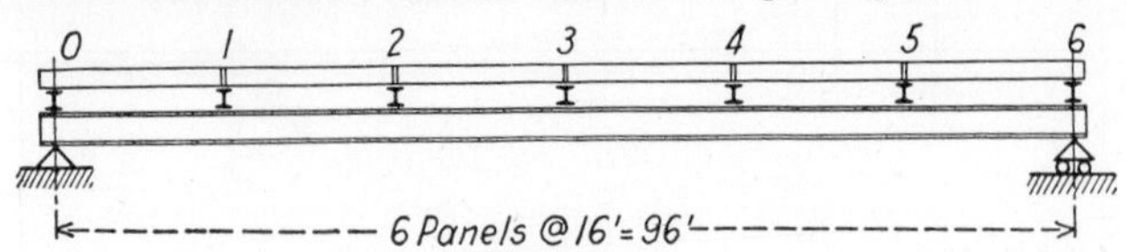

PROB. 98.

99. As a unit load moves from U_0 to U_9 on the truss, draw the influence line for:

(1) Shear in panel U_5U_6.
(2) Moment at panel point U_5.

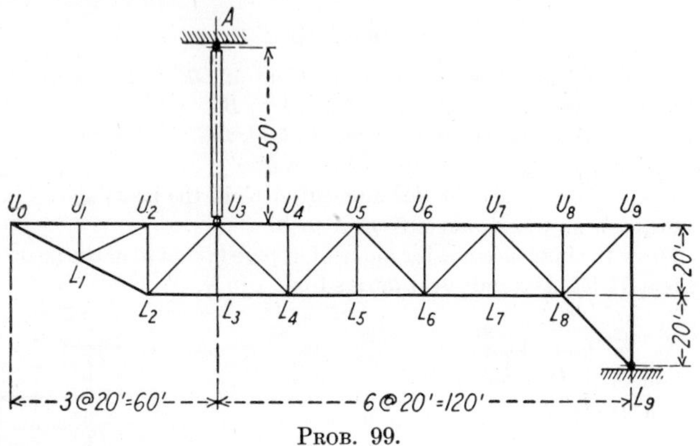

PROB. 99.

100. Draw the influence line for:

(*a*) vertical component of reaction at *G*,
(*b*) shear in panel 2–3,
(*c*) shear in panel 11–12,
(*d*) bending moment at panel point 23,

as a unit load moves between *A* and *B*.

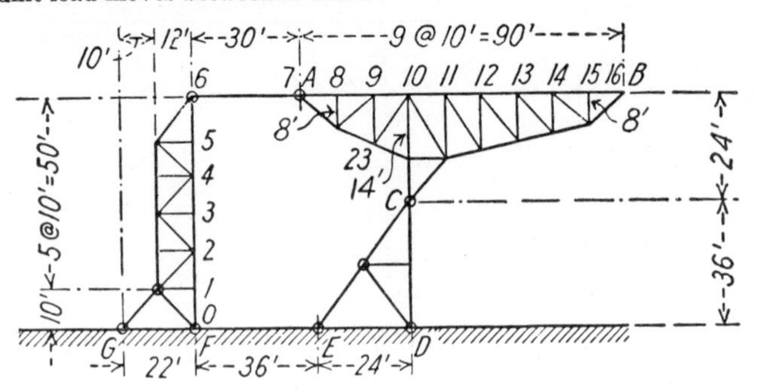

PROB. 100.

101. Draw the influence line for:

(*a*) Reaction at *A*.
(*b*) Shear in panel 3–4.
(*c*) Bending moment at panel point 5.

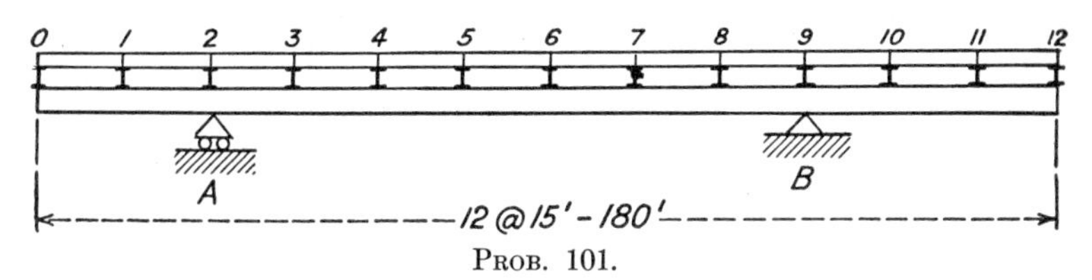

PROB. 101.

102. From the influence lines drawn for Problem 101, determine:

(*a*) the maximum positive and maximum negative reaction at *A*,
(*b*) the maximum positive and maximum negative shear in 3–4,
(*c*) the maximum positive and maximum negative moment at 5,

due, first, to a single concentrated load of 60^k, and second, to a movable uniform load of 4 kips per ft.

103. By means of influence lines, calculate the maximum negative shear and maximum negative moment at *E* due to a moving uniform load of 4 kips per ft.

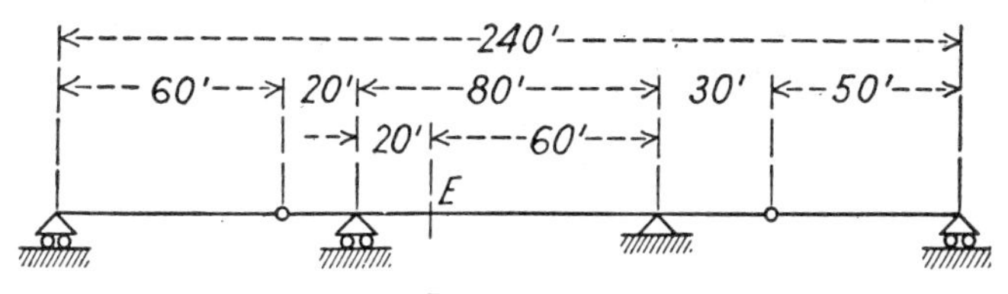

PROB. 103.

104. (*a*) Draw the influence line for shear at a point 30 ft. to the right of support *A* for the structure shown.

(*b*) From the influence line just drawn, compute the maximum positive shear at the section in question due to a moving uniform load of 3 kips per ft. *Ans.* 73.5^k.

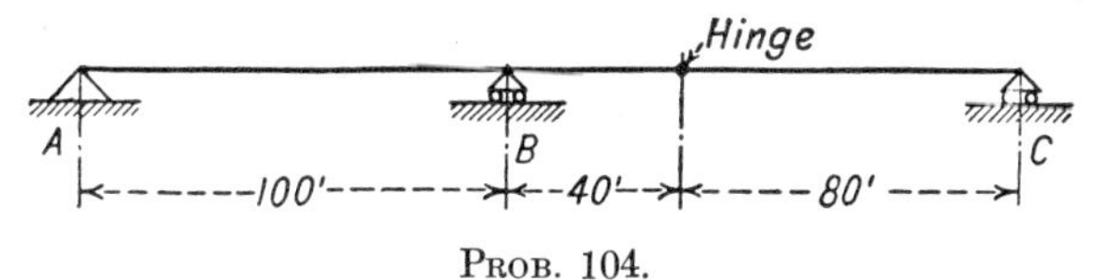

PROB. 104.

105. (*a*) Draw the influence line for moment at a point 30 ft. to the right of support *A* for the structure shown in Problem 104.

(*b*) From the influence line just drawn, compute the maximum negative moment at the section in question due to a moving uniform load of 3 kips per ft.

106. (*a*) From an inspection of the influence lines drawn for (*a*) and (*b*) Problem 89, determine where a single concentrated load should be placed to give:

(1) Maximum positive shear at point *c*.
(2) Maximum positive shear at point *b*.
(3) Maximum moment at point *c*.

(*b*) From an inspection of the same influence lines, determine what part of the beam should be loaded with uniform load to give:

(1) Maximum positive shear at point *c*.
(2) Maximum positive shear at point *b*.
(3) Maximum moment at point *a*.

107. (*a*) From the influence lines drawn for Problem 98, determine the exact maximum positive shear in panels 0–1 and 2–3 resulting from a uniform live load of 4000 lb. per ft. of stringer.

(*b*) Compute by the approximate method the maximum shear in the same panels resulting from the same uniform live load.

(*c*) Compute from the influence lines the maximum moment at panel points 1, 2, and 3 resulting from the same uniform live load.

108. From an inspection of the influence line drawn for Problem 94 (*a*):

(*a*) What part of the beam should be loaded with a uniform live load of 4 kips per ft. to produce maximum *upward* reaction at *K*?

(*b*) What part of the beam should be loaded with the same uniform live load to produce maximum *downward* reaction at *K*?

109. In the structure shown, draw influence lines for:

(*a*) shear in panel 4–5,
(*b*) moment at U_3,
(*c*) shear in panel 2–3,
(*d*) moment at L_5,

as a unit load moves from L_0 to L_9.

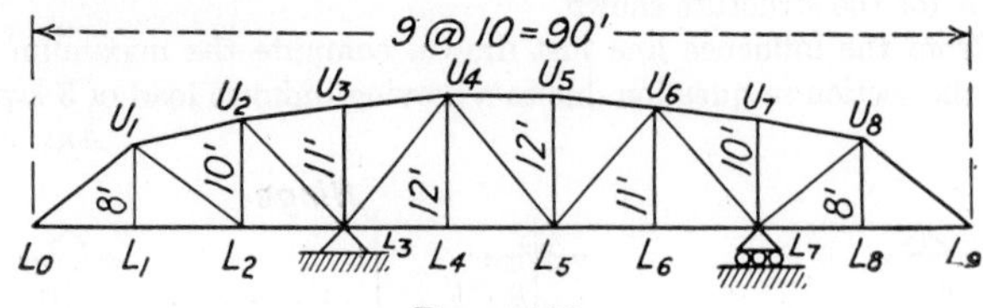

PROB. 109.

110. From the above influence lines find:

(*a*) maximum positive and negative moment at L_5,
(*b*) maximum positive and negative shear in 4–5,

due to a moving uniform load of 5 kips per ft.

(*c*) maximum moment at U_3,
(*d*) maximum shear in 2–3,

due to moving concentrated load of 50^k.

Ans. (*a*) +1000 ft.-kips, −1625 ft.-kips.
(*b*) $+89.6^k$, -33.4^k.
(*c*) −1500 ft.-kips.
(*d*) -50^k.

111. From an inspection of the influence lines drawn for Problem 94:

(*a*) What part of the beam should be loaded with a uniform live load of 4 kips per ft. to produce maximum positive shear at *DE* in the beam of Problem 94, Fig. (*a*)? Maximum negative shear at the same section?

(*b*) What part of the beam in Problem 94, Fig. (*b*) should be loaded with a uniform live load of 4 kips per ft. to produce maximum positive shear at *DE*? Maximum negative shear at the same section?

(*c*) From the influence lines drawn for Problem 95, what part of the beam in Fig. (*b*) should be loaded with a uniform load of 4 kips per ft. to produce maximum positive moment at *DE*? Maximum negative moment at the same point?

112. The figure shows a suspended floorbeam for a through arch. The panel lengths are 40 ft. 0 in.; i.e., the floorbeams are 40 ft. 0 in. center to center. The live load is to be taken as 100 lb. per sq. ft. of roadway surface.

(*a*) What part of the roadway should be loaded to give maximum negative moment in the floorbeam? What and where is the maximum negative moment due to live load given above?

(*b*) What part of the roadway should be loaded to give maximum positive moment in the floorbeam? What and where is the maximum positive moment due to the live load given above?

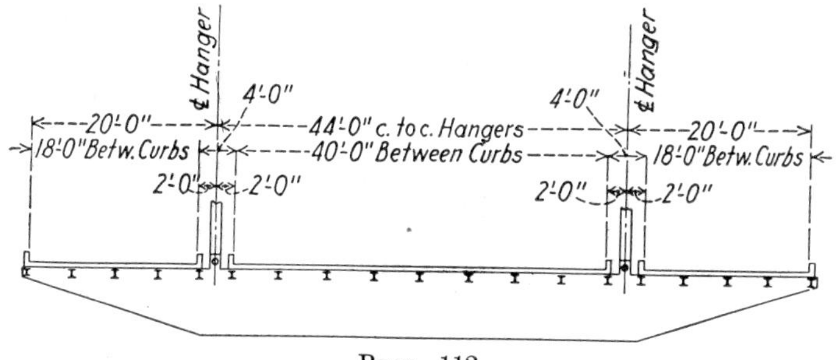

PROB. 112.

113. From the influence lines drawn for Problem 88, determine where to load to produce, and from the influence lines calculate:

(*a*) the maximum positive and negative shear at *B*,
(*b*) the maximum positive and negative shear at *C*,
(*c*) the maximum positive and negative moment at *C*,

due to a uniform load of 4 kips per ft.

Ans. (*a*) $+150^k$, $-3\frac{1}{3}^k$.
(*b*) $+60^k$, $-33\frac{1}{3}^k$.
(*c*) +1800 ft.-kips, −1000 ft.-kips.

114. A deck plate girder bridge and the loading diagram for which it is to be designed are shown. Compute:

(*a*) The maximum live load shear at the end.
(*b*) The maximum live load shear at the center.
(*c*) The maximum live load moment at the center.

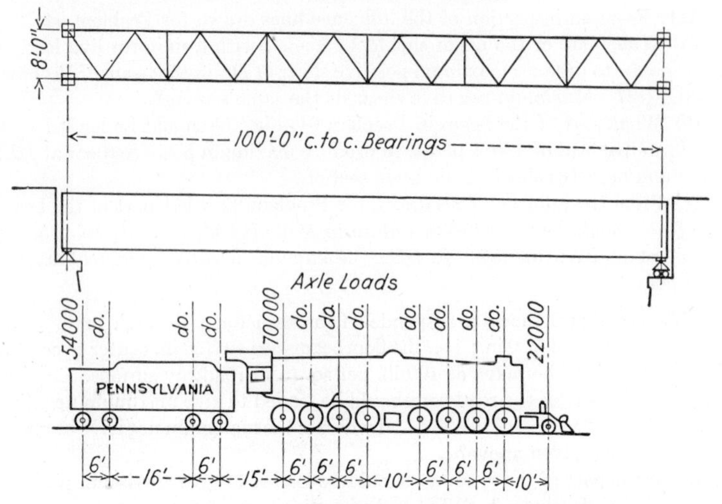

PROB. 114.

115. The figure shows the axle loads and spacings for two units of an electric locomotive for freight service.

(*a*) What position of the wheels will produce maximum reaction at the left end of one girder of the bridge span shown in Problem 114? Compute the reaction.

(*b*) What position of the wheels will produce maximum shear at the quarter point of one girder of the span? Compute the shear.

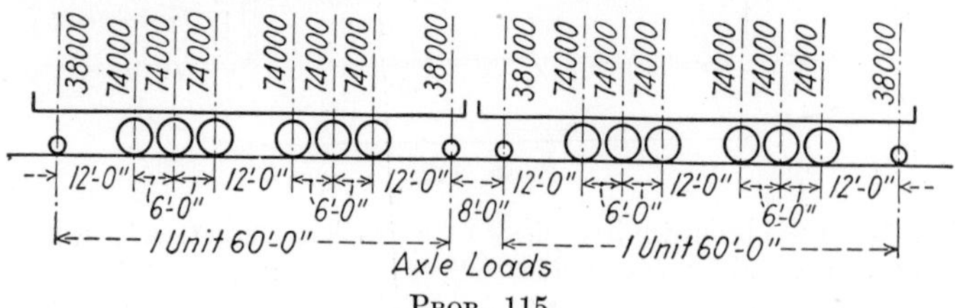

PROB. 115.

116. The figure shows the axle loads of a heavy freight locomotive. Calculate the maximum live load shear due to this loading on one girder of a 100-ft. deck plate girder span:

(*a*) At the end.
(*b*) At the quarter point.
(*c*) At the center.

Ans. (*a*) 247^k wheel 3.
(*b*) 152^k wheel 3.
(*c*) 73^k wheel 3.

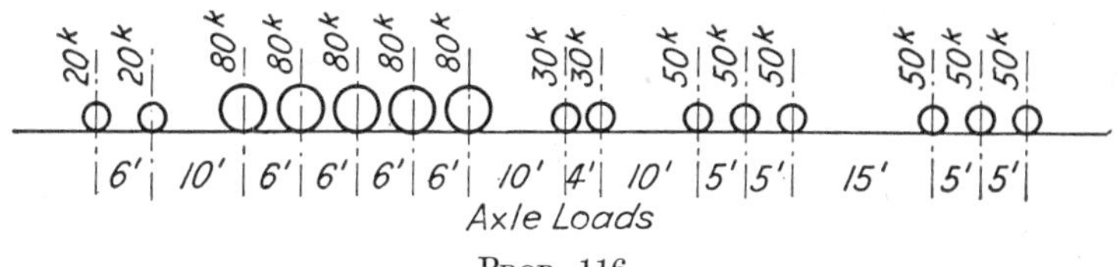

PROB. 116.

117. Calculate the maximum end shear and the maximum center moment for the beam due to the moving loads shown.

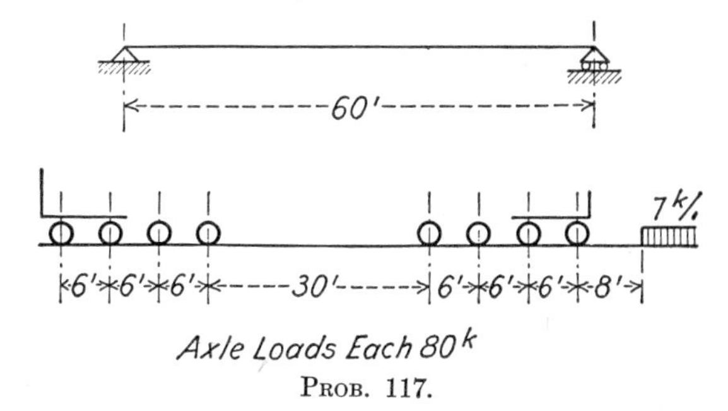

PROB. 117.

118. Calculate the maximum shear at a point 30 ft. from the left end of a deck girder 80 ft. long, due to the loads shown.

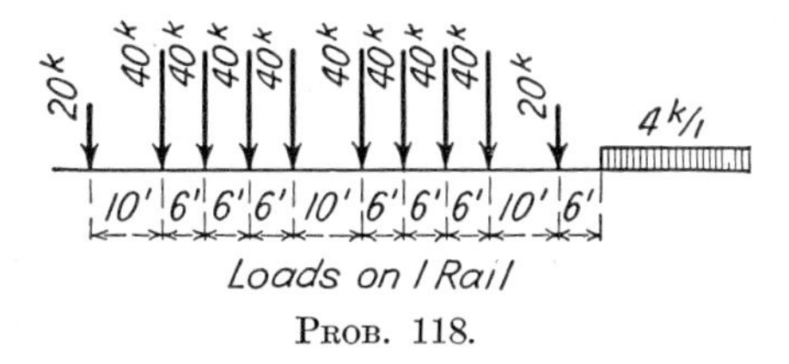

PROB. 118.

119. Calculate the maximum moment at a point 30 ft. from the left end of a deck girder 80 ft. long, due to the loads shown in Problem 118.

120. Due to the axle loading shown, calculate the maximum moment at the quarter point of a span of 80 ft. *Ans.* 2792 ft.-kips wheel 4.

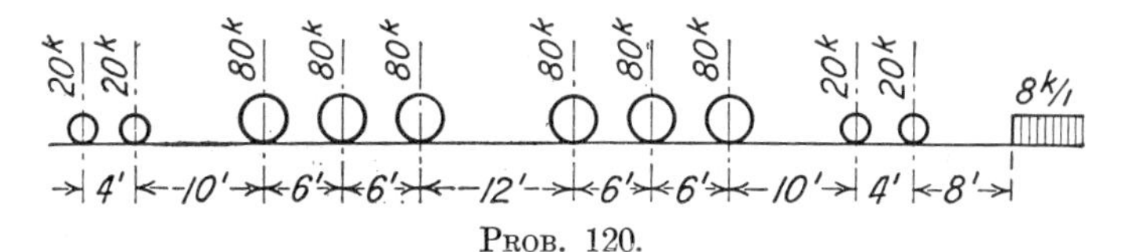

PROB. 120.

121. The wheel spacing and loads for two 50-ton O. E. T. cranes are shown. The columns supporting the crane runway girder are spaced 25 ft. center to center, there being several spans. Calculate the following:

(*a*) The maximum live load end shear on one crane runway girder.
(*b*) The maximum live load quarter point shear.
(*c*) The maximum live load center bending moment.

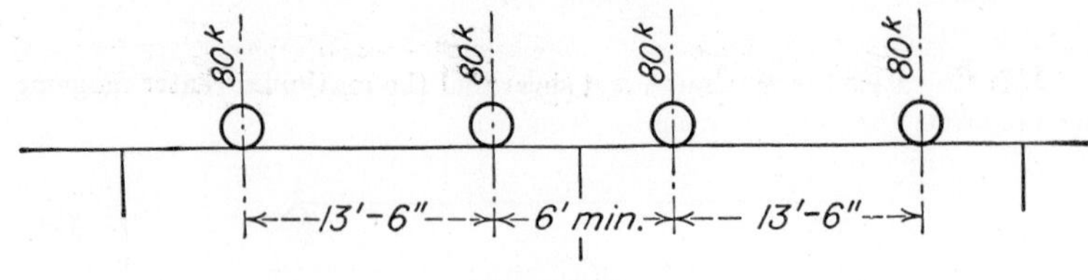

Prob. 121.

122. Using the axle loads and spacing for the new A-64 loading proposed by the Conference of Committees for Specifications for Steel Railway Bridges. For a single-track 100-ft. deck girder span calculate:

(*a*) Maximum end shear for one girder.
(*b*) Maximum center shear for one girder.
(*c*) Maximum center moment for one girder.

123. The truck and trailer axle loads resulting from the transportation by highway of an 80-ton bridge girder are shown. To reach the bridge site these loads must pass over a deck girder highway bridge having a span of 120 ft. Calculate for one girder:

(*a*) The maximum live load end shear.
(*b*) The maximum live load quarter point shear.
(*c*) The maximum live load center bending moment.

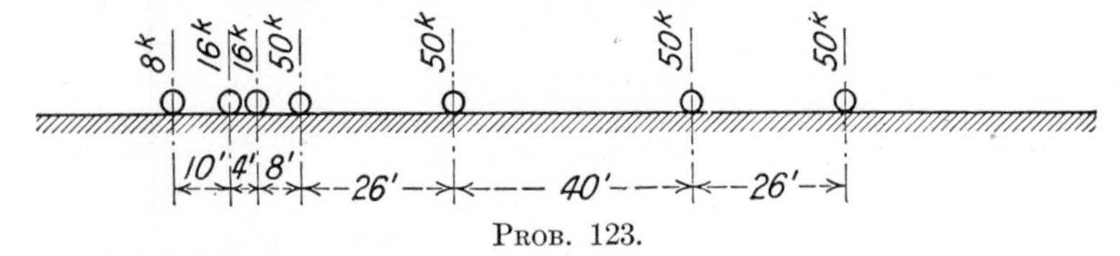

Prob. 123.

124. The figure shows the axle loads and spacing for a new mountain freight locomotive. For a single-track 90-ft. deck girder span calculate:

(*a*) Maximum end shear on one girder.
(*b*) Maximum center shear on one girder.
(*c*) Maximum center moment on one girder.

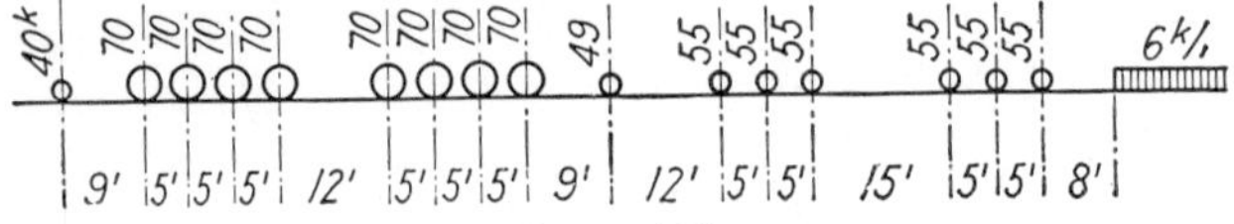

Prob. 124.

125. The span is a deck plate girder cantilever. Draw the influence lines for:

(*a*) moment at A,
(*b*) moment at B,
(*c*) shear at B (just to the right of the support),
(*d*) reaction on pier at B,

as a unit load moves from E to F.

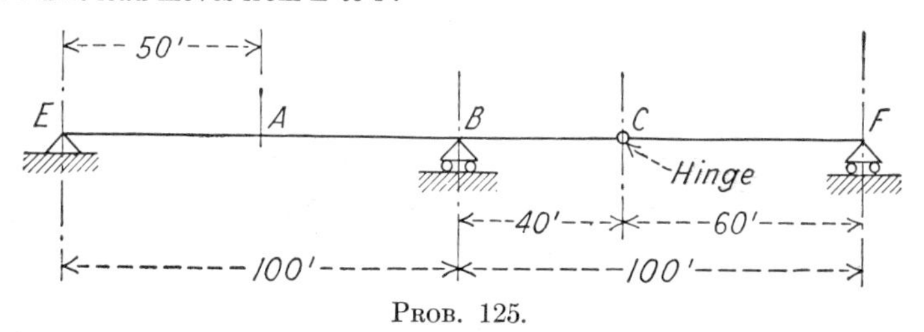

PROB. 125.

126. From study of the influence lines drawn for Problem 125 and application of the proper criteria, determine where to place the loads shown in Problem 116 to produce:

(*a*) Maximum positive moment at A.
(*b*) Maximum negative moment at A.
(*c*) Maximum negative moment at B.
(*d*) Maximum shear just to the right of B.
(*e*) Maximum reaction on the support at B.

127. For a span of 50 ft. calculate, due to the loading shown:

(*a*) The maximum moment at the center.
(*b*) The maximum moment.

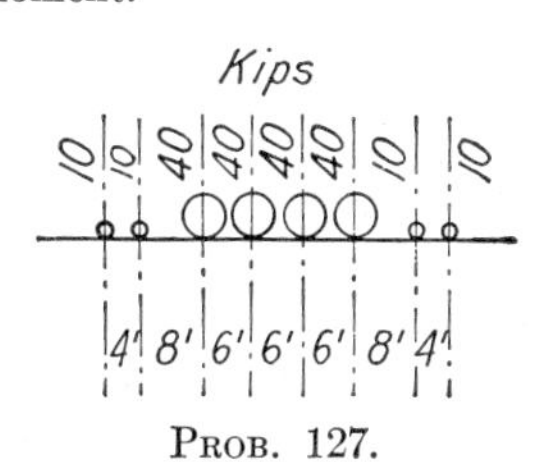

PROB. 127.

128. Calculate the absolute maximum moment on the span of Problem 123.

129. Using one unit of the locomotive shown in Problem 115:

(*a*) What position of the wheels will produce maximum moment at the center of one girder of a 100-ft. span? Compute the moment.

(*b*) What position of the wheels will produce maximum moment in the same girder? Where is the section of maximum moment? What is the magnitude of the moment?

130. The loads shown are *axle* loads.

(*a*) Calculate the maximum moment on a span of 24 ft.

(*b*) Calculate the maximum moment on a span of 30 ft.

Ans. (*a*) 100.8 ft.-kips.
(*b*) 137.5 ft.-kips.

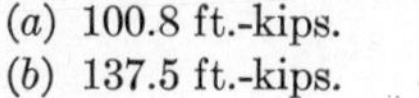

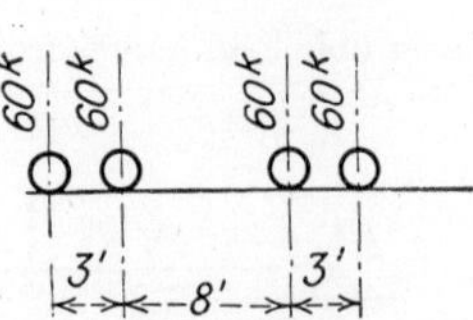

PROB. 130.

131. The loads shown are *wheel* loads. Due to the loading shown, calculate:

(*a*) The maximum bending moment in a span of 20 ft.

(*b*) The maximum bending moment in a span of 40 ft.

PROB. 131.

132. The loading diagram for which the through plate girder bridge is to be designed is the same as for Problem 114. Compute:

(*a*) The maximum live load shear in panel 0–1.
(*b*) The maximum live load shear in panel 2–3.
(*c*) The maximum live load moment at panel point 1.
(*d*) The maximum live load moment at panel point 3.

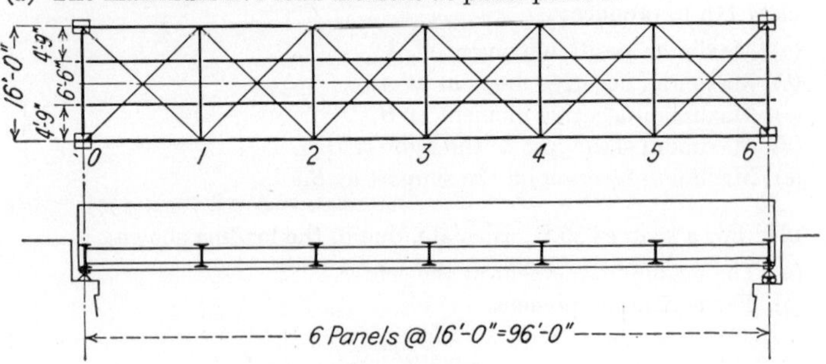

PROB. 132.

133. A through plate girder span is shown. It is to be designed for the loads shown in Problem 115. Compute:

(*a*) The maximum shear in panel 0–1.
(*b*) The maximum shear in panel 2–3.
(*c*) The maximum moment at panel point 1.
(*d*) The maximum moment at panel point 2.

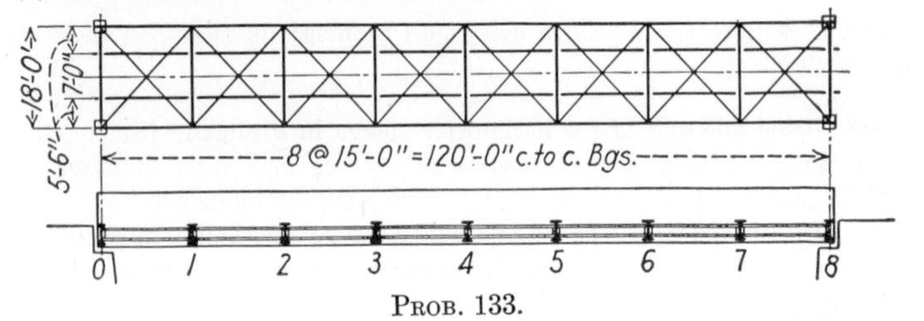

PROB. 133.

134. Calculate the maximum shear in the third panel of a span of 8 panels at 15 ft. due to the load shown. *Ans.* 119^k, wheel 3.

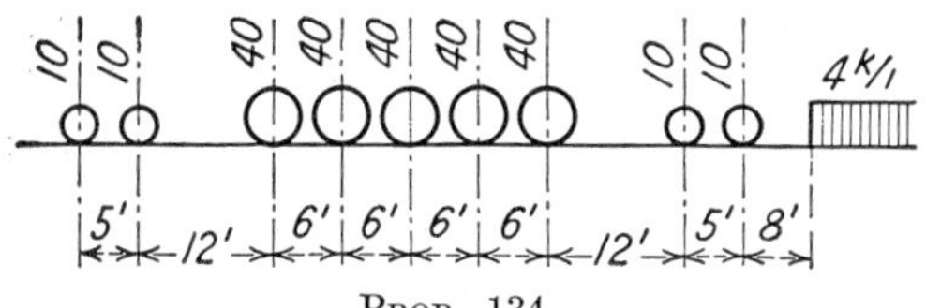

PROB. 134.

135. A through plate girder span is shown in plan. Using the locomotive shown in Problem 116, compute:

(*a*) The maximum shear in panel 0–1.
(*b*) The maximum shear in panel 2–3.
(*c*) The maximum moment at panel point 1.
(*d*) The maximum moment at panel point 2.
(*e*) The maximum moment in an intermediate floorbeam.

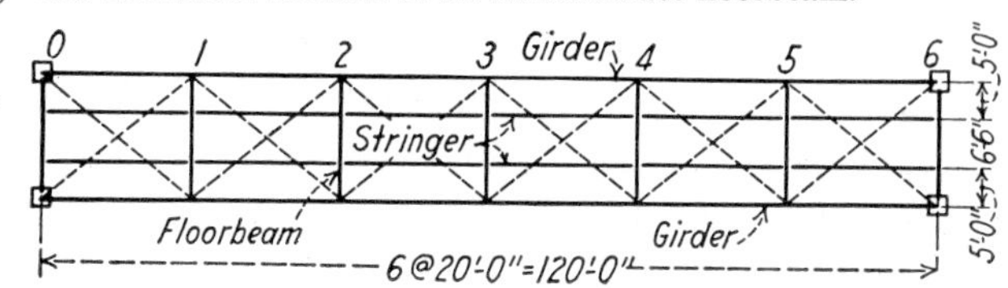

PROB. 135.

136. The wheel spacing and maximum wheel loads for two cranes operating in the main aisle of an industrial building are shown; also an elevation of part of the runway girders. Calculate:

(*a*) The maximum reaction on the intermediate support *A*.
(*b*) The maximum shear on the intermediate runway girder, G_1.
(*c*) The maximum moment on the intermediate runway girder, G_1.

In all cases state the position of the loads producing the maximum value in question.

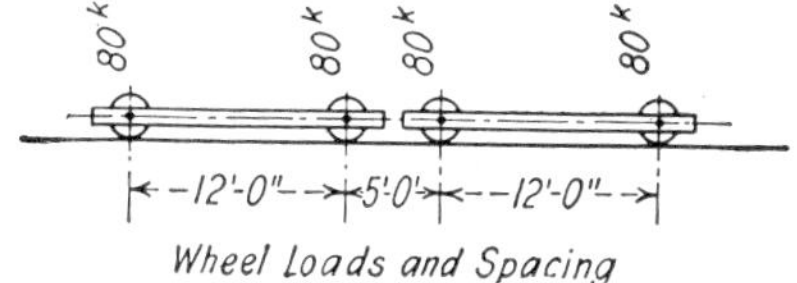

Wheel Loads and Spacing

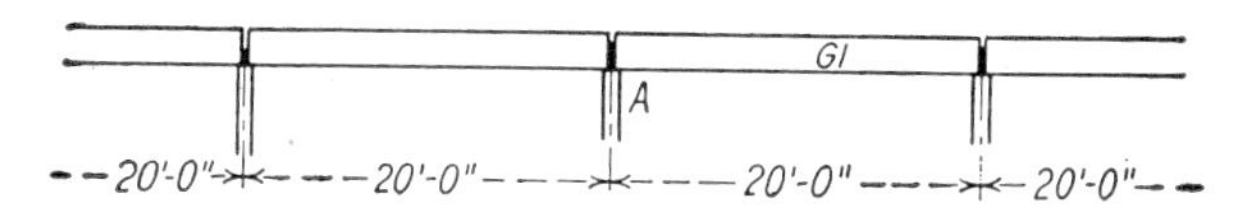

Elevation of Runway Girders

PROB. 136.

137. Using the crane runway girder and loads of Problem 121, calculate:

(*a*) Maximum possible moment on one span.
(*b*) Maximum column reaction for one column. (Use interior column.)

Ans. (*a*) 774 ft.-kips.
(*b*) 195.2^k.

138. Two bridge spans are supported on a common bent at B. What position of the loads shown in Problem 115 will produce maximum reaction on the bent? Compute the reaction from one rail.

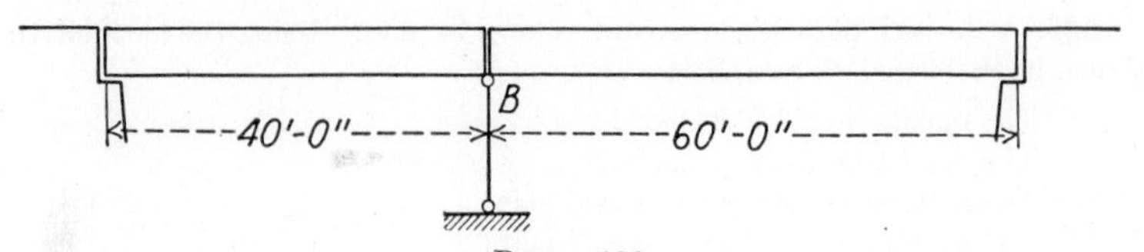

PROB. 138.

139. Given a single track through girder span having 8 panels of 15 ft. each. Calculate for the A-64 loading shown on p. 28:

(*a*) The maximum shear and moment for one stringer.
(*b*) The maximum interior floorbeam reaction.
(*c*) The maximum shear in panel 1–2 of the main girder.
(*d*) The maximum moment at panel point 3 of the main girder.

Ans. (*a*) 64^k, 200 ft.-kips.
(*b*) 96^k.
(*c*) 175^k, wheel 2.
(*d*) 7380 ft.-kips, wheel 17.

140. Given a single track through girder span having 9 panels of 12 ft. each. Calculate for Cooper's E-70:

(*a*) The maximum shear and moment for one stringer.
(*b*) The maximum interior floorbeam reaction.
(*c*) The maximum shear in panel 1–2 of the main girder.
(*d*) The maximum moment at panel point 4 of the main girder.

CHAPTER V

COMMON FRAMED STRUCTURES

74. The word **truss,** although frequently defined more broadly, will be used in this text to denote a jointed frame or structure which is designed to sustain inclined, vertical, or horizontal loads, occurring at or between its points of support, and which has the following characteristics:

(*a*) Straight members.
(*b*) Members connected at their intersections by means of frictionless pins or hinges.
(*c*) Members so arranged that the truss is loaded only at the joints.

It should be clearly understood that the above definition describes an *ideal* structure. The practical truss is subject to many modifications, some of which will be discussed later.

The triangle is the basic geometric figure in a truss. A truss frame may include other geometric figures, but stability cannot be secured without the use of some triangles. This matter will be more fully discussed in the next article.

The members which form the outline or perimeter of a truss are generally called the **chord members,** or simply **chords.** The interior members connecting the joints of the chords are called the **web members,** or more specifically, **diagonals** or **verticals,** depending on their direction in the web system. Some outside members, such as the end posts of bridge trusses, are generally considered as part of the web system. In (*a*), Fig. 79, U_0U_1, U_1U_2, L_1L_2, and so on, are chords, and U_0L_1, U_1L_1, U_2L_1, and so on, are web members.

75. Necessary Number of Bars.—It is necessary that a truss be composed primarily of a series of triangles because the triangle is the only geometric figure which cannot be changed in shape without changing the length of one or more of its sides. In (*a*) of

Fig. 78, for example, is shown a triangle subjected to a single load, and it should be clear to the student by inspection that the figure cannot change its shape under the action of the load shown unless one or more of its sides change in length. On the other hand, it should be equally clear that, if the members are connected at the joints by frictionless pins, the figures shown in (*b*), (*c*), and (*d*) of Fig. 78 will immediately collapse under the action of the load shown. If the frame shown in (*d*) is supported by another bar connected to a rigid support, as shown in (*e*), it will not collapse under the action of the load.

After the student has become familiar with the application of the laws of statics in calculating stresses in trussed structures he

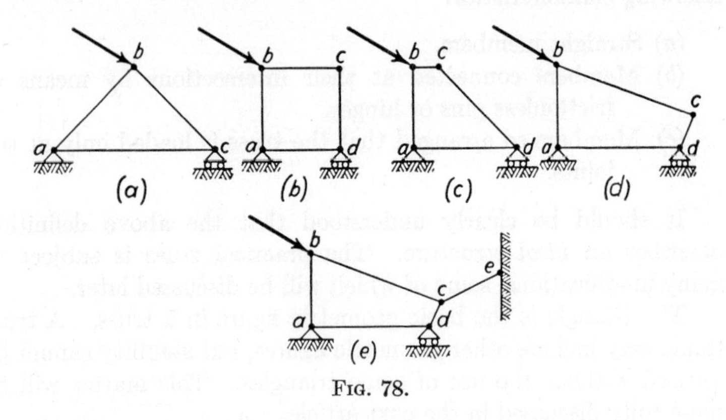

FIG. 78.

will, in most cases, be able to tell by inspection whether a truss has a sufficient number of bars to be stable or whether it has more than the number necessary to secure stability. Until such familiarity has been gained, or in less obvious cases, it may be helpful to study a truss from the standpoint of the number of bars necessary to hold the various joints in a fixed relation to each other. Referring again to (*a*) of Fig. 78 it is clear that the three joints, *a*, *b*, and *c*, are rigidly held in position with respect to each other. Evidently we may say that the bar *ac* holds the joints *a* and *c* in a fixed relation to each other, and that to hold the joint *b* in a fixed relation to these two requires the addition of two bars *ab* and *bc*, forming the basic triangle *abc*. The same procedure will apply in any case. In (*a*) of Fig. 79, for example, the two joints U_0 and L_0 are held in position with respect to each other by the bar

U_0L_0. The position of L_1 may be definitely established with reference to U_0 and L_0 by connecting it to them with the two additional bars U_0L_1 and L_0L_1 (forming a basic triangle). The joint U_1 may then be established with reference to the three already fixed by the addition of *two* more bars U_0U_1 and U_1L_1.

The student should follow through the rest of the structure, noting that the fixing in position of each new joint requires the addition of two bars. Studying the structure in (*b*) of Fig. 79 in the same manner shows at once that there is not a sufficient number of bars, since U_2, for example, is not fixed in position with reference to L_1, nor is L_2 fixed in position with reference to U_1. Similarly, study of (*c*) in the same figure shows that there are more

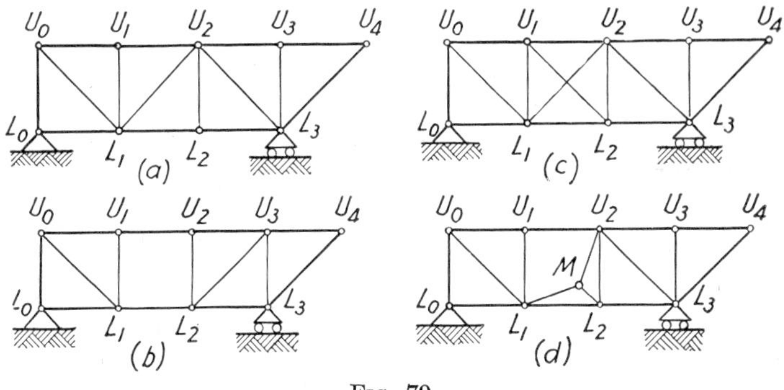

FIG. 79.

bars than necessary, since U_2 may be considered as fixed in relation to U_1 and L_1 by the bars U_1U_2 and U_2L_1, and is also fixed with reference to U_1 and L_2 by bars U_1U_2 and U_2L_2. Applying the same line of reasoning to the structure in (*d*) will show that it has just enough bars even though the part U_1–U_2–M–L_1 is not a triangle. The latter structure illustrates the statement that although the triangle is the basic truss figure, some other geometric shapes may occur. Subdivided trusses to be discussed later will furnish other illustrations of this.

These considerations lead to the general statement that to establish a fixed relation between a series of joints requires one bar and its end joints as a beginning, and two more bars for each additional joint. Although it is easy and probably better to examine a structure in the fundamental way outlined, the conclusion reached may be expressed algebraically as follows:

If

$$n = \text{number of necessary bars,}$$

$$j = \text{number of joints,}$$

the relation

$$n = 1 + 2(j - 2)$$

or

$$n = 2j - 3$$

follows at once from the general statement. This expression will tell at once whether a single structure has the proper number of bars, but confusion will result if an attempt is made to apply it to a framework which consists of more than one unit. It is applicable to (*a*), (*b*), (*c*), or (*d*) in Fig. 79, but not to (*k*) in Fig. 80. Structures such as that shown at (*k*) in Fig. 80 must be divided into separate units before applying this expression.

Generally speaking, fewer bars than are given by this expression will result in an unstable structure, and more bars in one which is more than stable — a condition usually called indeterminate, since the stresses in such a frame cannot be calculated by application of the laws of statics alone. There are exceptions to both cases. For example, it should be clear that (*b*) in Fig. 79 will be stable if the joints U_1, L_1, U_2, and L_2 are made stiff enough so that the angles between the four connecting members cannot change and the members themselves are made strong enough to resist the resulting shears, moments, and direct stresses; and as will develop later the structure in (*c*) Fig. 79 is not indeterminate if the diagonals U_1L_2 and U_2L_1 are too slender to resist compression.

76. Common Types of Trusses.—Trusses are used a great deal in bridge and building construction. In buildings their most common use is for the support of roofs of long clear span, and less often for supporting floors. In bridge construction, trusses are used for most spans exceeding 125 ft. and sometimes for spans as short as 60 or 70 ft.

Figures 80 and 81 show a few common types of trusses used for buildings and bridges, and these will be briefly described.

Building Trusses, Fig. 80.—The trusses shown in (*a*), (*b*), and (*c*) are common types of trusses used for roofs of moderate span when a sloping or pitched roof is wanted. The **Howe** truss in (*b*) is best suited to timber construction but is sometimes built with steel, although, when constructed of this material, it is less economical than the **Pratt** truss, in (*a*), or the **Fink** truss, in (*c*). The Pratt truss, in (*a*), is limited to moderate spans because of the wasteful use of material resulting when the vertical members

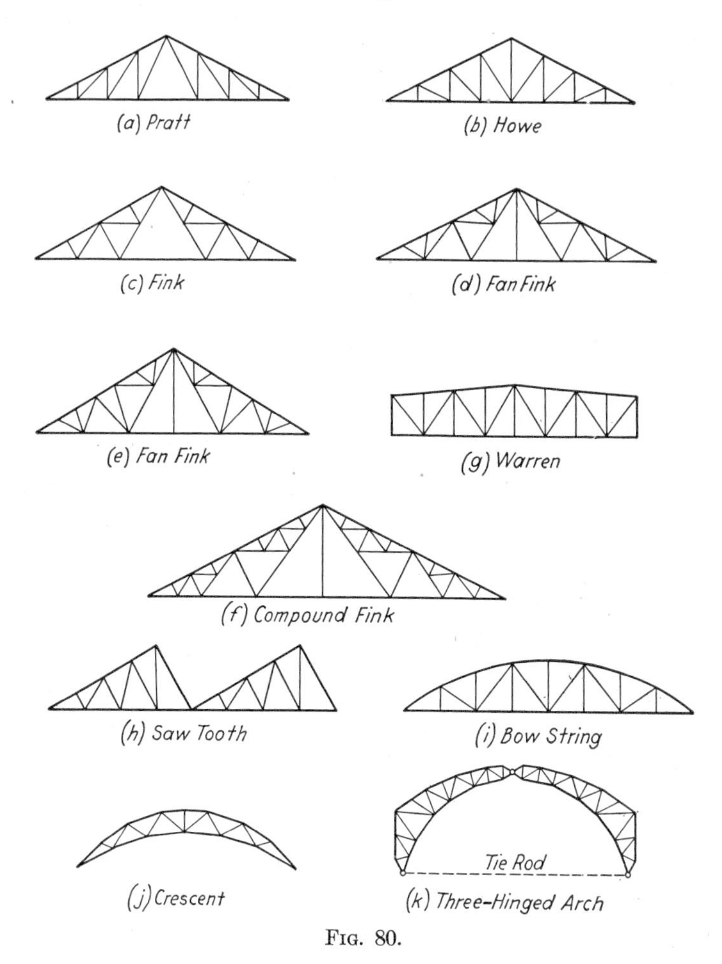

Fig. 80.

become long. The Fink truss may be used for spans of greater length if the roof does not require support at close intervals. When the spans are long and the roof must be supported at shorter intervals, the Fink truss may be modified and used in the forms shown in (*d*), (*e*), and (*f*). The **compound Fink** in (*f*) may be "fanned," i.e., its web system modified to that used for the truss in (*e*), resulting in a truss suitable for fairly long spans with the roof supported at relatively short intervals. All these trusses may be built with the bottom chord arched upward, or cambered, resulting in a cambered Pratt, cambered Howe, or cambered Fink truss, the latter sometimes being referred to as a *French* truss. When a flat roof, or one which is nearly flat, is suitable, a **Warren** truss as shown in (*g*) may be used. The Pratt and Howe trusses are also used for flat roof trusses. The **saw tooth** trusses shown in (*h*) are especially useful for buildings in which relatively close spacing of columns is not objectionable and in which uniform lighting is important, such as textile mills. In such cases the steep face on each truss supports a continuous skylight, and this side is generally placed toward the north. **Bow string** and **crescent** trusses, (*i*) and (*j*), are much used for garages and small hangars, with the roofing laid on closely spaced timber purlins which rest directly on the top chords. **Arch** trusses for roofs, (*k*), are relatively expensive and are used only for long spans with high rise. Some notable examples of this form have been used for large armories, field houses, skating rinks, and so on. As shown in (*k*), the arch is *three-hinged*, but the center or crown hinge is sometimes omitted, resulting in the two-hinged arch, which is statically indeterminate with respect to reactions. The necessary horizontal components are usually provided by a tie rod as shown in (*k*). Figure 80 shows only the more common forms, and many modifications and combinations of these have been used.

Bridge Trusses.—Figure 81 shows the most common forms of bridge trusses. Study of these diagrams will show that there are four fundamental types, the others being modifications of these elementary forms. The **Pratt** truss (*a*) has probably been used more than any other form, but with the decline in use of pin connections has lost much of its popularity to the **Warren** truss with verticals (*d*). The **Howe** truss (*b*) has been much used for timber, or combination timber and steel, bridges, but the great increase in the use of steel and concrete for bridge construction has caused it to practically disappear from most sections of the United States. It still is fairly common in the Pacific Northwest. The true Warren truss (*c*) has been used a great deal for elevated railroad work and is occasionally used for relatively short-span highway bridges of the **half-through** or "Pony" type. The Warren truss with verticals (*d*) has become very popular for modern bridges with riveted joints. The bridge trusses so far mentioned have been parallel chord types, and these are most suitable for spans up to 180 to 200 ft. in length. For longer spans the use of non-parallel, or polygonal, chords results in some saving in weight,

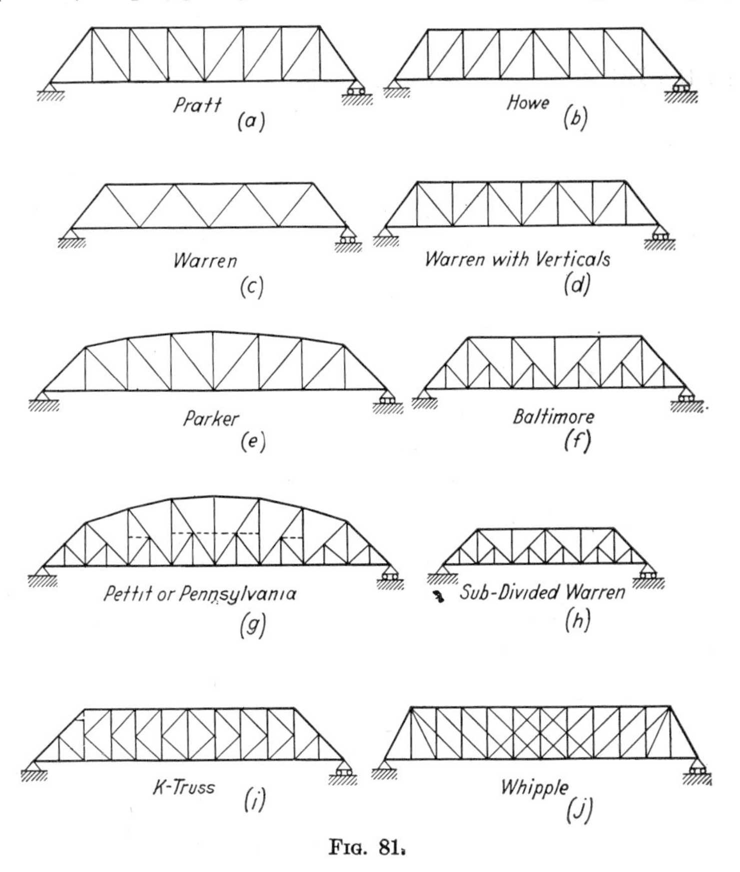

FIG. 81.

and the truss in (*e*) is shown as an example of a Pratt truss with polygonal top chord — a type often called a **Parker** truss. Warren trusses with verticals are also often made with non-parallel chords for long spans. Parker trusses have been used for spans up to 360 ft. For the greatest economy of material the diagonals of a truss should have a slope of between 45° and 60° with the horizontal, and as the depth between chords must increase as the span gets longer, this results in very long panels and heavy floor systems if trusses of the type already discussed are used. In order to use diagonals having a favorable slope and yet keep the weight of the floor system within reasonable limits, *subdivided* trusses have been developed. Typical subdivided trusses are shown in (*f*), (*g*), and (*h*). The diagram in (*f*) represents a subdivided Pratt truss with parallel chords, a type often referred to as the **Baltimore** truss. The Baltimore truss has been used a great deal in locations requiring spans of only moderate length but abnormally shallow floors — the moderate span calling for parallel chords and the limited floor depth for very short panels. The subdivided Warren type shown in (*h*) is also useful in such cases. The subdivided Pratt with non-parallel chords as shown in (*g*) has been commonly used for long spans requiring great truss depths; this form is often called the **Pettit** truss or the **Pennsylvania** truss. The horizontal dotted members shown in (*g*) are to support the long verticals: they are secondary members not subjected to calculated direct stress. The non-parallel chord Warren truss with verticals is also built as a subdivided truss for long spans. A relatively new form of truss which accomplishes the purpose of the subdivided truss is the **K truss** shown in (*i*). It has been built with both parallel and non-parallel chords. It is said to be especially favorable from the standpoint of secondary stresses, but has not as yet attained the popularity of the older types.

In the early days of iron and steel bridge development the **Whipple** truss, (*j*), was very extensively used to secure short panels, and at the same time economical slope for diagonals. Whipple trusses have not been built for more than thirty years, but there are a few still in service. These trusses now have historic interest only and will not be further discussed in this text. It may be remarked in passing, however, that although the Whipple truss is statically indeterminate its analysis was carried out by means of rather ingenious simplifying assumptions. The student who is interested in the methods used should consult "Stresses, Graphical Statics, and Masonry,"[1] by George Fillmore Swain, or "Framed Structures and Girders,"[1] by Edgar Marburg.

Figures 82, 83 and 84 are presented to illustrate actual examples

[1] McGraw-Hill Book Company.

Courtesy of McClintic Marshall Company

FIG. 82.—Monongahela River Bridge.

Courtesy of McClintic Marshall Company

FIG. 83.—Kennebec River Bridge, Bath, Maine.

Courtesy of McClintic Marshall Company

Fig. 84.—Alfred E. Smith Memorial Bridge Over the Hudson River, Castleton, N. Y.

of some of the common types discussed. Figure 82 shows a Parker truss for the main span, with Warren trusses with verticals as approach spans. The center span is of the **through** type and the side spans of the **deck** type. Figure 83 shows a crossing composed of double deck trusses of the Warren type with verticals. Figure 84 shows a construction view of an outstanding example of the Pettit or Pennsylvania truss.

CHAPTER VI

STRESSES IN TRUSSED STRUCTURES — FIXED LOADS

77. Fundamental Method of Analysis.—As stated at the beginning of Chapter III, there is *one* and *only one* method of studying the internal stresses in a structure. We may repeat here for emphasis that the method is to pass an imaginary section cutting the structure into two parts, choose one of the parts and apply the laws of statics to determine what internal forces must act on the cut section to hold the part under consideration in equilibrium against the known external forces. Too much emphasis cannot be placed on the importance of **passing a section,** and a section which completely separates the structure into two parts. Students often cause themselves needless confusion by attempting to visualize or reason about the action of a member in an uncut structure, or after passing a partial section.

It follows from the above that if the stress in a particular bar is to be found, that bar must be cut by the section which is passed. Either part of the structure may be chosen for study after passing the section, but the part offering the greater convenience and the smaller amount of calculation is of course to be preferred.

78. Assumptions.—In applying the fundamental method of analysis just stated, two assumptions are made which should be clearly understood and kept in mind:

First: It is assumed that the joints of a truss are made with frictionless pins or hinges.

Second: It is assumed that the change in shape of the truss due to changes in the length of members under stress is so small as to have negligible effect on the computation of axial stresses.

If the first assumption were correct, the stress in a member would always be axial. The facts are, of course, that the joints are never frictionless and in modern construction are seldom made with pins. The consequence is that the axial stresses are accompanied by bending moments due to the tendency of the joints to turn as a result of changes in the length of the various members under stress. In ordinary structures the neglect of these bending moments does not seriously affect the accuracy of the calculation of primary or axial stresses. The second assumption is taken as exact for ordinary structures and with the first assumption forms a satisfactory basis for the analysis of the trusses commonly met.

The effect of rigidity of the joints in trusses with extremely heavy and short members, such as those in some modern tall buildings, and the effect of change in shape of long and relatively flexible trusses, such as the stiffening trusses of long-span suspension bridges, may require special consideration. More exact analysis is often desirable in such cases, but the methods applicable are beyond the theory of simple structures.

79. Choice of Section.—As stated above, after an imaginary section has been passed cutting the structure into two parts, the part to be considered depends only on convenience. The choice of a section, however, is important and depends on how many bars in the structure will be cut by it as well as on convenience. The bar in which the stress is to be found must be cut by the section passed, and generally the most convenient section is fairly clear. The section which will cut the bar under consideration and the smallest number of additional bars is often best. It frequently happens, however, that a section which cuts a number of additional bars may be equally or more convenient if all or most of the bars cut, other than the one being studied, meet at a common point. It is difficult, and unwise, to attempt to lay down general rules. The experienced computer soon develops a routine technique in dealing with familiar forms of trusses, but the student should make a point of considering each case without reference to the kind of structure or the kind of member in the structure until the fundamental procedure is firmly fixed in his mind.

Since the unknown internal forces acting on the part considered are to be determined by application of the laws of statics to that part, it should be clear that not more than three unknown internal forces can be determined from a given section. If a section is passed around a joint so that all the forces acting on the part under consideration meet at a common point (the joint), evidently not more than two unknowns may be determined from that section. These facts should be kept in mind and will be helpful in choosing sections, but it will be found that facility in the selection and use of sections depends as much, and perhaps more, on practice in the solution of problems.

80. Signs.—In describing the character of the stress in the various bars of a truss, it has become nearly universal practice to call tension **positive** stress and compression **negative** stress. Thus a tension of one hundred and twenty kips is generally written: + **120k,** and a compression of two hundred and sixty kips is written: − **260k.** This convention will be followed as being the most convenient and the most widely used.

The student should from the very first form the habit of determining the character of a stress, i.e., tension or compression, by picturing in his mind how the part of the structure under consideration would move (up or down, right or left, turn clockwise or counter-clockwise) under the action of the forces acting on it *excluding* the stress in the bar in question, and then deciding whether that bar would have to *pull* (tension) or *push* (compression) to hold the part in equilibrium. In nearly every case it is possible in this manner to tell in advance of any calculation whether a bar is in tension or in compression. In those cases in which the sign of the stress cannot be determined in advance, the direction will quickly become apparent as the calculations proceed. The student should **never** assume the stress to be tension or compression and then by means of his calculations prove the assumption to be incorrect.

Particular attention should be given to the above method of determining sign in studying the discussion of the application of the fundamental method of analysis.

81. Application of Fundamental Method.—The use of the fundamental method of analysis stated above may best be shown by applying it to a number of general cases, and there follow calculations for stress in various bars of a miscellaneous collection of frames, with comments on the procedure.

82. Methods of Attack.—In Fig. 85 (*a*) there is shown a small roof truss supporting loads such that the panel concentrations are 3200 lb. each with resulting reactions of 8000 lb. each as shown. The lengths of the members are written on the right-hand side of the figure. In Fig. 85 (*b*) to (*e*) are shown parts cut off by sections 1–1, 2–2, 3–3, and 4–4 with the calculations for stress in bars L_0U_1

and L_0L_1, U_1L_1, U_2L_1, and U_2U_3 and L_2L_3. The calculations shown should be studied in conjunction with the following comments.

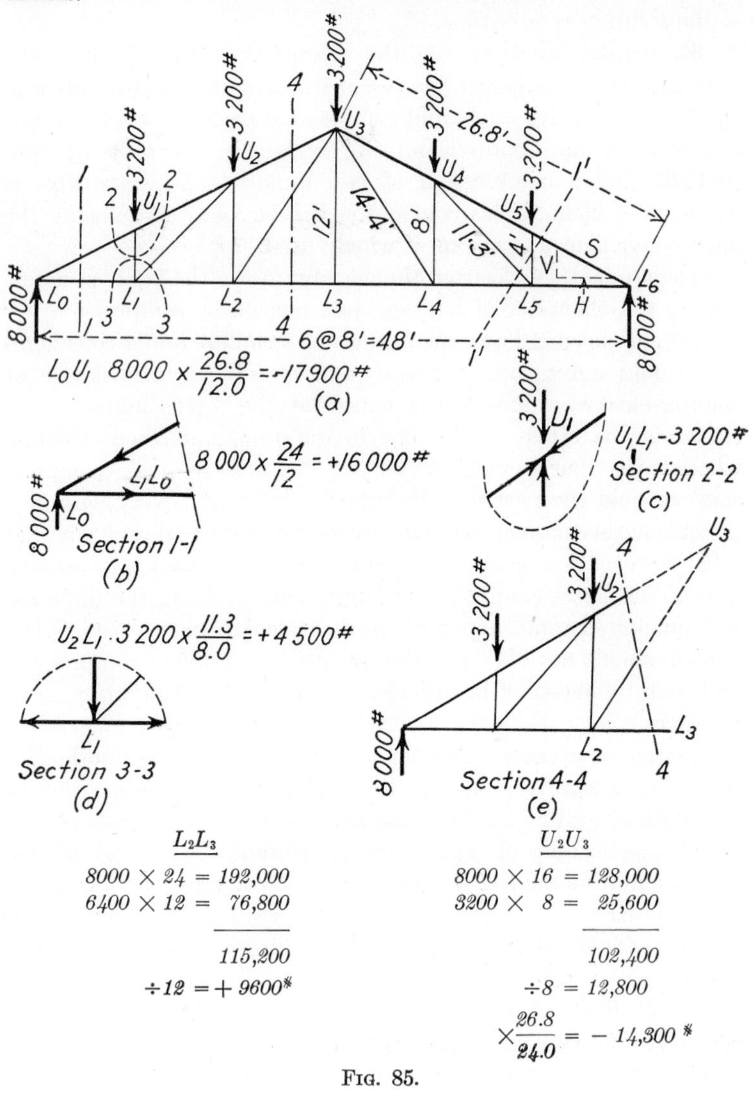

FIG. 85.

Bars L_0U_1 and L_0L_1.—In finding the stress in the bar L_0U_1 the section 1–1, shown in Fig. 85 (*a*), is the most obvious. Considering the part on the left of this section, shown in (*b*), the only external force acting is the upward reaction of 8000 lb. Since the bar L_0L_1, also cut by this section, is horizontal, it cannot have a vertical component, consequently the only vertical force acting other than the reaction is the vertical component of the stress in L_0U_1, which must be equal and opposite to the reaction. Knowing the vertical component, the stress is easily found as shown on the figure. The sign of the stress should be determined as explained in Art. 80. As a result of the forces acting, other than the stress in L_0U_1, the part of the structure under consideration would tend to move *up*, and, to hold the part in equilibrium, it would be necessary to *push* on the bar L_0U_1 — therefore, it is in compression as indicated.

Instead of 1–1, a section similar to 1′–1′, shown on the right in Fig. 85 (*a*), could have been used. Since the structure is symmetrical and symmetrically loaded, the stress in U_5L_6 must be the same as the stress in L_0U_1, and to show the use of section 1′–1′, the calculations will be given for the stress in the former. The part of the structure on the right of the section will be considered and is shown in Fig. 86. Four bars were cut by this section, but since three of them pass through the panel point L_5, they may be eliminated by taking moments about this point. The only external force acting on the part of the structure under consideration is the upward reaction of 8000 lb. Since the stress in U_5L_6 is the only internal force acting on this part which has a moment about L_5, its moment about that point must be equal to the moment of the reaction about the same point. The stress may be found by dividing this moment by the perpendicular distance from L_5 to the bar U_5L_6. However, this distance is not known, and although it is easily calculated, it is more convenient to resolve the stress in U_5L_6 into horizontal and vertical components acting at U_5 or at L_6. If the components are taken as acting at U_5, the vertical component passes through the center of moments and the horizontal component must equal the moment about L_5 divided by the distance from L_5 to U_5, which is known.

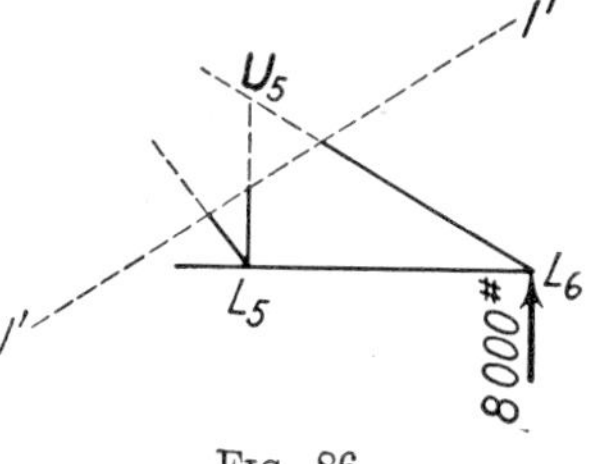

FIG. 86.

If the components are taken as acting at L_6, the horizontal component passes through the center of moments and the vertical component must equal the moment about L_5 divided by the distance from L_5 to L_6, which is known. The calculations for the two cases are as follows:

Components acting at U_5:

$$H \text{ comp.} = \frac{8000 \times 8}{4} = 16{,}000 \text{ lb.}$$

$$\text{Stress} = 16{,}000 \times \frac{26.8}{24.0} = -17{,}900 \text{ lb.}$$

Components acting at L_6:

$$V \text{ comp.} = \frac{8000 \times 8}{8} = 8000 \text{ lb.}$$

$$\text{Stress} = 8000 \times \frac{26.8}{12.0} = -17{,}900 \text{ lb.}$$

The sign of the stress should be determined in the same manner as before. As a result of the forces other than the stress in U_5L_6, the part under consideration would tend to turn around the joint L_5 to the left, or counter-clockwise, and to hold the part in equilibrium against this tendency it would be necessary to *push* on U_5L_6 — therefore, it is in compression as indicated.

Particular attention should be given to the method used in finding the stress from the components. At the right end of Fig. 85 (*a*), the vertical and horizontal components of the stress, S, are shown in dotted lines on the bar U_5L_6. The sides of this triangle, S, H, and V, are parallel to the sides of the truss triangle, U_3L_6, U_3L_3, and L_3L_6 and these triangles are, therefore, similar. From this similarity the relations:

$$\frac{S}{V} = \frac{26.8}{12.0}, \quad \frac{S}{H} = \frac{26.8}{24.0}, \quad \text{and} \quad \frac{V}{H} = \frac{12}{24}$$

follow at once.

It is important for the student to form the habit of calculating stresses from the *geometry* of the frame and not from the trigonometric functions of the angles between members or between members and the horizontal. In the actual performance of structural work the lengths and slopes of the various members in a truss must be known or determined whereas the angles between members or between members and the horizontal are not required or used and are seldom calculated. To calculate these angles in order to have their functions available is to do unnecessary work, which is poor engineering. It is true, of course, that the trigonometric functions may be determined without actually calculating the angles themselves, but calling the ratios of the sides of known triangles by trigonometric names is an unnatural and indirect procedure in structural work. In other words, to say that the stress S is equal to the horizontal component H multiplied by the secant of the angle between them and that the secant is the ratio of the side U_3L_6 to the side L_3L_6, is to introduce an unnecessary step and an artificial name. On the other hand, to say that the ratio of the stress S to its horizontal component H is equal to the ratio of the side U_3L_6 to the side L_3L_6 is natural and direct. The authors believe that the geometric conception is much to be preferred and that it should be cultivated.

L_0L_1.—The stress in L_0L_1 is determined in Fig. 85 (*b*) from the relation between the horizontal and vertical components of the stress in L_0U_1. Since the reaction is vertical, it should be clear that the stress in L_0L_1 must equal the horizontal component of the stress in L_0U_1 in order to have $\Sigma H = 0$. As to sign, under the action of the forces other than the stress in L_0L_1, the part of the structure shown in (*b*) tends to move to the left, and, to hold it in equilibrium, it is necessary to *pull* on the bar L_0L_1; it is, therefore, in tension as indicated.

It is also possible, and equally convenient, to pass a section cutting U_1U_2, U_1L_1, and L_0L_1, and to determine the stress in L_0L_1 by moments about U_1. The calculations would be as follows:

$$\text{Stress in } L_0L_1 = 8000 \times \tfrac{8}{4} = +16{,}000 \text{ lb.}$$

U_1L_1.—To determine the stress in U_1L_1 a section has been passed around the joint U_1 and the part of the structure cut off is shown in Fig. 85 (*c*). Since the member U_1L_1 is vertical it can have no horizontal component, consequently, in order to satisfy the requirement that $\Sigma H = 0$, the horizontal component of the stress in U_1U_2 must be equal and opposite to the horizontal component of the stress in L_0U_1. It should be clear from the figure that these vertical components are also equal and opposite and that the stress in U_1L_1 must therefore equal the panel load 3200 lb. to satisfy the requirement $\Sigma V = 0$. As to sign, under the action of the forces other than the stress in U_1L_1 the part of the structure under consideration tends to move *down*, and to hold it in equilibrium it is necessary to *push* on U_1L_1; it is therefore in compression as indicated.

An equally convenient section would be the second one used in calculating the stress in L_0L_1. Taking moments about L_0 the following calculations result:

$$\text{Stress in } U_1L_1 = 3200 \times \tfrac{8}{8} = -3200 \text{ lb.}$$

U_2L_1.—Several sections may be used in investigating the stress in U_2L_1. In Fig. 85 (*d*) there is shown the part cut off by a section around the joint L_1. The bars L_0L_1 and L_1L_2 which meet at this joint are both horizontal and, therefore, cannot have vertical components. Consequently the vertical component of the stress in U_2L_1 must be equal and opposite to the stress in U_1L_1 in order to satisfy the condition of equilibrium $\Sigma V = 0$. The stress in U_1L_1 has been found previously as $-$ 3200 lb. from which the stress in U_2L_1 is found to be $+$ 4500 lb. as shown in the figure, the sign having been determined by the method used in connection with the other bars.

The stress in this bar may also be calculated by passing a section cutting U_1U_2, U_2L_1 and L_1L_2 and taking moments about L_0. In this case it will be convenient to resolve the stress in the bar into vertical and horizontal components acting at L_1. The horizontal component will then pass through the center of moments leaving only the vertical component to be determined. The complete calculation is as follows:

$$\text{Stress in } U_2L_1 = 3200 \times \frac{8}{8} \times \frac{11.3}{8.0} = +\,4500 \text{ lb.}$$

It is unnecessary to write the part $3200 \times \frac{8}{8}$, as inspection of the section should show that the vertical component of the stress in U_2L_1 is 3200 lb.

U_2U_3 and L_2L_3.—As is true of the other bars discussed, there are several sections which may be used in calculating the stress in U_2U_3. Since the stresses in U_1U_2 and U_2L_1 are known, their horizontal components may be easily found and a section around the joint U_2 makes determination of the horizontal component of the stress in U_2U_3 very simple. It may just as readily be found by passing a section cutting U_2U_3, U_2L_2, and L_1L_2, or the section 4–4, shown in Fig. 85 (*a*), and taking moments about L_2. Figure 85 (*e*) shows the part cut from the structure by the section 4–4 and also the calculations for the stress by taking moments about L_2. As should be clear, the stress was considered as resolved into vertical and horizontal components and applied at U_2 so that the vertical component passed through the center of moments.

The stress in L_2L_3 may be found from the same section, as may also the stress in U_3L_2, and the necessary calculations for the stress in L_2L_3 are shown in the figure. As indicated by the dotted lines, the members U_2U_3 and U_3L_2 were considered as extended from their cut ends to their intersection at U_3 and moments taken about this point, thus obtaining directly the stress in L_2L_3.

The calculations for the stress in U_3L_2 are not given in the figure and are as follows:

$$\text{Stress in } U_3L_2 = 2 \times 3200 \times \frac{12}{16} \times \frac{14.4}{12.0} = +\ 5760 \text{ lb.}$$

As should be clear, the stress in U_3L_2 was taken as resolved into vertical and horizontal components and acting at L_2, L_0 being the center of moments, and the quantity $2 \times 3200 \times \frac{12}{16}$ the vertical component of the stress.

No attempt has been made in the above discussion to calculate the bar stresses in any particular order, nor have all the bars been considered. The discussion has, however, treated certain bars in considerable detail in an effort to form in the student's mind an accurate *picture* of the fundamental method of analysis. At this point the authors would like to emphasize the importance to the beginner of carefully going through each step in the fundamental method of analysis each time it is used in calculating a bar stress. If, when beginning the study of stresses, the student is careful to pass a correct and complete section, and to make in his own mind a clear and accurate statement of the reasoning in each step of the application of the laws of statics to the part chosen, he will soon form correct habits of thought in stress analysis. The importance of getting an exact understanding of the *fundamental* principles, definitions, and methods in studying the theory of structures cannot be overemphasized. This is equally true, of course, in any other field of study.

83. Illustrative Example.—In Fig. 87 is shown a truss with parallel chords supporting loads of 8000 lb. at each panel point. Calculations are given below for stress in the bars U_2L_3, U_2U_3,

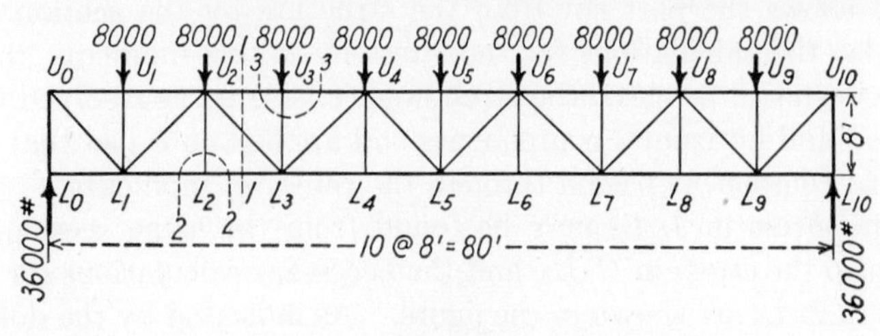

Fig. 87.

U_2L_2, U_3L_3. The sections passed are as indicated, 1–1 being for bars U_2L_3 and U_2U_3, 2–2 for bar U_2L_2, and 3–3 for U_3L_3.

U_2L_3 Section 1–1

$$36{,}000 - 2 \times 8000 = 20{,}000$$

$$\times \frac{11.31}{8.0} = +\ 28{,}300 \text{ lb.}$$

by application of $\Sigma V = 0$

U_2U_3 Section 1–1

$$\begin{aligned} 36{,}000 \times 24 &= & 864{,}000 \\ 8{,}000 \times 16 &= 128{,}000 & \\ 8{,}000 \times 8 &= 64{,}000 & \\ \hline & 192{,}000 & 192{,}000 \\ \hline & & 672{,}000 \div 8 = -\ 84{,}000 \text{ lb.} \end{aligned}$$

U_2L_2 Section 2–2

Stress = 0

U_3L_3 Section 3–3

Stress = − 8000 lb.

Comment on these calculations should be unnecessary with the possible exception of those given for U_2L_3. The part of the structure on the left of section 1–1 was considered. Since the bars U_2U_3 and L_2L_3 are horizontal they cannot have vertical components, consequently the vertical component of the stress in U_2L_3 must be equal to the algebraic sum of all the external forces acting on the part of the structure considered in order to make $\Sigma V = 0$. In other words, the vertical component of the stress in U_2L_3 must be equal to the *shear* in the panel 2–3. As to sign, the part of the structure under consideration tends to move *up* under the action of all the forces acting except the stress in U_2L_3, and to hold the part in equilibrium it is necessary to *pull* on U_2L_3, which is therefore in tension as shown in the calculations.

84. Illustrative Example.—In all the illustrative calculations so far discussed it has been possible to determine the stress in the bar in question without reference to the stress in any other bar.

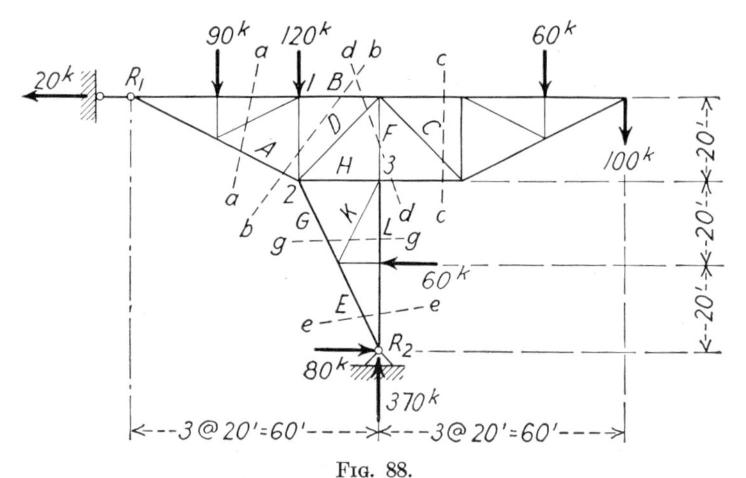

FIG. 88.

Sometimes it is impossible to pass a section which will enable the calculation of stress in a particular bar unless the stress in some other bar is known or determined in advance. The bars D and F in the structure shown in Fig. 88 are examples of this situation. A little study will show that it is impossible to pass a section which will enable the calculation of the stress in either of these members without reference to the stress in other bars. This is also true of the member H in the same structure. This difficulty may be overcome by determining the stress in such bars as will reduce the number of unknowns on a section through the bar in question to that which may be calculated from the data available. For example, the stress in bar D may be found by applying the principle $\Sigma V = 0$ to a section cutting B, D, H, and G, *provided* the stress in the bar G is previously calculated from some other section. The stress in G may be conveniently determined by passing the section g–g, considering the part of the structure below this section and taking moments about the joint marked 3. The stress in D may also be determined by passing the section d–d and taking moments about the joint marked 3, if the stress in B has been previously calculated. The stress in B can be easily found by passing the section b–b, or a section cutting B, D, H, and G, and taking moments about the joint marked 2. After the stress in D has been computed, the stress in F may be found by applying the principle $\Sigma V = 0$ to the section d–d.

To illustrate the discussion above and as further illustration of the discussion in Art. 82, the calculations for stress in bars A, B, C, D, E, F, and G of the structure in Fig. 88 are given below. The reactions must first be calculated and they are shown on the figure.

A Section a–a moments about joint marked 1

$$90 \times \frac{20}{20} = 90$$

$$\times \frac{22.36}{20.00} = -\ 101^k \text{ stress in } A \text{ (22.36 ft. is the length of } A\text{)}$$

B Section b–b moments about joint 2

$$\begin{aligned} 20 \times 20 &= 400 \\ 90 \times 20 &= \underline{1800} \\ & 2200 \end{aligned}$$

$$\div\ 20 = +\ 110^k \text{ stress in } B$$

C Section c–c $\Sigma V = 0$

$$\begin{aligned} &60 \\ &\underline{100} \\ &160 \times \frac{28.28}{20.0} = +\ 226^k \text{ stress in } C \end{aligned}$$

D Section d–d moments about joint 3

$$\begin{aligned} 60 \times 40 &= 2400 \\ 100 \times 60 &= \underline{6000} \\ & 8400 \\ 110 \times 20 &= \underline{2200} \\ & 6200 \div 20 = 310^k \quad H \text{ comp. stress in } D \end{aligned}$$

$$\times \frac{28.28}{20.00} = +\ 438^k \text{ stress in } D$$

E Section e–e $\Sigma H = 0$

$$80 \times \frac{22.36}{10} = +\ 179^k \text{ stress in } E$$

F Section d–d $\Sigma V = 0$

$$\begin{array}{r} 100 \\ 60 \\ 310 \\ \hline -\ 470^k \text{ stress in } F \end{array}$$

G Section g–g moments about joint 3

$$\begin{array}{r} 80 \times 40 = 3200 \\ 60 \times 20 = 1200 \\ \hline 2000 \end{array}$$

$$\div\ 20 = 100^k\ V \text{ comp. stress in } G$$

$$\times \frac{22.36}{20.00} = +\ 112^k \text{ stress in } G$$

The calculations above should not require further comment. They should be checked by the student, who should also calculate

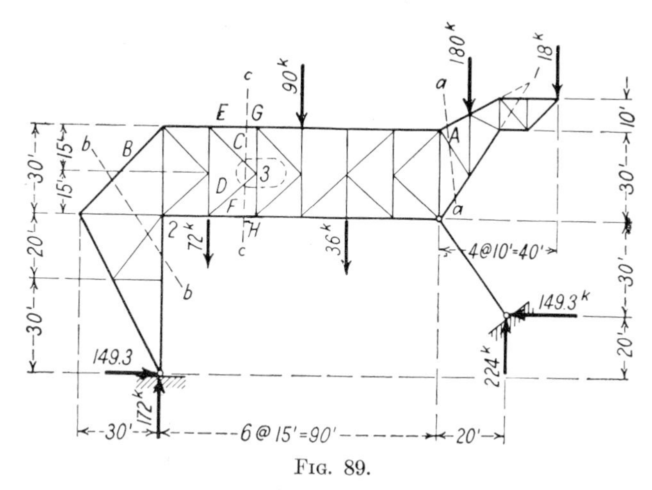

Fig. 89.

the stress in H by passing a section cutting B, D, H, and G and using the stresses already calculated.

85. Illustrative Example.—Determine the stress in bars A, B, C, and D of the structure shown in Fig. 89. The reactions are as shown.

A Section a–a moments about 1

$$
\begin{array}{r}
180 \times 20 = 3600 \\
18 \times 10 = \underline{180} \\
3420 \div 60 = 57^k \quad H \text{ comp. of stress} \\
\times \dfrac{18.03}{10.0} = +\ 102.7^k \text{ stress in } A
\end{array}
$$

B Section b–b moments about 2

$$149.3 \times \frac{50}{30} = 249 \quad H \text{ or } V \text{ comp.}$$

$$\times \frac{42.43}{30.00} = +\ 352^k \text{ stress in } B$$

C and **D**

$$
\begin{array}{l}
172 \\
\underline{72} \\
100 \div 2 = 50^k \quad V \text{ comp. in each bar}
\end{array}
$$

$$\times \frac{21.21}{15.0} = +\ 70.7^k \text{ stress in } C$$

$$= -\ 70.7^k \text{ stress in } D$$

The stress in A was resolved into vertical and horizontal components, and taken as acting in the line of A extended, at a point vertically under the center of moments. The vertical component then passed through the center of moments and the horizontal component was determined directly. The calculation of stress in B does not require comment. It should be noted that section c–c, passed for the calculation of stress in C and D, cuts four members. The stress in the bars cut, therefore, cannot be determined by application of the laws of statics to either part of the structure unless additional information is available. A section passed around joint 3 cutting out of the structure the part shown in Fig. 90 gives the necessary data. It should be clear from this figure that since $\Sigma H = 0$ the horizontal component of C must be equal and opposite to the horizontal component of D. Since the two bars have the same slope their vertical components must also be equal and act in the same direction, as shown. The members E and F are horizontal and cannot have vertical com-

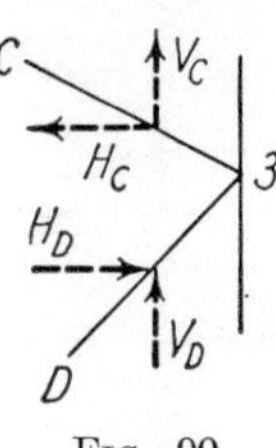

Fig. 90.

ponents. Consequently the sum of the vertical components of the stress in members C and D must be equal to the algebraic sum of the external forces acting on the part of the structure to the left (or right) of section c–c, or equal to the shear on section c–c. Since the vertical components of these members are equal, they divide equally the shear on section c–c as indicated in the calculations. If C and D have unequal slopes, their vertical components will be proportional to the slopes since their horizontal components must be equal. Calculate the stress in bars C and D when joint 3 is 10 ft. above H and 20 ft. below G. Calculate the stress in the same bars when a load of 60^k acts at joint 3 with a slope of 4

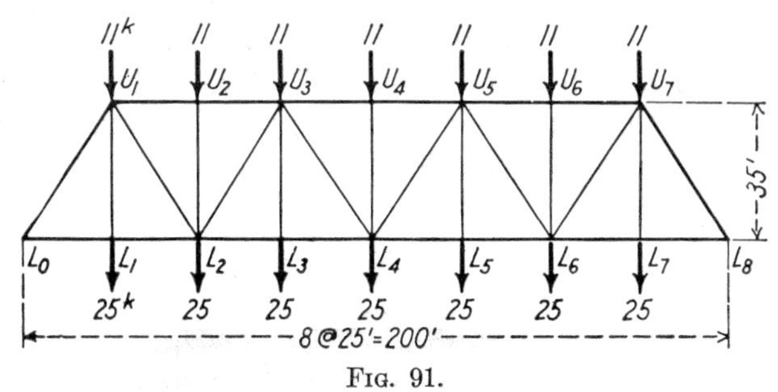

FIG. 91.

vertical to 3 horizontal; (*a*) when joint 3 is located as shown in Fig. 89, and (*b*) when it is 10 ft. above H.

86. Problems for Practice.—Figures 91 and 92 show two trusses of identical overall dimensions which differ in web triangulation. The dead load of each structure is assumed to be as follows:

Track	=	520 lb. per ft. of bridge
Floor	=	600
Trusses and bracing	=	1760
Total	=	2880 lb. per ft. of bridge

This dead load results in panel concentrations for each structure of 11^k at each top chord joint and 25^k at each bottom chord joint, as shown in Fig. 91. The student should calculate the stress in members U_1U_2, U_2U_3, L_2L_3, L_3L_4, and U_2L_2 for each structure and compare the results. He should also calculate the stress in U_3L_2 in the structure of Fig. 91 and compare with the stress in U_2L_3 of the structure in Fig. 92.

87. Illustrative Example.—The non-parallel chord Pratt truss shown in Fig. 93 — often called the Parker truss — is assumed to weigh the same as the trusses shown in Figs. 91 and 92; i.e., there

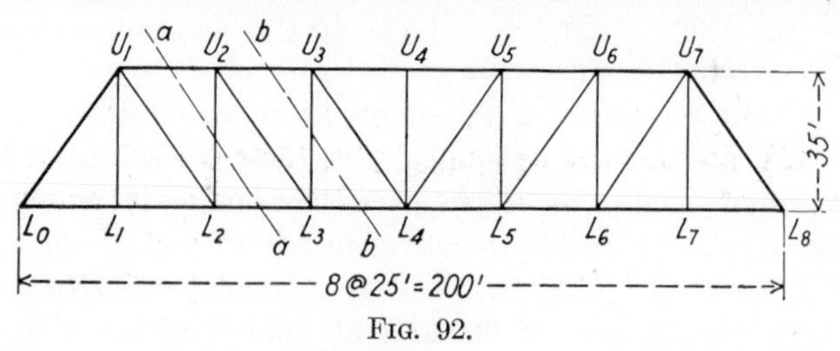

Fig. 92.

are dead load panel concentrations of 11^k at each top chord joint and 25^k at each bottom chord joint. The calculations for stress in the bars of this truss follow the lines already discussed, but a few detail differences may be illustrated by determining the stress in U_2L_2 and U_2L_3.

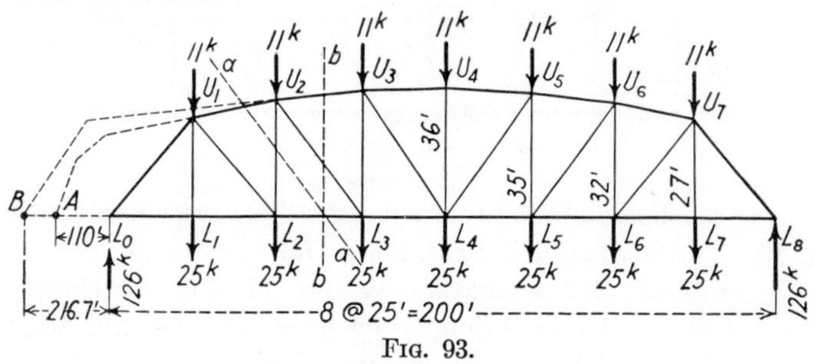

Fig. 93.

U_2L_2.—A number of different sections may be used in calculating the stress in U_2L_2, but only one section, marked a–a in Fig. 93, makes possible its determination independently of any other bar. If the members U_1U_2 and L_2L_3 are extended to their intersection at A, 110 ft. to the left of L_0, moments may be taken about this point, eliminating all unknown quantities but the stress in U_2L_2. It should be clear that either the part to the left of the section or the part to the right may be used in the calculation, but the part to the left involves fewer loads and is the more convenient.

$$
\begin{array}{lll}
126 \times 110 = & & 13{,}860 \\
11 \times 135 = & 1485 & \\
50 \times 147.5 = & 7375 & \\
\hline
& 8860 & 8{,}860 \\
\hline
& & 5{,}000 \div 160 = -\,31.3^k
\end{array}
$$

A little study of the calculations just given will show that the 25^k load at L_2 may be excluded from the moments about A and the 25^k load at L_1 added to the 11^k load at U_1. The calculations are then:

$$\begin{array}{rrl} 126 \times 110 = & 13{,}860 & \\ 36 \times 135 = & 4{,}860 & \\ \hline & 9{,}000 \div 160 = & 56.3^k \\ & & 25.0 \\ \hline & & -\,31.3^k \text{ stress in } U_2L_2. \end{array}$$

If the stress in U_1U_2 has already been calculated, the stress in U_2L_2 may be determined from the application of $\Sigma V = 0$ to the part of the structure on the right or left of section a–a. Or, if the stress in U_1L_2 is known, a section around the joint L_2 gives the stress in U_2L_2 very conveniently. The student should see that the second calculation given above is really the same as passing a section cutting U_1U_2, U_1L_2, and L_1L_2, finding the vertical component of the stress in U_1L_2 to be $+\,56.3^k$, and then passing a section around joint L_2. The part cut out by the latter section and the forces acting are shown in Fig. 94.

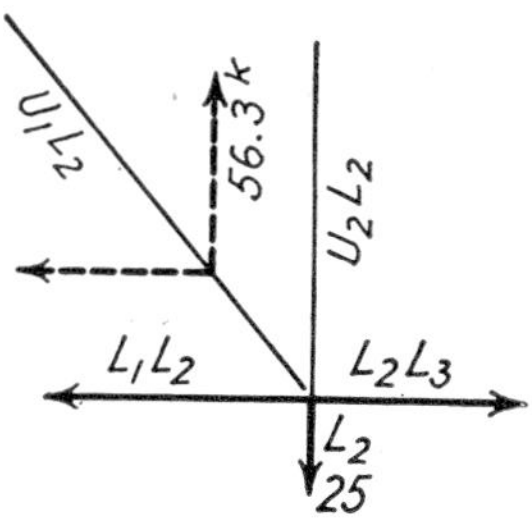

Fig. 94.

It should be clear from this figure that the stress in U_2L_2 is $56.3^k - 25.0^k = 31.3^k$ compression.

U_2L_3.—The calculation for stress in U_2L_3 is very similar to that for stress in U_2L_2. Section b–b is the most convenient. If the stress in U_2U_3 is known, its vertical component may be found and the vertical component of the stress in U_2L_3 found by applying the principle $\Sigma V = 0$ to the part of the structure on the right or that on the left of the section. If the stress in U_2U_3 is not known, the stress in U_2L_3 may be calculated independently by extending the bars U_2U_3 and L_2L_3 to their intersection at B, 216.7 ft. to the left of L_0. The stress in U_2L_3 is most conveniently resolved into vertical and horizontal components at L_3 as the horizontal component then passes through the center of moments leaving the vertical component as the only unknown and acting at a point a known distance from B. The calculations are then as follows:

$$\begin{array}{rrl} 126 \times 216.7 = & 27{,}300 & \\ 2 \times 36 \times 254.2 = & 18{,}300 & \\ \hline & 9{,}000 & \\ & & \div\ 291.7 = 30.9^k \text{ vert. comp.} \\ & & \times \dfrac{40.6}{32.0} = +\,39.2^k \text{ stress in } U_2L_3. \end{array}$$

The sign of the stress in U_2L_3 was determined in the manner outlined in Art. 80 and attention should be called to the statement made there, that if the character of the stress is not at once apparent it will become so as the calculations develop. This statement may be illustrated by referring to the calculations just made. The part of the structure to the left of section *b–b* and the forces acting are shown in Fig. 95.

In taking moments about the point *B* it may not be clear by inspection whether the moment of the reaction is greater than the moment of the two 11^k and two 25^k loads. As soon, however, as these moments have been calculated it is clear at once that the part of the structure shown in

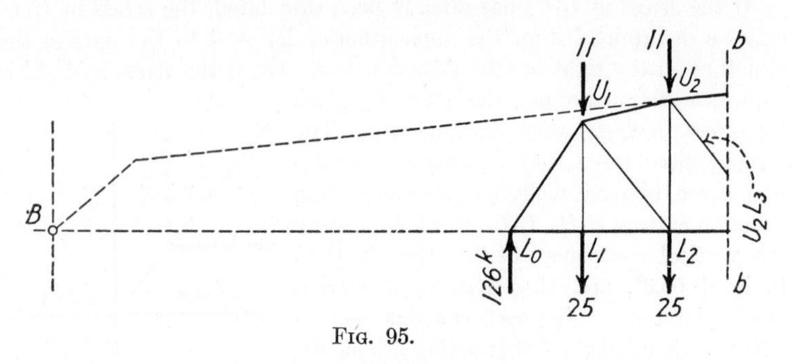

FIG. 95.

Fig. 95 tends to rotate counter-clockwise about *B* and that to prevent this rotation it is necessary to *pull* on the bar U_2L_3, which is therefore in tension.

88. Chord Stresses — Uniform Fixed Loads.—The principles discussed in Arts. 39 and 46, Chapter III, may be conveniently used in calculating the chord stresses in trusses supporting a uniformly distributed fixed load. Study of the trusses in Figs. 91, 92, and 93 shows that a chord stress or its horizontal component is always the bending moment at some joint (usually a top chord or bottom chord panel point) divided by the depth of the truss at that joint. As stated in Art. 46, Chapter III, the bending moment at any panel point in a girder or truss is the same as the bending moment at the same point in a beam of the same length to which the loads are directly applied. And, as stated in Art. 39, Chapter III, the bending moment at any point in a beam uniformly loaded is $\frac{1}{2}$ *wab*, the symbols having the significance there given.

The dead load per foot of bridge for each of the spans shown in Figs. 91, 92, and 93 is assumed to be 2880 lb. per ft. of bridge or 1440 lb. per ft. of truss. Applying the above relation to members

U_1U_2 in Fig. 91, L_3L_4 in Fig. 92, and U_2U_3 in Fig. 93, the following calculations result:

U_1U_2 *Fig. 91*:

$$\frac{1.44 \times 50 \times 150}{2 \times 35} = -\ 154.4^k \text{ stress in } U_1U_2$$

L_3L_4 *Fig. 92*:

$$\frac{1.44 \times 75 \times 125}{2 \times 35} = +\ 193.0^k \text{ stress in } L_3L_4$$

U_2U_3 *Fig. 93*:

$$\frac{1.44 \times 75 \times 125}{2 \times 35} = -\ 193.0^k\ H \text{ comp.}$$

$$\times \frac{25.18}{25.0} = -\ 194.5^k \text{ stress in } U_2U_3$$

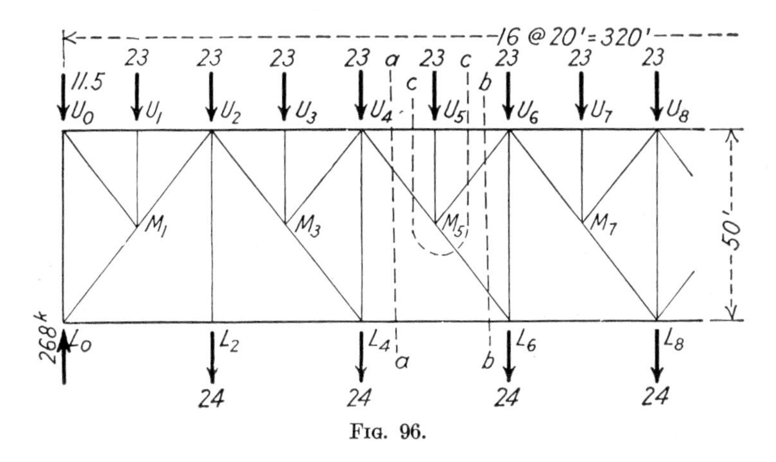

Fig. 96.

89. Subdivided Trusses.—As stated in Chapter V, the most economical slope for the diagonals of a truss is between 1 to 1 and 2 to 1. If such a slope is maintained with the great depths necessary in long spans, the panel length becomes too great for convenience and the weight of the floor becomes excessive. In such cases some form of "subdivided" truss, such as shown in Figs. 96 and 97, or the K truss in Fig. 101, may be used.

The vertical dotted members U_3M_3, U_5M_5, and U_7M_7 in Fig. 97 are sometimes used to reduce the unsupported length of the double-panel top chords. They are not affected by live load, but support some of the weight of the top chord and its bracing in the panels in which they are located. The horizontal dotted members M_4M_5 and M_6M_7 in the same figure are to provide lateral support for the long web columns U_4L_4 and U_6L_6. Unless inclined loads are applied at the joints M_4 and M_6, these members have no effect on, and are disregarded in, the calculation of primary stresses.

The short diagonals in subdivided trusses such as U_4M_3, U_6M_5, etc., in Fig. 96, and M_3L_2, M_5L_4, etc., in Fig. 97 are usually called sub-diagonals. If they are tension members, as in Fig. 96, they

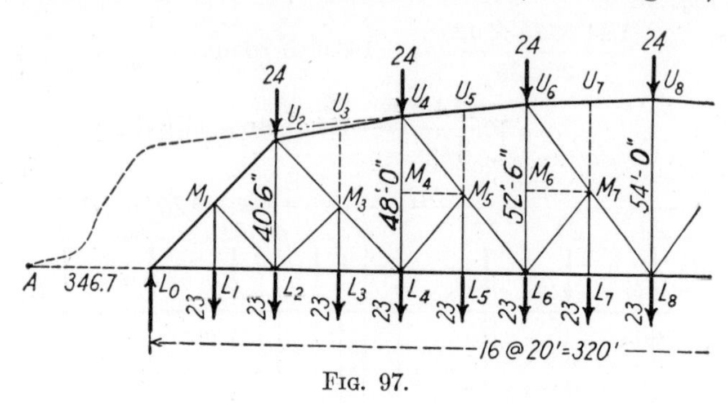

FIG. 97.

are often referred to as sub-ties, and if compression members, as in Fig. 97, as sub-struts.

90. Stresses in Subdivided Trusses. Fixed Loads.—The fundamental method of analysis which has been discussed in this chapter is adequate for the determination of stresses in any statically determinate truss, regardless of type, and the student is prepared to analyze the subdivided trusses shown in the above-mentioned figures when subjected to fixed loads only. However, the calculations for stress in several bars of these trusses are given below to illustrate some detail differences in procedure.

The dead load of the structure in each figure will be assumed as follows:

Track	=	520 lb. per ft. of bridge
Floor	=	580 lb. per ft. of bridge
Trusses and bracing	=	2400 lb. per ft. of bridge
Total	=	3500 lb. per ft. of bridge.

The weight of the trusses will be assumed to be divided equally between the top and bottom chords, but the track and floor will in each case be applied at the loaded chord. The panel loads for the truss in Fig. 96 are then

$$\text{Top} \quad \tfrac{1}{2} \times 20 \times 2300 = 23{,}000 \text{ lb.} = 23^k \text{ per panel}$$

$$\text{Bottom} \quad \tfrac{1}{2} \times 40 \times 1200 = 24{,}000 \text{ lb.} = 24^k \text{ per panel.}$$

These figures, based on uniform distribution of the dead load, are approximate. Actually the panel concentrations at U_2, U_4, U_6, U_8, etc., are larger than those at U_1, U_3, U_5, U_7, etc., and there are concentrations of dead load at M_1, M_3, M_5, M_7, etc. In long, heavy spans, the assumption of uniform distribution of dead load may not be sufficiently accurate, but for ordinary spans such as are shown in Figs. 96 and 97, the results are satisfactory for design purposes.

91. Subdivided Truss with Parallel Chords.—The stress in the members in the panel 4–6 of the truss in Fig. 96 will be considered.

$\mathbf{L_4L_6}$ Section a–a moments about U_4

$$\tfrac{1}{2} \times 1.75 \text{ kips per ft.} \times 80 \text{ ft.} \times 240 \text{ ft.} = 16{,}800 \text{ ft.-kips} \div 50 \text{ ft.} = +336^k$$

1.75 kips per ft. in the above expression is the weight per foot applied on one truss.

$\mathbf{U_4U_6}$ Section a–a moments about L_6

$$\begin{aligned}
268 \times 120 &= & & 32{,}160 \\
4 \times 23 \times 70 &= & 6{,}440 & \\
11.5 \times 120 &= & 1{,}380 & \\
2 \times 24 \times 60 &= & 2{,}880 & \\
& & \overline{10{,}700} & \ 10{,}700 \\
& & & \overline{21{,}460} \div 50 = -429.2^k
\end{aligned}$$

The student should note the difference between the calculations for stress in these two chords. Why is it not correct to use the simpler procedure of the calculations for stress in L_4L_6 in finding the stress in U_4U_6?

$\mathbf{U_4M_5}$ Section a–a $\Sigma V = 0$

$$268 - (11.5 + 4 \times 23 + 2 \times 24) = 116.5^k$$

$$\times \frac{32.02}{25.0} = +149.4^k$$

U_5M_5 Section around U_5 $\Sigma V = 0$

$$-23^k.$$

U_6M_5 Section c–c moments about U_4

$$23 \times \frac{20}{40} = 11.5\ V.\ \text{comp.}$$

$$\times \frac{32.02}{25.0} = +14.7^k$$

The stress in U_6M_5 was resolved into vertical and horizontal components at U_6. The stress in this bar will be further discussed later.

M_5L_6 Section b–b $\Sigma V = 0$

$$268 - (11.5 + 5 \times 23 + 2 \times 24) + \tfrac{1}{2} \times 23 = 105$$

$$\times \frac{32.02}{25.0} = +134.5^k$$

In this expression the last term on the left, $\frac{1}{2} \times 23$, is the vertical component of the stress in U_6M_5.

U_6L_6 Section around joint L_6 $\Sigma V = 0$

$$105 - 24 = -81^k$$

U_4L_4 Section cutting U_3U_4, U_4M_3, U_4L_4, L_4L_6

$$268 - (11.5 + 3 \times 23 + 2 \times 24) + \tfrac{1}{2} \times 23 = -151^k$$

92. Subdivided Truss with Non-parallel Chords.—The Pettit or Pennsylvania truss in Fig. 97 may be analyzed by proceeding in a manner similar to that used in the calculations just made above for the parallel chord subdivided truss. The assumed panel concentrations are shown on the figure. The stresses in the members of a typical panel such as 4–6 should be calculated as an illustrative exercise.

The non-parallel chord subdivided through truss is sometimes made with sub-ties instead of sub-struts. Figure 98 shows a double panel 4–6 of a truss like that in Fig. 97 rearranged to use a sub-tie instead of a sub-strut. No new principles are involved but the calculation of stress in U_6M_5 may be discussed briefly. Passing the section a–a as shown in Fig. 98, the part cut out from the structure is shown in Fig. 98 in full lines, the dotted lines completing the panel. The dimensions are given in general terms and the following discussion concerns the general case.

Let

W = the total load applied along the line $U_5M_5L_5$;
V = the vertical component of the stress in U_6M_5;
H = the horizontal component of the stress in U_6M_5.

$$H = V\frac{p}{h_2 - \frac{h_1}{2}}$$

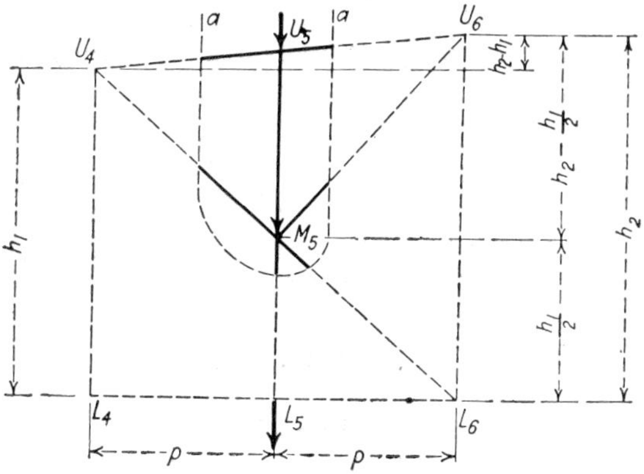

FIG. 98.

Resolving the stress in U_6M_5 into horizontal and vertical components at U_6 and taking moments about U_4

$$Wp = V2p - H(h_2 - h_1)$$

$$= V2p - V\frac{p}{\left(h_2 - \frac{h_1}{2}\right)}(h_2 - h_1)$$

and

$$V = W\frac{h_2 - \frac{h_1}{2}}{h_2}$$

That is, the vertical component of the stress in a sub-diagonal is a fraction of the load applied at the center of the main panel in which the sub-diagonal occurs, the fraction being the vertical projection of the sub-diagonal divided by the length of the vertical to which it connects. When the chord to which the sub-diagonal connects is horizontal (i.e., when $h_2 = h_1$) the fraction is one-half.

This relation is very convenient in calculating the stresses in subdivided trusses. It is not correct if the main diagonal in the panel in which the sub-diagonal occurs is not straight throughout its length, or if the chord to which the sub-diagonal connects is not straight throughout the panel in which the sub-diagonal occurs. In the panel shown in Fig. 98 the relation is not correct if U_4L_6 and U_4U_6 are not straight lines. Cases in which these members are broken lines are rare.

93. Secondary System in Subdivided Truss.—A subdivided truss may be considered as an ordinary truss with a small secondary

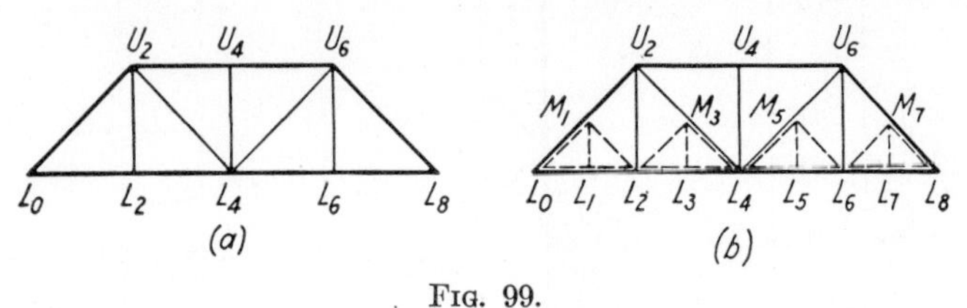

FIG. 99.

truss added in each subdivided panel to support a floorbeam at the center of the main panel. For example, in Fig. 99 (*a*) is shown an ordinary truss which may be considered as converted to the subdivided truss in Fig. 99 (*b*) by the addition of the secondary trusses shown in dotted lines. Of course the only members actually added are the sub-diagonals M_1L_2, M_3L_2, M_5L_6, and M_7L_6 and the hangers M_1L_1, M_3L_3, M_5L_5, and M_7L_7. The stresses in the subdivided truss may be correctly determined by calculating the stresses in the truss of Fig. 99 (*a*) and adding to those members or parts of members which coincide with members of the secondary trusses the stresses in the secondary truss due to the loads applied to it. That is, to find the stress in U_2L_4 we may calculate the stress in U_2L_4 in the truss of Fig. 99 (*a*); this stress will be correct for the part U_2M_3, but for the part M_3L_4 we must add the stress in M_3L_4 of the secondary truss due to the load at L_3. Similarly the stress in L_2L_4 may be calculated as the stress in L_2L_4 of the ordinary truss in Fig. 99 (*a*) *plus* the stress in L_2L_4 of the secondary truss due to the load at L_3. It should be clearly understood that in calculating stresses in this manner the loads applied at L_1, L_3, L_5, and L_7 must be considered as distributed to the adjacent panel points before the stresses are determined in the truss of Fig. 99 (*a*).

The student should show that the proof of the relation between the vertical component of stress in the member U_6M_5 of Fig. 98, and the load W is also proof that the same relation will hold in the secondary truss shown in Fig. 100 and that this secondary truss may be removed from the main truss without changing the stress in any remaining members, except U_4M_5 and U_4U_6, provided the load W is distributed to the panel points U_4 and U_6.

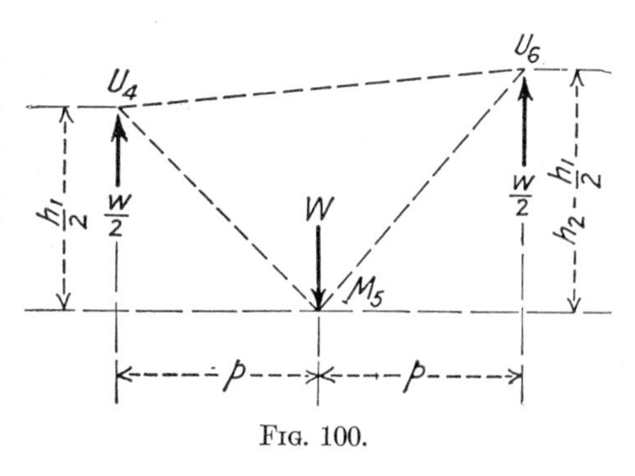

FIG. 100.

94. K Truss.—Analysis of a K truss such as shown in Fig. 101 presents no difficulty for fixed loads. The discussion of members C and D in Fig. 89 covers the details of the application of the fundamental method. The fact that the chords are not parallel

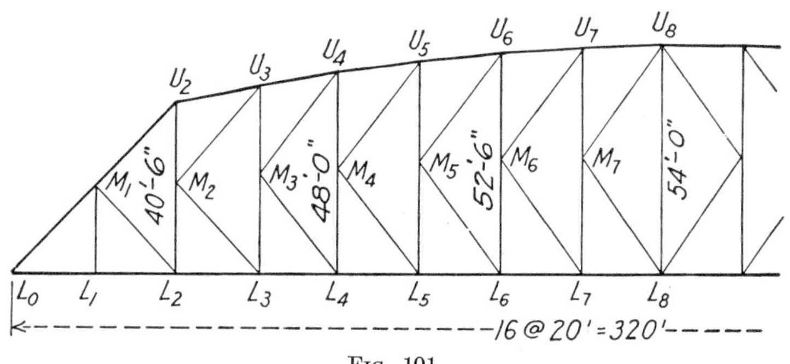

FIG. 101.

in the truss in Fig. 101 has the same effect on the procedure as non-parallel chords have in the ordinary truss. Considering panel 4–5, for example, the shear in the panel is not equal to the sum of the vertical components of the diagonals since the upper chord is inclined. If the stress in the upper chord is known, its vertical component may be included in applying $\Sigma V = 0$ to a vertical section through the panel. If the chord stress is not known, the sum of the vertical components of the diagonal stresses may be found by taking moments about the intersection of the upper and lower chords. If there are no horizontal or inclined loads applied at the intersection of the diagonals, the horizontal components of their stresses must be equal and opposite, and the vertical components in proportion to the slopes of the diagonals, and stresses proportional to the lengths. In the truss shown in Fig. 101 the diagonals in each panel have equal slopes. The chord stresses may be found by passing a section cutting U_4U_5, U_4M_4, M_4L_4, and L_4L_5, for example, and taking moments about U_4, M_4 or L_4. The horizontal components of these chord stresses must

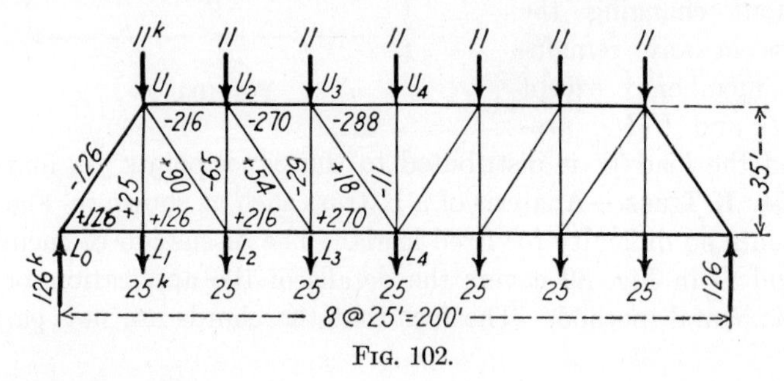

FIG. 102.

be equal and opposite provided there are no horizontal forces applied to the truss.

95. Index Stresses.—The stresses in a parallel chord truss which has equal panel lengths and which is supporting fixed loads may be found very conveniently by writing the **index stresses.** Index stresses are based on the vertical components of the stresses in the web members. They are found by passing sections around successive joints and by mental addition or subtraction, calculating and writing on the web bars cut by the sections the vertical components necessary to hold the joint in equilibrium against the forces known to be acting. The calculation and use of index stresses may best be shown by a few examples. In Fig. 102 is shown a truss with known external loads applied at the joints. The index stresses are shown on the bars and may be obtained as follows. It is necessary to start at a joint where there is only one member having an unknown vertical component, or at a joint where symmetry of structure and loading make possible the determination of more than one unknown vertical component. In the truss in Fig. 102 the start may be made at either end or at the center top chord joint, U_4. When the loading and the truss are symmetrical it is generally most convenient to start at the center. Passing a section around the joint U_4, inspection shows that the stress in U_4L_4 is -11^k, which is written on the bar. Passing a section around L_4 the part cut out is as shown in Fig. 103. Since the truss is symmetrical, it is clear that the vertical components of the two center diagonals must be equal and together must be 36^k to make $\Sigma V = 0$. Therefore the **index stress** of $+18^k$ is written on U_3L_4. A section may then be passed around U_3, cutting out the portion of structure shown in Fig. 104. The vertical com-

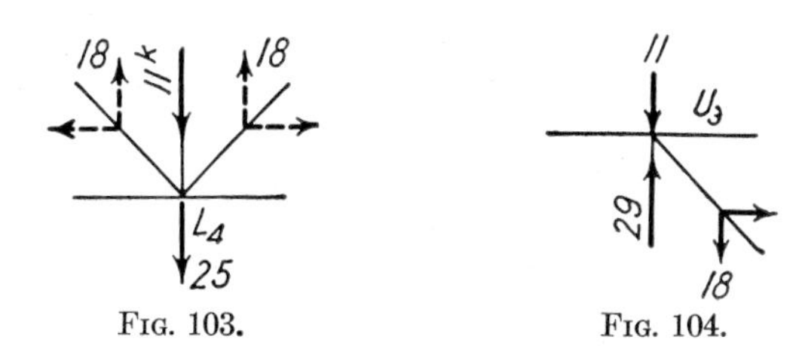

FIG. 103. FIG. 104.

ponent of the diagonal U_3L_4 which connects to this joint is known to be 18^k acting down as shown, the external load at the joint is known to be 11^k acting down, and inspection shows that for equilibrium the vertical U_3L_3 must *push* up with a force of 29^k: the **index stress** -29 is therefore written on U_3L_3. Proceeding in the same manner to joint L_3, inspection shows that the bar U_2L_3 must pull up with a force of 54^k to hold the joint in equilibrium, and the index stress $+54$ is written on the bar. By passing sections around successive joints in this manner, the index stresses for the web members may be written by inspection. The next step is to write the index stresses for the chords. Passing a section around L_0, the part cut out is as shown in Fig. 105. The vertical component of the stress in the diagonal U_1L_0, or its index stress, is 126^k as shown. If p is the length of the panel and h the depth of the truss, the horizontal component of the stress in U_1L_0 is $126\frac{p}{h}$ as shown. It is clear that there must be a *pull* of $126\frac{p}{h}$ in L_0L_1 to hold the joint L_0 in equilibrium, and the quantity 126 is the index stress for L_0L_1. Passing a section around the joint U_1 the part of the structure cut off is as shown in Fig. 106. Inspection shows that for equilibrium the bar U_1U_2 must push on the joint U_1 with a force of $126\frac{p}{h} + 90\frac{p}{h} = \frac{p}{h} \times 216$. The quantity 216 is the index stress for the chord U_1U_2 and is written on the bar with a minus sign since the member is in compression. Pro-

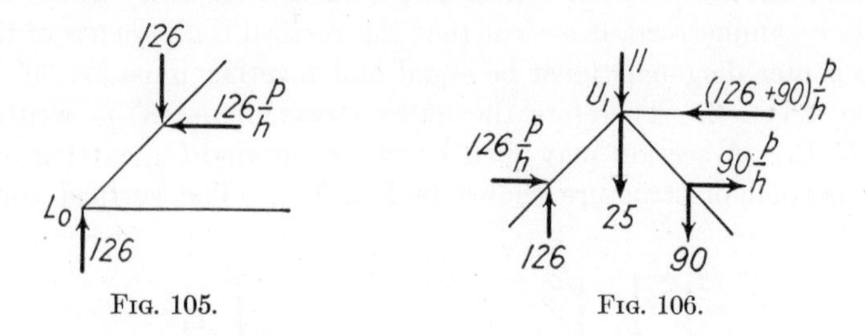

Fig. 105.

Fig. 106.

ceeding to joint U_2, the section passed cuts out a portion of the structure shown in Fig. 107. The bar U_2U_3 must push against the joint U_2 with a force of $216\frac{p}{h} + 54\frac{p}{h} = 270\frac{p}{h}$. The quantity 270 is the index stress and is written on the member with a minus sign to indicate compression.

The discussion above indicates the method of writing index stresses and should show that **the true stress in any bar is the index stress for that bar multiplied by the length of the bar and divided by the depth of the truss.**

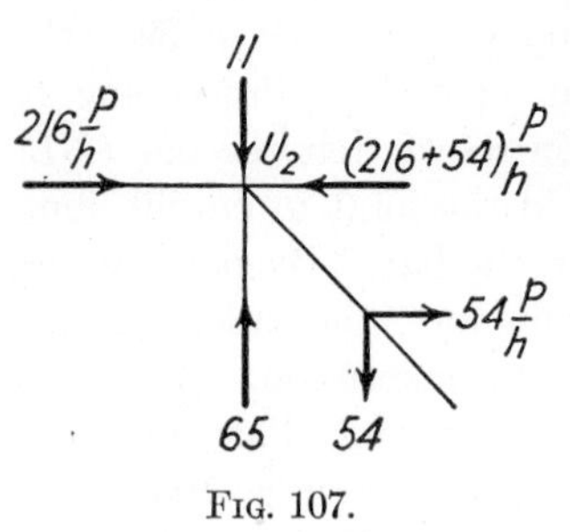

Fig. 107.

Index stresses may be written just as easily for unsymmetrical loading, but must, in such cases, be written for the entire truss, and must be started at one end. An example is shown in Fig. 108. Index stresses may also be written for subdivided or K trusses; as examples the index stresses for the truss of Fig. 96 and for a K truss are shown in Figs. 109 and 110, respectively.

It should be noted that, in obtaining the stress in a sub-diagonal or in a half main diagonal, the index stress must be multiplied by the ratio of the length of a full diagonal to the depth of the truss, or by the ratio of the length of a half or sub-diagonal to *half* the depth of the truss.

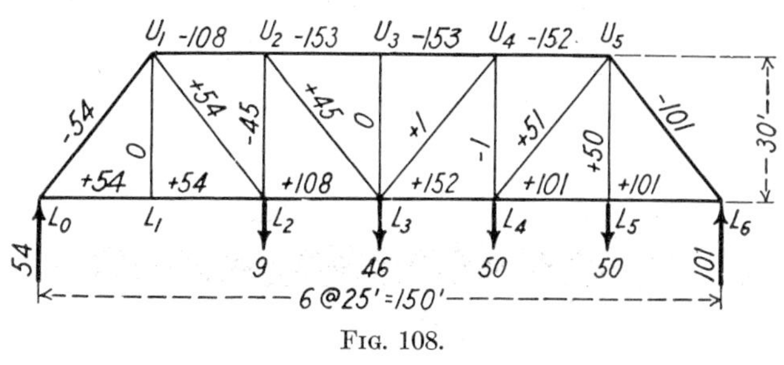

FIG. 108.

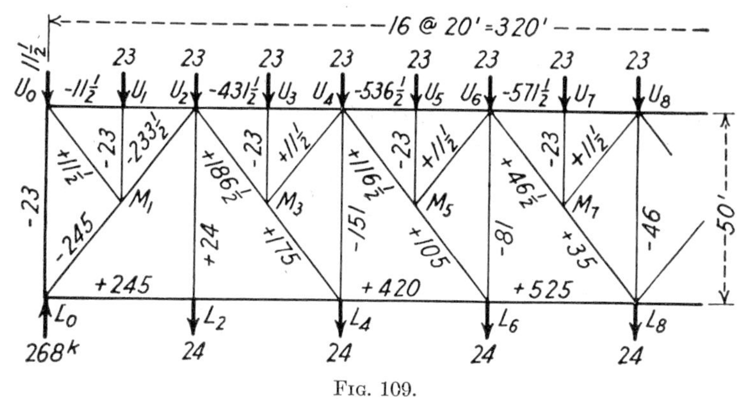

FIG. 109.

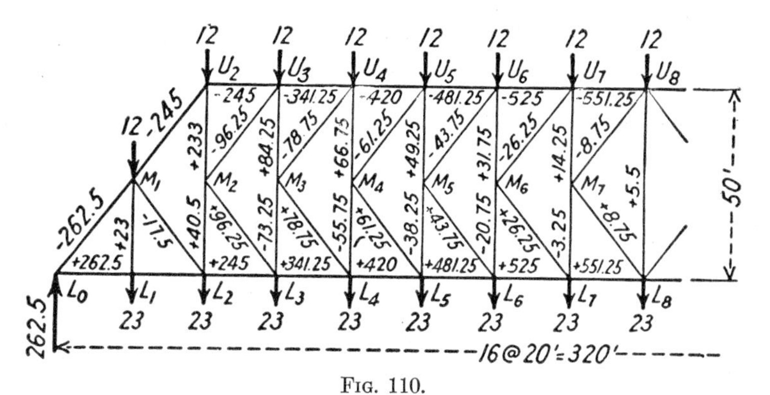

FIG. 110.

Index stresses are sometimes written for a *unit* load at each panel point, and in such cases may be called *index coefficients*. An example is shown in Fig. 111. These coefficients, when multiplied by the length of the member in question and divided by the depth of the truss, give the stress in the member in question due to the unit loads at the panel points. The stresses due to panel loads of any other magnitude are in direct proportion to the loads. The student should note that if the loads are not applied to the chord joints for which the stress coefficients were written, or if the loads are divided between the chords, the stresses in the verticals

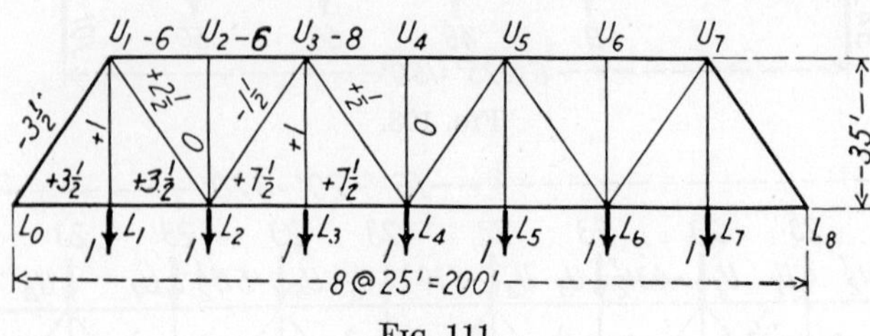

FIG. 111.

found from the coefficients must be corrected; the stresses in the other bars will be correct no matter to which chord the loads are applied.

It is possible to write index stresses for non-parallel chord trusses, or for trusses with varying panel lengths, but the necessary corrections for the differences in slope so lengthen and complicate the procedure that it does not offer any advantage over ordinary calculation of the stresses.

PROBLEMS

141. Compute the stress in bars a to k inclusive of the structure shown.

Ans. $a = -\ 114^k$. $e = +\ 645^k$. $i = -\ 63.7^k$.
$b = -\ 1161^k$. $f = -\ 807^k$. $j = +\ 121^k$.
$c = +\ 299^k$. $g = +\ 31.5^k$. $k = +\ 40.3^k$.
$d = +\ 35.5^k$. $h = +\ 114^k$.

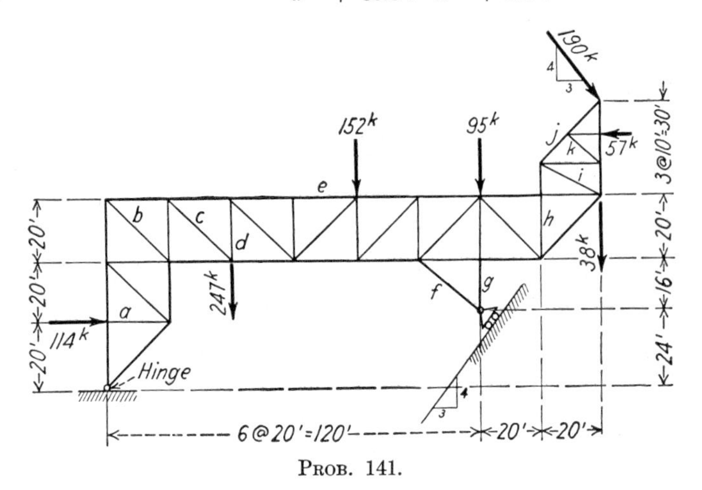

PROB. 141.

142. Calculate for each case the stress in bars a and b of the structures shown in (a) and (b).

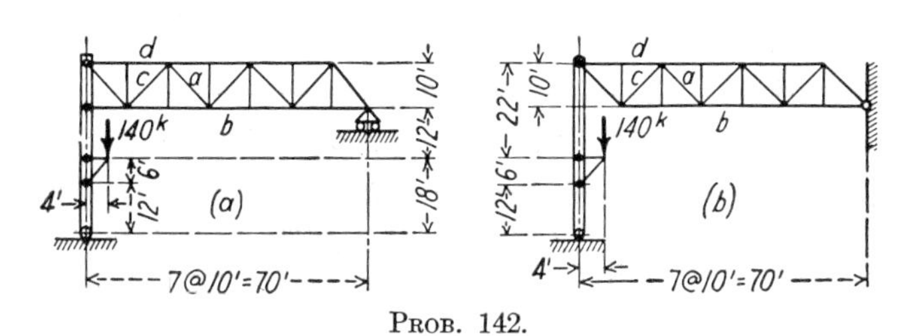

PROB. 142.

143. Calculate the stress in bars c and d, in each case, for the structures shown in Problem 142.

144. Calculate: (a) The stress in L_8L_9.
(b) The stress in U_6U_7.
(c) The stress in U_5L_4.

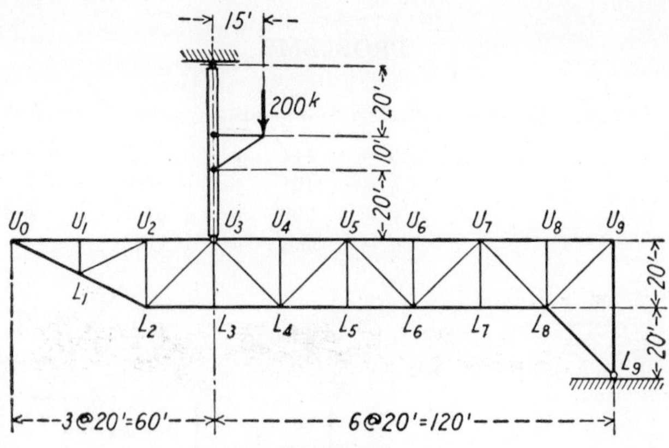

PROB. 144.

145. Compute the stresses in the bars a, b, c, d, e, and f of the structure shown.

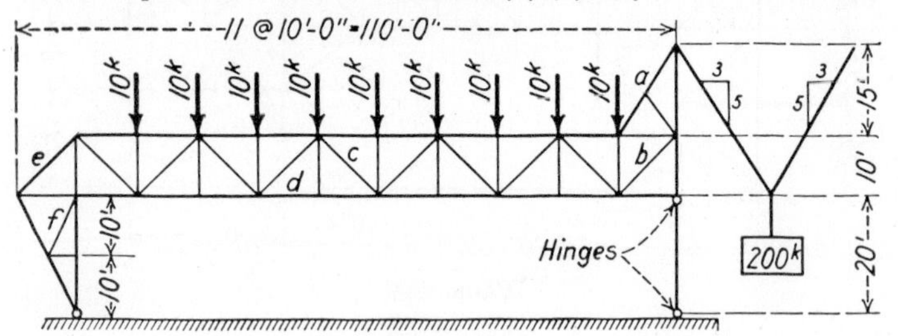

PROB. 145.

146. Calculate the stress in the bars a, b, c, and d of the structure shown

Ans. $a = -285^k$. $c = +236^k$.
$b = -327^k$. $d = -198^k$.

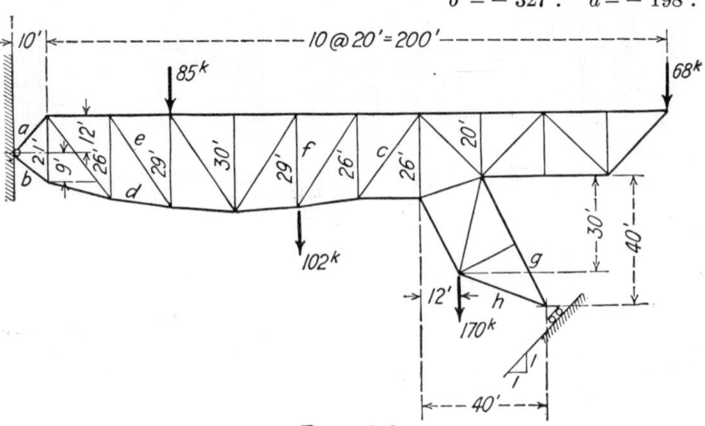

PROB. 146.

147. Calculate the stress in the bars e, f, g, and h of the structure shown in Problem 146.

Ans. $e = +\,35.8^k$. $g = -\,372^k$.
$f = -\,99.7^k$. $h = -\,274^k$.

148. Compute the stress, due to the loads shown, in bars a to n inclusive of the structure.

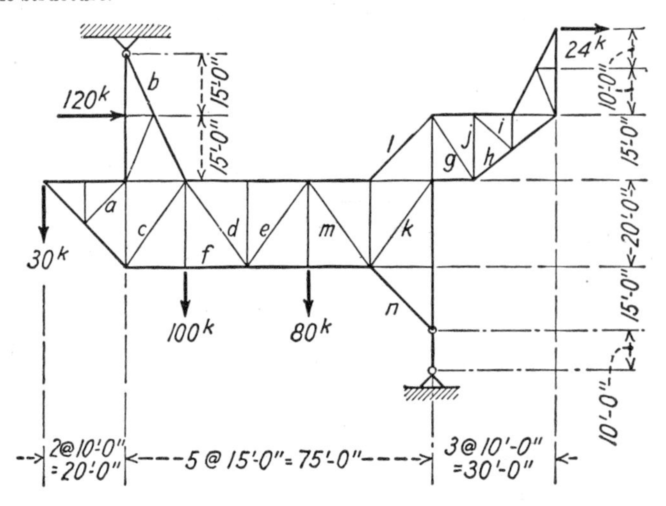

Prob. 148.

149. Compute the stress, due to the loads shown, in bars a to j inclusive of the structure.

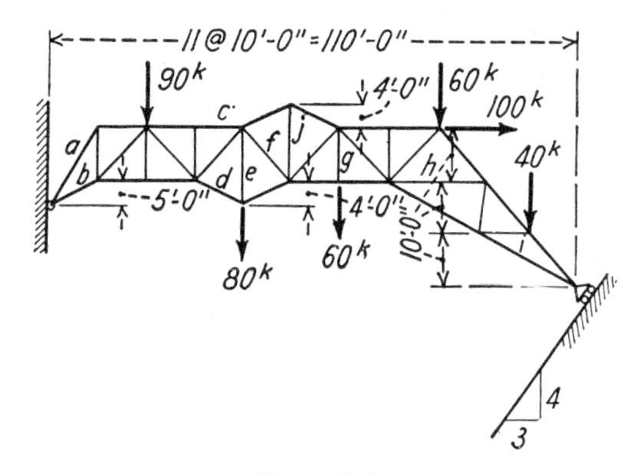

Prob. 149.

150. Calculate the stress in bars a, b, c, and d of the structure.

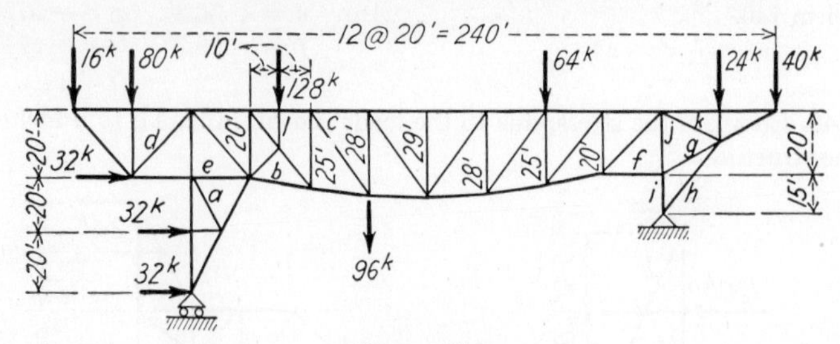

PROB. 150.

151. Calculate the stress in bars e, f, g, and h of the structure shown in Problem 150.

152. Calculate the stress in bars i, j, k, and l of the structure shown in Problem 150.

153. Owing to a rise in temperature the horizontal component of the temperature reaction at $A = 80^k$, acting to the right. Calculate the other reactions and the resulting stress in U_2L_3 and L_2L_3.

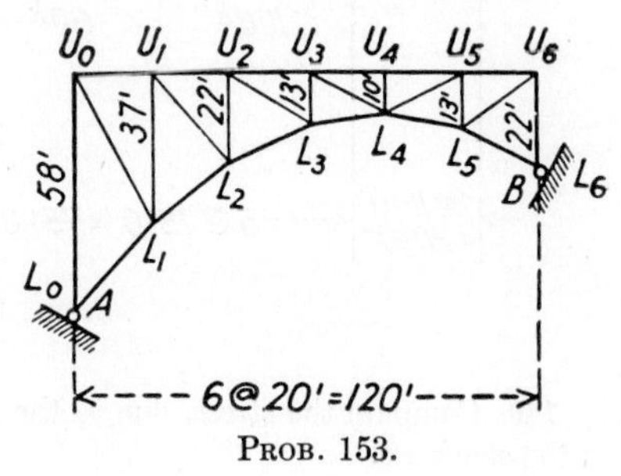

PROB. 153.

154. Compute the stress in bars a to g inclusive of the structure shown.

Ans. $a = -\ 68^k$. $e = -\ 80.9^k$.
$b = -\ 357^k$. $f = +\ 5.5^k$.
$c = +\ 137^k$. $g = -\ 78.3^k$.
$d = -\ 23.6^k$.

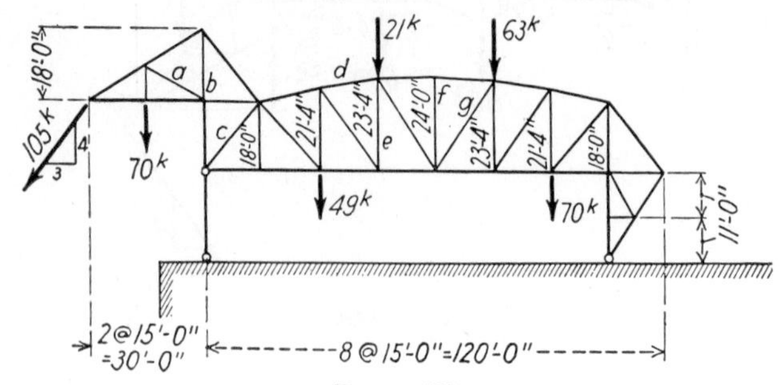

PROB. 154.

155. Calculate the stress in bars *a*, *b*, *c*, and *d* of the structure shown.

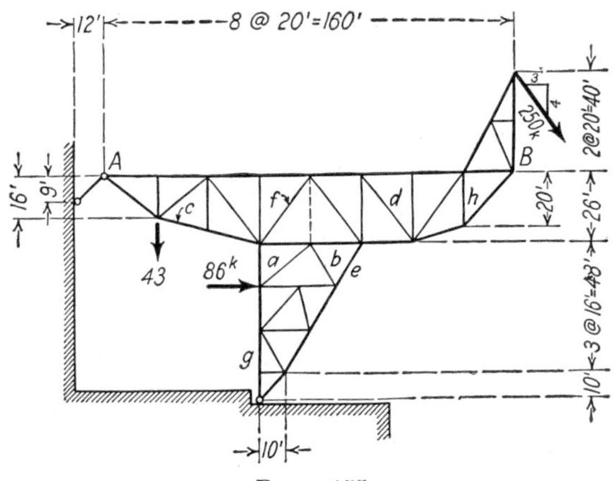

Prob. 155.

156. Calculate the stress in bars *e*, *f*, *g*, and *h* of the structure shown in Problem 155.

Ans. $e = -173.8^k$.
$f = -66.5^k$.
$g = -400^k$.
$h = +350^k$.

157. Compute the dead load stress in each bar of the bridge.
Dead load in pounds per foot of bridge:

applied to top chord	1000 lb. per ft.
applied to bottom chord	2200
Total	3200 lb. per ft.

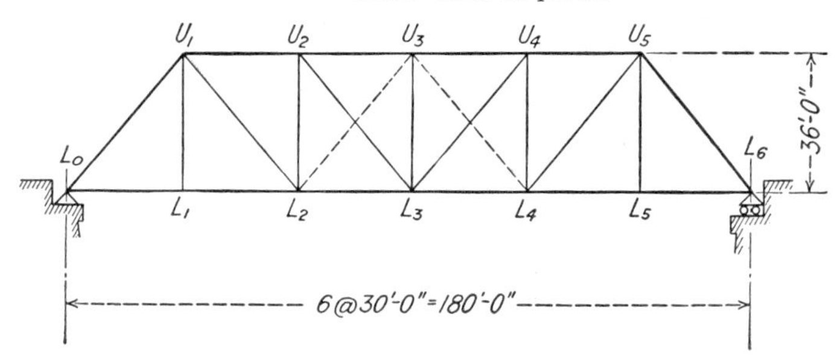

Prob. 157.

158. Compute the dead load stress in bars U_2U_3, L_2L_3, U_2L_2, and U_2L_3 of the bridge.

Dead load in pounds per foot of bridge:

applied to top	chord	1200 lb. per ft.
applied to bottom	chord	2400
	Total	3600 lb. per ft. of bridge.

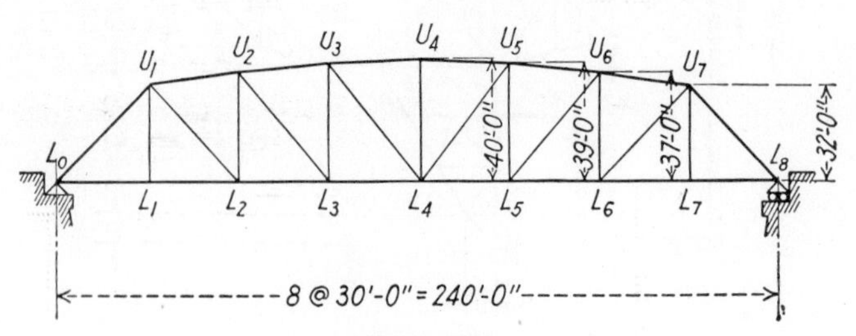

PROB. 158.

159. Given the following weights:

Track	=	560 lb. per ft. of bridge
Floor	=	640
Trusses and bracing	=	2800
Total	=	4000 lb. per ft. of bridge.

Calculate the dead load stress in the bars U_2U_3, U_2L_3, U_3L_3, and L_3L_4 of the single-track bridge shown.

Ans. $U_2U_3 = -\ 380^k$.
$U_2L_3 = +\ 90.1^k$.
$U_3L_3 = -\ 36.8^k$.
$L_3L_4 = +\ 374^k$.

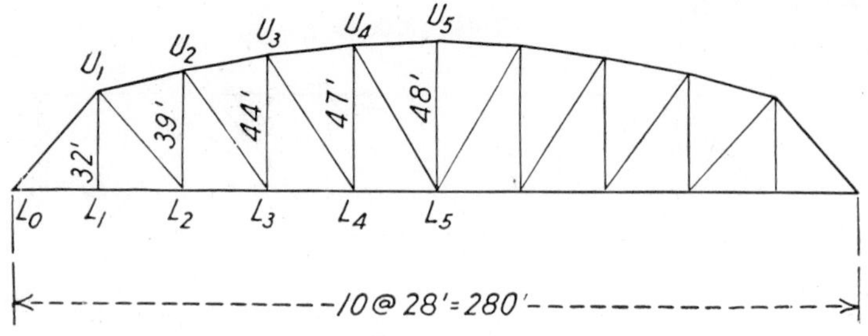

PROB. 159.

160. Given the following weights:

Track	=	600 lb. per ft. of bridge
Floor	=	700
Trusses and bracing	=	3200
Total	=	4500 lb. per ft. of bridge.

Calculate the dead load stress in the bars U_3U_4, U_3L_4, U_3L_3, and U_1L_1 of the single-track bridge shown.

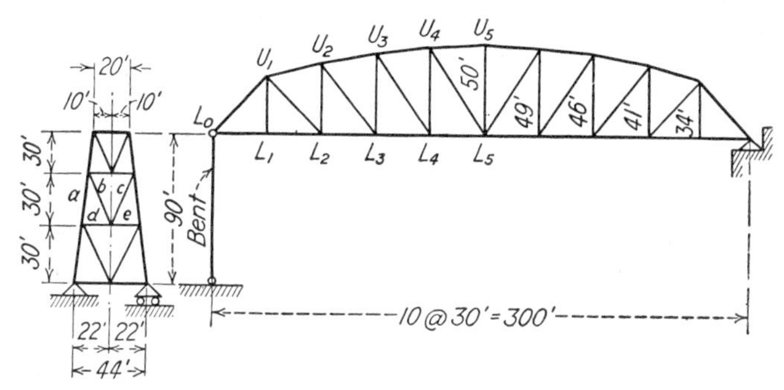

PROB. 160.

161. Calculate the stress in members a, b, c, d, and e of the bent at L_0 in Problem 160, due to a horizontal load of 1200 lb. per ft. applied along the bottom chord of the truss.

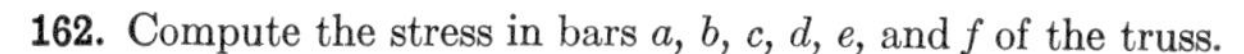

162. Compute the stress in bars a, b, c, d, e, and f of the truss.

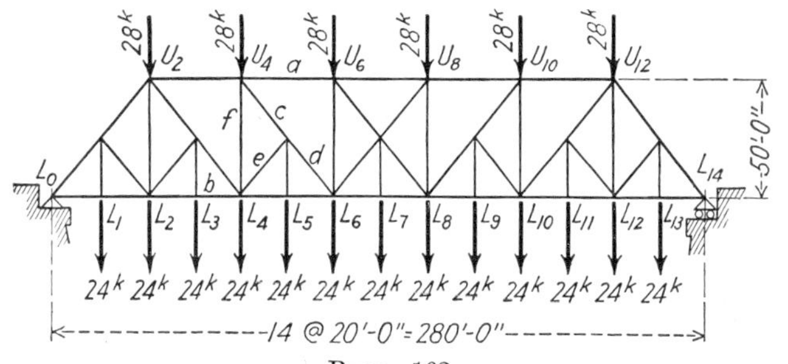

PROB. 162.

163. Compute the stress in bars c, d, e, and f of the structure in Problem 162:

(a) With panel loads of 60^k each at panel points 6 to 13, inclusive.
(b) With panel loads of 60^k each at panel points 5 to 13, inclusive.

164. Calculate the stress in bars a, b, c, and d of the structure shown.

Ans. $a = -\ 74.5^k$.
$b = +\ 94.3^k$.
$c = -\ 256^k$.
$d = -\ 1633^k$.

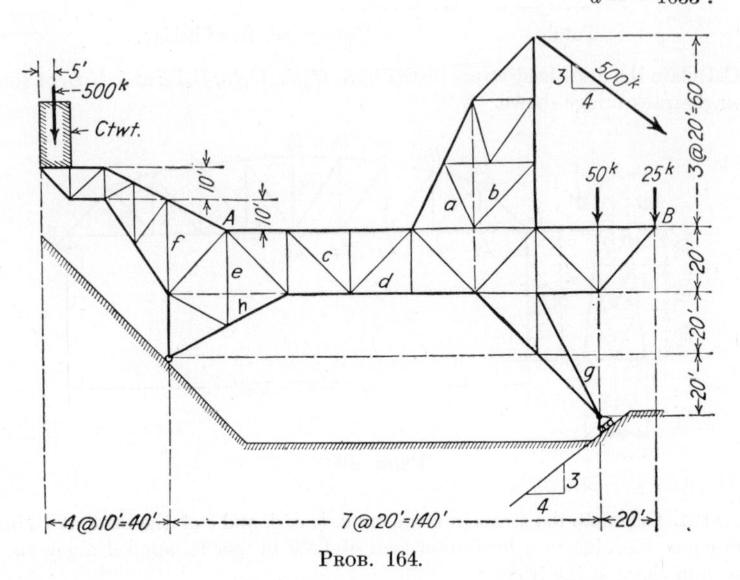

PROB. 164.

165. Calculate the stress in bars e, f, g, and h of the structure shown in Problem 164.

166. Calculate the stress in the members U_6U_8, L_6L_8, U_6L_6, U_6M_7, and M_7L_8. Load = 3600 lb. per ft. of bridge: one-third at top chord panel points and two-thirds at bottom.

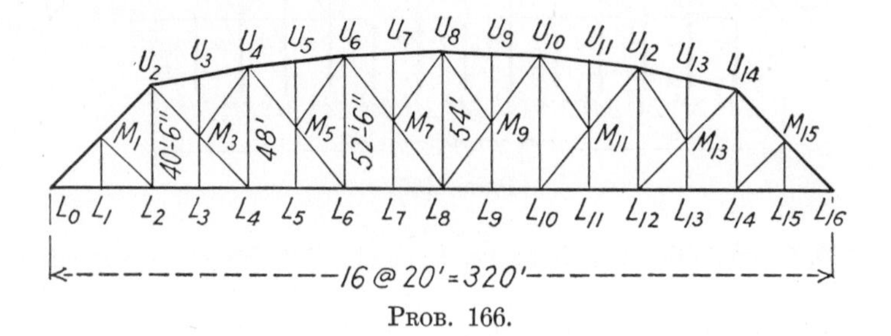

PROB. 166.

167. Calculate the stress in bars a, b, c, and d of the structure.

Ans. $a = +\,52.7^k$.
$b = 0$.
$c = -\,61.3^k$.
$d = +\,61.3^k$.

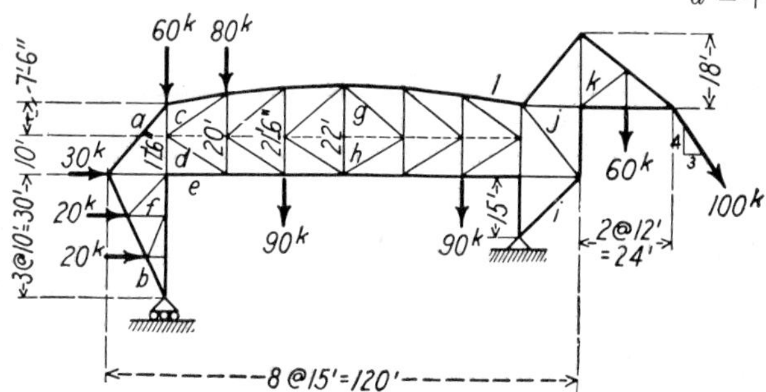

Prob. 167.

168. Calculate the stress in bars e, f, g, and h of the structure shown in Problem 167.

169. Calculate the stress in bars i, j, k, and l of the structure shown in Problem 167.

170. Calculate the stresses in a, b, and c.

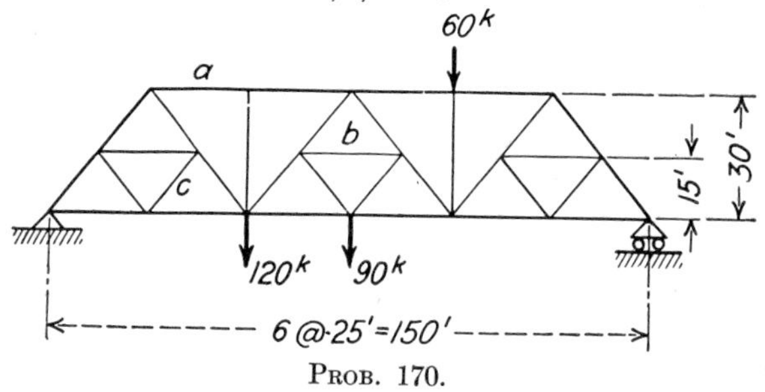

Prob. 170.

171. Calculate the stresses in a, b, c, and d.

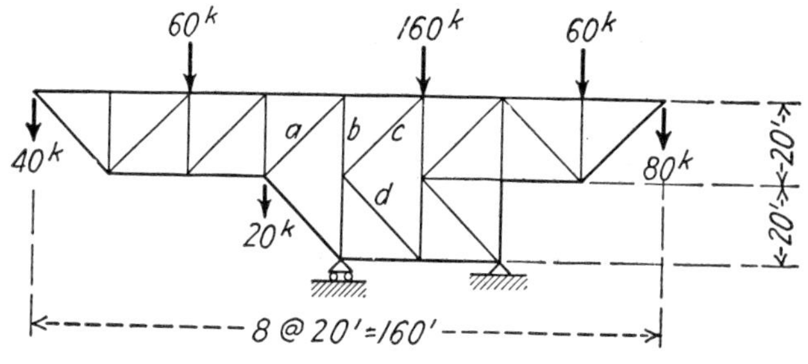

Prob. 171.

172. Write the index stresses for the structure shown. Each top chord panel point supports a load of 12.5^k, and each bottom chord panel point a load of 27.5^k.

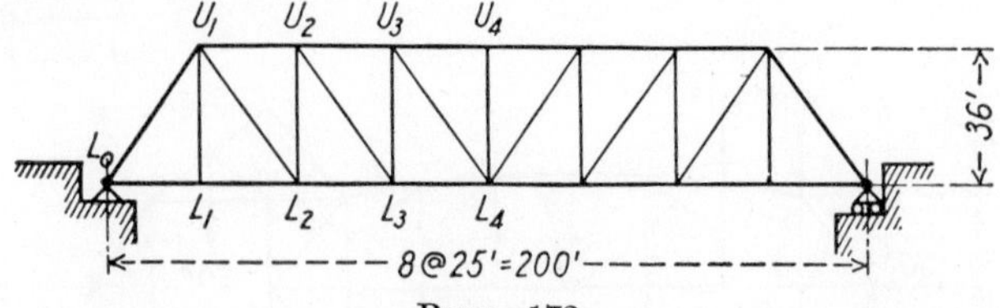

PROB. 172.

173. A through Warren truss with verticals has 8 panels of 28 ft. each and is 40 ft. deep center to center of chords. Write the index stresses for loads of 16^k at each top chord joint and 32^k at each bottom chord joint.

174. Write the index stresses for the truss shown in Problem 142 (*b*), due to loads of 10^k at each top chord joint and 3^k at each bottom chord joint.

175. Determine by means of index stress the dead load stresses in all the bars of the truss. The dead loads are to be taken as follows:

Track	=	600 lb. per ft.
Floor	=	500
Trusses and bracing	=	1900
Total	=	3000 lb. per ft. of bridge.

Assume that one-third of the load is applied at the top chord and two-thirds at the bottom chord.

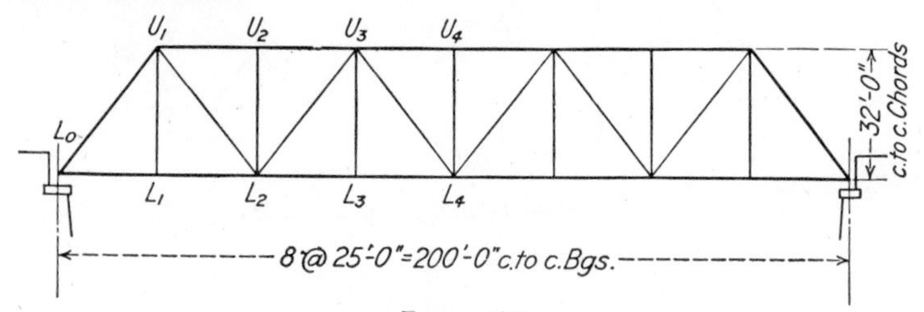

PROB. 175.

176. Write the index stresses for the structure shown, for a uniform fixed load of 4^k per ft. of truss, all applied on the bottom chord.

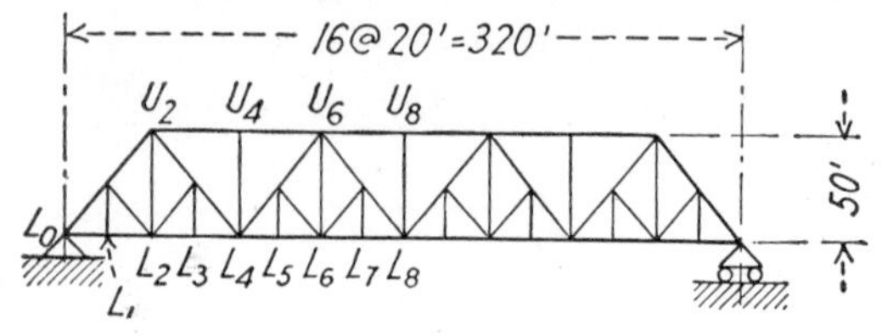

PROB. 176.

177. Given top chord panel loads of 1^k and bottom chord panel loads of 2^k for the truss, write index stresses.

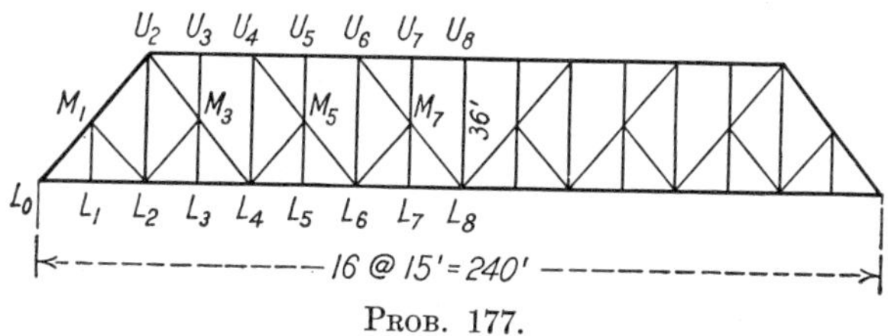

PROB. 177.

178. Write the index stresses for the loads shown.

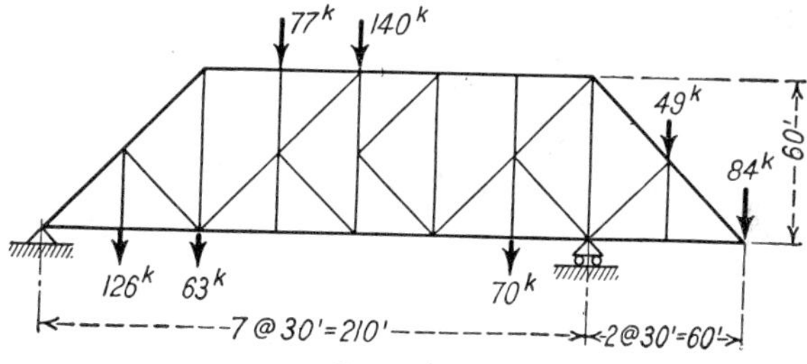

PROB. 178.

CHAPTER VII

GRAPHIC STATICS

96. Graphic Statics is the term commonly applied to the general procedure used in the solution of problems in statics by means of geometric constructions. Graphic statics is not a separate science nor a separate branch of the science of statics, but merely the substitution of the methods of graphical calculation for those of simple arithmetic and geometry. The fundamental laws of statics remain the same, and the use of graphical methods of calculation adds nothing to and subtracts nothing from their range of application.

In engineering work many problems in statics arise in which graphic methods of calculation are quicker and more convenient than those of arithmetic. For example, it will generally be found simplest to determine graphically:

(*a*) The stresses in non-parallel chord trusses supporting fixed loads, such as:

the common types of simple roof trusses;
roof arches;
steel centering for concrete arch construction, etc.

(*b*) The dead load stresses in non-parallel or polygonal chord bridge trusses.

(*c*) The stresses due to unit loads or unit reactions, necessary in certain calculations in connection with deflection studies and indeterminate structures.

On the other hand, it will seldom be found worth while to calculate graphically the stresses in any parallel chord truss, whether the loads are fixed or not, or the shears, moments or stresses resulting from moving loads in any structure. Nor does it seem likely that many engineers would care to determine the wind stresses in a high building by graphical methods.

Between these extremes lie many cases in which the choice between graphic and arithmetic methods of calculation is largely a matter of personal preference or immediate convenience, i.e., in such cases the choice may depend on whether the engineer does or does not like to calculate graphically, or on whether he does or does not have immediately at hand and in use the necessary drawing equipment.

It is important for the student to have a thorough understanding of the fundamental methods of graphical analysis, not only because of their usefulness in engineering work, but also because they form part of the language used by engineers in technical literature and discussions. Furthermore, a simple free-hand sketch outlining a procedure for a graphical analysis may often indicate an easier arithmetical solution; many, if not most, engineers use elementary graphical methods in this manner more or less unconsciously as an aid in thinking.

Only the fundamental methods of graphical analysis, as applied to statics, will be discussed in this chapter; nevertheless a thorough grasp of the material given here will enable the reader to use it as a convenient tool, to easily understand and use the elaborations presented in larger texts devoted exclusively to graphical analysis, if and when such elaborations offer any advantage, or to develop for himself more advanced methods especially adapted to the problems he is particularly concerned with.

The treatment in this text will be restricted to forces acting in a plane. Graphical methods may be extended to space statics, and, although space statics will not be specifically considered in what follows, it is important for the student to remember that if any system of forces in space is in equilibrium its projection on any plane must form a system of forces, acting in that plane, which is also in equilibrium. All problems in space statics can be solved as a series of problems in plane statics — either graphically or arithmetically — after being so projected.

97. Fundamental Principles.—The application of graphical methods of calculation to problems in statics rests on three fundamental principles already known to the student. These are:

First: A force may be represented by a line; the length of which, to some scale, represents the magnitude of the force; and the direction of which shows the direction of the line of action of the force in the plane. In order to have the force fully defined it is necessary also to know the location of its line of action in the plane.

Second: Two intersecting forces may be combined into a single force, usually called their resultant, by means of the parallelogram or triangle of forces.

Third: Any three non-parallel forces acting in a plane must, if they are in equilibrium, pass through a common point.

It is necessary, of course, in the development of graphical methods to extend these principles, draw corollaries from them, and in some cases to introduce additional considerations, but these three facts are fundamental and should be clearly understood.

98. Graphical Representation of a Force.—The representation of a force by a line is illustrated by Fig. 112 (*a*), which shows a beam acted on by a single force P and held in equilibrium by

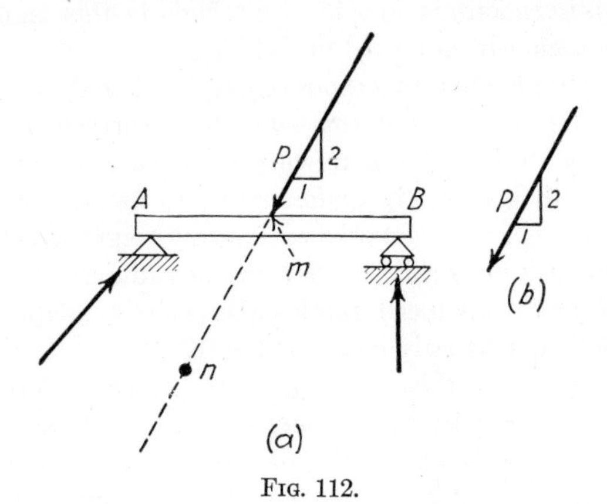

FIG. 112.

reactions at A and B. As stated above, the magnitude of this force is given by the length of the line representing it. If the force has a magnitude of 120^k and a scale of 1 in. = 100^k is to be used, the length of the line must be 1.2 in. The direction of the force is given by the slope of the line, shown as 2 to 1, and by the arrow-head indicating action down and to the left. This, however, is not sufficient fully to determine the force, since any line drawn in the plane at a slope of 2 to 1, having a length of 1.2 in. and an arrow-head pointing down and to the left will give this information. The line shown in Fig. 112 (*b*), for example, is parallel to P in Fig. 112 (*a*), has the same length and an arrow-head pointing in the same direction; it does not convey the information that this force is acting on the beam AB, and this fact can only be given by the location of the *point of application*, m, or the location of some other point on the *line of action*, such as n.

99. Parallelogram and Triangle of Forces.—The second fundamental principle is illustrated in Fig. 113, (a) and (b). P_1 and P_2 represent two loads applied to the beam AB. The lines of action of these forces, if extended, will intersect at the point m. In accordance with the principle of the parallelogram of forces, we may combine these two loads into a single load which will have the same effect on the reactions of the beam AB, by laying off from their intersection point, m, along the lines of action of P_1 and P_2, lengths mc and md, representing, respectively, the magnitudes of these forces, and completing the parallelogram $mcnd$ by

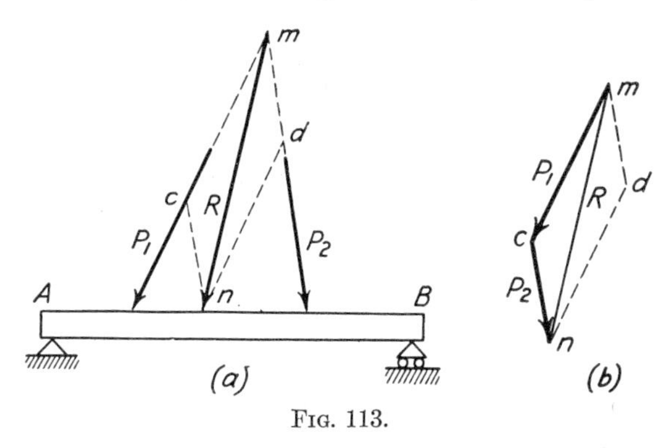

FIG. 113.

drawing cn parallel to md and dn parallel to mc. mn then represents, in magnitude, direction, and line of action, a single force R (the resultant of P_1 and P_2) which will have the same effect on the reactions of the beam AB as the forces P_1 and P_2.

It should be clear that it is not necessary that this parallelogram be constructed at the actual intersection of the lines of action of the forces P_1 and P_2: it may be constructed anywhere in the plane of the forces, as indicated at (b) in Fig. 113. Furthermore it should be clear that the resultant R may be obtained by constructing only half of the parallelogram of forces as shown by the full lines in Fig. 113 (b); this is the triangle of forces.

The parallelogram or triangle of forces may be used to obtain the resultant of any number of forces acting in a plane. For example, in Fig. 114 (a) is shown a beam subjected to forces P_1, P_2, P_3, and P_4. As shown at (a) in Fig. 114 the forces P_1 and P_2

may be extended to an intersection at e and there combined into a single force R_1 by means of either the parallelogram or triangle of forces. The resultant of P_1 and P_2 may then be extended to an intersection with P_3 at f and there combined with P_3 into a single force R_2. Similarly, the force R_2 may then be extended to an intersection with P_4 at g and there combined with P_4 to form R_3, a single force which will have the same horizontal component, the same vertical component, and the same moment about any point in the plane of forces as will be found from the algebraic sum of

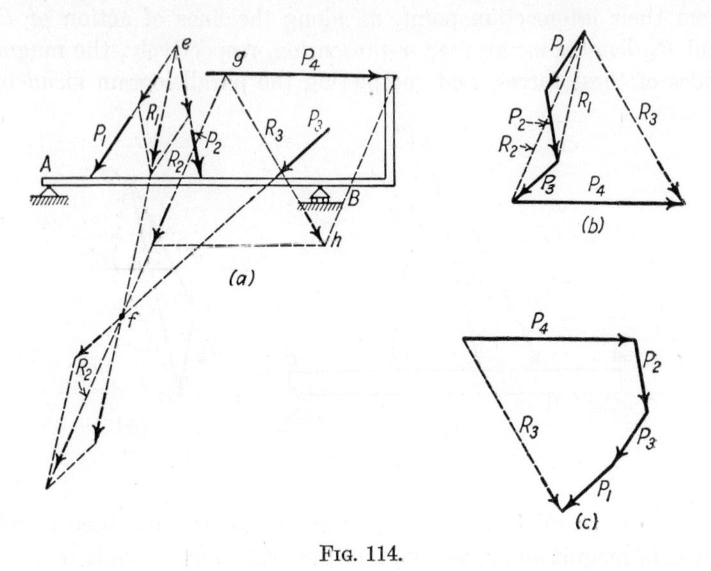

Fig. 114.

the horizontal components, vertical components, and moments of the forces P_1, P_2, P_3, and P_4.

Although it will usually be convenient to combine a series of forces in some definite order, such as in succession passing around the structure in either a clockwise or counter-clockwise direction, it is important for the student to see clearly that no particular order is necessary. For example, in Fig. 114 (a), P_4 may be extended to an intersection with P_2 and combined with it to form a single force which may in turn be extended to an intersection with either P_1 or P_3, a new combination effected, and so on until the entire system has been replaced by a single force. A little study should make it clear that, regardless of the order in which the forces are combined, the single force finally obtained must always be the same in magnitude, direction, and line of action, since there can be only one force having exactly the same effect on the body or structure as a whole as the original system.

It is unnecessary to make the various combinations of forces at their actual intersection points. As in the case shown in Fig. 113, the forces may be combined in a separate diagram. As shown at (*b*) in Fig. 114, P_1 and P_2 may be combined into R_1, which may be combined with P_3 into R_2, and finally R_2 and P_4 may be combined into R_3. The resulting diagram is called the **force diagram** or **force polygon.** As constructed in Fig. 114 (*b*), the force polygon consists of a series of force triangles. A little study of this figure should show clearly that it is not necessary to determine the intermediate resultants R_1 and R_2, but that the final resultant R_3 may be determined directly by laying off the various forces end to end, being careful of course to draw the lines representing the various forces exactly parallel to their respective lines of action.

The force polygon in Fig. 114 (*b*) was constructed taking the forces in order in a clockwise direction around the structure, and in (*c*) is shown the resultant R_3 determined from a force polygon drawn taking the forces at random.

Although the magnitude and direction of the resultant of the forces P_1 to P_4, inclusive, may be determined by means of a force polygon, as at (*b*) or (*c*) in Fig. 114, this polygon will not fix the location of the resultant in the plane, i.e., a point on its line of action. To find the position of the resultant R_3 we may follow the procedure first used in finding its magnitude, except that the parallelograms drawn in (*a*) for the determination of R_1, R_2, and R_3 are not necessary. That is, having drawn P_1 and P_2 to their intersection at *e*, we may draw through *e* a line parallel to R_1, its direction being taken from the force polygon in (*b*); from the intersection of this line with the line of action of P_3 at *f* draw a line parallel to R_2 (the direction of which may also be taken from the force polygon in (*b*)) to an intersection with P_4 at *g*, which is a point on the line of action of the resultant R_3. The resulting figure will be exactly the same as (*a*) in Fig. 114, omitting the lines drawn to form the parallelograms there used. Drawing a separate force polygon to give the magnitude and direction of the resultant, and finding its position as just described, will usually be more convenient than drawing several separate parallelograms as was done at (*a*). This method must be modified, however, when forces are parallel, or nearly so, and this will be discussed later.

100. Division of a Force into Components.—It is sometimes convenient to reverse the procedure just discussed, i.e., to change a single force into two or more forces which will have the same effect on the structure as a whole. The two or more forces which are to take the place of the original force are called its **components,** and the procedure itself is called the **resolution** of forces, or resolving a force into its components. In a force triangle any two sides may be thought of as components of the other side. Evidently any force may be resolved into two components by drawing, from the extremities of the line which represents it, lines parallel to the directions in which the required components are to act. For example, the force P, Fig. 115, may be resolved into vertical and horizontal components by drawing a vertical line through A to an intersection at C with a horizontal line drawn through B. Furthermore, it should be evident that there are an infinite number of pairs of components into which the force P may be resolved. Since the H and V components together with the force P form a force triangle (this would be true for any other pair of components), it is easy to see that the components acting together must have the same effect on the body or structure as a whole as the original force P, *provided they intersect at some point on the line of action of* P. It is very important to understand clearly the necessity for the intersection of the components at some point on the line of action of the original force, and it may be illustrated by referring again to Fig. 113, (*a*) and (*b*). If we choose to do so the force triangle in (*b*) may be looked upon as the resolution of the force R into components P_1 and P_2, instead of their combination into R. It is then clear by inspection that P_1 and P_2 together will have the same effect horizontally and vertically as R, and the only additional condition of equivalence is that the sum of their moments about any point in the plane must be the same as the moment of R about

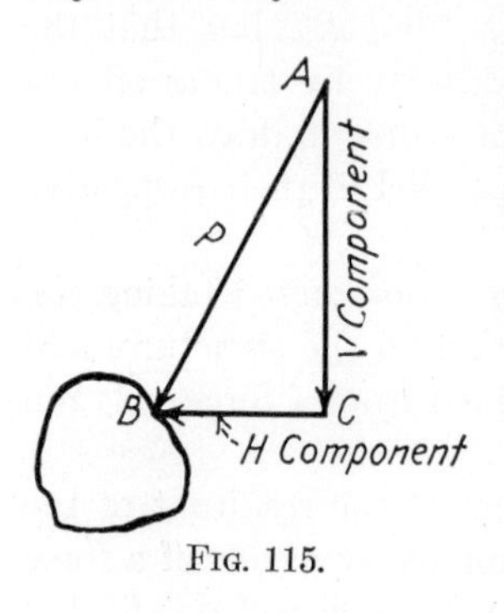

Fig. 115.

that point. Reference to (*a*) will show at once that this can be true only if P_1 and P_2 intersect at some point on the line of action of R, for at whatever point P_1 and P_2 intersect we may combine them into a single force which will have the same magnitude and direction as R and which must coincide with its line of action in order to have the same moment about any point.

101. Use of Substitute Forces.—As stated above in Art. 99, when the forces acting on a body or structure are parallel, or so nearly so that they will not intersect on the drawing, the method

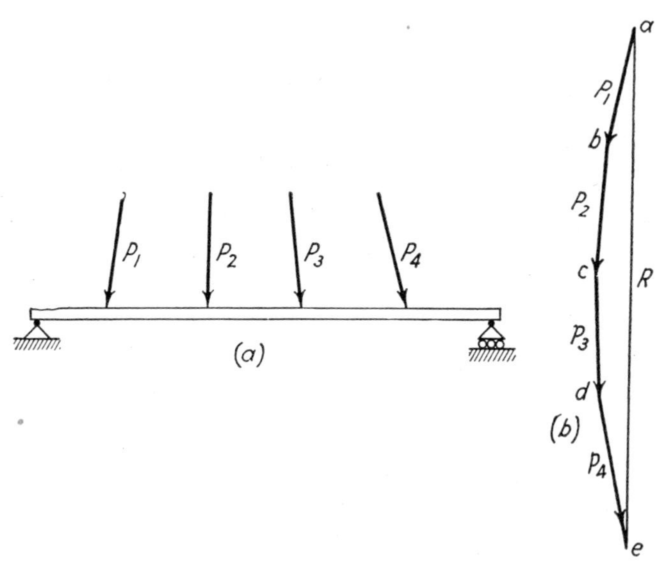

Fig. 116.

of finding the position of the resultant already described must be modified.

In Fig. 116 (*a*) is shown a beam acted on by several forces which are so nearly parallel that it would be impracticable to find the location of their resultant as in Art. 99. At (*b*) is drawn the force polygon determining the resultant, R, of all the forces. It is the location of the line of action of this resultant which we now wish to consider.

Using the principle of the previous article, we may resolve any one of the forces acting on the beam into two components making a pronounced angle with each other and the rest of the forces, and in this way obtain a new but equivalent series of forces which will intersect within the limits of the paper. Making such a substitution for P_1, the new system of forces acting on the beam is shown in Fig. 117 (*a*), and at (*b*) is shown the corresponding force polygon in full lines. The directions of the components of P_1 (1 and 2) may be drawn at random, except that fairly abrupt angles of intersection with the remaining forces are desirable. In accordance with the principle of the previous article, the components of P_1 must intersect at some point on its line of action, and they are introduced at the point *m*. We may now proceed to combine

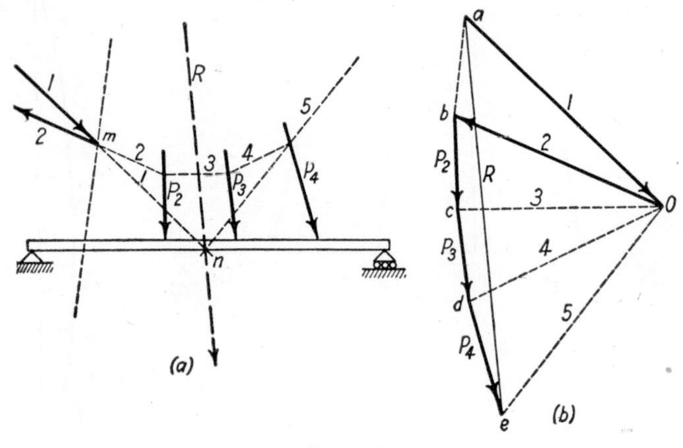

FIG. 117.

the forces as previously described, either at their actual intersection points or in a separately drawn force polygon; the latter procedure has been chosen here. The line of action of the force 2 is extended to an intersection with the line of action of P_2, from which point the line of action of the resultant of 2 and P_2 (which is evidently parallel to 3 in the force polygon) is drawn to its intersection with P_3. At the latter point *Oc* is combined with P_3 and the line of action of their resultant (4 in the force polygon) extended to intersect P_4, which is then combined with 4 to form 5. We have now reduced the system to the forces 1 and 5 which the force polygon shows clearly to be components of *R*, the resultant of the original forces P_1, P_2, P_3, and P_4. It should be evident that this resultant must act through the intersection of its components, or the point n, and of course parallel to R in the force polygon.

It is important to see clearly that any force in the system could have been replaced as well as P_1. For example, 2 and 3 could have been considered as replacing P_2, 3 and 4 as replacing P_3, or 1 and 5 as replacing R. Evidently exactly the same result would have followed.

The use of auxiliary or substitute forces, which has just been described, is a very useful device in graphical calculations, and the student should be careful to gain a thorough understanding of the procedure. The point at which the substitute forces intersect, O in Fig. 117 (b), is generally referred to as the **pole.**

The diagrams shown in (a) of Figs. 114 and 117 are commonly called **space diagrams** whereas the polygon shown in (a) of Fig. 117 and composed of the forces, 1, 2, 3, 4, and 5, is usually called the **string polygon** or **equilibrium polygon.** Other names are used, but those given are preferred by the authors; in what follows, the terms space diagram and string polygon or equilibrium polygon will be used with the meaning here given. The line of forces in the force polygon (a–b–c–d–e in [b] of Fig. 117) is often called the **load line.**

102. Center of Gravity.—Use may be made of this method of locating the resultant of a series of forces in finding the center of gravity of an irregular area. For example, consider the figure shown in Fig. 118 (a). The area has been divided into a triangle A_1 and two rectangles A_2 and A_3, the centers of gravity of which may be easily located. If we assume applied at the center of gravity of each of these areas a vertical force proportional to the area, it seems clear that the line of action of the resultant of this series of forces passes vertically through the center of gravity of the entire figure. In (b) of Fig. 118 is the force polygon for the vertical forces, and just above the figure in (a), the equilibrium polygon which determines the line m–n as the line of action of the resultant of the three forces A_1, A_2, and A_3. In a similar manner, if the forces proportional to the elementary areas are applied horizontally through the respective centers of gravity, the line of action of the resultant of this horizontal system of forces must pass horizontally through the center of gravity of the whole figure. In (c) is shown the force polygon and at the right of (a) the equilibrium polygon which establishes the line p–q as the line of action of the resultant of the horizontal system of forces. The center of gravity of the figure must, then, be at the intersection of the lines m–n and p–q as indicated.

The student should see clearly that it is not *necessary* that the two systems of forces be taken at right angles to each other. They

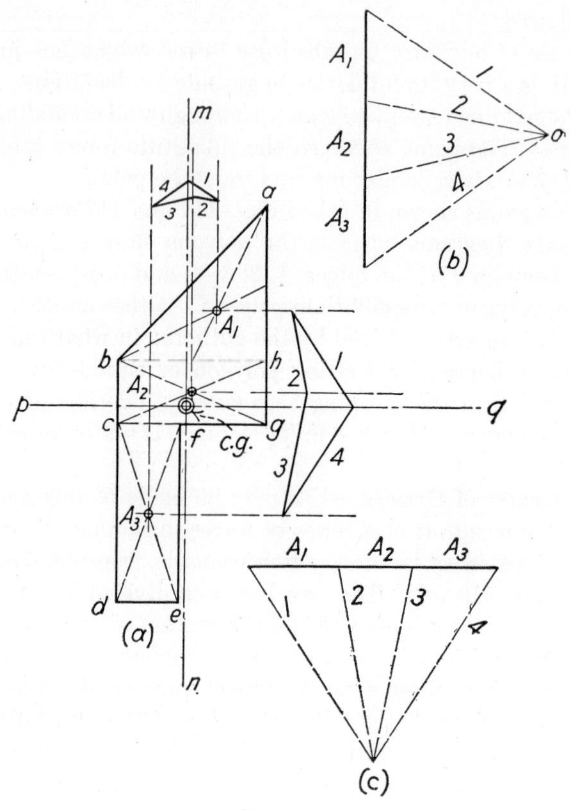

Fig. 118.

are, however, usually so taken as a matter of convenience in construction.

103. Equilibrium.—Since we are concerned primarily with the application of graphical methods of calculation to problems in statics it is necessary that we consider carefully how we may determine whether the laws of statics have or have not been satisfied. These laws of course remain the same:

$$\Sigma H = 0$$

$$\Sigma V = 0$$

and

$$\Sigma M = 0$$

are still the three conditions of equilibrium which must be fulfilled.

Consider first the case of a single force acting on a beam as shown in Fig. 112 (*a*). It seems obvious that the force P can be held in equilibrium by a force equal in magnitude and opposite in direction, provided its line of action coincides with that of P. The first two requirements evidently satisfy the first two laws of statics. It should be clear, however, that *any* force parallel to P, having equal magnitude and opposite direction, will satisfy these two laws, and that equilibrium can be obtained only if the line of action of the force holding P in equilibrium coincides with the line of action of P, thus satisfying the third law of statics.

The force P may also be held in equilibrium by any system of forces which can be combined into a single force equal in magnitude, opposite in direction, and of coincident line of action. The reactions at A and B evidently must form such a system if the beam is in equilibrium. Since these two forces may be combined into a single force equal and opposite to P and having the same line of action it is clear that they must intersect each other on the line of action of P, and thus illustrate the principle previously stated, that if three non-parallel forces are in equilibrium they must intersect in a common point. It should be clear that if three forces which meet in a common point are in equilibrium any two of them may be combined into a single force equal and opposite to the third.

Consider now the forces acting on the beam shown in Fig. 114 (*a*). Since a force R_3, which may be found in magnitude and direction as in (*b*) or (*c*), will have the same effect on the structure as a whole as the forces P_1, P_2, P_3, and P_4, if it acts along the line R_3 in (*a*), a force *equal and opposite* to R_3, will hold these forces in equilibrium provided it also acts along the line of R_3 in (*a*).

The reader should see clearly that any force parallel to R_3, having the same magnitude, and acting in the *opposite* direction, will, in combination with the forces P_1 to P_4, inclusive, satisfy the first two laws of statics. If such a force acts in the plane of the other forces we may call it P_5 and add it to the force polygon shown in (*b*) [or (*c*)] of Fig. 114. This polygon will then be as shown in Fig. 119 (*b*), and it should be obvious by inspection that the sum of the horizontal components of all the forces in the polygon, as well as the sum of their vertical components, is equal to zero.

It should be noted also that the forces P_1 to P_5, inclusive, form a closed figure with the forces all acting in the same direction (counter-clockwise) around the figure. Brief consideration of any force polygon will make it clear that whenever the last force is equal and opposite to the resultant of the rest of the forces this will always be true, and there follows at once the general statement: **If a system of forces acting on a body or structure is in equilibrium**

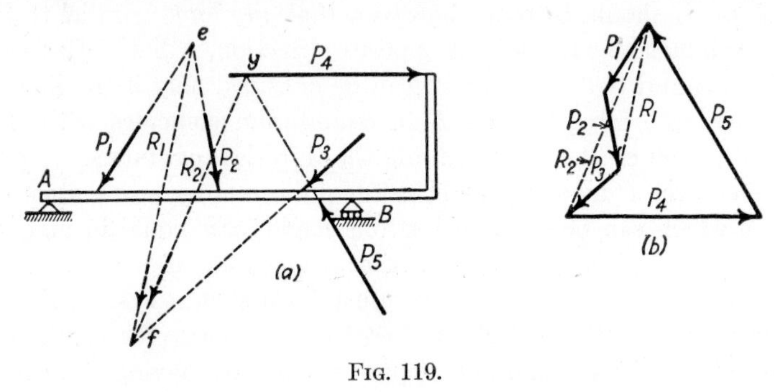

FIG. 119.

a polygon drawn to include all the forces, taken in any order, will form a closed figure, and the forces will all act in one direction around that figure.

Closing of the force polygon is an essential condition of equilibrium, but, except for a series of forces meeting at a common point, it does not alone establish equilibrium as a fact. The first two laws of statics have been satisfied when the force polygon closes, but the third law, $\Sigma M = 0$, cannot be satisfied unless the line of action of the last force in the system coincides with the line of action of the resultant of all the other forces — the direction of the last force must of course be opposite to that of the resultant of the rest of the forces. This is perfectly general and has already been illustrated in what precedes. In the discussion above, P_5 has been taken as the last force in the system, but since the force polygon closes, any one of the forces may be considered as holding the rest in equilibrium and as being the last force in the system. It will be well for the reader to call some other force, say P_2 or P_3, the last force and go through the reasoning for that case.

The student should very carefully note that the system of forces in the space diagram reduced to three forces meeting in a common point — R_2, P_4, and P_5 meeting at g Fig. 119 (a). As noted above, these three may be further reduced to two equal, opposite, and coincident forces — R_2 and P_5 may be combined into one force equal and opposite to and coincident with P_4 — P_4 and P_5 may be combined into a force equal and opposite to and coincident with R_2 — or any other combination of two of the three forces made.

104. Equilibrium of Forces Which Are Parallel or Nearly Parallel.—Although the discussion above was based on a system of forces intersecting within a narrow area, the line of reasoning applies equally well to a system of parallel, or nearly parallel, forces. For example, consider the forces acting on the beam in Figs. 116 and 117. These forces will not intersect within a convenient area, but substituting the equivalent forces 1 and 2 for P_1 results in a system in which exactly the same reasoning may be followed. Replacing R in Fig. 117, (a) and (b), by an equal and opposite force P_5, we find that the force polygon closes and that all the forces act around the closed figure in a counter-clockwise direction. Also we find in the space diagram that the system may be considered as reduced to three forces meeting in a common point. These three forces may be taken as 1, 5, and P_5; 2, 3, and P_2; or any one of several other combinations.

105. Application of Principles Discussed.—With the principles discussed before well in mind the application of graphical calculation to the determination of reactions, moments, stresses, etc., follows very directly.

As stated before, graphical methods cannot add to the range of application of the laws of statics. It follows therefore that not more than three unknown quantities may be found in any case, and that if all the forces to be dealt with meet in a common point, only two unknown quantities may be found.

106. Reactions.—The application of graphical methods to the determination of reactions may now be discussed in connection with problems previously considered.

The beam shown in Fig. 112 is repeated here as Fig. 120 and

the reactions determined graphically. There are in this case only three forces acting on the beam, and if the structure is to be in equilibrium they must meet in a common point. The rollers at B fix the direction of R_2 as vertical, and the hinge at B fixes a point on its line of action. Therefore a vertical line drawn through the hinge at B intersecting the line of action of the force P at e locates the common point and determines the direction of R_1, which must pass through the hinge at A as well as point e. In the force polygon shown in (b) lines drawn from the extremities of P parallel to the now known directions of R_1 and R_2 complete

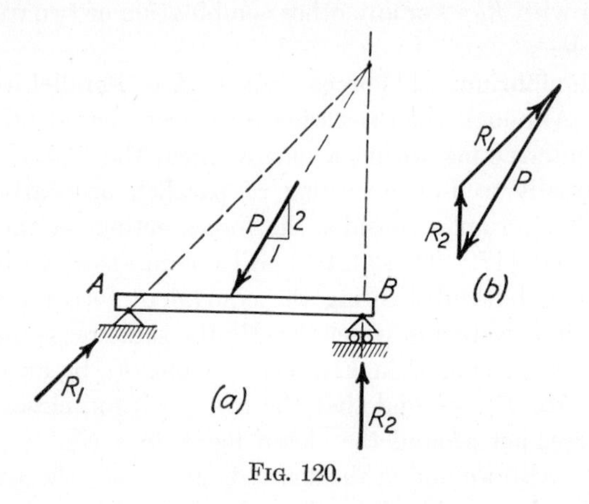

FIG. 120.

the force polygon and determine the magnitude of these reactions. It is evidently immaterial whether the force polygon is completed by drawing R_2 from the lower end of P as was done in (b) Fig. 120, or by drawing it from the upper end. The student should see that in this case three unknowns have been determined: the magnitude of R_2, and the magnitude and direction of R_1. At the start it was known that R_2 must be vertical and must act through the hinge at B, and the hinge at A was known to be a point on the line of action of R_1.

The beam shown in Fig. 27 of Chapter II is reproduced here as Fig. 121 and the reactions found graphically. Here we know that the left reaction must be vertical and must pass through the hinge at this end; we do not know its magnitude. We know that the right reaction must pass through the hinge at the right end; we do not know its direction or its magnitude. In this case it is a simple matter to combine the two forces acting on the beam into a single force, which must pass through the point *e* and be parallel to the dotted line in the force polygon. The system of forces acting on the beam has now been reduced to three non-parallel forces, and as the resultant of the 700-lb. and 600-lb. loads makes a fairly abrupt inclination with the left reaction (which is known to

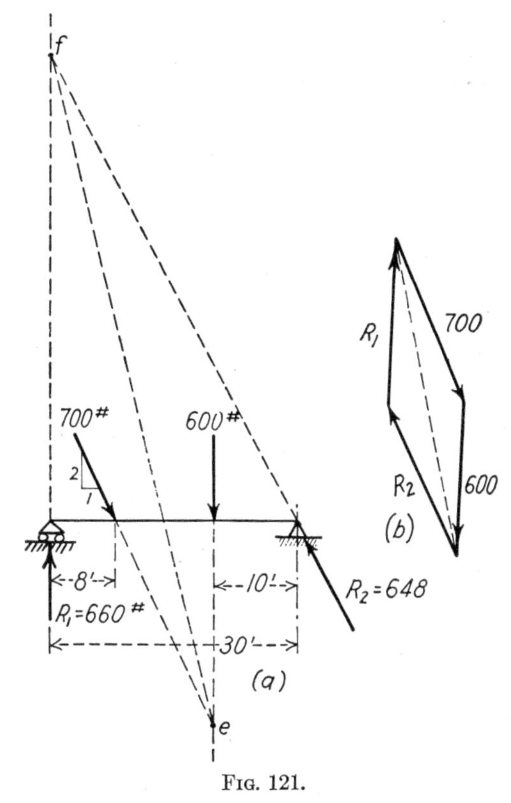

Fig. 121.

be vertical), it is easy to locate the point *f* through which the three forces must pass. The determination of the left and right reactions then follows directly as shown in the force polygon. As before it evidently makes no difference whether the lines representing reactions R_1 and R_2 are drawn from the upper and lower ends, respectively, of the dotted line in the force polygon, or the reverse.

If the forces acting on a beam or other structure are parallel or nearly parallel the method of substituting inclined components for one of the forces may be used.

To illustrate the use of this method in the determination of reactions refer again to the beam and forces shown in Fig. 117. In this figure the auxiliary forces 1 and 2 were substituted for P_1 and the line of action of the resultant R then determined by intersecting and combining the forces in the usual manner. The resultant R in magnitude and line of action having been found by means of the force polygon and equilibrium polygon, the system has been reduced to three forces in equilibrium, the two reactions R_1 and R_2 (their magnitudes yet to be determined), and the resultant of the applied loads, R. These forces, however, are so

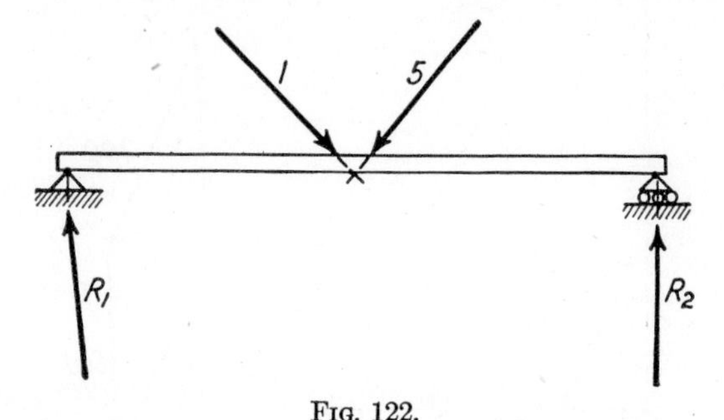

Fig. 122.

nearly parallel that they will not intersect within the area of the drawing, and it is necessary to substitute for one of them, components which make a pronounced angle with the other forces. We already have drawn in the force polygon the forces 1 and 5 which are components of the resultant of the forces P_1 to P_4, inclusive, and we may replace this resultant R by these components. When this substitution is made we have four forces acting on the beam, the two reactions R_1 and R_2 and the components of R, 1 and 5. These four forces are shown in Fig. 122, and it must be understood that although we know the direction of R_2 we do not yet know its magnitude, nor the magnitude and direction of R_1. These four may be reduced to three by combining two of them at their intersection. We have already found, however, that combining 1 and 5 results in three forces which are too nearly parallel to intersect within the area of the paper. It is therefore necessary to combine either 1 or 5 with R_1 or R_2. If we combine 1 (or 5) with R_2 we must then pass the resultant of these forces through the intersection of 5 (or 1) and R_1, but we do not know the line of action of R_1 and cannot therefore find the intersection of this force with either 1 or 5. It should be clear then that we must combine 1 (or 5) with R_1 and pass the resultant of these forces through the intersection of 5 (or 1) and R_2, which we can easily find since we know that the line of action of R_2 must be normal to the surface on which the rollers are supported and pass through the hinge at B. Since we are substituting the forces 1 and 2 for P_1, we must draw them through some point on the line of action of P_1, but it is immaterial where this point is taken so long as it

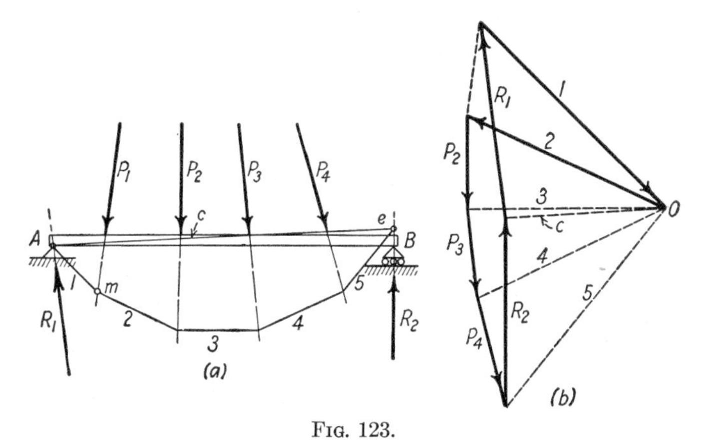

FIG. 123.

is in the line, and it will evidently be convenient to take it so that 1 will also pass through the hinge at A. In Fig. 123 (a) the string polygon is now drawn, the point m on the line of action of P_1 having been so chosen that its component 1 will also pass through the hinge at A. The system of forces then reduces to three non-parallel forces, 5, the reaction R_2, and the resultant of 1 and R_1. Since 5 and R_2 intersect at e the resultant of 1 and R_1 must pass through this point if the forces are to be in equilibrium, and its line of action therefore is the line c. Since c, 5, and R_2 are in equilibrium we may determine the magnitudes of c and R_2 by drawing lines parallel to them from the extremities of 5, as is done in the force polygon (b) of Fig. 123. Since c is the resultant of 1 and R_1 the force R_2 just determined must represent the reaction at B, and we may now determine the magnitude and direction of

R_1 by completing the force triangle 1–c–R_1. These values of R_1 and R_2 also complete the polygon of forces as originally applied to the entire structure. It should be clear that in determining the magnitude of R_2 the line parallel to R_2 may be drawn from either end of 5, and the line parallel to c from the other end, but since R_2 is one of the forces in the force polygon it will evidently

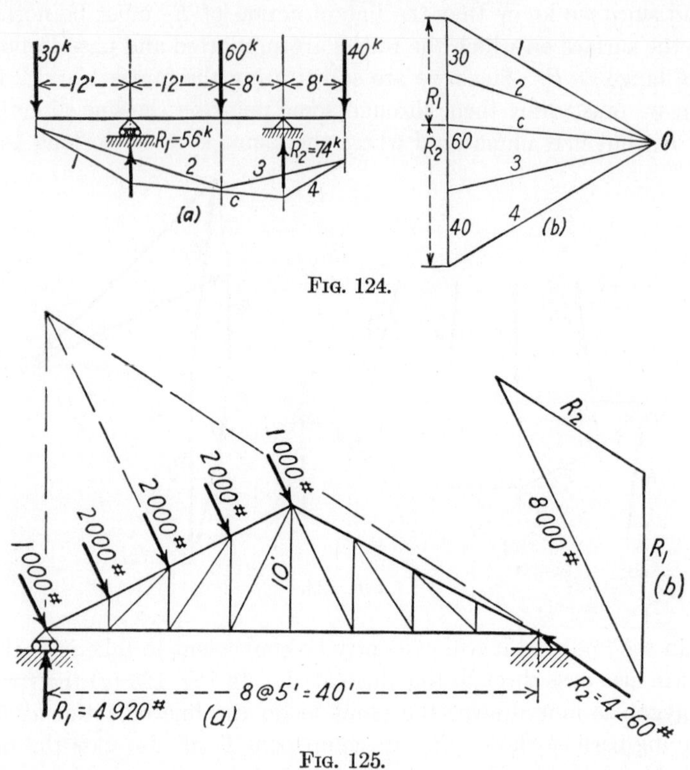

Fig. 124.

Fig. 125.

be more convenient to draw R_2 from the end of P_4, and c from the other end of 5. Then completing the triangle of forces composed of 1, c, and R_1 automatically completes the polygon of forces for the entire structure. This procedure of resolving 1 and R_1 into their resultant c which must pass through the point of intersection of R_2 and 5 is often called *closing the equilibrium polygon.*

The reaction problems solved arithmetically in Figs. 29, 31, 32, and 33 are solved graphically in Figs. 124, 125, 126, and 127 as illustrative examples.

107. Three-hinged Arch Reactions.—The structures shown in Figs. 34 and 36, Chapter II, have four unknown reactions, horizontal and vertical components at both A and C, and in the application of graphical calculation to the determination of these

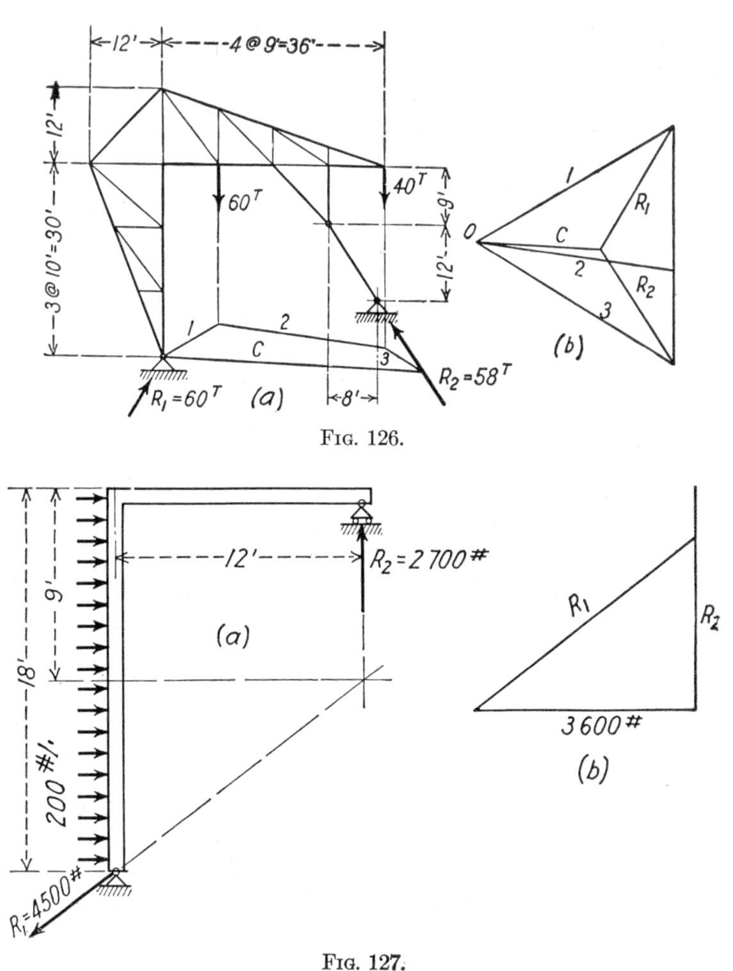

Fig. 126.

Fig. 127.

reactions use must be made of the fact that there cannot be any bending moment at the hinge at B. Two simple methods of determining the reactions for such structures will be discussed in connection with the arch of Fig. 36.

In Fig. 128 this arch is reproduced, showing in (*a*) the arch with the loads acting on the left side of the center hinge and in (*c*) the arch with the loads acting on the right side of the center hinge. It is a simple matter to find the resultant of the 120^k and 60^k forces shown in (*a*) and its line of action. The resultant of these forces is found in direction and magnitude by the force polygon in (*b*), and its line of action by means of the string polygon shown in (*a*). The forces then acting on the arch are the resultant of the 120^k and 60^k forces, which acts vertically through the point *d*, and the reactions at *A* and *C*. It should be clear that the reaction at *C*

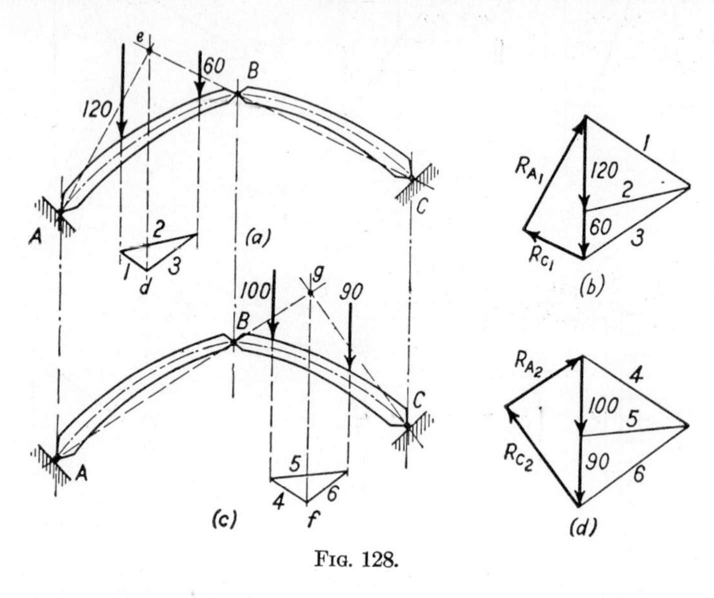

FIG. 128.

must not only pass through the hinge at *C* but also through the hinge at *B*, which determines its line of action. The three forces just mentioned are in equilibrium and therefore must meet in the common point *e*, the location of which is determined by the intersection of the lines of action of the resultant of 120^k and 60^k and the reaction at *C*. The line of action of the reaction at *A* is established by the fact that it must pass through the hinge at *A* and the common point *e*. The magnitude of the reactions at *A* and *C*, resulting from the loads shown in (*a*), may now be determined by drawing lines parallel to *Ae* and *Ce* from the ends of the load line as shown in (*b*). Proceeding in the same way, the reactions at A and C due to the loads of 100^k and 90^k acting on the right of the center hinge may be determined as shown in (c) and (d) of Fig. 128. Combining the reactions R_{A_1} and R_{A_2}, and R_{C_1} and R_{C_2}, will then give the true reactions at A and C due to all the loads acting on the arch.

The entire procedure, described above in two separate steps for clearness, may be combined into one diagram as shown in Fig. 129. In this figure the combination of the reactions R_{A_1}, R_{A_2}, and R_{C_1}, R_{C_2} into the true reactions R_A and R_C is also shown.

108. Equilibrium Polygon through Three Points.—If in Fig. 129 the reaction R_A is drawn through the hinge at A in the direction shown by the force polygon, it may be combined with the

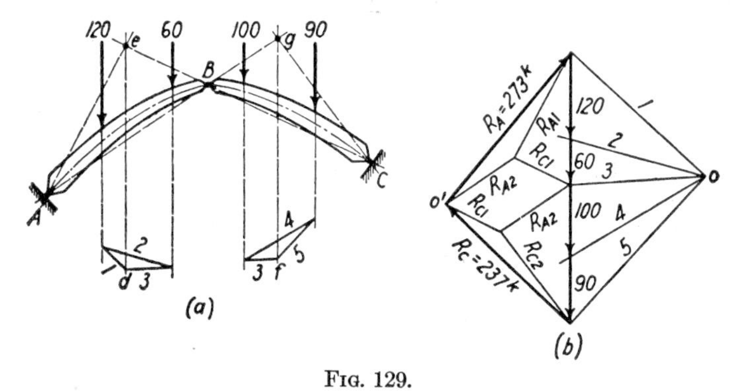

FIG. 129.

120^k load at their intersection. The resultant of these two forces will be given in magnitude and direction by a line connecting O' and the lower end of the 120^k load in the force polygon. The intersection of R_A and the 120^k load is a point on the line of action of their resultant, which may then be drawn through this point in the direction given by the force polygon to an intersection with the 60^k load. At this intersection the resultant of R_A and 120^k may be combined with the 60^k load into a new resultant, which will be given in magnitude and direction by a line connecting O' and the lower end of the 60^k load in the force polygon. In the same manner as before this new resultant may be extended to an intersection with the 100^k load and a new combination effected. This procedure may be continued until an equilibrium polygon has been constructed for the entire system of loads.

Since there can be no bending moment at the hinge at B, it should be clear that the resultant of the forces R_A, 120^k, and 60^k must pass through this hinge. And finally the resultant of the forces R_A, 120^k, 60^k, 100^k, and 90^k must pass through the hinge at C. In other words, the intersection of R_A and R_C locates a point O', which, taken as a pole, will pass the equilibrium polygon through the three points A, B, and C. Evidently when it is necessary to pass an equilibrium polygon through three points, the necessary pole may be found by determining in the above manner the reac-

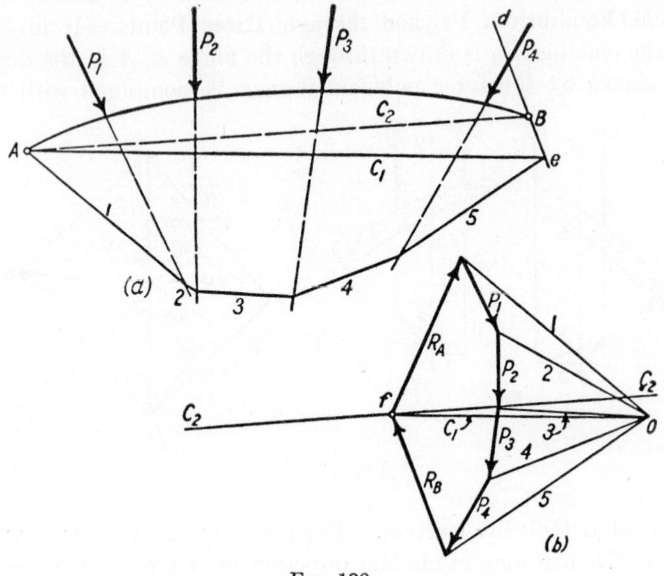

FIG. 130.

tions which would be developed by the given loads if applied to an arch of which the three points form the hinges.

A different method of passing an equilibrium polygon through three points, based on an extension of the procedure for passing such a polygon through two points, is often used.

In Fig. 130 (*a*) four forces are shown acting more or less at random. Suppose that we wish to pass an equilibrium polygon for these forces through the points A and B. Assume that the forces are acting on a beam supported at A and B in such a manner that the reaction at B must pass along the line d–e. Introducing the substitute forces 1 and 2, intersecting at O, construct the equilibrium polygon 1, 2, 3, 4, 5, and C_1 in the usual manner, finding the reactions R_A and R_B. In the equilibrium polygon, C_1 represents the line of action of the resultant of 1 and R_A, or it may be considered as the line of action of the resultant of 5 and R_B. If the equilibrium polygon passed through B as well as A, the resultant of R_A and 1 would necessarily pass through B. The reactions R_A and R_B are dependent only on the forces acting and the conditions of support and must be the same regardless of the location of the pole. Therefore the substitute forces must be so chosen that they will intersect on a line which passes through f in the force polygon parallel to C_2 in the space diagram. In other words, any point on the line C_2–C_2 in the force polygon, taken as a pole,

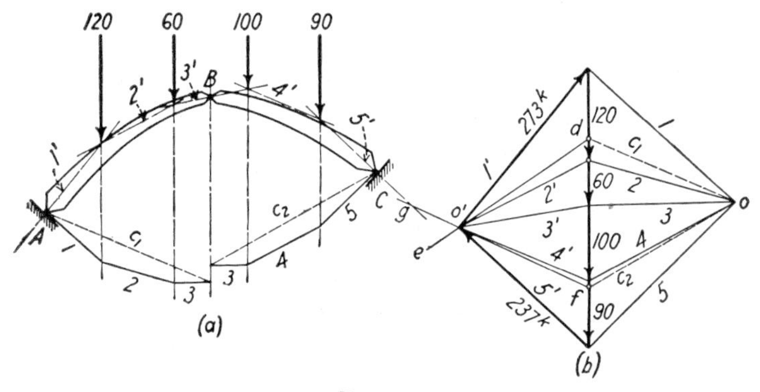

Fig. 131.

will pass an equilibrium polygon for the forces given through points A and B. From this it should be clear that an infinite number of equilibrium polygons for the forces P_1 to P_4, inclusive, may be passed through the points A and B. If the pole is chosen to the right of the load line the equilibrium polygon will evidently be concave upward as shown in (a), and concave downward if taken to the left.

In Fig. 131 this method is extended to determine the pole which will pass the equilibrium polygon for the forces shown through the three points A, B, and C. Proceeding in the manner just described, we find that a pole lying in the line d–e will pass an equilibrium polygon for the forces between A and B through A and B, and similarly that a pole lying on the line f–g will pass an equilibrium polygon for the forces between B and C through

B and C. It seems clear that if we take the intersection of these lines as a pole the equilibrium polygon will pass through A, B, and C, and furthermore that there can be only one polygon for these forces passing through these three points. Having found the pole $0'$, it follows directly that $1'$ and $5'$ are the reactions at A and C for a three-hinged arch supporting the loads shown, and that the equilibrium polygon $1'$, $2'$, $3'$, $4'$, and $5'$ shows the true line of thrust on the arch for the given loads.

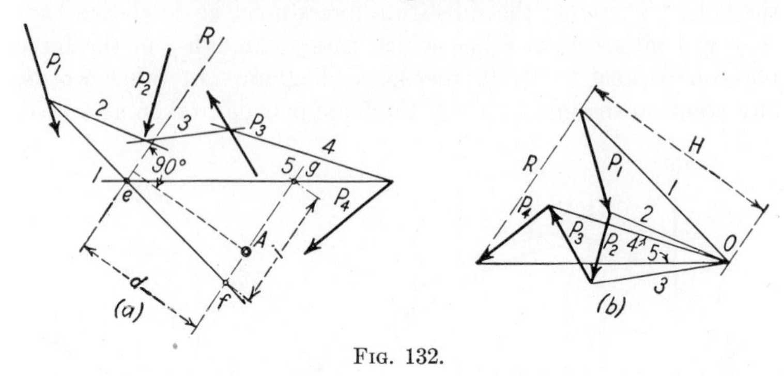

FIG. 132.

109. Bending Moments Determined Graphically.—In Chapter III, bending moment is defined as: "The algebraic sum of the moments of *all* the external forces acting on *either* side of the section taken about the center of gravity of the section." It follows that the algebraic sum of the moments of *all* the external forces acting on one side of the section is the moment of the *resultant* of those forces about the point in question. This fact is the basis of the common methods of calculating bending moments graphically, and as an introduction to the subject the moment of a group of forces about some point in their plane will be discussed.

In Fig. 132 (a) four forces, P_1 to P_4, inclusive, are shown acting in a common plane, and their moment about the point A is to be calculated. The force polygon is shown in Fig. 132 (b). Although it would be possible to determine the magnitude and direction of these forces by intersecting them and combining at their intersections, it would require considerable space, and the method of substitute forces has been used. Substitute forces 1 and 2 replace P_1 and the system is reduced to the resultant R. Its direction and magnitude are determined from the force polygon, and a point on its line of action is given by the intersection of 1 and 5 (components of R) in the space diagram. Measuring the perpendicular distance from the point A to the line of action of R in the space diagram and multiplying this *distance* by the magnitude of R, taken from the force polygon, at once gives the moment of all the forces (P_1 to P_4, inclusive) about A. In other words:

$$M_A = R \times d$$

This method of determining moments graphically is universally applicable and generally as easy as any other when the forces to be included are not parallel. For forces which are parallel, or nearly parallel, a method introduced by a Swiss engineer, Professor Carl Culmann of Zurich, is very convenient. This method is as follows:

In the space diagram (a) of Fig. 132, draw a line through the point A parallel to the resultant R in the force polygon and extend this line to an intersection with the lines of action (extended if necessary) of 1 and 5 at points f and g. The resulting triangle, efg, has its sides parallel to the sides of the triangle formed by R, 1, and 5 in the force polygon. These triangles are therefore similar and their altitudes and sides are proportional. Calling the perpendicular distance between the resultant, R, and the pole, O, in the force polygon, H, and the intercept which the lines of action of 1 and 5 in the space diagram cut from the line drawn through A parallel to R, i, the following proportion may be written:

$$\frac{\text{altitude of } efg}{\text{altitude of } R,\ 1,\ 5} = \frac{i}{R}$$

or

$$\frac{d}{H} = \frac{i}{R}$$

and

$$R \times d = H \times i$$

or since

$$M_A = R \times d$$

$$M_A = H \times i$$

The altitude H is generally referred to as the **pole distance,** and the distance i as the **intercept.** The above relation may then be stated in words as follows: The moment of any series of forces about a point, A, is equal to the product of the pole distance of the resultant of the forces and the intercept which the strings or forces of the equilibrium polygon determining the line of action of the resultant cut from a line drawn through A parallel to the resultant.

Culmann's method is perfectly general and may be applied to any number of forces, whether parallel or non-parallel, although, as previously stated, the direct method discussed above may be more or equally convenient for forces which are not parallel.

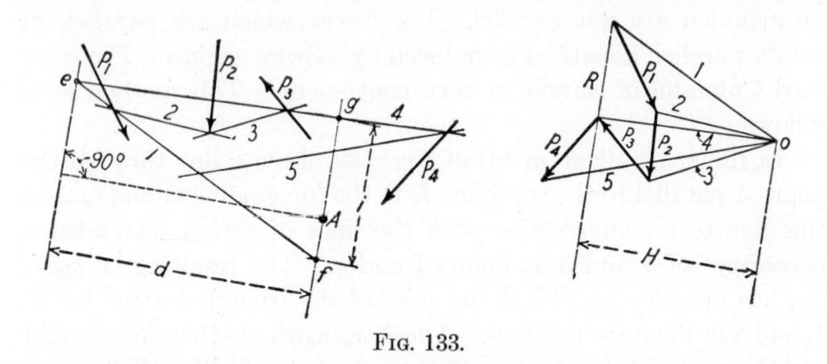

FIG. 133.

Figure 133 shows the same forces as Fig. 132 and the construction necessary to determine the moment of P_1, P_2, and P_3 about A.

The student should see that the *pole distance* is a *force*, the magnitude of which is fixed by the scale of the force polygon, and the *intercept* a *distance* measured to the scale of the space diagram.

Culmann's method of determining moments may be used in drawing bending moment diagrams for beams supporting vertical loads. In Fig. 134 is shown a beam supporting four loads, P_1, P_2, P_3, and P_4, with the force polygon and space diagram for the determination of the reactions R_1 and R_2. The bending moment at A is the moment of the resultant of R_1 and P_1. Inspection of the force polygon shows that the intersection of the substitute forces 2 and c will determine the location of this resultant in the space diagram. In accordance with the principles described above, drawing a vertical line through A determines the intercept i_A, and the bending moment at A then is:

$$M_A = H \times i_A$$

and similarly the bending moment at B is:

$$M_B = H \times i_B$$

Study of Fig. 134 should make it clear that the bending moment at any point in the beam shown is equal to the pole distance H times the intercept within the equilibrium polygon on a vertical line drawn through the point. In other words, ordinates in the bending moment diagram may be found by multiplying the corresponding ordinate in the equilibrium polygon by H. From this it follows that the moment diagram is proportional to the equilibrium polygon, and if the pole distance, H, is made some multiple of 10, the moment may be scaled directly from the equilibrium polygon using the scale of the space diagram with the proper change in the location of the decimal point. The same result may be obtained, of course, by using units of measure for the space diagram and force polygon such that their product may be measured with a commonly available scale. For example, suppose that the space diagram is so drawn that 1 in. = 20 ft. and the force diagram so that $H = 150^k$; then, since $150^k \times 20$ ft. per in. = 3000 ft.-kips per in., the equilibrium polygon may be considered the bending moment diagram to a scale of 3000 ft.-kips per in., and bending moments measured directly from the diagram with the readily available engineer's "30-scale."

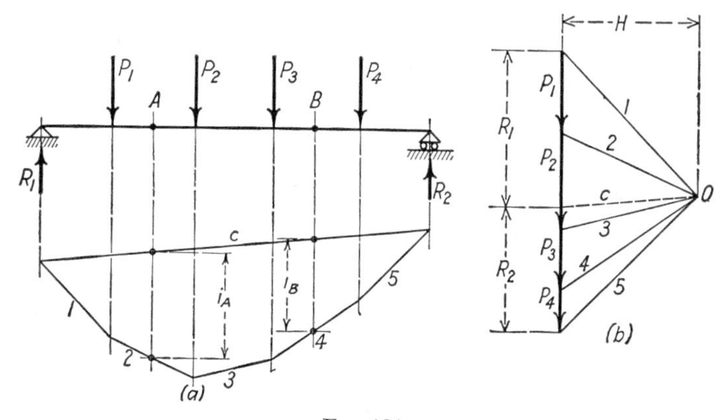

Fig. 134.

Bending moment diagrams for beams supporting a distributed

load (either uniform or varying) may be constructed graphically, using the method described above, by dividing the load up into short lengths, applying the total over each section at the center of gravity of the section, and then constructing the equilibrium polygon as usual for the resulting series of concentrated loads.

Figure 135 illustrates this procedure. The beam shown in this case supports a uniformly distributed load which is divided into ten equal sections. The moments determined from the equilibrium polygon will be exactly correct (within the limits of accuracy attainable by graphical methods) at the lettered sections. Between these sections the moments obtained from the construction shown will be in error by an amount equal to the difference

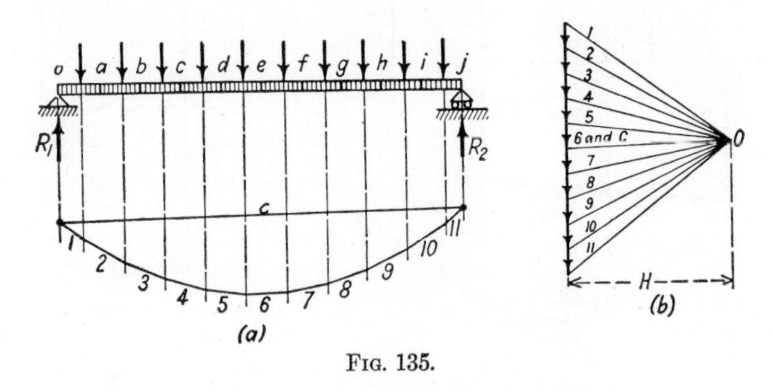

Fig. 135.

between the equilibrium polygon as drawn and an inscribed parabola tangent to the polygon at verticals drawn through the lettered sections — evidently inappreciable for the case given.

If it is sufficient to obtain the bending moment at only one or two points in a beam supporting a distributed load, it is not necessary to divide the load up into a series of concentrated loads and draw an equilibrium polygon. Figure 136 shows a beam AE supporting a distributed load from B to E. Assume that the bending moment at D is required and that the reactions have already been determined, considering the entire load concentrated at its center, by means of the force and equilibrium polygons shown. To determine the bending moment at D correctly, proceed as follows: Draw a vertical line through the center of gravity of the load between B and D and a vertical line through the center of gravity of the load between D and E. Connect the intersections of these lines with the segments 1 and 2 by the line b–e. Draw a vertical line through D; then the bending moment at this section is equal to the product of the pole distance and the intercept on the line through D, between c and b–e; i.e.,

$$M_D = H \times i_D$$

The student should demonstrate the correctness of this construction, which he is prepared to do if he has properly understood the preceding discussion of bending moments graphically determined.

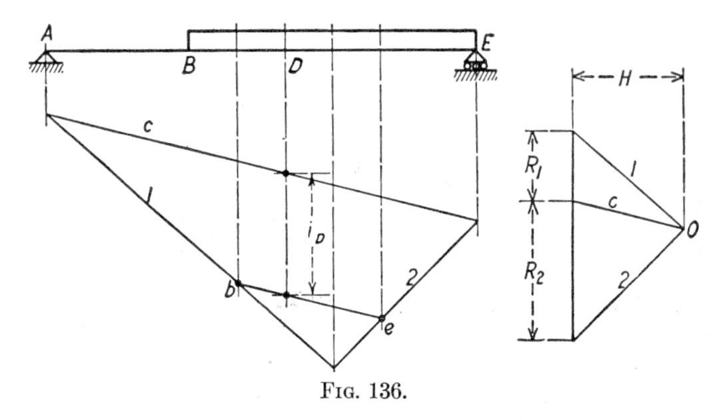

FIG. 136.

110. Moment of Inertia.—The graphical calculation of moments may be easily extended to include "second moments," or moment of inertia.

Three vertical forces, P_1, P_2, and P_3, are shown in Fig. 137, and it is proposed to calculate their moment of inertia graphically about a vertical axis through the point A. By definition the moment of inertia is given by

$$I = P_1d_1^2 + P_2d_2^2 + P_3d_3^2$$

$$= P_1d_1d_1 + P_2d_2d_2 + P_3d_3d_3$$

In accordance with the principles already discussed, the first moments, P_1d_1, P_2d_2, and P_3d_3, may be found from the product of the pole distance H and the respective intercepts shown in the space diagram; i.e.,

$$P_1d_1 = Hy_1$$

$$P_2d_2 = Hy_2$$

$$P_3d_3 = Hy_3$$

$$I = H(y_1d_1 + y_2d_2 + y_3d_3)$$

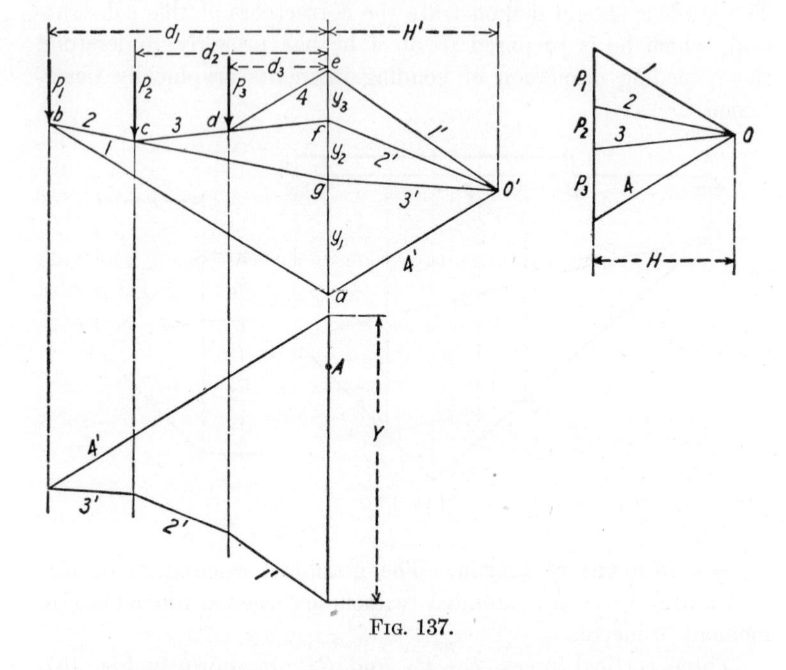

FIG. 137.

The product y_1d_1 is the moment about A of a force y_1, having the line of action of P_1, and similarly with respect to y_2d_2 and y_3d_3. From this it follows that the moment of inertia, I, may be obtained by multiplying the moment about A of the new series of forces y_1, y_2, and y_3 by H. The moment of the forces y_1, y_2, and y_3 about A may be found graphically by drawing a new equilibrium polygon, as shown in Fig. 137, with a new pole $0'$. Then since:

$$y_1d_1 + y_2d_2 + y_3d_3 = H'Y$$

$$I = HH'Y$$

This is known as Culmann's method of graphically calculating moment of inertia.

The expression above:

$$I = H(y_1d_1 + y_2d_2 + y_3d_3)$$

furnishes at once another method of calculating I.

$$y_1d_1 = 2 \times \text{area } \Delta abg$$

$$y_2d_2 = 2 \times \text{area } \Delta gcf$$

$$y_3d_3 = 2 \times \text{area } \Delta fde$$

from which

$$I = H \times 2 \times \text{area of } abcdea,$$

which is known as Mohr's graphical method of calculating moment of inertia.

The above methods of determining moment of inertia and the method of determining center of gravity in Art. 102 are sometimes made use of in connection with the graphical analysis of the elastic arch and are included here as a matter of interest for that reason. In general, the authors doubt whether graphical determination of center of gravity and moment of inertia will have any advantages over arithmetical calculation.

The moment of inertia of irregular areas may also be approximated by the graphical methods discussed. The closeness of the approximation will evidently depend on the size of the elementary areas into which the figure is divided — the smaller the elementary areas the smaller the error resulting from the neglect of the moment of inertia of each portion about its own center of gravity. Error from this source may be eliminated by applying the area of each element at its radius of gyration with respect to the axis in question instead of at its center of gravity. These methods, though of some academic interest, seldom offer much advantage in structural work, and the reader is referred to the larger treatises devoted exclusively to graphical calculation for a complete discussion.

111. Stresses in Trussed Structures — Graphically Determined.—The use of graphical methods in calculating the stresses in the various members of a truss does not change the fundamental method of attack, which, as stated in Chapter VI, is to pass a section, completely separating the structure into two parts, and apply the laws of statics to one of the parts cut off by the section. In calculating stresses graphically the most convenient section will generally be one going completely around some joint. Since purely axial stresses are assumed, we are, for such a section, dealing with a series of forces meeting at a common point.

Evidently for a given truss all the forces meeting at a joint are known in line of action, and all but two must be known in magnitude, since only two of the laws of statics are available. It should be clear from the previous discussion that for any joint where this condition exists, i.e., all but two forces known in magnitude, and of course all known in line of action, we may pass a section around the joint and by means of a force polygon calculate the stress in the two bars in which the magnitude of the stress is not known.

The application of this fundamental method of attack will be illustrated in connection with the truss which is shown in Fig. 85, and which was analyzed in Chapter VI. This truss is repeated in Fig. 138 (*a*).

Before proceeding with the discussion it will be well to call attention to the system of marking loads, members, and stresses which will be used in what follows. A letter is placed between adjacent forces and a number in each triangle in the truss as shown in (*a*) of Fig. 138. Each force is then designated by the adjacent letters, and each bar by the adjacent letter and number or by the adjacent numbers. The left reaction will be the force A–B if reading around the structure in a clockwise direction, and B–A if reading in a counter-clockwise direction. Similarly, the bar previously called L_0U_1 will now be referred to as B–1 or 1–B, depending on whether we read around the joint L_0 in a clockwise or counter-clockwise direction. The student should note that reading around joint U_1 reverses this order of notation. In the same manner the bar U_2L_1 will be known as 2–3 or 3–2. In the force polygons or stress diagrams the line representing the force or stress in a particular bar will be marked by placing at the ends of the line the letter and number (or numbers alone) which designate that bar in the truss. For example, in (*b*) of Fig. 138 the inclined line represents the stress in B–1 and is marked at its ends with this letter and figure. This system is generally known as *Bow's notation* and seems to the authors the most satisfactory of the various marking schemes in use in determining stresses graphically.

in drawing the polygon for joint U_1, simply by laying off B–C from B in (*b*) and completing the polygon by drawing C–2 and 2–1 just as in (*c*). The polygon for joint L_1 may then be drawn merely by adding 2–3 and 3–A to A–1 and 1–2 which have previously been drawn. Continuing in this manner, all the polygons will combine into one figure in which each bar has its stress represented only once. The stress polygons for this truss are thus combined in (*f*). As previously stated, it is immaterial in what order the forces are drawn in the force polygon if a separate diagram is to be constructed for each joint, **but if all the diagrams are to be combined into a single figure it is necessary to pass around each joint in the same direction and to draw the forces in the polygon in the order in which they are met in passing around the joint.** Thus, in drawing the stress diagram (*f*) in Fig. 138, each joint was passed around in a clockwise direction and the forces drawn in order: for joint L_0 the order was A–B, B–1, and 1–A; for joint U_1, 1–B, B–C, C–2, and 2–1; for joint L_1, A–1, 1–2, 2–3, and 3–A; for joint U_2, 3–2, 2–C, C–D, D–4, and 4–3; and so on. Whether the direction chosen is clockwise or counter-clockwise is not important, *but having started in one direction it must be followed for the entire diagram.* This is very important. The student should firmly fix it in mind by resketching the separate diagrams (*b*), (*c*), (*d*), and (*e*) of Fig. 138, noting that so far as the individual diagrams are concerned the order in which the various forces are drawn does not matter, and then try combining the diagrams without passing around each joint in the same direction. In so doing the observant student will quickly see the reason and necessity for this procedure.

112. Determination of Sign.—The character of the stress in a bar, i.e., whether tension or compression, can be quickly determined by observing the direction in which the stress acts around the force polygon for either joint to which the member connects and noting whether this direction is *away* from the joint (tension) or *toward* the joint (compression). For example, consider the member 3–4 in the truss just analyzed. The stress diagram in (*f*) was drawn going around the joints in a clockwise direction, therefore if we refer to joint L_2 this member must be read 3–4, and if we read *from* 3 *to* 4 in the stress diagram the direction is *towards* the joint L_2 and the bar must be in compression. Evidently the same result will be obtained referring to joint U_2, for in this case the member must be read 4–3, and reading *from* 4 *to* 3 in (*f*) the direction is towards the joint U_2, denoting compression in the bar.

Figure 139 (*a*) shows the same truss as in Fig. 138 but subjected to wind loads acting normal to the roof, and in (*b*) is shown the stress diagram assuming rollers under the right end. The student should draw a stress diagram for the same truss and loads with rollers under the left end.

In Fig. 140 the truss used in the previous discussion is shown with symmetrical top chord loads and in addition somewhat

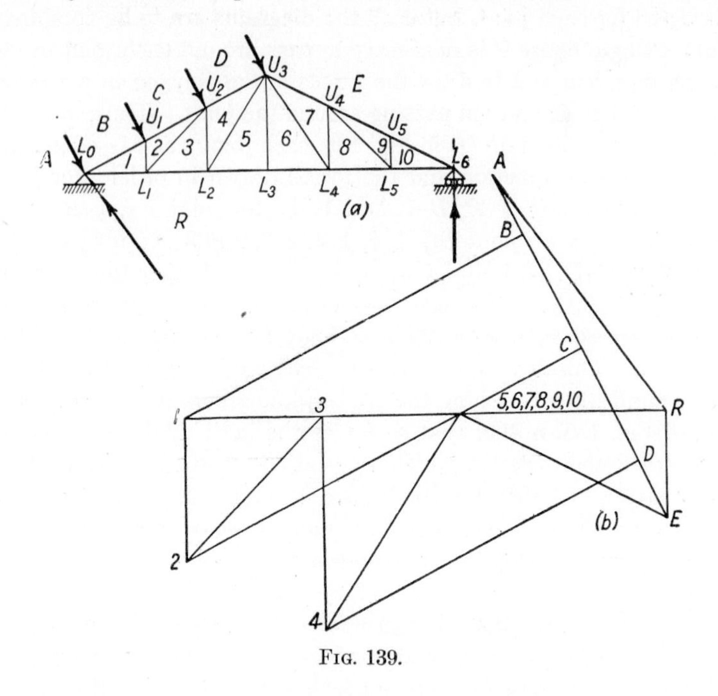

Fig. 139.

larger loads at L_4 and L_5. There are no new principles involved in the solution of such a problem, and the student who thoroughly understands the preceding discussion should be able to make an analysis without further explanation. Nevertheless the following suggestions may prove helpful. If the reactions are to be calculated graphically all the loads acting in one line should be taken together, e.g., the loads applied at U_4 and L_4 should be combined into a single load of 20^k which may be applied at either the top chord point U_4 or the bottom chord L_4; the same is true for the loads at U_5 and L_5. After the reactions have been determined either graphically or arithmetically, the construction of the stress diagram proceeds as usual.

Students often seem to have difficulty in laying off the load line when there are loads applied on the bottom chord as well as the top chord. It is not necessary that all the loads be laid off before the stress diagram is started, and beginners may find it advantageous not to attempt it, but instead lay off a load when

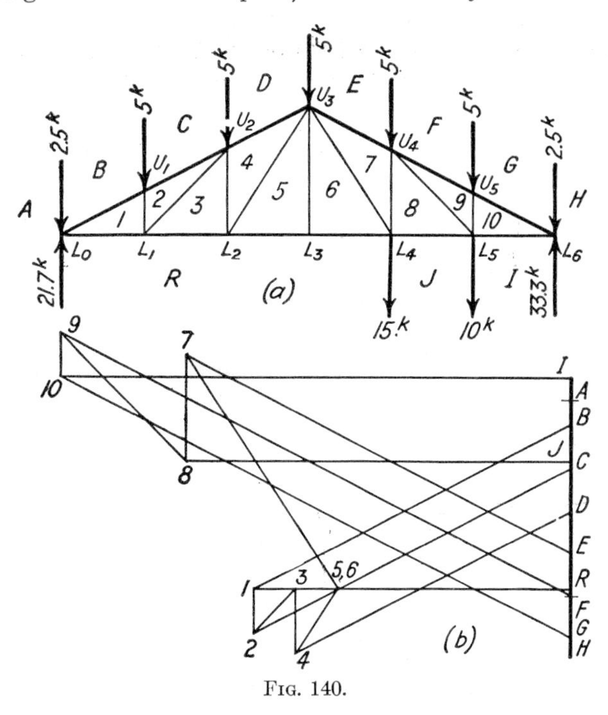

FIG. 140.

the joint at which it acts is dealt with. For example, in drawing the stress diagram for the truss and loads in Fig. 140: start with joint L_0 and lay off the loads R–A and A–B which act at that joint, complete the polygon for this joint; pass to joint U_1, lay off the load B–C *down* from point B, which has already been established, and complete the polygon for this joint; pass to L_1 and draw the polygon for that joint (no loads act at L_1 and none need be laid off); pass to U_2, lay off C–D from the point C, already established, and complete the polygon. This procedure may be followed for the entire truss, and since one end of a load is always located in the stress diagram *before* the load is reached, there can never be any difficulty in determining where it should be drawn: it should simply be drawn in the direction in which it acts to or from the point already established. It is necessary of course in this case — as in all cases when the various force polygons are to combine into one figure — to take care to pass around all joints in the direction decided on for the first joint.

If the computer wishes to lay off the load line completely before starting the stress diagram (and doing so adds somewhat to the accuracy of the construction) it may be done without difficulty if the loads and reactions are taken in order, passing around the structure in the direction (clockwise or counter-clockwise) in which it is intended to pass around each joint in constructing the stress diagram.

113. Substitute Members.—Occasionally a truss is encountered in which the triangulation is of such form that when certain joints are reached during the construction of the stress diagram there are more unknowns (more than two) than can be determined from a force polygon. In such cases it is necessary to calculate the stress in one or more bars arithmetically, before continuing with the construction of the stress diagram, or to make use of a substitute triangulation. An example of this kind is shown in Fig. 141. In (*b*) there is shown enough of the stress diagram to illustrate the point. The stress diagram may be started at the left reaction and constructed as usual without difficulty until the stresses in members H–1, H–2, 2–1, 2–3, B–1, B–3, 3–4, and B–4 have been determined. It is next necessary to draw the force polygon for joint U_1 or joint M_1, and at each of these joints there are three unknown forces acting: those at U_1 being B–6, 6–5, and 5–4, and those at M_1 are 4–5, 5–7, and 7–H. It is a simple matter to calculate the stress in either B–6 or 7–H arithmetically, introduce the calculated stress into the diagram, and proceed with the force polygons for joints U_1 and M_1. Or members 7–5, 5–6, 6–8, and 8–7 may be replaced by the dotted member U_2M_1 and a full vertical U_2M_2. If this substitution is made there will be only two unknowns at U_1, and a force polygon may be drawn for this joint, but will not of course give stresses in the bars B–6 and 5–4 which are correct for the original truss. The stresses, however, are correct for the substitute triangulation and permit drawing a polygon for joint M_1. The stress thus found in bar 7–H is correct for the original truss, since the stress in this member may be calculated arithmetically as a bar in either the original or in the substitute truss, by dividing the bending moment at panel point U_2 by the depth of the truss U_2–M_2. The correct stress in 7–H having been found, there are only two unknowns at the joint M_1 in the original truss, and the substitute members may then be replaced

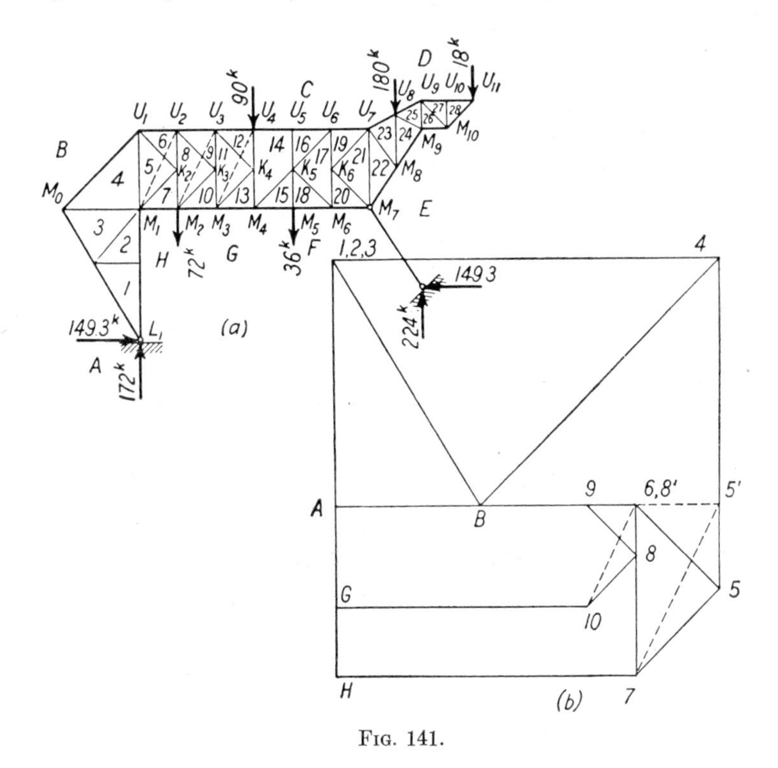

FIG. 141.

by the original members and polygons drawn for joints M_1 and U_1, which will give the correct stresses. The same procedure may be followed for succeeding joints, using the substitute members U_3M_2 and U_4M_3, shown dotted in the truss diagram. The stress diagram in (b) has been carried only far enough to get the correct stresses up to and including B–9, 9–8, 8–10, and 10–G from the left reaction. The student should be able to follow the construction of the diagram, keeping in mind that substitute members U_2M_1

and U_3M_2 appear in the stress diagram as 5′–7 and 8′–10 respectively.

Some study is sometimes necessary in the choice of a convenient substitute triangulation, and the student should keep in mind the two requirements which must be satisfied in such a choice:

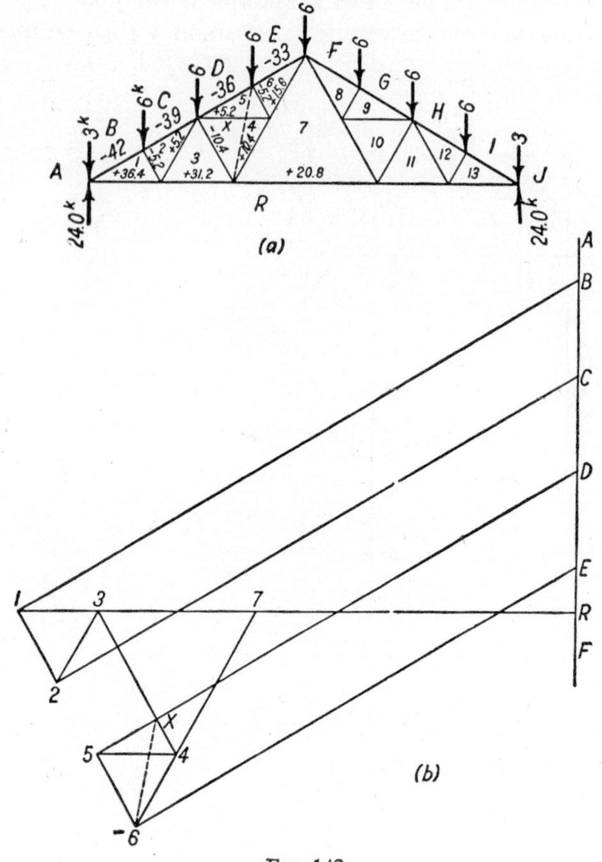

Fig. 142.

First: The truss must be a stable structure with the substitute members replacing the originals.

Second: The triangulation chosen must be such as to permit the determination of the *true* stress in some member beyond the joint at which too many unknowns are encountered, but as close thereto as possible.

In meeting the second requirement it may be necessary to go several joints beyond the one which first stops the construction of the diagram and work backwards when a true stress is finally determined. This is illustrated in the problem above by the fact that it was necessary to go from U_1 to M_1 before a true stress was found (stress in 7–H), after which it was possible to work backwards to U_1, determining the true stresses in all bars meeting at these two joints. A member in which the true stress may be determined will have been reached when it is possible to pass a section which cuts the member but which need not cut either

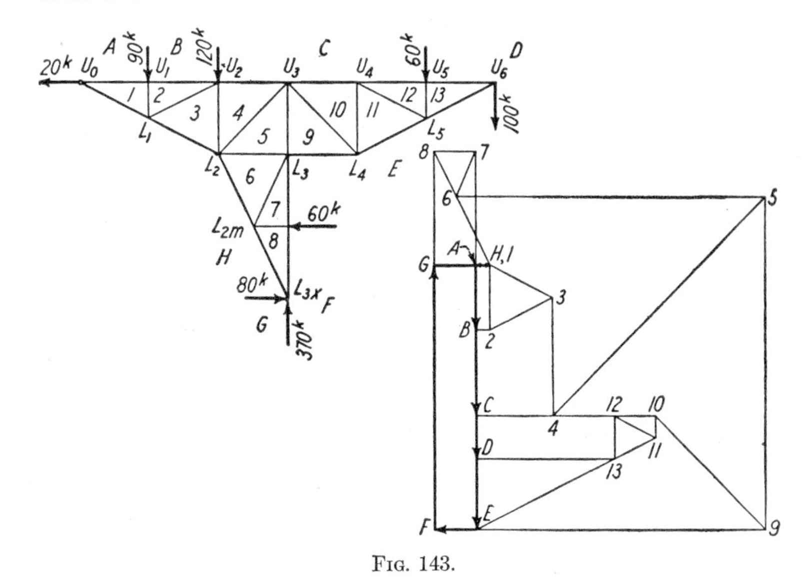

FIG. 143.

the substitute member being used or the members which the substitute member replaces.

In Fig. 142 is shown the classic illustration of a substitute member in the form of the common Fink roof truss. Here the substitute member is shown dotted in (*a*) and the stress diagram in (*b*). Familiarity with a particular type of truss will sometimes suggest methods other than arithmetical calculation of some stress, or the use of a substitute member, for overcoming the difficulty just discussed. For example, close scrutiny of Fig. 142 and comparison with stress diagrams for Fink trusses under other kinds of loading will disclose that a substitute member need not be used in drawing the stress diagram for a symmetrically loaded symmetrical truss of this form.

Another illustration of this kind of problem is given in Fig. 143. Study of this truss will show that the stress diagram may be started at U_0, L_{3x}, or U_6 but that too many unknowns will soon be encountered whichever is chosen as the starting point. In this case the remedy is to lay off the entire load line and work from two starting points. The student should follow the stress diagram in (b) all the way through, starting at any one of the three points mentioned above.

As stated at the beginning of this chapter, the authors wished to present here only the fundamental principles essential for the understanding and use of graphical calculation in the solution of simple problems in structural analysis. It is believed, however, that a thorough understanding of the material presented will enable the student to extend the principles to more complicated applications and to follow understandingly the more elaborate treatises devoted exclusively to graphical methods.

PROBLEMS

179. Determine graphically the reactions for the structure due to the loads shown.

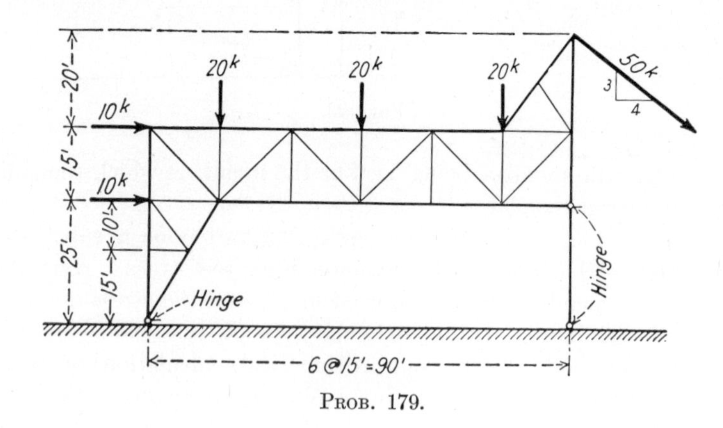

PROB. 179.

180. Determine graphically the reactions for the beam shown. Divide the uniform load into 6-ft. sections.

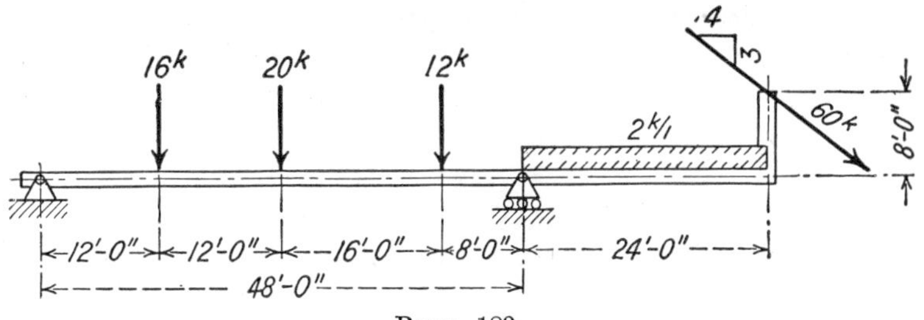

PROB. 180.

181. Determine graphically the reactions for the beam shown.

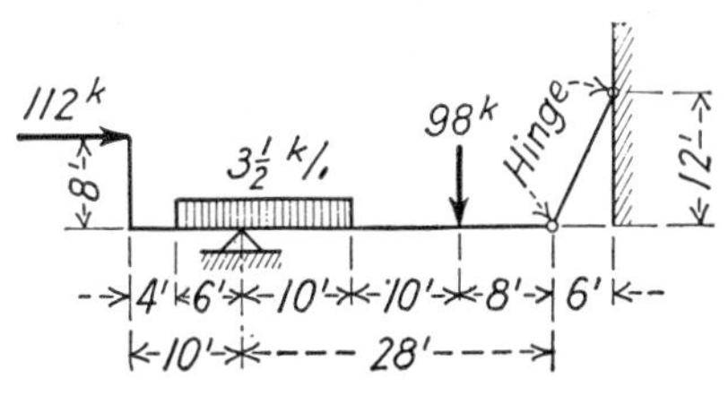

PROB. 181.

182. Calculate graphically the reactions on the structure shown in the figure.

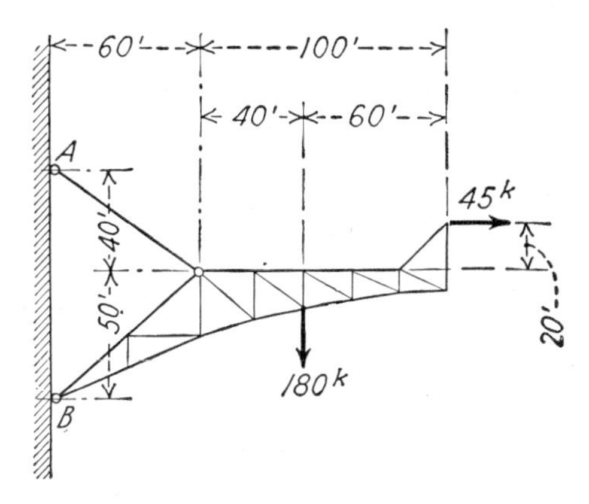

PROB. 182.

183. Calculate graphically the reactions on the structure shown in the figure.

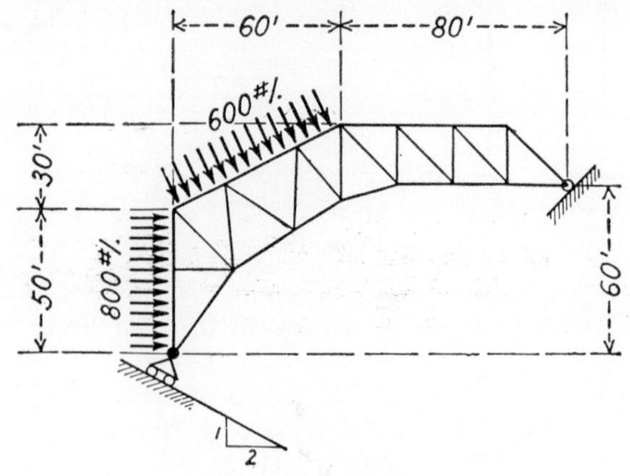

PROB. 183.

184. Calculate graphically the reactions on the structure shown in the figure.

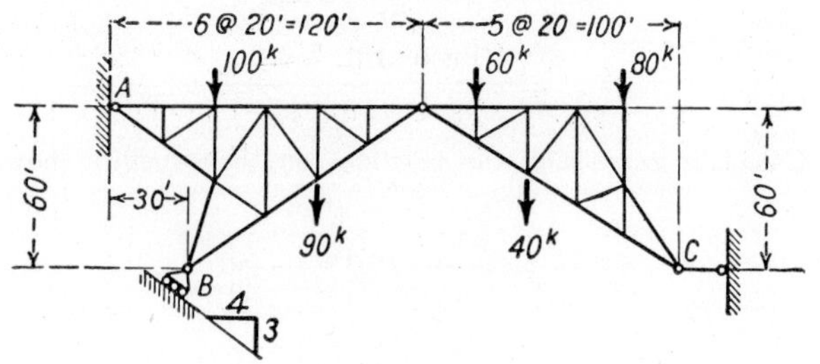

PROB. 184.

185. Determine graphically the reactions for the structures shown.

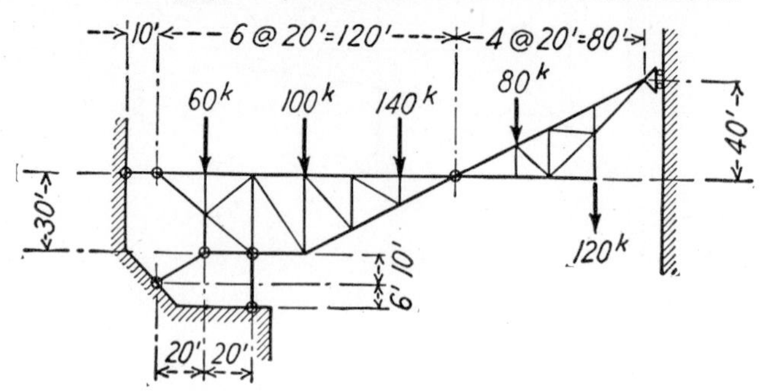

PROB. 185.

186. Calculate graphically the reactions on the structure shown in the figure.

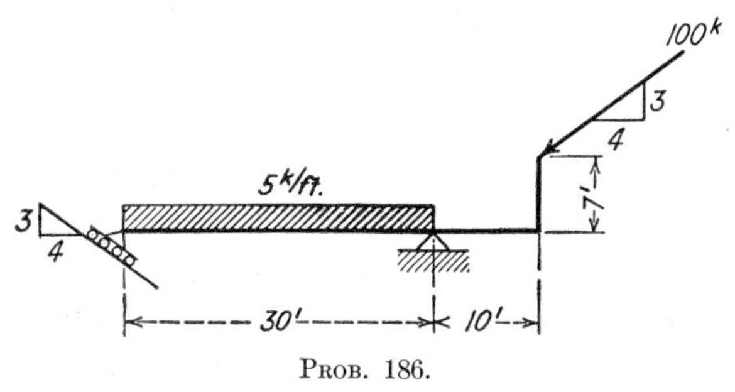

PROB. 186.

187. From the equilibrium polygon drawn for Problem 186, determine the bending moment at the center of the span and at the right support.

188. (*a*) Determine graphically the reactions on the beam due to the loads shown.

(*b*) From the equilibrium polygon determine the bending moment at *a*, *b*, and *c*.

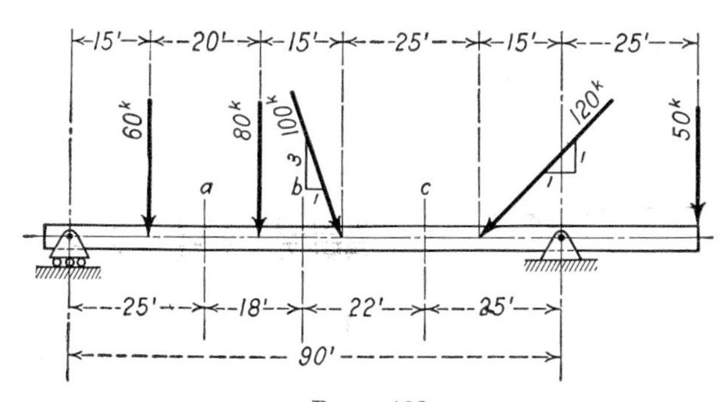

PROB. 188.

189. From the string polygon drawn for Problem 180, determine the bending moment:

(*a*) At a section 16 ft. to the right of the left reaction.
(*b*) At a section 44 ft. to the right of the left reaction.
(*c*) At a section 12 ft. to the right of the right reaction.
(*d*) At a section 6 ft. below the top of the vertical portion.

190. From the equilibrium polygon drawn for Problem 181, determine the bending moment at points measured horizontally to the right 4 ft., 25 ft. and 34 ft. from the base of the mast.

191. (*a*) Apply a uniform load of 2 kips per ft. to the beam shown, and calculate the reactions graphically in such a way that the equilibrium polygon may be used for a bending moment diagram.

(*b*) From the diagram determine the bending moment at panel points 3, 6, and 9.

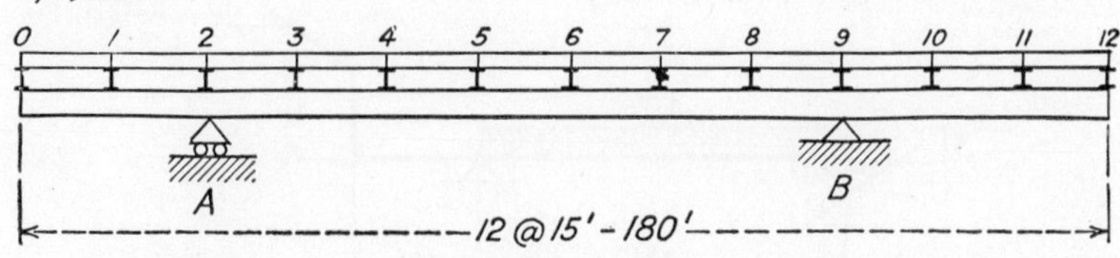

PROB. 191.

192. (*a*) Determine graphically the dead load stresses for the single-track truss span shown. The dead load may be taken as follows:

Track	= 600 lb. per ft.	All applied at top chord.
Floor	= 600	
Trusses and bracing	= 2800	One-half applied at each chord.
Total	= 4000 lb. per ft. of bridge.	

(*b*) Check arithmetically the stress in U_4U_5 and U_4L_5.

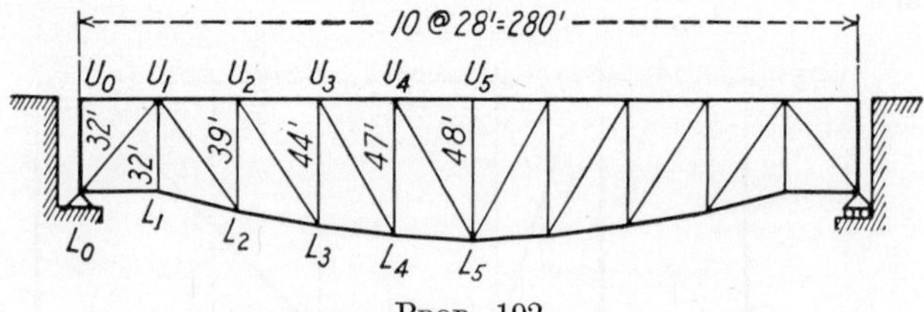

PROB. 192.

193. Determine graphically the stresses in all the bars of the structure in Problem 179 due to the loads shown.

194. Determine graphically the stresses in all the bars of the structure due to the loads shown.

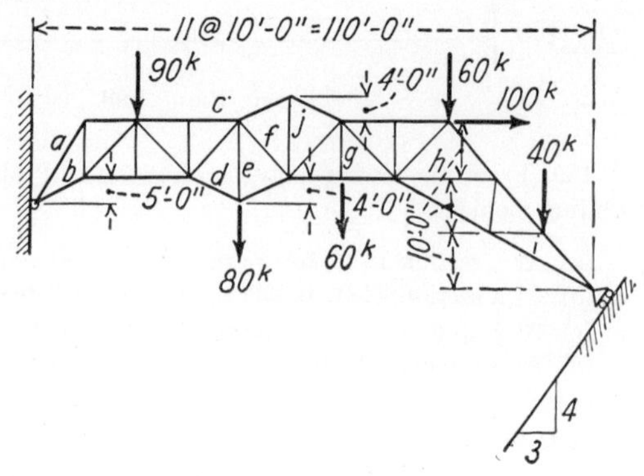

PROB. 194.

195. Calculate graphically the stresses in all the bars of the structure shown in Problem 182.

196. Calculate graphically all the stresses in the bent shown in Problem 160 on p. 201, using the loads given in Problem 161.

197. Calculate graphically all the stresses in the structure shown.

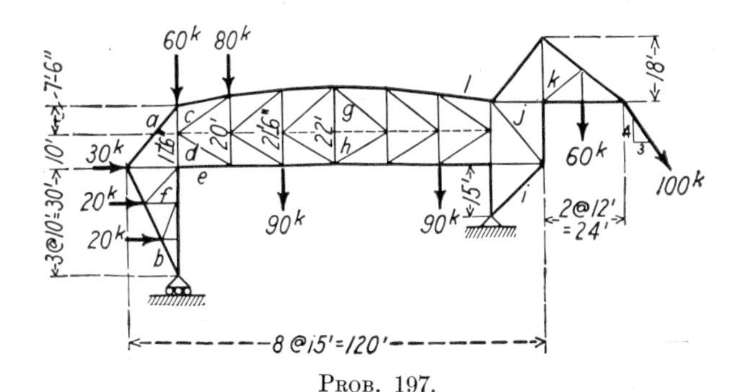

PROB. 197.

198. Determine the reactions on the structure graphically by:

(*a*) Passing an equilibrium polygon through the three hinges.

(*b*) Determining the reactions due to the loads on each half of the structure separately and then combining them, all graphically.

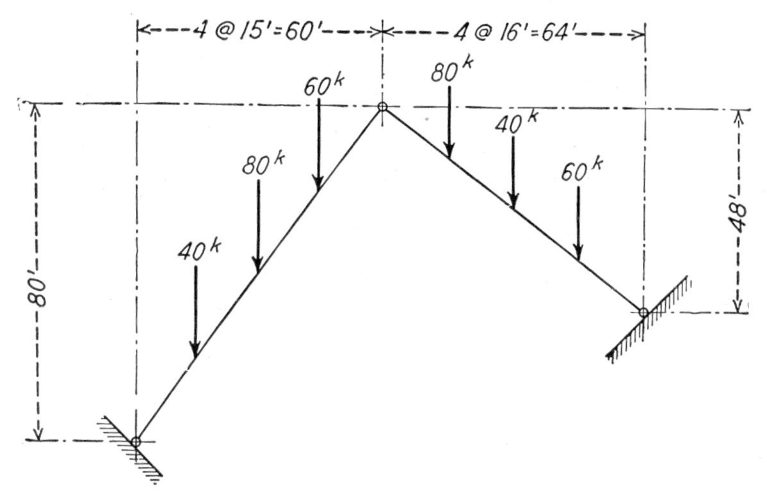

PROB. 198.

199. (*a*) Determine graphically the reactions for the structure shown.

(*b*) Using the reactions found for (*a*), compute graphically the stress in bars U_3U_4, U_3L_4, and L_3L_4.

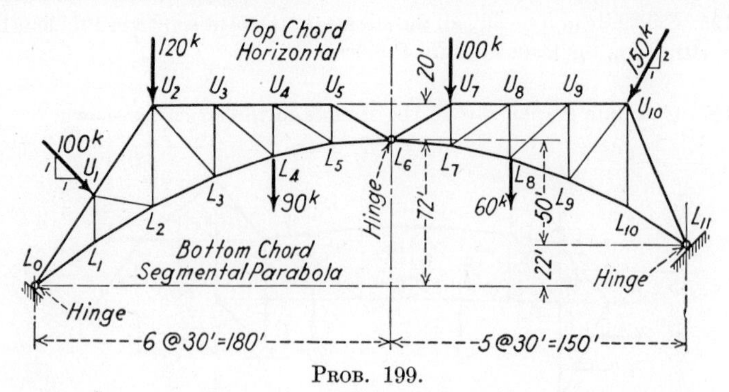

PROB. 199.

200. Locate *X* and *Y* axes through the center of gravity graphically.

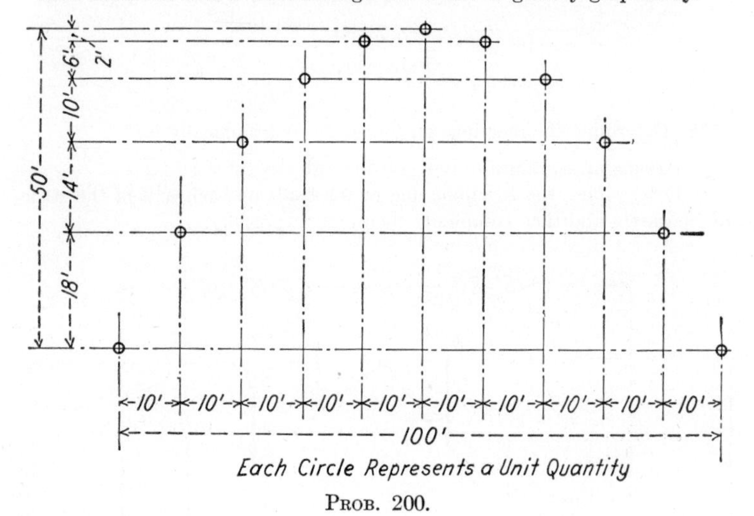

PROB. 200.

201. Determine graphically the moment of inertia about the axis *X–X* found in Problem 200.

202. Determine graphically the moment of inertia about the axis *Y–Y* found in Problem 200.

NOTE: Problems 141, 145, 150, 153, 154, 158, 159, 160, 170, 171 and 178 are also recommended for practice in graphical determination of stresses.

CHAPTER VIII

STRESSES IN TRUSSED STRUCTURES—MOVING LOADS

114. As stated in Chapter IV, it is seldom that an engineer is called upon to design a structure to support only loads which do not change in magnitude or position. Most structures must support, in addition to their own weight, loads which move or are movable. In order to prepare a safe and economical design for such a structure it is necessary to know the greatest stress to which any part may be subjected, and if the loads are moving or movable, it is necessary to determine the position in which they will have the greatest effect on the part in question.

In Chapter IV there were discussed methods for obtaining the position of moving loads to produce: maximum reaction; maximum shear at a section, or within a panel; and maximum moment at any point in a beam or girder to which the loads are directly applied, or at any panel point of a beam or girder to which the loads are applied through a floor system. In Chapter VI the fundamental method of truss analysis was discussed. In the present chapter the application of these principles and methods to the determination of maximum stresses in trusses will be discussed and illustrated. In some cases extension of the methods already presented will be necessary, but for the most part they are sufficient for the calculation of the maximum stresses resulting from moving loads.

115. Influence Lines.—Influence lines for stress in some bars of a truss are often convenient in calculating the stress due to a moving uniform load or a moving uniform load combined with a single concentrated load. The definition of an influence line given in Chapter IV and the methods of construction presented there furnish sufficient information to enable the drawing of an influence line for stress in any bar of any statically determinate truss.

It is desirable here to re-emphasize the importance of constructing influence lines by means of the fundamental method previously discussed. It is very important for the student in drawing an influence line for stress to:

First: Decide *how* the stress is to be calculated.

Second: Move the unit load along the span and observe the effect on the stress in question.

Third: Calculate the controlling ordinates on the influence line and complete the diagram.

While constructing an influence line for stress in a bar, the authors prefer not to pay especial attention to plotting positive or negative values on a particular side of the reference line, but merely to be sure that values of opposite sign are placed on opposite sides of the reference line and after completing the diagram to

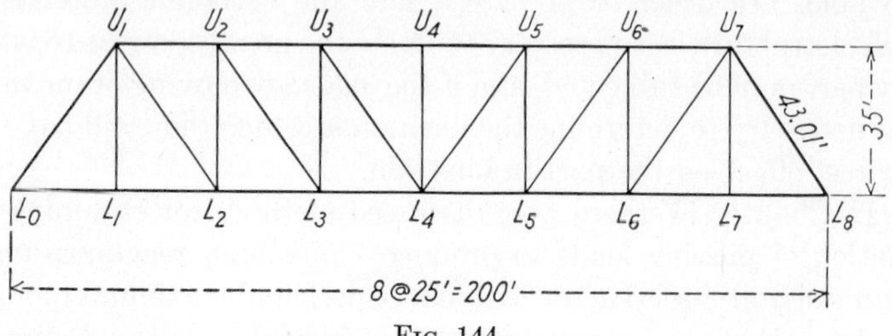

FIG. 144.

determine by inspection which parts represent positive stress, which negative, and to mark them plus or minus accordingly.

As used in this text, influence lines need not be drawn to scale, but the controlling ordinates should be computed and marked on a free-hand sketch of the diagram. The procedure described will be illustrated by examples.

116. Use of Principles Previously Discussed.—The application of the principles and methods already discussed may be shown best in connection with illustrative examples.

In Fig. 144 is shown one of the trusses given as a problem for practice in Art. 86, Chapter VI. As an illustration of the use of methods already known, the maximum live load stress in bars U_3U_4, L_3L_4, U_3L_4, U_2L_2, and U_1L_1 due to Steinman's M–50 loading will be discussed and the necessary calculations made. The actual calculations are given in the following article (Art. 117), and should be studied in connection with the discussion in this article. The moment table given in Chapter IV (Table IV) will be used.

U_3U_4.—In calculating the stress due to live load in any bar, the student should first decide *how* the stress is to be calculated and then study the effect of the moving loads. For the bar U_3U_4 the stress should be calculated by passing a section cutting U_3U_4, U_3L_4, L_3L_4, and finding the bending moment about L_4 (the intersection point of U_3L_4 and L_3L_4), this moment divided by the depth of the truss evidently being the stress in U_3U_4. From this it follows that the *maximum* stress in U_3U_4 will result when the maximum bending moment at L_4 occurs. As shown in Chapter IV, the maximum moment at L_4 will occur when the average load to the left of L_4 is equal to the average load on the span.

L_3L_4.—The section passed for the calculation of stress in U_3U_4 is also suitable for determining the stress in L_3L_4, but moments must be taken about U_3, the intersection of U_3U_4 and U_3L_4. It should be clear that maximum stress in L_3L_4 will result when maximum moment at U_3 occurs. Since the loads acting are *vertical* only, the moment at U_3 must be the same as the moment at any point in a vertical line passing through U_3. Or the moment at U_3 is the same as the moment at L_3, and maximum moment at L_3 occurs when the average load to the left of L_3 is equal to the average load on the span.

Since the moment at L_3 is equal to the moment at U_3, it is clear that the maximum stress in U_2U_3 is equal to the maximum stress in L_3L_4, but of opposite sign. This also follows from passing a section cutting U_2U_3, U_3L_3, and L_3L_4.

U_3L_4.—The section passed in discussing the stress in U_3U_4 and L_3L_4 is also the one most convenient for calculating the stress in U_3L_4. Since U_3U_4 and L_3L_4 are horizontal, their stresses can have no vertical components and consequently the vertical component of the stress in U_3L_4 must equal the shear in the panel in order to have $\Sigma V = 0$. Then *maximum* stress in U_3L_4 must result when its vertical component is a maximum or when the shear in panel 3–4 is a maximum. As shown in Chapter IV, the shear in a panel is a maximum when the average load in the panel is equal to the average load on the span.

The floor system for the truss under consideration is connected to bottom panel points; that is, the bridge is a " through " bridge. Consequently, all the live loads are applied at the bottom chord panel points. From this it follows that, if a section is passed around joint U_3, the only vertical forces acting on the part of the structure cut out by the section are the vertical component of the stress in U_3L_4 and the stress in U_3L_3. It should be clear then that maximum live load stress in U_3L_3 occurs when the stress in U_3L_4 is a maximum and that it is equal to the vertical component of the stress in U_3L_4, but of opposite sign.

U_2L_2.—There are three sections which may be passed in calculating the stress in U_2L_2, but the most convenient one is a section cutting U_1U_2, U_2L_2, and L_2L_3. Since U_1U_2 and L_2L_3 are horizontal their stresses can have no vertical components, from which it follows that the stress in U_2L_2 must be equal to the algebraic sum of all the external forces acting on either side of the section, or the stress in U_2L_2 must be equal to the *shear* on the section passed. Evidently the stress in the bar will be greatest when the shear on the section is greatest. Since the live loads are applied to the bottom chord only, the shear on the section is the same as the shear in panel 2–3.

From the discussion under U_3L_4 it should be clear also that the maximum stress in U_2L_2 is the vertical component of the maximum stress in U_2L_3, which occurs of course when the shear in panel 2–3 is a maximum.

U_1L_1.—Passing a section around joint L_1 shows clearly that the only vertical forces acting on the part of the structure cut off by the section are the stress in U_1L_1 and whatever external load is applied at the joint. Consequently the stress in U_1L_1 must be equal to the floorbeam reaction at L_1 and is a maximum when the floorbeam reaction is a maximum. The position of a series of concentrated loads which will produce maximum floorbeam reaction has already been discussed in Chapter IV, Article 72.

117. Calculations.—

$\mathbf{U_3U_4}$

Wheel 10 at L_4 $\left.\begin{matrix}555\\630\end{matrix}\right\}622.5$ satisfies criterion.

Wheel 11 at L_4 $\left.\begin{matrix}630\\705\end{matrix}\right\}637.5$ satisfies criterion.

Change in moment from 10 at L_4 to 11 at L_4 will be 0 by inspection.[1]

[1] When two adjacent wheels satisfy the criterion for moment (or shear) because of an additional portion of the uniform load moving on the span, *and that only*, it is possible to determine by inspection which wheel gives the maximum. It will be that wheel for which the value of the average load on the span differs most from the average value of the loads to the left (or in the

Stress for 10 at L_4

$$\begin{array}{rrl} & 22{,}725'^k & \\ 705 \times 90 = & 63{,}450 & \\ 6 \times 90 \times 45 = & \underline{24{,}300} & \\ & 110{,}475 \div 200 = 552.4^k & \\ & \times 100 = 55{,}240'^k & \\ & \underline{16{,}050} & \\ & 39{,}190'^k & \text{mom. about } L_4 \end{array}$$

$$\begin{array}{rll} \div 35 = & 1120 & \text{M–60} \\ \times \frac{5}{6} = & -\ 933^k & \text{M–50 one track} \\ \times \frac{1}{2} = & -\ 467^k & \text{M–50 one truss} \end{array}$$

L_3L_4

Wheel 9 at L_3 $\left.\begin{array}{r}480\\555\end{array}\right\}$ $1365 \times \frac{3}{8} = 512$ satisfies criterion.

$$\begin{array}{rrl} & 22{,}725 & \\ 705 \times 110 = & 77{,}550 & \\ 6 \times 110 \times 55 = & \underline{36{,}300} & \\ & 136{,}575 \div 200 = 682.9 & \\ & \times 75 = 51{,}220 & \\ & \underline{13{,}275} & \\ & 37{,}945'^k & \text{mom. at } U_3 \\ & \div 35 = 1084^k & \text{M–60} \\ & \times \frac{5}{6} \times \frac{1}{2} = +\ 452^k & \text{M–50} \end{array}$$

---

panel for shear) which is common to both wheels. Thus, in the calculation above, since 622.5 and 637.5 differ from 630 by the same amount, wheels 10 and 11 give the same moment. If, in the locomotive in the above problem, wheel 11 were 4 ft. from wheel 10 (the uniform load then being 6 ft. from wheel 11), there would result the following:

Wheel 10 at L_4 $\left.\begin{array}{r}555\\630\end{array}\right\}$ 622.5 satisfies.

Wheel 11 at L_4 $\left.\begin{array}{r}630\\705\end{array}\right\}$ 634.5. also satisfies.

Maximum stress would then occur for wheel 10 at L_4, since the difference between 630 and 622.5 is greater than that between 630 and 634.5

The student should show that this is true by writing the expression for change in moment as two wheels a distance d apart are successively placed over the point of moments and a uniform load of w lb. per ft. $\times\, d$ ft. comes on the span during the movement. Many simple short cuts similar to the one described here will suggest themselves to one making numerous calculations involving wheel loads. Such short cuts, however, are not essential to a thorough understanding of the fundamental principles and are best developed as the result of experience.

U_3L_4

$$\left.\begin{matrix}30\\90\end{matrix}\right\}\frac{945}{8}\quad \text{Wheel 2 at } L_4$$

$$\left.\begin{matrix}90\\150\end{matrix}\right\}\frac{975}{8}\quad \text{Wheel 3 at } L_4 \text{ satisfies criterion.}$$

$$\begin{aligned} & 22{,}725 \\ 705 \times 45 = {} & 31{,}725 \\ 6 \times 45 \times 22.5 = {} & 6{,}075 \\ \hline & 60{,}525 \div 200 = 302.6 \end{aligned}$$

$$\frac{750}{25} = 30.0^k$$

$$272.6 \text{ shear in panel M–60}$$

$$\times \frac{43.01}{35.0} = 335^k \text{ M–60}$$

$$\times \tfrac{5}{6} \times \tfrac{1}{2} = +\,139.6^k \text{ M–50}$$

U_2L_2

$$\left.\begin{matrix}30\\90\end{matrix}\right\}\frac{1095}{8}\quad \text{Wheel 2 at } L_3$$

$$\left.\begin{matrix}90\\150\end{matrix}\right\}\frac{1125}{8}\quad \text{Wheel 3 at } L_3 \text{ satisfies criterion.}$$

$$\begin{aligned} & 22{,}725 \\ 705 \times 70 = {} & 49{,}350 \\ 6 \times 70 \times 35 = {} & 14{,}700 \\ \hline & 86{,}775 \div 200 = 433.9 \end{aligned}$$

$$\frac{750}{25} = 30.0^k$$

$$403.9 \quad \text{M–60}$$

$$\times \tfrac{5}{6} \times \tfrac{1}{2} = -\,168^k \quad \text{M–50}$$

U_1L_1

$$\left.\begin{matrix}150\\225\end{matrix}\right\}\frac{435}{2}\quad \text{Wheel 9 at } L_1 \text{ satisfies criterion.}$$

$$\left.\begin{matrix}225\\300\end{matrix}\right\}\frac{465}{2}\quad \text{Wheel 10 at } L_1 \text{ satisfies criterion.}$$

Inspection shows the stress will be the same for either wheel at L_1 — use 9.

$$\frac{4500}{25} = \qquad 180$$

$$\begin{array}{r} 1125 \\ 150 \times 10 = 1500 \\ 6 \times 10 \times 5 = \underline{\ 300} \\ 2925 \div 25 = \underline{117} \\ 297 \quad \text{M-60} \\ \times \frac{5}{6} \times \frac{1}{2} = +\ 123.8^k \quad \text{M-50} \end{array}$$

118. Reversal of Stress in Web Members.—In the calculations above, the train was brought on from the right in each case. Tension in U_3L_4 resulted from maximum shear in the panel 3–4 with loads coming on from the right. If the loads were brought on from the left, the bar U_3L_4 would be in compression, considering live loads only, as long as all loads on the span were between L_3 and the left end. As loads moved into the panel L_3L_4 from the left, the compression in U_3L_4 would approach a maximum value and reach it when the average load in the panel became equal to the average load on the span. Evidently the same thing could result as loads which came on from the right passed off at the left; i.e., as the loads moved to the left until all or most of the loads on the span were to the left of L_4, the stress in U_3L_4 would change to compression which would reach a maximum value when the average load in the panel L_3L_4 became equal to the average load on the span.

In designing a truss it is important to know the greatest compression which may occur in a bar, as well as the greatest tension, and it is necessary to consider the effect, on members such as U_3L_4, of the train, or other loads, coming on from either end, or passing off at either end. The calculations for stress in U_3L_4 due to a train coming on from the left and for a locomotive pushing a train passing off at the left are given below.

U_3L_4 *Train on from left:*

$$\left.\begin{array}{r} 30 \\ 90 \end{array}\right\} \frac{795}{8} \quad \text{Wheel 2 at } L_3$$

$$\left.\begin{array}{r} 90 \\ 150 \end{array}\right\} \frac{825}{8} \quad \text{Wheel 3 at } L_3 \text{ satisfies criterion.}$$

$$
\begin{aligned}
& & 22{,}725 & & \\
705 \times 20 &= & 14{,}100 & & \\
6 \times 20 \times 10 &= & 1{,}200 & & \\
& & \overline{38{,}025} \div 200 &= 190.1 & \\
& & \frac{750}{25} &= \underline{\ 30.0\ } & \\
& & & \quad 160.1 & \\
& & \times \frac{43.01}{35.00} &= -196.7 & \text{M-60} \\
& & \times \tfrac{5}{6} \times \tfrac{1}{2} &= -82.0^k & \text{M-50}
\end{aligned}
$$

U_3L_4 *Train passing off to left — uniform load* 8 *ft. ahead of wheel* 1:

$\left.\begin{matrix}0\\75\end{matrix}\right\}\frac{717}{8}$ Wheel 11 at L_3

$\left.\begin{matrix}75\\150\end{matrix}\right\}\frac{747}{8}$ Wheel 10 at L_3 satisfies criterion.

$$
\begin{aligned}
& & 26{,}625 & & \\
705 \times 15 &= & 10{,}575 & & \\
6 \times 7 \times 3.5 &= & 147 & & \\
& & \overline{37{,}347} \div 200 &= 186.7 & \\
& & \frac{375}{25} &= \underline{\ 15.0\ } & \\
& & & \quad 171.7 & \\
& & \times \frac{43.01}{35.00} &= -\ 211 & \text{M-60} \\
& & \times \tfrac{5}{6} \times \tfrac{1}{2} &= -\ 87.9^k & \text{M-50}
\end{aligned}
$$

The change in the stress in a diagonal or vertical from tension to compression, or *vice versa*, as a train crosses a bridge is called "reversal" of stress. Members in which reversal of stress takes [illegible]which tension or compression may exist for different [illegible]oad, even though the opposite signs do not occur [illegible]f a train, are said to be subject to "alternate"

[illegible] although apparent reversal of stress [illegible]nt end posts, considering live [illegible] when the dead load stress, which is alw[illegible] [illegible] load stress of opposite kind. For [illegible] according to the assumptions of Article 86, Chapter VI (see also Fig. 102), is $+ 22.1^k$. In this case there is actual reversal of stress since, as just found above, a live load stress of $- 87.9^k$ may occur in this member. On the other hand, the member U_2L_3 in this truss has a dead load stress of $+ 66.4^k$, whereas a live load stress of $- 43.3^k$ is the largest of opposite kind which M–50 loading can cause. In this case it is clear that, considering live load and dead load together, actual reversal does not occur. However, the effect of " impact " (see Art. 17, Chapter I), if included, might cause actual reversal in this case.

119. Uniform Load with Roving Concentrated Load.—It is becoming common in highway bridge design to specify for the trusses a moving uniform load of a constant weight per linear foot accompanied by a concentrated load which may occupy any point on the span independently of the position of the uniform load. It is entirely artificial of course and is intended as a convenient but reasonably representative substitute for the miscellaneous mixture of trucks, horse-drawn vehicles, and pedestrians to which a highway bridge is actually subjected. This type of loading is the same as the " locomotive excess " loading used to some extent in the past in railroad work, and recurrently suggested for modern railroad bridge specifications. The calculation of stresses in a structure using a load of this kind is rapid and easy, the principal argument in its favor.

For chord stresses a little reflection should show that the uniform load should cover the span, and the roving concentration be placed at, or in a vertical line through, the center of moments. For web stresses the use of influence lines is probably the most convenient. To illustrate the use of such a loading, the stress in the bars of the truss in Fig. 144, already considered, will be recalculated, using a moving uniform load of 1200 lb. per lin. ft. plus a roving concentration of 58,000 lb.

In Fig. 145 are shown the influence lines for the bars in question. The use of influence lines for calculating the chord stresses presents no advantage as can be seen since both methods are given. The influence lines are for *stress*, and the student should be able to understand their construction after reviewing the discussion of influence lines in Chapter IV.

120. Web Stresses — Non-parallel Chord Trusses.—No difficulty should be experienced in applying the methods of Chapters

IV and VI to the calculation of the stresses in chord members of a truss such as shown in Fig. 146, when subjected to a series of moving concentrated loads. The calculation of the stresses in

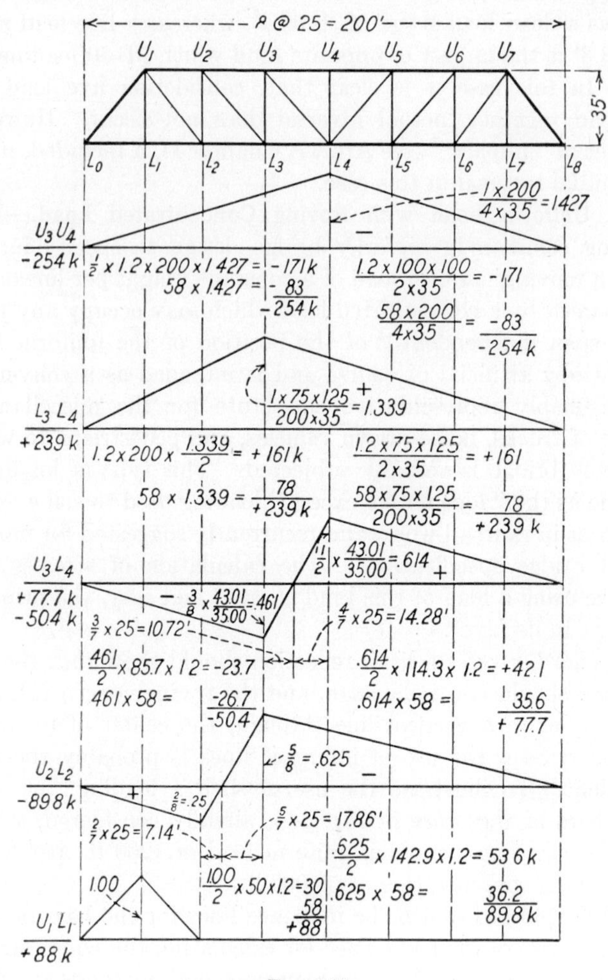

Fig. 145.

some of the web members, however, requires further study. Consider the bar U_2L_3, for example. The section a–a is evidently the only one which enables the calculation of the stress without reference to the stress in any other member. The procedure, as shown in Chapter VI, is to take moments about the intersection of the members U_2U_3 and L_2L_3, which is at B. The vertical component of the stress in U_2L_3 is the moment about B divided by the distance from B to L_3, and it should be clear that the maximum stress will result when the moment about B is a maximum. The position of

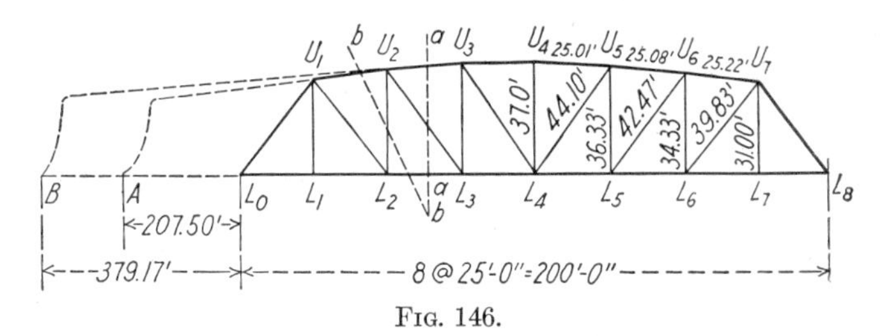

FIG. 146.

a series of loads to produce maximum moment about a point outside of the span cannot be determined from the criteria developed in Chapter IV, and it is necessary to extend the methods already discussed to include this case.

In Fig. 147 the full lines to the left of a–a show the part of the structure cut off by the section, and the dotted lines to the right,

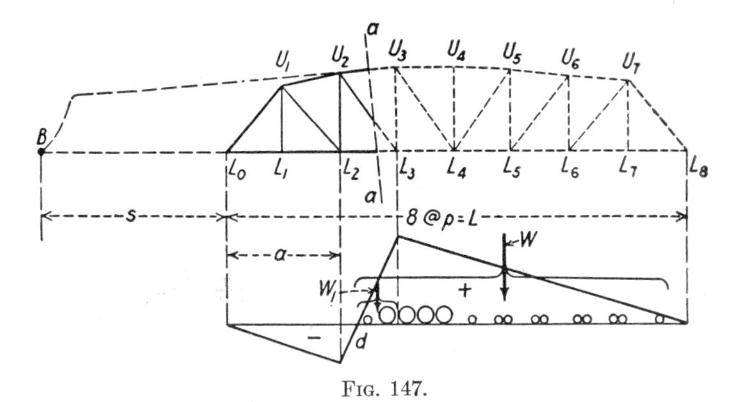

FIG. 147.

the remainder. Below the sketch of the truss is shown the influence line for stress in the bar U_2L_3. It is clear from the influence line that to produce the greatest *positive* stress in U_2L_3 as many loads as possible should be on the span between L_3 and the right-hand end and as few as possible between the point d on the influence line and the left-hand end. It is also clear that as loads pass L_3 moving to the left, their effect on positive stress in U_2L_3 rapidly decreases, and that they produce negative stress in the bar as soon as they pass the point d. Consequently in loading to produce maximum positive stress in U_2L_3 no load should be allowed to pass L_3 moving to the left unless the *increase* in stress due to the movement of those loads between L_3 and the right-hand end is greater than the *decrease* in stress due to the load passing L_3 into the panel 2–3. Usually maximum positive stress in a member such as U_2L_3 occurs before any loads move beyond the panel in which the member is located, i.e., in this case before any loads move to the left of L_2 out of the panel 2–3. It will be assumed for the present that there are loads in panel 2–3 and between L_3 and the right-hand end, but no loads between L_2 and the left-hand end, as shown on the influence line in Fig. 147. In order to establish the position of a series of moving concentrated loads which will produce the maximum positive stress in a bar such as U_2L_3, the *change* in stress in this member will be studied as the loads come on the span from the right and move to the left. It is clear that, as long as loads lie between L_3 and the right-hand end, the stress will be positive and will increase as the loads move to the left. That this statement is correct is apparent not only from the influence line but from the forces acting on the structure. Consider the part of the structure shown in full lines to the left of section a–a in Fig. 147. There is only one external force acting on this part as long as there are no loads to the left of L_3 and that force is the left reaction. The reaction tends to rotate the part under consideration counter-clockwise about the point B, and it is necessary to *pull* on the bar U_2L_3 to prevent rotation. The greater the left reaction, the greater the tension in U_2L_3, as long as the reaction is the only force acting on the part under consideration. As soon as a load passes to the left of L_3 there results a downward force at L_2 which tends to rotate the part of the structure to the left of section a–a in a clockwise direction, thus opposing the tendency of the reaction to rotate the part in a counter-clockwise direction. As movement to the left continues, the downward force at L_2 increases proportionately more rapidly than the reaction, and, as soon as the *change* in the moment of the reaction about B becomes equal to the *change* in the moment of the downward force at L_2 about B, the stress in U_2L_3 has reached a maximum value. This may be expressed mathematically as follows:

Let

W = the total load on the span;
W_1 = the load in the panel 2–3;
ΔS_v = the *change* in the vertical component of U_2L_3;
s = distance from B to the left reaction;
a = distance from left reaction to L_2;
p = panel length;
B is the point at which U_2U_3 and L_2L_3 intersect if projected;
L = the length of the span.

If the loads move to the left a distance dx

$$\Delta S_v = \frac{\frac{Wdx}{L}s - W_1\frac{dx}{p}(s + a)}{(s + a + p)}$$

A little study of this relation shows that as long as the first term in the numerator is larger than the second term, the stress is increasing, owing to movement to the left. If the stress in the bar is an *increasing* function, it cannot pass through a maximum value and become a decreasing function unless the first term in the numerator becomes smaller than the second or the second term becomes larger than the first. It is very improbable that any loads will even move out of the panel 2–3 to the left, much less move off the span to the left. Consequently, for practical purposes we may say that W cannot become smaller and in order to have the numerator of the above expression pass through zero and become negative W_1 *must* become larger, which can occur only if a load moves from the right of L_3 to the left of L_3. An increasing function passes through a maximum when it starts decreasing. In other words, the stress in U_2L_3 passes through a maximum when

$$\Delta S_v = 0$$

or

$$\frac{Wdx}{L}s = W_1\frac{dx}{p}(s + a)$$

$$\frac{W}{L} = \frac{W_1}{p}\frac{(s + a)}{(s)}$$

In words, this relation states that the stress in U_2L_3 (or a similar bar) is a maximum when the average load on the span is equal to the average load in the panel, multiplied by the quantity $\frac{(s + a)}{s}$.[2]

121. Stress Reversal Web Members — Non-parallel Chord Trusses.—If the train is brought on the span in Fig. 147 from the left, it is clear that the stress in U_2L_3 from live loads only will be compression as long as loads are between the point d on the influence line and the left end. As loads pass d, moving to the right, the compression in U_2L_3 will stop increasing and soon reverse to tension. The same thing will occur when loads which come on from the right pass off the span to the left, except that in that case the reversal will be from tension (due to live loads only) to compression. It is necessary to find the maximum compression which may occur in a web member such as U_2L_3, and the first requirement is to establish the position of the loads which will give this result. The method of attack is the same in principle. The loads should be brought on from the left, and it is more convenient in that case to consider the part of the structure on the right of the section a–a. Using the notation given above the mathematical statement is as follows:

$$\Delta S_v = \frac{W\frac{dx}{L}(s + L) - W_1\frac{dx}{p}(s + a + p)}{(s + a + p)}$$

For maximum

$$\Delta S_v = 0$$

$$\frac{Wdx(s + L)}{L} = W_1\frac{dx}{p}(s + a + p)$$

$$\frac{W}{L} = \frac{W_1}{p}\frac{(s + a + p)}{(s + L)}$$

[2] In developing the criterion for shear it was shown that no account need be taken of any loads to the left of the panel in question beyond including them in the total loads on the span. This would not be true in the case of criteria for maximum web stresses in a non-parallel chord truss such as above. There would seldom, if ever, be loads beyond the panel in question in such a case, but if the condition should occur the criterion can easily be developed by applying the principles already used. As an exercise the student should develop the criterion, and if he calls the sum of all loads beyond the panel in question, W_0, he will obtain

$$\frac{W}{L} + \frac{W_0}{s} = \frac{W_1}{p}\cdot\frac{s + a}{s}$$

in which all terms have the same significance as in previous criteria.

The student should note that the increase in the downward load at L_3 due to loads in the panel 2–3 is of interest in this case instead of that at L_2, and that the quantity $\frac{W_1 dx}{p}(s + a + p)$ is the increase in moment about B of the downward load at L_3. The student should also note the similarity between this criterion and the one previously developed.

It is very important to fix in mind the physical meaning of the distances s, $s + a$, $s + a + p$, and $s + L$ used in these criteria and not merely to use the ratios $\frac{s + a}{s}$ and $\frac{s + a + p}{s + L}$ as formulas.

122. Vertical Web Members — Non-parallel Chord Trusses.— If the maximum stress in U_2L_2 of the truss shown in Fig. 146 is to be calculated it will evidently be necessary to pass the section b–b cutting the chord U_1U_2 but the same lower chord as before. Inspection will show that the criteria developed above will apply, but the center of moments will be at A.

123. Illustrative Example.—In order to illustrate the application of the principles developed above, the maximum stresses in the member U_2L_3 of the truss shown in Fig. 146 will be calculated. The loading will be taken as Steinman's M–50 and the moment table given in Table IV in Chapter IV will be used.

$\mathbf{U_2L_3}$ Section a–a moments about B:

$$\frac{379.17 + 50}{379.17} = 1.13$$

Wheel 2 at L_3 $\left.\begin{matrix} 30 \times 1.13 \\ 90 \times 1.13 \end{matrix}\right\} \frac{1095}{8}$ does *not* satisfy criterion.

Wheel 3 at L_3 $\left.\begin{matrix} 90 \times 1.13 \\ 150 \times 1.13 \end{matrix}\right\} \frac{1125}{8}$ *does* satisfy criterion.

$$\begin{aligned} & 22{,}725 \\ 705 \times 70 = {} & 49{,}350 \\ 6 \times 70 \times 35 = {} & \underline{14{,}700} \\ & 86{,}775 \div 200 = 433.9^k \\ & \qquad \times 379.2 = 164{,}600 \\ & \frac{750}{25} = 30 \times 429.2 = \underline{12{,}880} \\ & \qquad 151{,}720 \\ & \qquad \div 454.2 = 334 \\ & \qquad \times \frac{42.47}{34.33} = 413 \\ & \qquad \times \tfrac{5}{6} \times \tfrac{1}{2} = +172.1^k \quad \text{M–50} \end{aligned}$$

U_2L_3 (Compression) train off to left:

$$\frac{379.17 + 50 + 25}{379.17 + 200} = .784$$

Wheel 11 at L_2 $\left.\begin{matrix} 0 \\ 75 \times .784 \end{matrix}\right\} \frac{555}{8}$ does *not* satisfy criterion.

Wheel 10 at L_2 $\left.\begin{matrix} 75 \times .784 \\ 150 \times .784 \end{matrix}\right\} \frac{615}{8}$ *satisfies* criterion.

Wheel 9 at L_2 $\left.\begin{matrix} 150 \times .784 \\ 225 \times .784 \end{matrix}\right\} \frac{675}{8}$ does *not* satisfy criterion.

$$19{,}875 \div 200 = 99.4$$

$$\times\ 579.2 = 57{,}570$$

$$\frac{375}{25} = 15$$

$$\times\ 454.2 = \underline{\ \ 6{,}810}$$

$$50{,}760$$

$$\div\ 454.2 = 111.7$$

$$\times \frac{42.47}{34.33} = 138.2$$

$$\times \tfrac{5}{6} \times \tfrac{1}{2} = -57.6^k \quad \text{M–50}$$

The method presented above is perfectly general and may be applied to any web member of a non-parallel chord truss without subdivided panels in which stress is computed by moments about a point lying outside the span. Care must be taken in determining the distances s and a. Students frequently become confused concerning these quantities and it is not safe to use the relations given above as formulas; the student should *see* clearly in each case how the stress is to be calculated and from that determine the distances s and a.

The calculation of web stresses in a non-parallel chord truss is simple but tedious, and, as will be shown later, if charts of equivalent uniform loads are available, the use of influence lines is simpler and more rapid.

124. Equivalent Uniform Loads.—The calculation of maximum stresses in the bars of a truss subjected to moving concentrated loads is a very tedious and time-consuming task. To facilitate such calculations most railroad companies, bridge companies and engineers in private practice keep on file tables giving the maximum shears in the panels and the maximum moments at the panel points for trusses with varying panel lengths and numbers of panels for standard loadings. These data are sufficient for the calculation of the stresses in all the bars of parallel chord trusses and in the chords of all non-parallel chord trusses, which lie within their range. Since the maximum web stresses for non-parallel chord trusses do not necessarily occur for the positions of the loads giving maximum shear in the panels, and since the stresses in the inclined chords in the panels have vertical components, the stresses in diagonal and vertical members cannot be determined from such tables. For use in such cases, and in others not within the range of the tables, elaborate charts of **equivalent uniform loads** for certain much-used standard loadings have been prepared. Examples of such charts are those prepared by D. B. Steinman for Cooper's E–60 loading and Steinman's M–60 loading and are reproduced as Plates I and II,[3] facing page 302.

These equivalent uniform load charts are based on the segments of the influence line triangles. Their construction involves an enormous amount of labor and cannot be discussed here. They are very easy to use, however, and there is given below an illustrative example showing their application.

Figure 148 shows the truss of Fig. 146 with influence lines for *stress* in bars U_2U_3, U_2L_3, L_2L_3, and U_2L_2 with the calculations for stress in these bars for M–50 loading, based on the chart given in Plate II. The chart in Plate II is for M–60 one track, and to obtain stresses for M–50 one rail it is necessary to multiply the loads taken from the chart by $\frac{1}{2} \times \frac{50}{60}$, or to multiply the stresses computed from the chart loads by the same ratio.

The student should be able to check the construction of the influence lines after having mastered the discussion of influence lines in Chapter IV, but it may be pointed out that no effort was made to plot positive values above or below the line. The diagrams were drawn and the signs placed on them by inspection.

After the diagrams had been drawn, the equivalent uniform loads were taken from the chart as follows. Consider the bar U_2U_3, for example. The two segments of the triangular influence

[3] "Locomotive Loadings for Railway Bridges," D. B. Steinman, *Trans. Am. Soc. C. E.*, Vol. 86, pp. 606–723, Plates IV and XIII.

line are 75 ft. and 125 ft. Going into the chart with 75 ft. as the shorter segment (read at the top of the diagram) follow down the 75-ft. line vertically to its intersection with the longer segment of 125 ft. (read at the side of the chart) and from this intersection

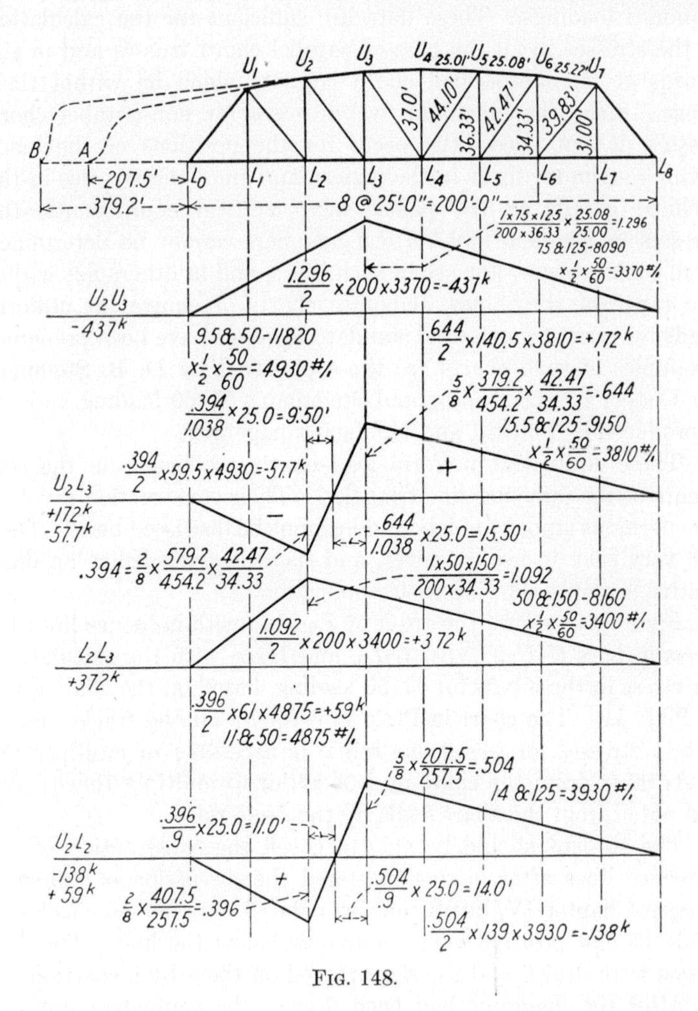

FIG. 148.

follow the curve to a reading on the diagonal edge. The reading is 8090 lb. per ft., which is for M–60 and one full track as stated above. This is reduced to M–50 one rail by multiplying by $\frac{1}{2} \times \frac{50}{60}$ as shown in the figure. In the same manner the segments for the positive stress in U_2L_3, 15.5 ft. and 125 ft., give a reading of 9150 lb. per ft., which is reduced to 3810 lb. per ft. as shown. The shorter segment, 9.5 ft., for the negative stress in U_2L_3, is outside the chart and the value was obtained by extrapolating by eye. As will be noted, the stresses obtained from the influence line calculations check very closely those obtained from the wheel loads. This is to be expected for chord stresses, as the equivalent uniform loads shown on the diagrams were calculated for moment influence lines. For influence lines where l_1 is short, one wheel may be outside of the triangular influence line. For moment this wheel would be off the span, and therefore have no effect, but for web stress it would cause a slight modification as there would

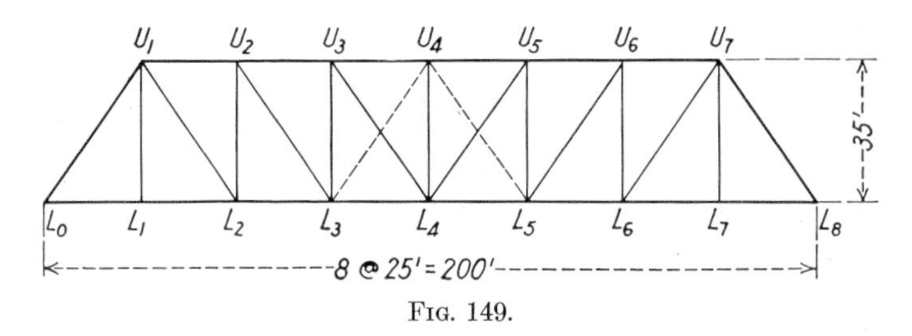

Fig. 149.

be a small amount of stress of the opposite kind caused by this wheel.

125. Counters.—In Art. 118 it was shown that web members may be subjected to reversal of stress; i.e., a diagonal which is normally in tension may for some positions of a series of moving loads be subjected to a compressive stress. If the diagonal is composed of eye bars or is of riveted section so slender that it is incapable of resisting compression, it is necessary to provide an additional diagonal in the panel sloping in the opposite direction to prevent collapse of the structure. This additional diagonal is called a **counter diagonal** or more commonly a **counter.** In Fig. 149 is shown the truss of Fig. 144 with counters shown in panels 3–4 and 4–5. Counters are generally indicated by dotted lines since they are not normally in action.

In considering the action of counters and in calculating stresses in them it will be helpful to think of all diagonals as being wire ropes which would instantly buckle if subjected to compression. For example consider the diagonal U_3L_4 and its counter U_4L_3.

As shown by the index stresses in Fig. 102, the dead load stress in U_3L_4 is $+ 22.1^k$. It should be clear that, as a train comes on from the left-hand end of the bridge, compression develops in U_3L_4 owing to the live loads. Of course there is no actual compression but merely a relief or lessening of the dead load tension. However, as soon as the live load compression becomes greater than the dead load tension, the diagonal U_3L_4 will buckle out of line, since it is unable to resist compression, and the counter diagonal will come into action. The maximum stress in the counter will be the maximum compression calculated for U_3L_4 in Art. 118, minus the normal dead load tension or

$$\text{Stress in } U_4L_3 = 87.8 - 22.1 = + 65.7^k$$

It should be noted that this is neglecting impact which would act to *increase* the counter stress.

Counters are required in non-parallel chord trusses if the diagonals are incapable of resisting compression. In such cases counter stress may be determined by calculating the maximum compression to which the main diagonal would be subjected if capable of resisting compression and multiplying this by the ratio of the length of the counter to the length of the main diagonal. That this statement is correct may be seen by passing a horizontal section through the entire web of the truss shown in Fig. 146. Since the fact that there is or is not a counter in the panel 3–4, for example, will not affect the stress in any member outside of that panel, it should be clear that if the main diagonal U_3L_4 is replaced by a counter U_4L_3 (not shown in the figure), the horizontal component of the counter stress must be equal to that of the replaced main diagonal in order to maintain equilibrium horizontally. Since the horizontal components and horizontal projections of the two members are equal, their stresses must be proportional to their lengths.

123. Tension in Verticals.—A problem of some difficulty which may sometimes require attention is the determination of the greatest tension in the verticals of a non-parallel chord truss with counters. For example, if a counter is required in the panel 2–3 of the truss in Fig. 146 it may be desirable to determine the greatest tension which can occur in U_3L_3. The greatest tension in this vertical is most likely to occur when the counter U_3L_2, the main diagonal U_3L_4, and the counter U_4L_3 all have zero stress, if this condition is possible, as is generally the case. The problem is somewhat troublesome, and when concentrated loads are involved, a solution can be obtained only by trial calculations which simultaneously include live load, impact, and dead load. If a uniform load is used for the calculation of stresses, the solution of this problem still requires computations which simultaneously include live load, impact, and dead load, but if the percentage of impact can be assumed in advance, a direct solution, which leads to a quadratic equation, can be developed.

Tension in the verticals will not be important in a truss having a gradual chord angle change as the one in Fig. 146. When there

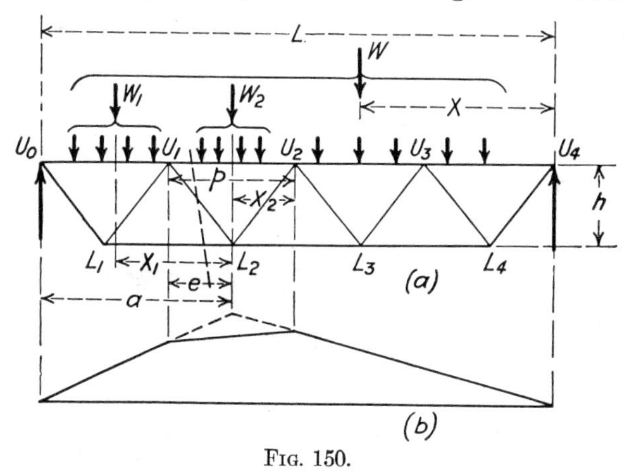

FIG. 150.

is a sharp break in angle between chord segments as often occurred in old " camel-back " trusses, the tension in a vertical may exceed its greatest compression. The matter will not be discussed further as the problem is one not likely to arise frequently, if at all, under present practice in design. Should it occur, the student is prepared to reach a reasonable solution if he thoroughly understands the principles and methods already discussed.

127. Trusses without Verticals.—The positions of a system of concentrated loads which will cause maximum stress in the various members of a truss such as that shown in (*a*) of Fig. 150 may be determined by the same methods used for other parallel chord trusses, except for members of the loaded chord. The necessity for excluding the loaded chord from this statement may be seen by studying the influence line for stress in a top chord of the truss shown in the figure. Figure 150 (*b*) shows the influence line for stress in U_1U_2 of the truss shown in (*a*). It should be clear that so long as the unit load is to the right of U_2, or to the left of U_1, the influence line for bending moment at L_2 (and therefore for stress in U_1U_2) will have the same shape as for any other truss. However, as soon as the unit load passes U_2, moving to the left, a downward reaction at U_1 begins to develop, and during the movement of the unit load between U_1 and U_2 the bending moment at L_2 is, of course, the moment of the reaction at U_0 (which varies as a straight line) minus the moment of the reaction at U_1 (which also varies as a straight line). The influence line for bending moment at L_2 (and therefore for stress in U_1U_2) must, then, be a straight line throughout the panel 1–2, as shown in (*b*).

The shape of the influence line just discussed should make it clear that the criterion for placing the loads in position to produce maximum stress in U_1U_2 (and in similar members) will not be the same as previously developed. The method of attack, however, is the same, and the necessary criterion may be derived as follows:

W = total load on the span;
W_1 = total load to the left of U_1;
W_2 = total load in the panel 1–2;
a = distance from the left support to center of moments;
e = distance from U_1 to center of moments;
p = length of panel 1–2;
h = depth of truss;
L = span length;
dx = small distance moved to the left;
ΔS = change in stress in U_1U_2 due to the movement dx.

Taking moments about L_2

$$\Delta S = \frac{\dfrac{Wdx}{L}a - W_1dx - \dfrac{W_2dx}{p}e}{h}$$

Since $\Delta S = 0$ is necessary in order to have a maximum stress

$$\frac{Wdx}{L}a = W_1dx + \frac{W_2dx}{p}e$$

$$\frac{W}{L} = \frac{W_1 + \dfrac{W_2e}{p}}{a}$$

which is the criterion for maximum moment at any point in a panel. In the common Warren truss the panels are equal and $e = \frac{p}{2}$; the criterion then reduces to the common form,

$$\frac{W}{L} = \frac{W_1 + \frac{W_2}{2}}{a}$$

It should be noted that the expression for change in stress can change from an increasing to a decreasing function by increasing

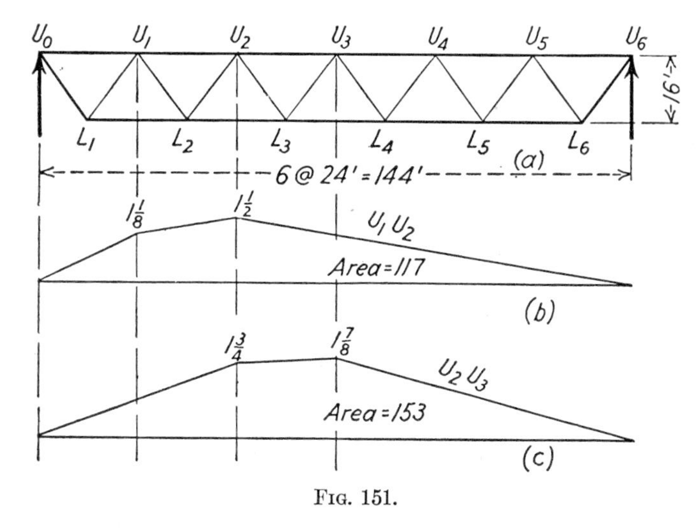

Fig. 151.

W_2 or by moving a load from W_2 to W_1, and the criterion can therefore be satisfied for maximum stress with a load at either U_1 or U_2.

Illustrative Example.—The stresses will be calculated for the members U_1U_2 and U_2U_3 in the truss shown in Fig. 151 (*a*), using an E–40 loading.

Member U_1U_2 (Using Table III)

Wheel 3 @ U_1 and 7 @ U_2 $\left.\begin{matrix} 90 + 109.5 \\ 150 + 99 \end{matrix}\right\} \frac{36}{144} 996 = 249$ just satisfies.

Wheel 4 @ U_1 $\left.\begin{matrix} 150 + 99 \\ 210 + 69 \end{matrix}\right\} \frac{36}{144} 1026 = 256.5$ satisfies.

Wheel 8 @ U_2 does not satisfy.

Inspection indicates wheel 4 gives maximum but moving from 3 @ U_1 to 4 @ U_1

$$\left(996 + \frac{30}{2}\right)\frac{5}{144}36 - 150 \times 5 - \frac{198}{2}5 = +\,18.75 \qquad \text{Use 4.}$$

$$\begin{array}{lrl}
 & 49{,}092 & \\
852 \times 29 = & 24{,}708 & \\
174 \times 14\tfrac{1}{2} = & 2{,}523 & \\ \hline
 & 76{,}323 \times \dfrac{36}{144} = 19{,}081 & \\
 & 1440 & \\
210 \times 12 = & \underline{2520} \quad 3960 & \\
 & 138 & \\
\dfrac{1587}{24} = & 66 & \\
 & 72 \times 12 = \underline{864} & \\
 & & 4{,}824 \\
 & & 14{,}257 \times \dfrac{4}{16 \times 6 \times 2} = -\,297^k \quad \text{E–40}
\end{array}$$

Member U_2U_3

$$\text{Wheel } 7 \text{ @ } U_2 \qquad \left.\begin{array}{l} 309 + 73.5 \\ 348 + 54 \end{array}\right\}\frac{60}{144}\,996 = 415$$

$$\text{Wheel } 11 \text{ @ } U_3 \qquad \left.\begin{array}{l} 348 + 54 \\ 348 + 84 \end{array}\right\}\frac{60}{144}\,1014 = 422.5 \quad \text{satisfies.}$$

$$\begin{array}{lrl}
 & 49{,}092 & \\
852 \times 27 = & 23{,}004 & \\
162 \times 13\tfrac{1}{2} = & 2{,}187 & \\ \hline
 & 74{,}283 \times \dfrac{60}{144} = 30{,}950 & \\
 & 6465 & \\
348 \times 15 = & 5220 & \\
\dfrac{1683}{24} \times 12 = & \underline{841} & 12{,}526 \\
 & & 18{,}424 \times \dfrac{4}{16 \times 6 \times 2} = -\,384^k \quad \text{E–40}
\end{array}$$

Stress in U_1U_2 and U_2U_3 by Equivalent Uniform Loads.—The influence lines for stress in the two members in which stresses were just calculated are shown in (*b*) and (*c*) of Fig. 151. Since these are not triangles, precise values of equivalent uniform loads should not be expected from the diagram in Plate I, but approximate values may be obtained which should be accurate enough for most purposes. These diagrams may be used in connection with influence lines which are not exactly triangular in shape, by assuming a truly triangular influence line which approximates the true one as closely as possible. It may be well here to caution the student against the unthinking use of equivalent uniform load charts in connection with non-triangular influence lines.[4] In this particular case the divide between the two segments may be taken at the high point of the influence line, or at the intersection of the two extreme slopes (the latter being the center of moments). Either choice of segments will give good results for this problem, but in general greater accuracy will result if the center of moments is assumed as the dividing point between the segments. Using the areas shown on the influence lines in Fig. 151:

U_1U_2 36 and 108 $7630 \times \frac{1}{2} = 3815$

$117 \times 3815 \times \frac{4}{6} = -298^k$

U_2U_3 60 and 84 $7610 \times \frac{1}{2} = 3805$

$153 \times 3805 \times \frac{4}{6} = -388^k$

128. Subdivided Trusses.—The calculation of maximum live load stresses in the members of ordinary subdivided trusses follows for the most part along the lines already discussed. The positions of a series of concentrated loads which will produce maximum stresses in the various members may be found in most cases from criteria already developed. In determining the positions for maximum stresses in the chords to which the secondary system connects, a slight modification is necessary.

In Figs. 152 and 153 are shown a parallel chord or Baltimore truss, and a non-parallel chord or Pettit truss, with influence lines for typical members. Inspection of these influence lines shows that it is only the chords to which the secondary trussing connects which have influence diagrams differing from those for which criteria have been developed. Two cases will be briefly discussed.

In Fig. 154 is shown a subdivided deck truss with a series of wheel loads applied to the top chord. The *change* in stress in

[4] Judgment is necessary, and judgment must be based on experience as well as on careful study. The student or engineer having occasion to use the equivalent uniform load charts given in this text for calculation of stresses from influence lines which are not triangular should read the article on this matter by Mr. Steinman, published in *Engineering News–Record*, Aug. 1, 1918.

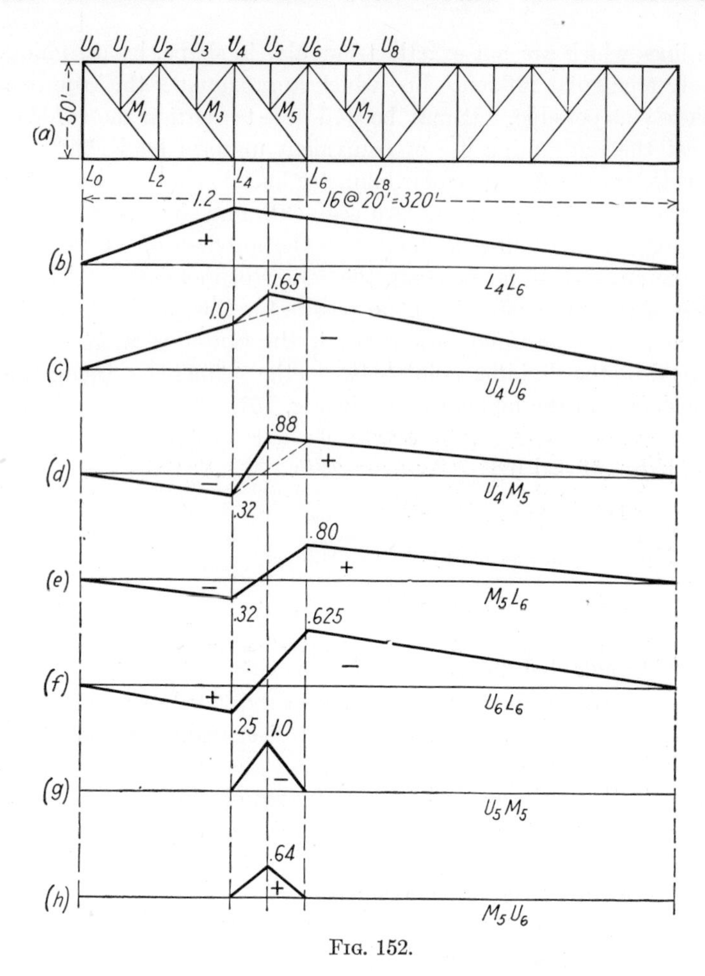

FIG. 152.

U_4U_6 due to a movement to the left of these loads may be expressed as follows:

W = total load on the span;
W_1 = total load to the left of U_4;
W_2 = total load in the panel 4–5;
a = distance from the left support to L_6;
h = depth of truss;
dx = small distance moved to the left;
ΔS = *change* in stress in U_4U_6 due to the movement dx;
L = span length;
p = panel length.

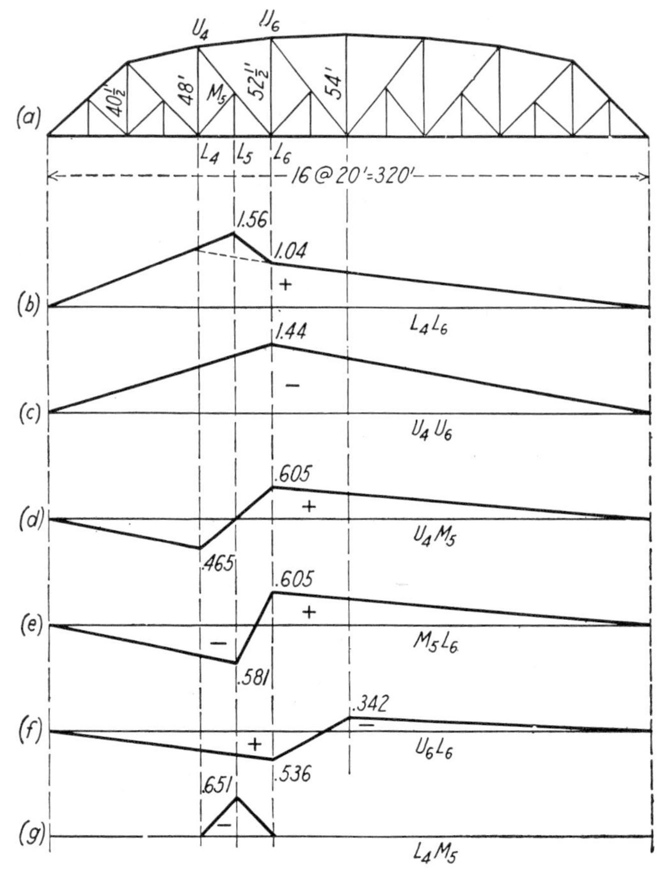

Fig. 153.

Taking moments about L_6

$$\Delta S = \frac{\dfrac{W dx}{L} a - W_1 dx - W_2 \dfrac{dx}{p} 2p}{h}$$

If the stress in U_4U_6 is an increasing function ΔS must become equal to zero to have the stress pass through a maximum value. Therefore, when $\Delta S = 0$

$$\frac{W dx}{L} a = W_1 dx + W_2 \frac{dx}{p} 2p$$

$$\frac{W}{L} = \frac{(W_1 + 2W_2)}{a}$$

Inspection of the expression for ΔS or of the influence line in Fig. 152 (*c*) will show that for a maximum value (i.e., ΔS changing from an increasing to a decreasing function) a load must be just entering the panel 4–5 and therefore the criterion can be satisfied only when a load is at U_5.

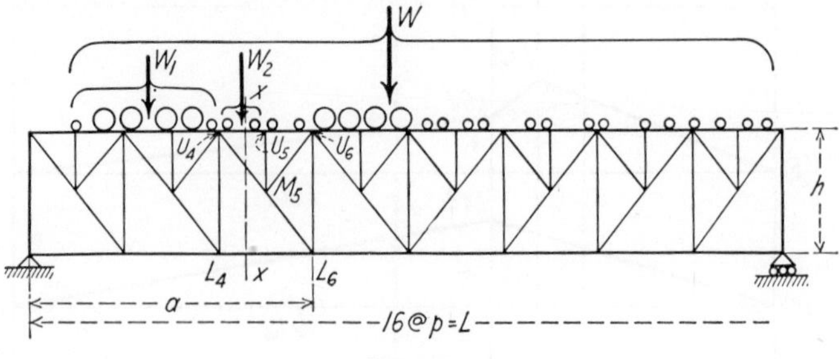

FIG. 154.

It should be clear that in writing the expression for ΔS the part of the structure to the left of section x–x was considered. In this case all the forces acting on the part under consideration were to the left of the center of moments.

In Fig. 155 is shown a subdivided through Pettit truss with loads which actually are applied along the floor at the bottom

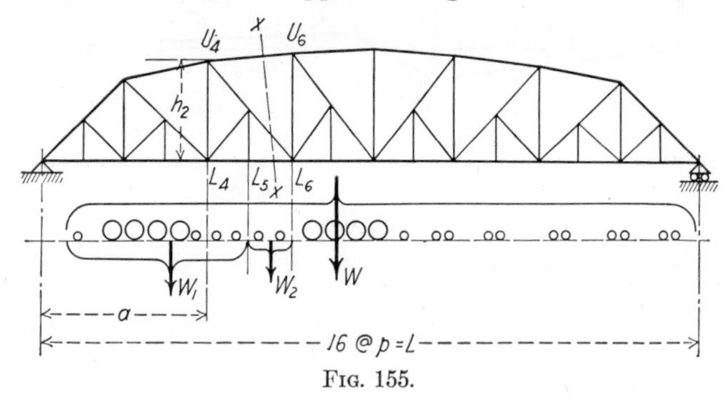

FIG. 155.

chord shown below the truss for clearness. In calculating the stress in L_4L_6, section x–x is passed and moments taken about U_4. In this case the changing floorbeam reaction at L_5 is on the right of the center of moments while the other forces acting on the part of the structure to the left of x–x are on the left of U_4, the center of moments. This modifies the criterion for position for maximum stress. The notation shown on the figure is self-explanatory, and

S. & V. RAILROAD—CLEAR CREEK BRIDGE

Preliminary Design	
4–15–31	J. R. D.
Sheet 1 of 4	

Live Load Stresses

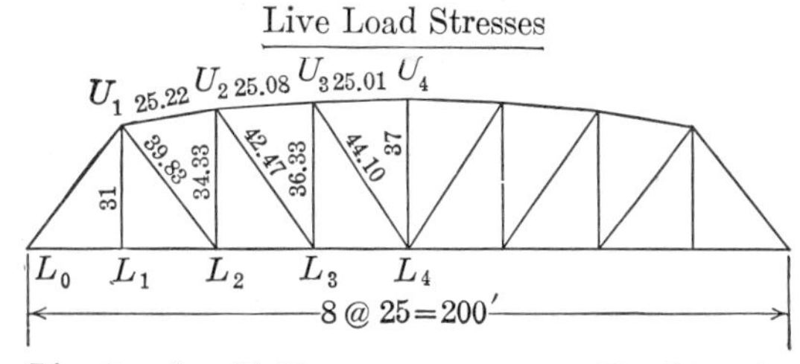

Live Load = E–60

$$\text{Impact} = S\frac{2000 - L}{1600 + 10L}$$

U_1L_0

Load 25 and 175 = 7460 lb. per ft.

$$\frac{7460 \times 25 \times 175}{4 \times 31}\ \frac{39.83}{25} = -\ 419^k$$

U_1U_2

Load 50 and 150 = 7200 lb. per ft.

$$\frac{7200 \times 50 \times 150}{4 \times 34.33}\ \frac{25.22}{25} = -\ 397^k$$

U_2U_3

Load 75 and 125 = 7170 lb. per ft.

$$\frac{7170 \times 75 \times 125}{4 \times 36.33}\ \frac{25.08}{25} = -\ 464^k$$

U_3U_4

Load 100 and 100 = 7140 lb. per ft.

$$\frac{7140 \times 100 \times 100}{4 \times 37}\ \frac{25.01}{25} = -\ 483^k$$

U_1L_1

Load 25 and 25 = 9100 lb. per ft.

$$\frac{9100 \times 25}{2} = +\ 114^k$$

$U_2\ L_2$

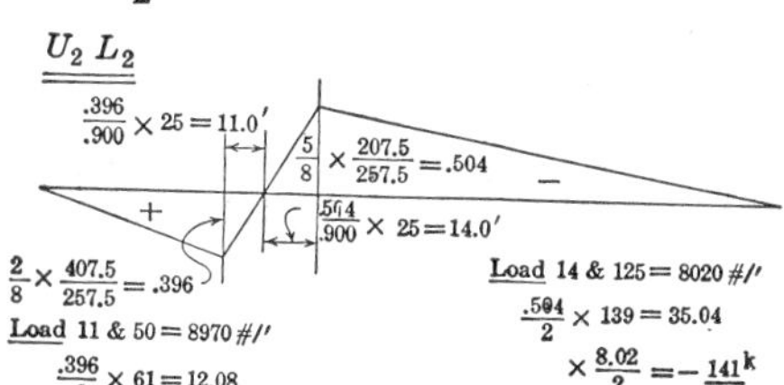

$$\times \frac{8.970}{2} = +54^k$$

Dead Loads

Track	=	520 lb. per ft. of Br.
Floor	=	600
Tr. and Br.	=	1840
		2960 lb. per ft. of Br.
÷ 2	=	1480 lb. per ft. of Tr.

$$\frac{1.120}{2} \times 25 = \qquad 14.0$$

$$\frac{1.840}{4} \times 25 = 11.5 \qquad 11.5$$

Panel Loads = T 11.5 B 25.5

L_0L_2

$$\frac{7460 \times 25 \times 175}{4 \times 31} = +\ 263^k$$

L_2L_3

$$\frac{7200 \times 50 \times 150}{4 \times 34.33} = +\ 393^k$$

L_3L_4

$$\frac{7170 \times 75 \times 125}{4 \times 36.33} = +\ 462^k$$

U_4L_4

$$483 \times \frac{0.67}{25.01} \times 2 = +\ 25.8^k$$

Intersection Distances

$$U_1U_2\left(\frac{31}{3.33} - 1\right) 25 = 207.50$$

$$U_2U_3\left(\frac{34.33}{2} - 2\right)25 = 379.17$$

$$U_3U_4\left(\frac{36.33}{0.67} - 3\right)25 = 1287.5$$

terms not defined there are as used before. The expression for *change* in stress in L_4L_6 due to a movement dx to the left is:

$$\Delta S = \frac{\frac{W dx}{L} a - W_1 dx + W_2 \frac{dx}{p} p}{h_2}$$

and for a maximum

$$\Delta S = 0$$

Therefore

$$\frac{W}{L} = \frac{(W_1 - W_2)}{a}$$

Inspection of the expression for ΔS or of the influence line in Fig. 153 (*b*) will show that for a maximum value a load must be at L_5.

If the student understands the reasoning used in developing the various criteria given in this chapter and in Chapter IV, he should be able to make such modifications as are necessary for trusses with triangulation different from those discussed above.

129. K-Truss with Concentrated Loads.—The truss shown in Fig. 101 is repeated here in Fig. 156 (*a*). The two diagonals in each panel have the same slope, and consequently equal stresses which are opposite in sign. The top chord is straight between even-numbered panel points. Influence lines for typical members are shown in Fig. 156, (*b*) to (*i*). The student should check the ordinates by placing a unit load at the proper points and making the appropriate calculations.

It will be observed that the tension in the lower chord is equal to the horizontal component of the compression in the upper chord. Also, the influence line for stress in U_5M_5 is proportional to that for M_4U_5, and the same position of the loads will therefore produce maximum stress in either member. All influence lines, except the one for M_5L_5, are similar to those previously shown for non-parallel chord trusses and the criteria already used are applicable. Since the most convenient section for M_5L_5 also cuts M_4U_5, the stress in this member must be included in developing a criterion for M_5L_5. This lengthens the procedure, although for maximum compression the criterion simplifies to $\frac{W}{L} = \frac{W_1}{p} \frac{2(s + a)}{s}$, in which a is the distance from L_0 to L_4 and the other nomenclature is as

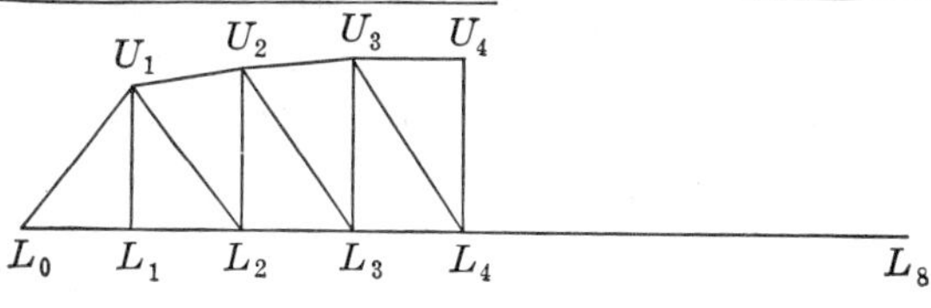

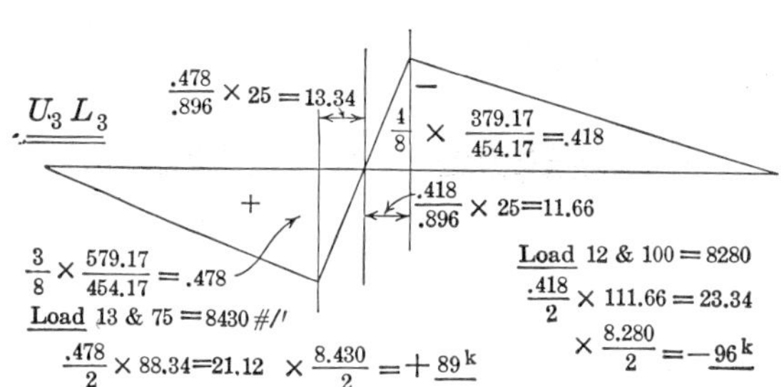

$U_3 L_3$
$\frac{.478}{.896} \times 25 = 13.34$
$\frac{4}{8} \times \frac{379.17}{454.17} = .418$
$\frac{.418}{.896} \times 25 = 11.66$
$\frac{3}{8} \times \frac{579.17}{454.17} = .478$
Load 13 & 75 = 8430 #/′
$\frac{.478}{2} \times 88.34 = 21.12 \quad \times \frac{8.430}{2} = +89^k$
Load 12 & 100 = 8280
$\frac{.418}{2} \times 111.66 = 23.34$
$\times \frac{8.280}{2} = -96^k$

$\frac{.254}{1.031} \times 25 = 6.16$

$U_1 L_2$

$\frac{6}{8} \times \frac{207.5}{257.5} \times \frac{39.83}{31} = .777$

$\frac{.777}{1.031} \times 25 = 18.84$

$\frac{1}{8} \times \frac{407.5}{257.5} \times \frac{39.83}{31} = .254$

$\frac{.254}{2} \times 31.16 = 3.96$

Load 19 & 150 = 7710 #/′

$\frac{.777}{2} \times 168.84 = 65.60$

$\times \frac{7.710}{2} = +253^k$

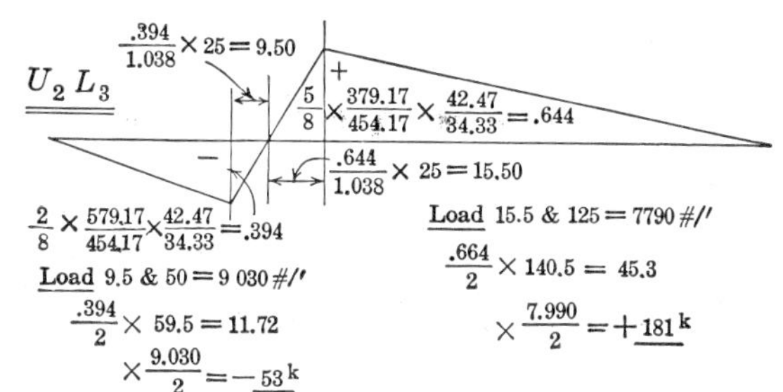

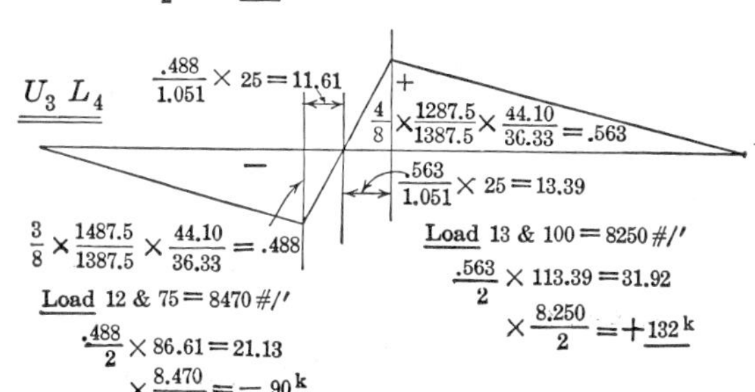

previously used. For maximum tension the criterion is not so simple. For standard loading the equivalent uniform load could conveniently be used for maximum compression, but if it were

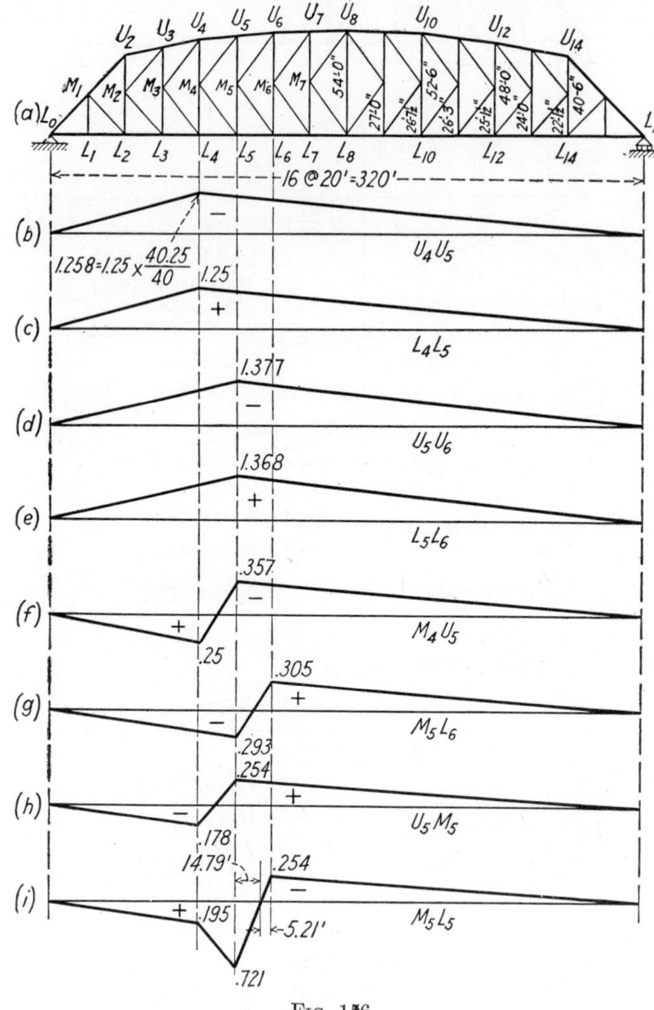

FIG. 156.

necessary to compute the stresses for a special locomotive loading the criterion could conveniently be derived from the influence line.

In obtaining the criterion for maximum moment in Art. 65, use was made of the principle that the change in any function due

S. & V. RAILROAD—CLEAR CREEK BRIDGE

Dead Load Stresses

Preliminary Design	
4–15–31	J. R. D.
Sheet 3 of 4	

$\underline{U_1L_0}\quad \dfrac{419}{7460} \times 2960 = -\,166^k$

$\underline{U_1U_2}\quad \dfrac{397}{7200} \times 2960 = -\,163^k$

$\underline{U_2U_3}\quad \dfrac{464}{7170} \times 2960 = -\,192^k$

$\underline{U_3U_4}\quad \dfrac{483}{7140} \times 2960 = -\,200^k$

$\underline{U_1L_1}\quad = +\,25.5^k$

$\underline{L_0L_2}\quad \dfrac{263}{7460} \times 2960 = +\,104^k$

$\underline{L_2L_3}\quad \dfrac{393}{7200} \times 2960 = +\,162^k$

$\underline{L_3L_4}\quad \dfrac{462}{7170} \times 2960 = +\,191^k$

$\underline{U_4L_4}\quad \dfrac{25.8}{7140} \times 2960 = +\,10.7$

$\quad -\,11.5$

$\quad -\,0.8^k$

$\underline{U_2L_2}$ 35.04 − 12.08 = 22.96

$22.96 \times \dfrac{2960}{2} = -\,34$

$\quad 11.5$

$\quad -\,45.5^k$

$\underline{U_3L_3}$ 23.34 − 21.12 = 2.22

$2.22 \times \dfrac{2960}{2} = -\,3.3$

$\quad 11.5$

$\quad -\,14.8^k$

$\underline{U_1L_2}$ 65.60 − 3.96 = 61.64

$61.64 \times \dfrac{2960}{2} = +\,91^k$

$\underline{U_2L_3}$ 45.33 − 11.72 = 33.61

$33.61 \times \dfrac{2960}{2} = +\,50^k$

$\underline{U_3L_4}$ 31.92 − 21.13 = 10.79

$10.79 \times \dfrac{2960}{2} = +\,16^k$

to a movement of loads is equal to the loads times the slope of the influence line times the distance moved. For maximum compression in M_5L_5, loads will be on the right portion of the span and extend into the panel 5–6. Let W_1 represent the loads in the panel 5–6 and W_2 represent the loads to the right of L_6, then for a unit movement to the left,

$$\Delta S = W_2 \frac{.254}{200} - W_1 \frac{.975}{20} = 0 \text{ for maximum.}$$

$W_1 = .0261\ W_2$, which is the criterion for maximum compression in M_5L_5 for this truss. Inspection of the influence line will show that this can be satisfied for a maximum only when a load is at L_6.

For maximum tension the left portion of the span will be loaded and it will be assumed that no loads extend to the right of L_6. Let W_1 represent the loads in panel 5–6, W_2 the loads in the panel 4–5, and W_3 the loads to the left of L_4. For unit movement to the right,

$$\Delta S = W_3 \frac{.195}{80} + W_2 \frac{.526}{20} - W_1 \frac{.975}{20} = 0 \text{ for maximum.}$$

$W_1 = .54W_2 + .05W_3$, which is the criterion for maximum tension in M_5L_5. Inspection shows that a load will be at L_5 when the stress has a maximum value. Although the assumption that there were no loads to the left of L_5 was clearly correct for maximum compression, it is possible that some may extend to the right of L_6 for maximum tension. If this is found to be the case the criterion must be modified to include such loads.

If it is necessary to determine the maximum value of any function due to moving concentrated loads, a criterion can be developed from an influence line for that function whenever the influence line is composed of a series of straight lines.

130. Sample Computations for a Through Truss.—On the right-hand pages, 283 to 291, are shown the computations for maximum stress due to vertical loads in the various members of the Parker truss discussed heretofore. This truss is for a single track through bridge and is to be designed for E–60 loading. The dead loads and impact formula are shown on Sheet 1 of the calculations.

Live Load Chord Stresses.—Since for maximum stress in the chord members the entire span should be loaded, these stresses

S. & V. RAILROAD—CLEAR CREEK BRIDGE

Preliminary Design	
4-15-31	J. R. D.
Sheet 4 of 4	

Member	D.L.	L.L.	Imp. %	Imp.	Totals
U_1L_0	−166	−419	50	−210	−795
U_1U_2	−163	−397	50	−199	−759
U_2U_3	−192	−464	50	−232	−888
U_3U_4	−200	−483	50	−242	−925
L_0L_2	+104	+263	50	+132	+499
L_2L_3	+162	+393	50	+197	+752
L_3L_4	+191	+462	50	+231	+884
U_1L_1	+ 26	+114	93	+106	+246
U_2L_2	− 46	−141	60	−85	−272
		+ 54	82	+ 44	+ 52
U_3L_3	− 15	− 96	66	− 63	−174
		+ 89	73	+ 65	+139
U_4L_4	0	+ 26	50	+ 13	+ 39
U_1L_2	+ 91	+253	54	+137	+481
U_2L_3	+ 50	+181	60	+109	+340
		− 53	82	− 43	− 46
U_3L_4	+ 16	+132	66	+ 87	+235
		− 90	73	− 66	−140

can be most conveniently calculated by means of the equivalent uniform loads given in Plate I, the center of moments for the particular member dividing the span into the segments l_1 and l_2. The moment will be $\frac{w \times l_1 \times l_2}{2}$ and, since w is the load per foot of track, this divided by 2 times the height of the truss at the point of moments will give the stress in the lower chord or the horizontal component of stress in the upper chord.

The member U_4L_4 has been included with the chord members as its stress is the sum of the vertical components of U_3U_4 and U_4U_5.

Live Load Web Stresses.—The maximum stress in the hanger U_1L_1 occurs when the two panels are loaded, the equivalent uniform load being that for the two segments of 25 ft. For the other members of the web system the best procedure is to draw influence lines for each member and multiply the compression and tension areas by the appropriate equivalent uniform load. Compression need not be calculated for the diagonals near the end as reversal does not occur.

Dead Load Stresses.—Since equivalent uniform loads have been used in the calculation of the chord stresses, and influence lines have been drawn for the web members, the most direct procedure in computing the dead load stresses is by simple proportion for the chord members and the net areas of the influence lines for the others, the amount of the dead load per foot being used. If this procedure is followed a correction for top chord loads must be made for correct results in calculating the stresses in verticals, as shown in the calculations.

When tables of moments are available for the computation of chord stresses or when equivalent uniform load diagrams are not available for the computation of the live load stresses, it will generally be found most advantageous to determine the dead load stresses graphically. On page 291 is shown the stress diagram for this truss for the dead loads given. The stresses are shown on the figure.

Combined Stresses.—The stresses are tabulated on page 289, and the total stresses are given. Where there is a reversal of stress in the member the maximum value of each kind is shown. The dead load compression in U_4L_4 is so small that it has no meaning in design, and has been tabulated as zero.

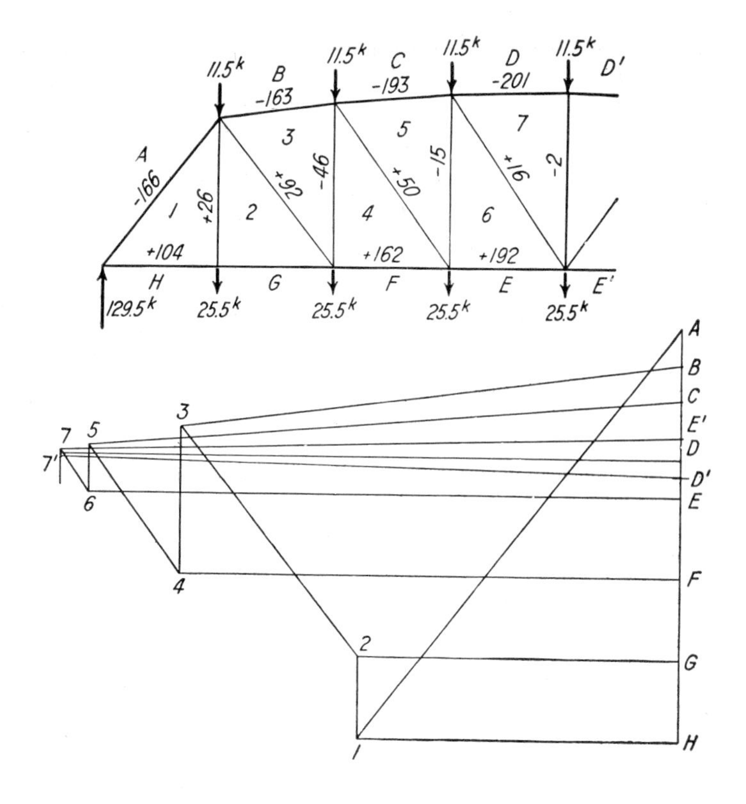

PROBLEMS

203. Calculate the stress in bars L_3L_4 and U_1L_2 of the structure here shown, due to the live load shown in Problem 117 on p. 147.

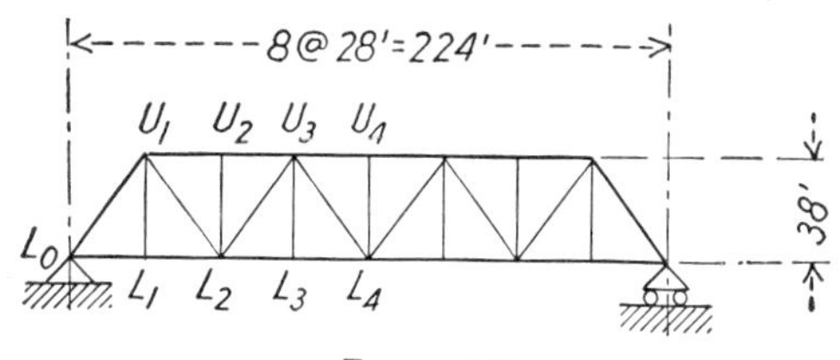

Prob. 203.

204. Calculate the stress in the following members of the truss due to an E-60 loading,

(*a*) U_2U_3. *Ans.* $U_2U_3 = -651^k$ wheel 12.
(*b*) L_3L_4. $L_3L_4 = +642^k$ wheel 12.

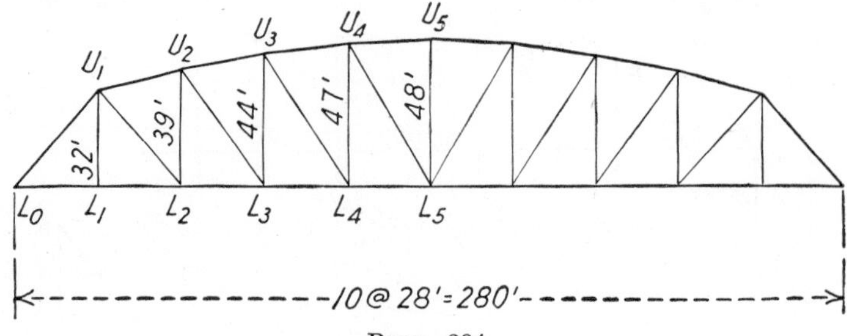

Prob. 204.

205. As a unit load moves from *A* to *B* on the structure, draw:

(*a*) The influence line for stress in bar *e*.
(*b*) The influence line for stress in bar *g*.

Give ordinates in each case.

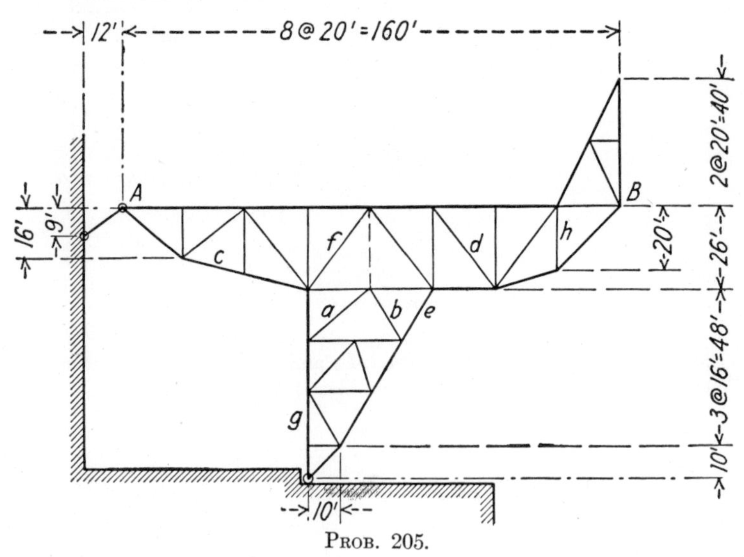

Prob. 205.

206. Due to the axle loads shown, calculate the maximum stress in:

(*a*) U_3L_3 (maximum compression)
(*b*) L_3L_4

of an 8-panel S. T. deck Pratt truss having panel lengths of 28 ft. and a depth of 38 ft. *Ans.* $U_3L_3 = -208^k$ wheel 4.
$L_3L_4 = +619^k$ uniform load.

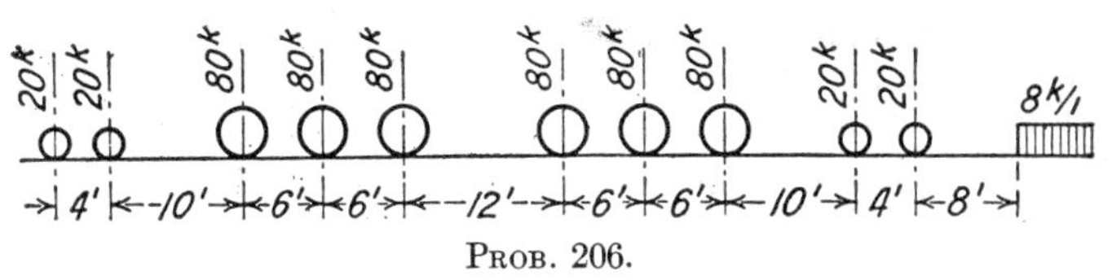

Prob. 206.

207. As a unit load moves from A to B:

(a) Draw the influence line for stress in the bar h.

(b) Draw the influence line for stress in bar g.

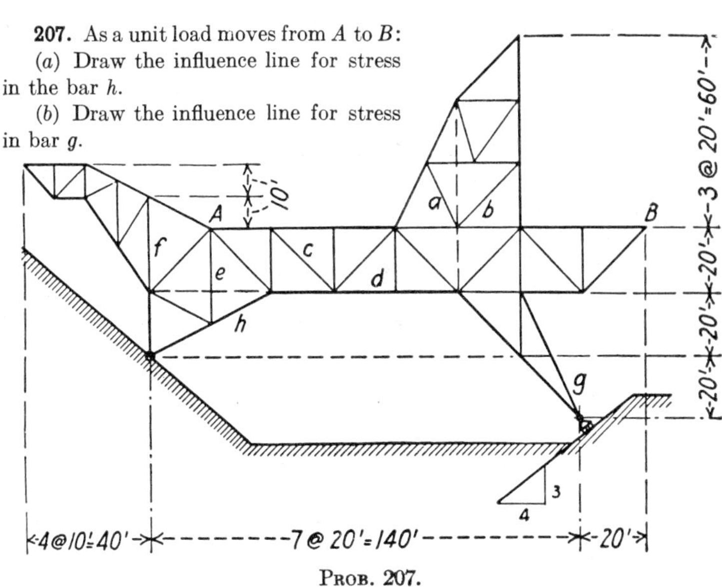

Prob. 207.

208. Draw the influence lines for stress in bars a, c, e, f, and k of the figure, as a unit load moves across the top chord from the left end to the right reaction.

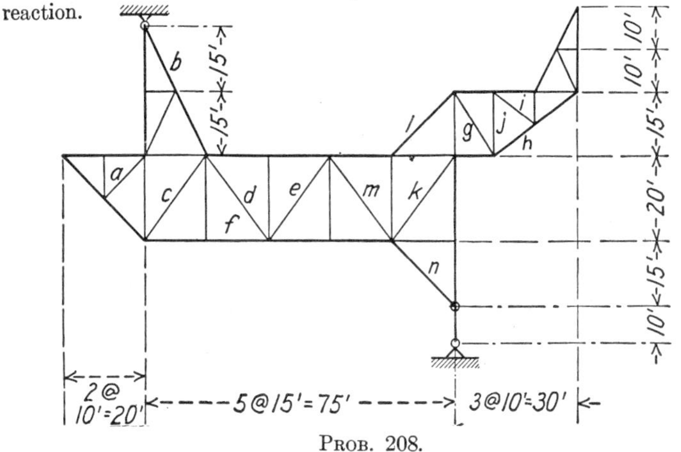

Prob. 208.

209. Compute the maximum stress in the bars given in Problem 208, due to a single concentrated load of 100^k which may occupy any point on the top chord between the left end and the right reaction.

210. Compute the maximum stress in bars *a*, *d*, *f*, and *h* of the figure, caused by a single load of 100^k which can occupy any point on the top chord between the hip points.

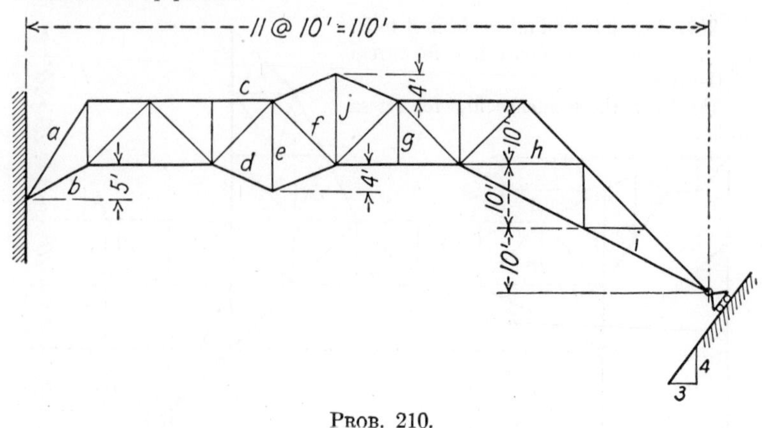

Prob. 210.

211. Draw the influence lines for stress in bars *a*, *b*, *c*, and *d* of the structure shown, as a unit load moves from *A* to *B*, assuming rollers at *B*.

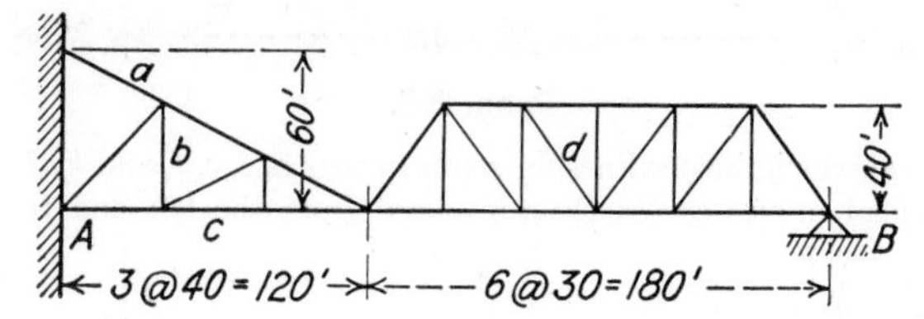

Prob. 211.

212. (*a*) Draw the influence lines for stress in bars *a* and *b* of the structure, as a unit load moves from *A* to *B*.

(*b*) Calculate the maximum stress in bars *c*, *d*, and *e* due to the loads shown. These loads may take any position between *A* and *B*.

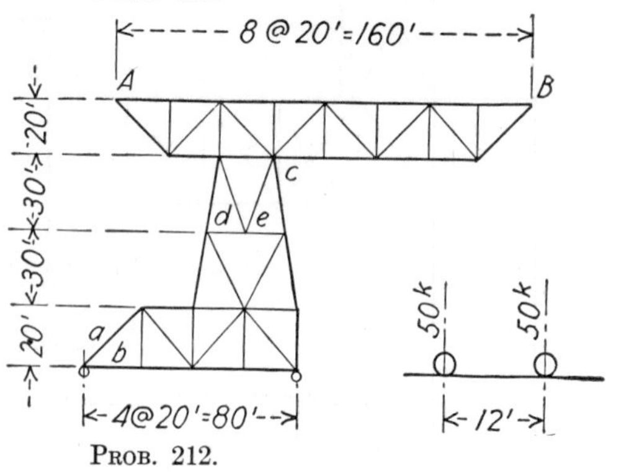

Prob. 212.

(*c*) Is the structure statically determinate for every bar?

$$Ans.\quad (b)\ \left.\begin{array}{l} c = -\ 370^k \\ d = +\ 183^k \\ e = -\ 183^k \end{array}\right\}\text{right wheel at B.}$$

213. The loads shown may occupy any position between *A* and *B* on the structure in Problem 205. Calculate the maximum stress in bars *a* and *d*.

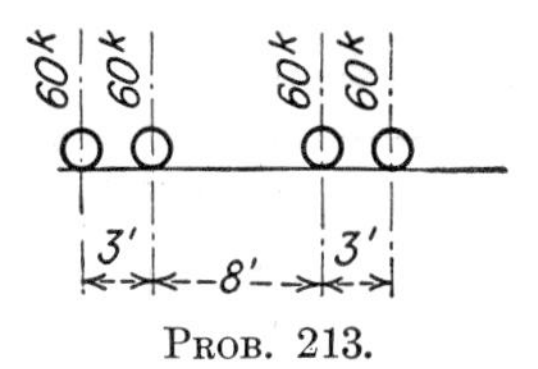

PROB. 213.

214. Compute the maximum live load stress in U_1U_2 and L_3L_4 of the figure shown, due to a uniform moving load of 7000 lb. per ft. of track.

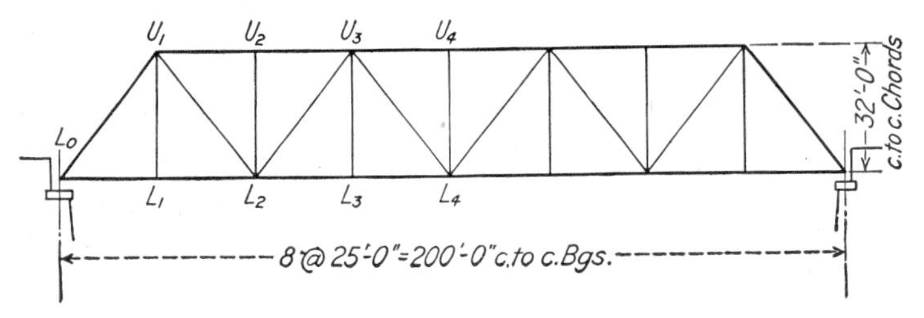

PROB. 214.

215. Calculate the maximum stress in bar *a* of the truss shown, due to the loads in the same figure. *Ans.* $+583^k$ wheel 8.

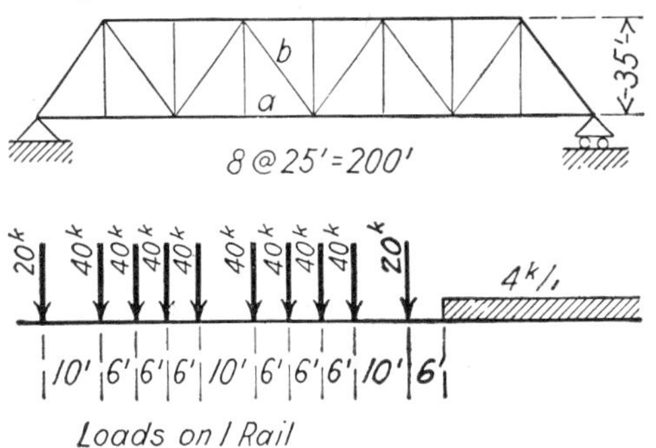

PROB. 215.

216. Calculate the maximum tension in bar *b* of the truss shown in Problem 215, due to the loads shown in the same figure.

217. (*a*) Compute the maximum live load stress of both kinds in U_3L_4 of the figure for Problem 214, due to the same uniform moving load, using the conventional full panel load method.

(*b*) Compute the maximum live load stress of both kinds in U_3L_4 due to the same uniform moving load, using the influence line.

218. A deck Pratt truss has 10 panels of 25 ft. each and is 38 ft. deep center to center of chords. Calculate the maximum compression in bars U_3U_4 and U_4L_4 due to the loads shown.

Ans. $U_3U_4 = - 652^k$ $6\frac{2}{3}$ ft. uniform load.
$U_4L_4 = - 196^k$ wheel 2.

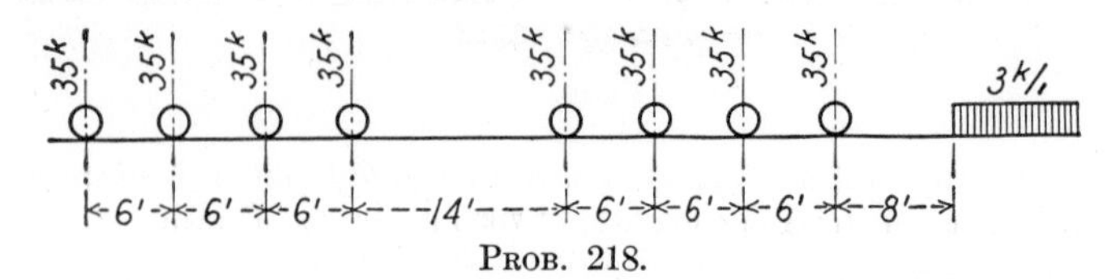

PROB. 218.

219. A through Warren truss with verticals has 8 panels of 28 ft. each and is 40 ft. deep center to center of chords. Calculate the maximum tension in bars L_2L_4 and U_3L_2, due to the loads shown.

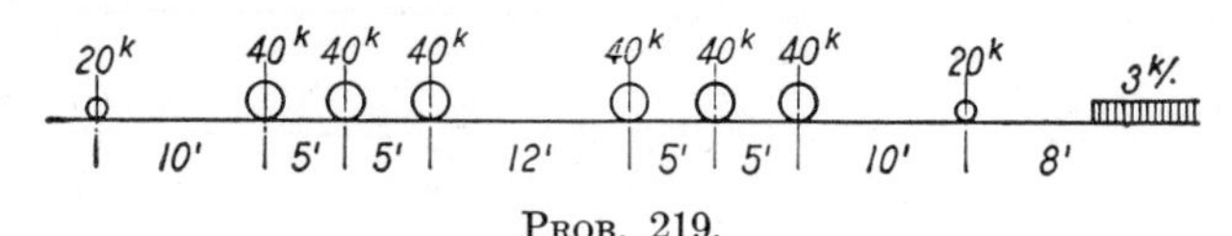

PROB. 219.

220. Compute live stress in each bar due to Steinman's M-50 loading, for the figure shown.

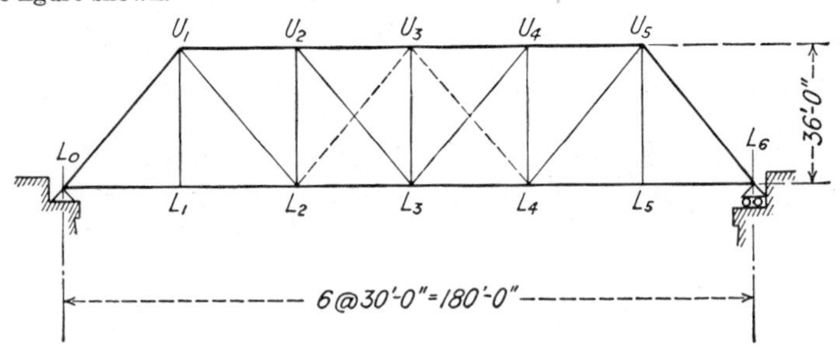

PROB. 220.

221. Compute the stress, in the following bars of the structure shown, due to Steinman's M-60 loading.

(*a*) U_3U_4 Maximum compression. *Ans.* $U_3U_4 = - 544^k$ wheel 10 or 11.
(*b*) L_3L_4 Maximum tension. $L_3L_4 = + 527^k$ wheel 9.

(*c*) U_3L_4 Maximum tension and maximum compression. $U_3L_4 = +\ 166^k$ wheel 3. $\begin{cases} -\ 97.5^k \text{ wheel } 3. \\ -\ 104^k \text{ wheel } \overline{10}. \end{cases}$

(*d*) U_2L_2 Maximum compression. $U_2L_2 = -\ 202^k$ wheel 3.

(*e*) U_1L_1 Maximum tension. $U_1L_1 = +\ 148.5^k$ wheel 9 or 10.

PROB. 221.

222. Calculate the stress due to Cooper's E-75 in:

(*a*) The chord L_4L_5

(*b*) The vertical U_3L_3

of a single-track deck Pratt truss having 10 panels of 28 ft. each and a depth of 48 ft. center to center of chords.

223. Compute the maximum live load stress of both kinds in the bars L_3L_4 and U_3L_4 of the structure shown in Problem 214, due to Cooper's E-60 loading.

224. Calculate the maximum stress in bars U_3L_3 and L_3L_4 of the structure due to a moving uniform load of 4^k per ft. of truss.

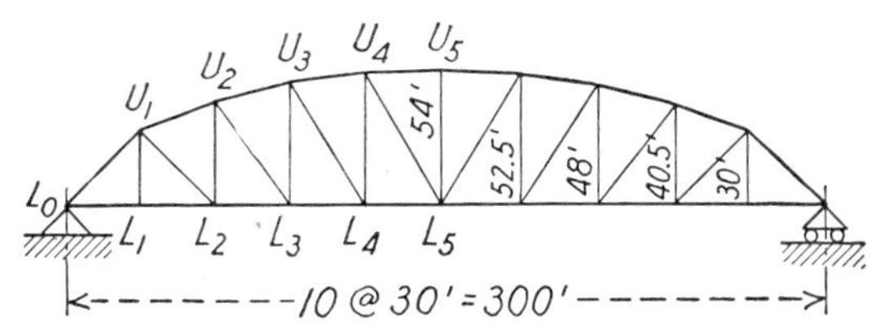

PROB. 224.

225. (*a*) Calculate the maximum stress in the bar *a* of the truss shown, due to a moving uniform load of 3^k per ft. of truss.

(*b*) Calculate the maximum stress of both kinds in the bar *b* due to the same load: first, by the approximate full panel load method; and second, exactly by any method you wish. *Ans.* (*a*) $+539^k$.

(*b*) 1st: -192^k, $+53.7^k$.

2nd: -182^k, $+43.6^k$.

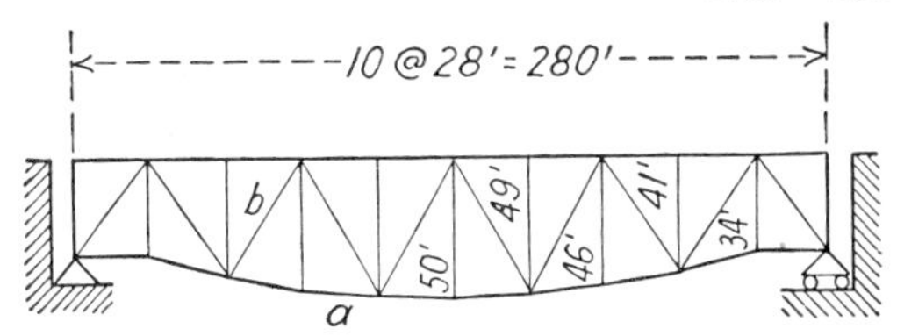

PROB. 225.

226. A through Pratt truss has 10 panels of 28 ft. each and the following depths:

At U_1L_1 depth = 32 ft.
U_2L_3 depth = 39 ft.
U_3L_3 depth = 44 ft.
U_4L_4 depth = 47 ft.
U_5L_5 depth = 48 ft.

Calculate the maximum compression in U_3U_4 due to a moving uniform load of 4^k per ft., and the maximum stress of both kinds in U_3L_3 due to a moving uniform load of 5^k per ft.

227. A through Warren truss with verticals has 8 panels of 30 ft. each and the following depths:

At U_1L_1 depth = 32 ft.
U_2L_2 depth = 37 ft.
U_3L_3 depth = 40 ft.
U_4L_4 depth = 41 ft.

Calculate the maximum tension in L_2L_4 due to a moving uniform load of 4^k per ft., and the maximum stress of both kinds in U_3L_2 due to a moving uniform load of 5^k per ft.

Ans. $L_2L_4 = +\ 678^k$.
$U_3L_2 = -\ 274^k$.
$+\ 84.1^k$.

228. (*a*) Compute the maximum live load stress of both kinds in bars U_3L_3 and U_3L_4 of the truss, due to a moving uniform load of 4000 lb. per ft. of truss, using the conventional full panel load method.

(*b*) Compute the maximum live load stress of both kinds in the same bars due to the same load, using the influence lines.

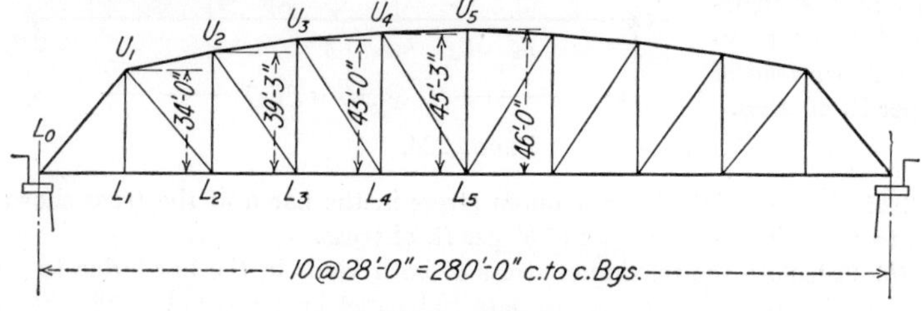

PROB. 228.

229. Due to a moving uniform load of 3^k per ft., combined with a roving concentration of 60^k:

(*a*) Calculate the maximum stress in the bar L_3L_4.

(*b*) Calculate the maximum stress of both kinds in the bar U_3L_2 of an 8-panel through Warren truss with verticals, having depths of:

31 ft. at U_1L_1	39 ft. at U_3L_3
36 ft. at U_2L_2	40 ft. at U_4L_4

and panel lengths of 30 ft.

Ans. $L_3L_4 = +\ 605^k$.
$U_3L_2 = -\ 204^k$.
$+\ 80^k$.

230. Due to a moving uniform load of 4^k per ft. and a roving concentration of 80^k, calculate:

(*a*) The maximum stress in bar L_2L_3.

(*b*) The maximum stress of both kinds in bar U_5L_4 of a Warren deck truss with verticals, having the following dimensions:

Length 10 panels at 28 ft.	= 280 ft.
U_0L_0 and U_1L_1	30 ft.
U_2L_2	37 ft.
U_3L_3	42 ft.
U_4L_4	45 ft.
U_5L_5	46 ft.

231. Compute the stress in the following bars of the structure shown, due to Cooper's E-60 loading.

(*a*) U_4U_5 Maximum compression.

(*b*) U_3L_4 Maximum tension and maximum compression.

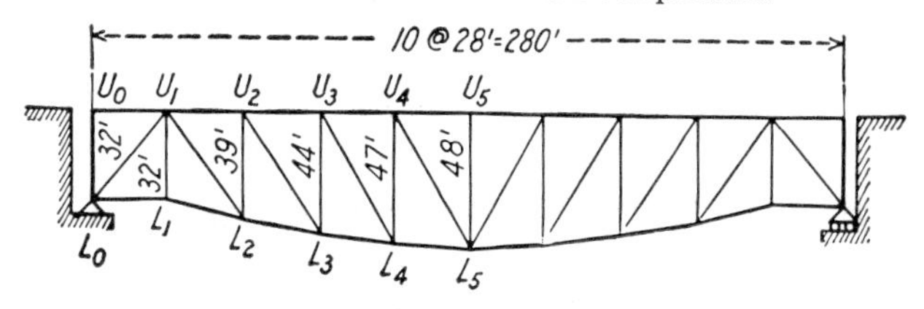

PROB. 231.

232. Calculate the stress of both kinds in member U_2L_3 of the truss shown in Problem 204, due to an E-60 loading.

Ans. $+225^k$ wheel 3.
$-\ 64^k$ wheel 3.

233. Calculate the stress of both kinds in member U_3L_3 of the truss in Problem 204, due to an E-60 loading.

Ans. -137^k wheel 2.
$+112^k$ wheel 3.

234. Compute the maximum tension in bars *c* and *d* of the single-track structure shown, due to the loading in the same figure.

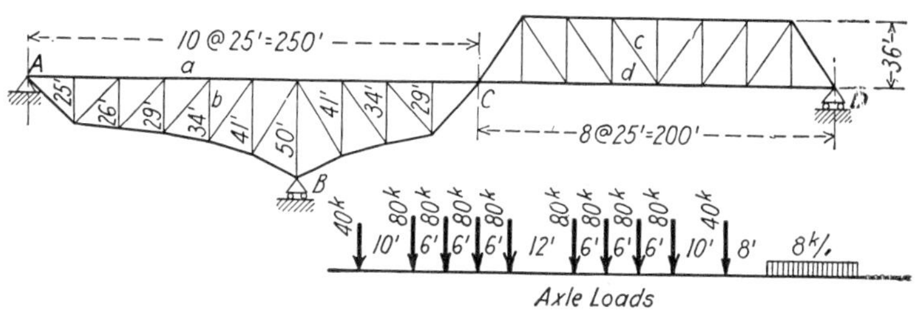

PROB. 234.

235. (*a*) Draw the influence line for stress in bar *a* of the structure shown in Problem 234, as a unit load moves from *D* to *A*.

(*b*) Compute from the influence line the maximum tension in *a* due to a moving uniform load of 8^k per ft. of track.

236. (*a*) Draw the influence line for stress in bar *b* of the structure shown in Problem 234, as a unit load moves from *D* to *A*.

(*b*) Compute from the influence line the maximum compression in *b* due to a moving uniform load of 8^k per ft. of track.

237. Draw the influence line for:

(*a*) Stress in L_5L_6

(*b*) Stress in U_7L_8

as a unit load moves from U_0 to L_{19} on the structure shown.

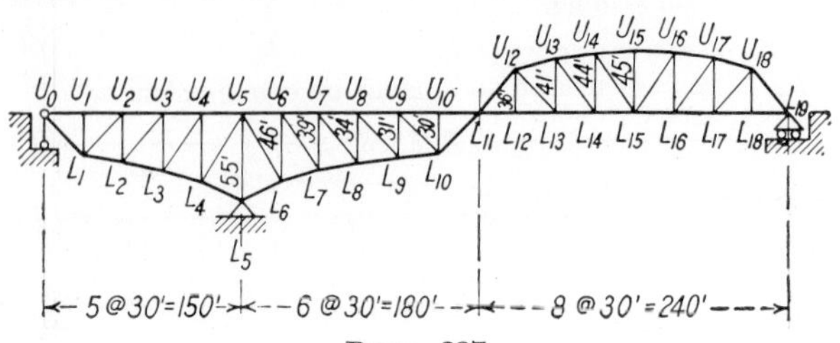

PROB. 237.

238. Draw the influence line for:

(*a*) Stress in U_3L_2

(*b*) Stress in $U_{14}L_{14}$

(*c*) Stress in $L_{15}L_{16}$

as a unit load moves from U_0 to L_{19} on the structure shown in Problem 237.

239. Calculate the maximum stress in L_5L_6 of the structure shown in Problem 237 due to the loads shown here.

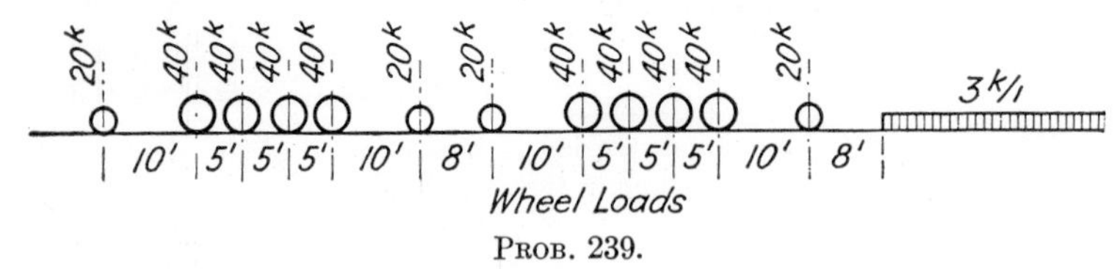

PROB. 239.

240. Calculate the maximum stress in $U_{14}L_{14}$ of the structure in Problem 237, due to the loads shown in Problem 239. *Ans.* $+132.7^k$.

241. Calculate the maximum tension in U_7L_8 due to a moving uniform load of 3^k per ft. of truss and a moving concentration of 80^k per truss, using the influence line previously drawn in Problem 237.

242. Calculate the maximum tension in U_3L_2 due to the load given in Problem 241, using the influence line previously drawn in Problem 238. Uniform load not to be divided. *Ans.* 744^k.

243. (*a*) Compute the live load stress of both kinds in bars U_2U_3, L_2L_3, U_2L_2, and U_2L_3 of the truss shown, due to Cooper's E–60 loading.

(*b*) Compute the live load stress in the same bars, using equivalent uniform loads.

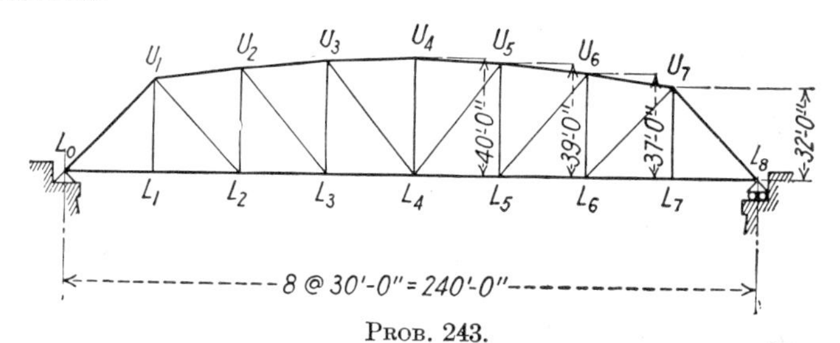

PROB. 243.

244. Given the following dead load weights for the truss shown:

Track	=	600 lb. per ft. of bridge.
Floor	=	560
Trusses and bracing	=	2240
Total		3400 lb. per ft. of bridge.

Calculate the stress in the counter L_3U_4 due to an E-60 loading.

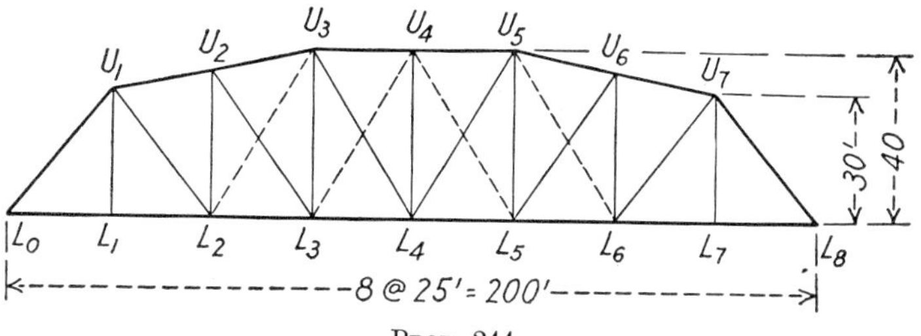

PROB. 244.

245. Calculate the maximum compression in the vertical U_3L_3 of the truss in Problem 244 due to an E-60 loading.

246. Check the stresses computed for Problem 231, using the equivalent uniform loads given by Plate I.

247. Calculate the live load stress in the bars L_3L_4, U_3L_4 of the truss shown in Problem 160 on p. 201, using the equivalent uniform load for an M-50 loading.

248. Calculate the stress in member L_4L_6 of the truss for an M-60 loading.
Ans. $+627^k$ wheel 10.

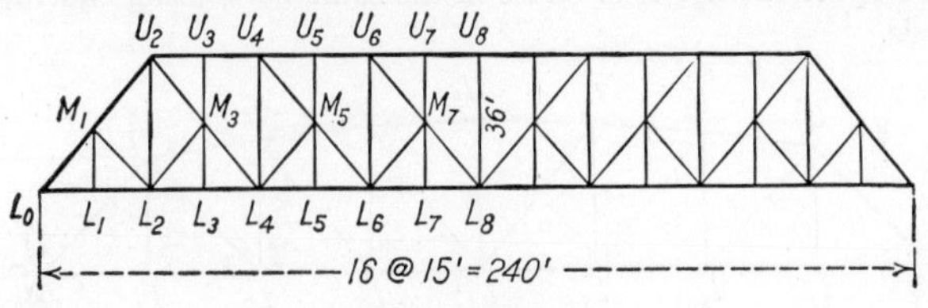

PROB. 248.

249. Draw the influence line for stress in the same member as in Problem 248 and, using the equivalent uniform load for the M-60 loading from the diagram, calculate the stress in the member:

(*a*) Assuming the segments divided at L_4.
(*b*) Assuming the segments divided at L_5.

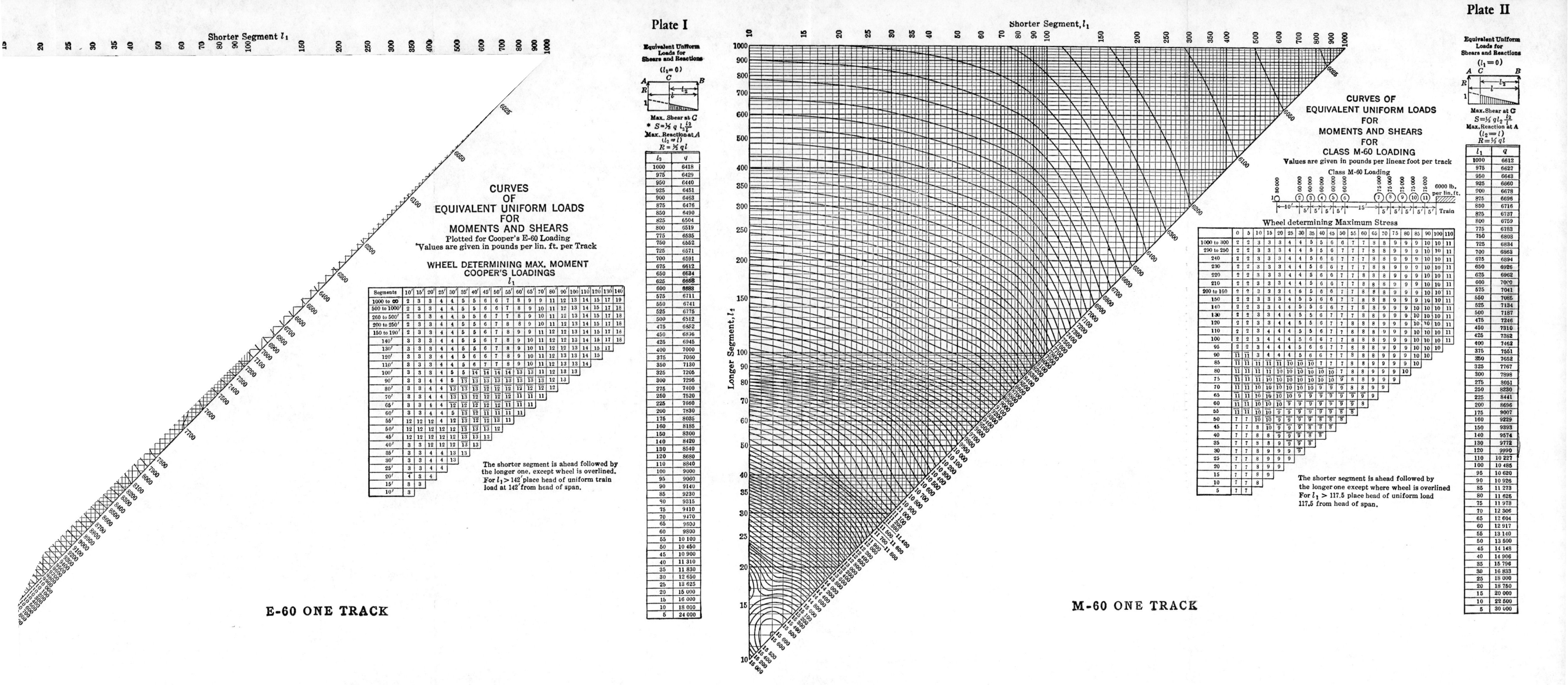

Wheel determining max. moment, Cooper's loadings (l_1)

Segments	10'	15'	20'	25'	30'	35'	40'	45'	50'	55'	60'	65'	70'	80'	90'	100'	110'	120'	130'	140'
1000 to ∞	2	3	3	4	4	5	5	6	6	7	8	9	9	11	12	13	14	15	17	19
500 to 1000'	2	3	3	4	4	5	5	6	6	7	8	9	10	11	12	13	14	15	17	18
260 to 500'	2	3	3	4	4	5	5	6	7	7	8	9	10	11	12	13	14	15	17	18
200 to 250'	2	3	3	4	4	5	5	6	7	8	8	9	10	11	12	13	14	15	17	18
150 to 190'	2	3	3	4	4	5	5	6	7	8	9	9	11	12	12	13	14	15	17	18
140'	3	3	3	4	4	5	5	6	7	8	9	10	11	12	12	13	14	15	17	18
130'	3	3	3	4	4	5	5	6	7	8	9	10	11	12	12	13	14	15	17	
120'	3	3	3	4	4	5	6	6	7	8	9	10	11	12	13	13	14	15		
110'	3	3	3	4	4	5	6	6	7	7	8	9	10	11	12	13	14			
100'	3	3	3	4	5	5	14	14	14	14	13	13	11	12	13	13				
90'	3	3	4	4	5	13	13	13	13	13	13	13	12	12	13					
80'	3	3	4	4	13	13	13	12	12	12	12	12	12	12						
70'	3	3	4	4	13	13	12	12	12	12	11	11	11							
65'	3	3	4	4	12	12	12	12	12	11	11	11								
60'	3	3	4	4	5	13	12	11	11	11	11									
55'	12	12	12	4	12	13	12	13	13	11										
50'	12	12	12	12	12	13	13	13	12											
45'	12	12	12	12	12	13	13	13												
40'	3	3	12	12	12	13	13													
35'	3	3	4	4	13	13														
30'	3	3	4	4	13															
25'	3	3	4	4																
20'	4	3	4																	
15'	3	3																		
10'	3																			

Equivalent Uniform Loads for Shears and Reactions (E-60)

l_2	q
1000	6418
975	6429
950	6440
925	6451
900	6463
875	6476
850	6490
825	6504
800	6519
775	6535
750	6552
725	6571
700	6591
675	6612
650	6634
625	6658
600	6688
575	6711
550	6741
525	6775
500	6812
475	6852
450	6896
425	6945
400	7000
375	7060
350	7130
325	7205
300	7295
275	7400
250	7520
225	7660
200	7830
175	8035
160	8185
150	8300
140	8420
130	8540
120	8680
110	8840
100	9000
95	9060
90	9140
85	9230
80	9315
75	9410
70	9470
65	9600
60	9800
55	10 100
50	10 450
45	10 900
40	11 310
35	11 830
30	12 650
25	13 625
20	15 000
15	16 000
10	18 000
5	24 000

Wheel determining Maximum Stress (M-60)

	0	5	10	15	20	25	30	35	40	45	50	55	60	65	70	75	80	85	90	100	110
1000 to 300	2	2	3	3	3	4	4	5	5	6	6	7	7	8	8	9	9	9	10	10	11
290 to 250	2	2	3	3	3	4	4	5	5	6	7	7	7	8	8	9	9	9	10	10	11
240	2	2	3	3	3	4	4	5	5	6	7	7	7	8	8	9	9	9	10	10	11
230	2	2	3	3	3	4	4	5	5	6	7	7	7	8	8	9	9	9	10	10	11
220	2	2	3	3	3	4	4	5	5	6	7	7	8	8	8	9	9	9	10	10	11
210	2	2	3	3	3	4	4	5	5	6	7	7	7	8	8	9	9	9	10	10	11
200 to 160	2	2	3	3	3	4	5	5	5	6	7	7	8	8	8	9	9	9	10	10	11
150	2	2	3	3	3	4	5	5	6	6	7	7	8	8	9	9	9	9	10	10	11
140	2	2	3	3	4	4	5	5	6	6	7	7	8	8	9	9	9	10	10	10	11
130	2	2	3	3	4	4	5	5	6	7	7	7	8	8	9	9	9	10	10	10	11
120	2	2	3	3	4	4	5	5	6	7	7	8	8	8	9	9	9	10	10	10	11
110	2	2	3	4	4	4	5	5	6	7	7	8	8	8	9	9	9	10	10	10	11
100	2	2	3	4	4	4	5	6	6	7	7	8	8	9	9	9	9	10	10	10	11
95	2	2	3	4	4	4	5	6	6	7	7	8	8	8	9	9	9	10	10	10	
90	11	11	3	4	4	4	5	6	6	7	7	8	8	8	9	9	9	10	10		
85	11	11	11	11	11	10	10	10	7	7	7	8	8	9	9	9	9	10			
80	11	11	11	11	10	10	10	10	10	10	7	8	8	9	9	9	10				
75	11	11	11	10	10	10	10	10	10	10	9	8	8	9	9	9					
70	11	11	11	10	10	10	10	10	10	9	9	9	8	9	9						
65	11	11	10	10	10	10	9	9	9	9	9	9	9	9							
60	11	11	10	10	9	9	9	9	9	9	9	9	8								
55	11	11	10	10	9	9	9	9	9	9	8	8									
50	7	7	10	10	9	9	9	9	8	8	8										
45	7	7	8	10	9	9	9	8	8	8											
40	7	7	8	8	9	9	9	8	8												
35	7	7	8	8	9	9	9	8													
30	7	7	8	9	9	9	9														
25	7	7	8	9	9	9															
20	7	7	8	9	9																
15	7	7	8	9																	
10	7	7	8																		
5	7	7																			

Equivalent Uniform Loads for Shears and Reactions (M-60)

l_1	q
1000	6612
975	6627
950	6643
925	6660
900	6678
875	6696
850	6716
825	6737
800	6759
775	6783
750	6808
725	6834
700	6863
675	6894
650	6926
625	6962
600	7000
575	7041
550	7085
525	7134
500	7187
475	7246
450	7310
425	7382
400	7462
375	7551
350	7652
325	7767
300	7898
275	8051
250	8230
225	8441
200	8696
175	9007
160	9229
150	9393
140	9574
130	9772
120	9990
110	10 227
100	10 485
95	10 620
90	10 926
85	11 273
80	11 626
75	11 978
70	12 306
65	12 604
60	12 917
55	13 140
50	13 500
45	14 148
40	14 906
35	15 796
30	16 833
25	18 000
20	18 750
15	20 000
10	22 500
5	30 000

CHAPTER IX

EFFECT OF LATERAL AND LONGITUDINAL FORCES

131. In the design of structures the engineer must consider the effect of lateral and longitudinal forces as well as that of the more definite vertical forces. Although the vertical forces, consisting of the weight of the structure, the moving or movable live load, and the vibration caused by the moving loads will in perhaps a majority of structures control the amount of material required in the various parts, there are many cases in which lateral forces have an important influence.

The principal lateral force which must be considered is that caused by wind at high velocity. Wind forces, of course, affect all structures and sometimes control the design of important members. Industrial buildings which contain traveling cranes are subject to both lateral and longitudinal forces resulting from the operation of the cranes, and in buildings which are high to provide large head room, these forces may be important.

Bridges must resist the wind acting on the structure itself as well as that acting on the trains or other loads passing over the structure, and in addition a lateral vibration set up by side sway or " nosing " of the locomotives. The magnitude of the latter is very uncertain but is generally fixed more or less arbitrarily as a percentage of the vertical loads. The longitudinal forces acting on a bridge result from the tractive effort necessary to start a train or other live load on the structure, and more particularly from the retarding force occurring when the brakes are suddenly applied to a train as it crosses the bridge. Tractive effort can be applied only through the driving wheels of the engine, but braking force occurs under practically every wheel in a train and is by far the most important longitudinal force acting on a railroad bridge. Lateral and longitudinal forces are seldom of controlling effect in the design of ordinary highway bridges, but may be important in narrow bridges of long span.

There are no new principles involved in the calculation of stresses resulting from lateral or longitudinal forces, and were it not for the fact that the framework provided for resisting these forces is generally statically indeterminate, no additional discussion would be needed. Although the framework provided for resisting lateral forces is generally indeterminate in character it is usual to estimate the stresses by making a sufficient number of simplifying assumptions to reduce the problem to one which may be solved by applying the laws of statics. So far as the shears, moments, and stresses resulting from lateral or longitudinal forces may be estimated in this manner they are a proper subject for discussion in a text dealing with simple structures, and the common methods of dealing with such problems will be shown by a series of illustrative examples.

132. Industrial Building Bents.—In Fig. 157 (*a*) there is shown an ordinary industrial building bent, one story in height and one aisle in width, subject to a horizontal wind load. The wind is assumed to exert a force equivalent to 30 lb. per sq. ft. of exposed vertical surface. The reactions are at *A* and *B*, and with the usual conditions of support for such frames (flat column bases bolted to the masonry) there are evidently six unknown reactions — vertical and horizontal components and a moment at each column base. Since there are available only three equations from statics, three additional conditions must be obtained from the elastic properties of the frame or from simplifying assumptions based on what seems to be a reasonable estimate of the action of the structure.

In (*b*) of Fig. 157 is shown to a greatly exaggerated scale the general shape which the frame will take in deflecting laterally under the action of the wind. In this sketch it is assumed that the columns are so firmly attached to the masonry at *A* and *B* and to a stiff truss at the top that tangents to their axes at the points of attachment to the masonry will be vertical, and that chords of the axes passing through the intersection points of the truss chords will be vertical. To secure absolute verticalness of these tangents to, and chords of, the column axes would require a truss of infinite stiffness and immovable foundations, and of course neither of these requirements can be fully met. However, it is generally assumed that the conditions are substantially met and that the shape shown in (*b*) is a reasonable approximation. Study of this figure will show that both the windward and leeward columns are so bent that the fibers on the left-hand side are in tension at the lower ends and in compression at the upper ends. It should be clear that somewhere between the ends there must be a point where the stress in the fibers changes from tension to compression and where the bending moment must be zero. Such

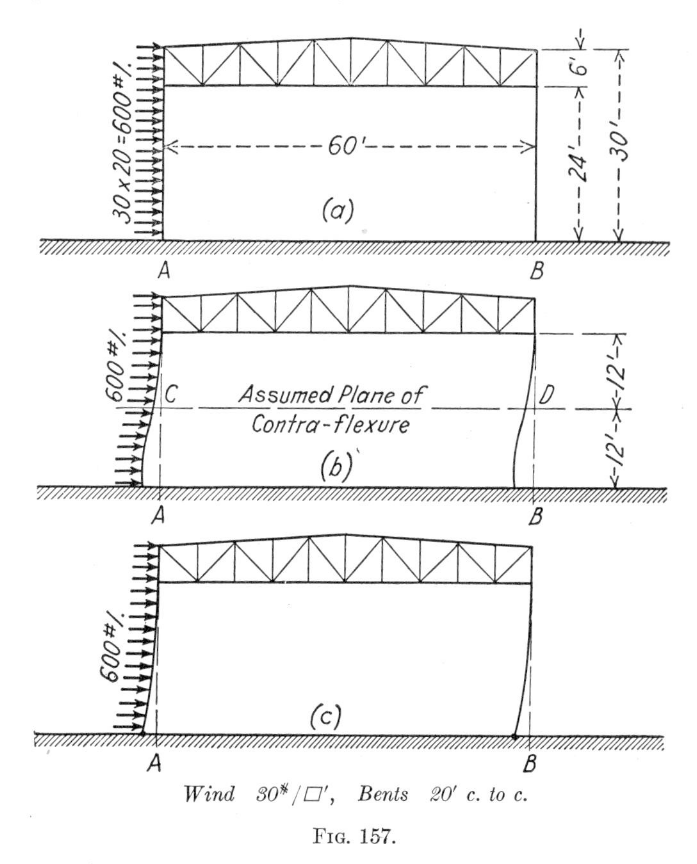

Wind 30#/□', Bents 20' c. to c.

FIG. 157.

a point is called a point of **contra-flexure,** and two of the necessary three additional conditions mentioned above are obtained by assuming the location of the point of contra-flexure in each column. In (*b*) of Fig. 157 there is shown an assumed plane of contra-flexure halfway between the bottom of the columns and the under side of the truss, which locates a point of zero bending moment in each column. If the conditions stated above were true (tangent to axis of column at bottom and chord of axis at top remaining vertical), the point of contra-flexure would be above the center. It is a simple matter to develop a formula locating the point of contra-flexure in accordance with these or other conditions, but it is doubtful whether our knowledge of foundation action justifies such precision. Rotation of the foundations will lower the point of contra-flexure, and it is probably sufficiently accurate to assume contra-flexure at the center — or lower if there is reason to believe that the column base or footing is not especially rigid. The third additional condition is obtained by assuming the distribution of the shear on the plane of contra-flexure between the two columns. When the columns are alike the shear on the plane of contra-flexure is assumed to be equally divided between them. If the columns differ much in section this assumption may be considerably in error and require modification. In such cases an accurate analysis may be made or the shear distributed in accordance with the stiffness of the columns; in either case consideration of the elastic properties is involved and the problem will not be discussed here.

133. Column Bases Fixed.—In Fig. 158 complete calculations and shear and moment diagrams are given for the columns of the bent in Fig. 157 (*b*). The three simplifying assumptions are as outlined above — a plane of contra-flexure halfway between the base of the columns and the under side of the truss, and the shear on this plane equally divided between the two columns. In (*a*) of Fig. 158 the bent is shown divided at the plane of contra-flexure and the internal forces acting at the plane of separation are calculated in accordance with these assumptions. The simplifying assumptions having been made, the calculations merely involve the application of the laws of statics, and the student should be able to follow the work given. In (*b*) of Fig. 158 the shear and moment diagrams have been sketched, and the forces acting on the columns shown. The student should draw the shear and moment diagrams for the truss and calculate the stress in a few members, taking the center depth of the truss as 7 ft. 8 in.; the bottom chord is horizontal, and the top chord straight between the ends and the center.

134. Column Bases Hinged.—In Fig. 159 the columns of the bent in Fig. 157 (*c*) are analyzed under the assumptions of hinged column bases and equal horizontal reactions at the bases of the columns. These assumptions may be appreciably in error but are sometimes used. The student should make an analysis under the assumption of hinged bases with the horizontal load

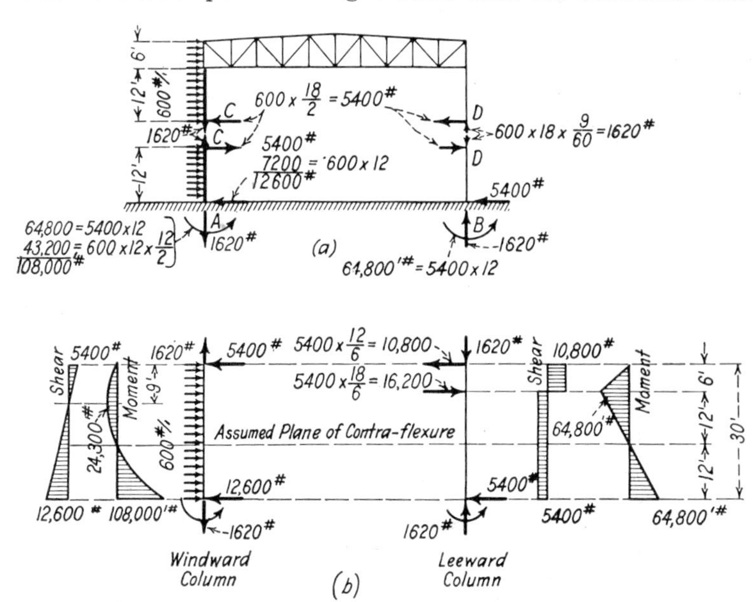

FIG. 158.

distributed about five-eighths to the windward column and three-eighths to the leeward column, and as before draw shear and

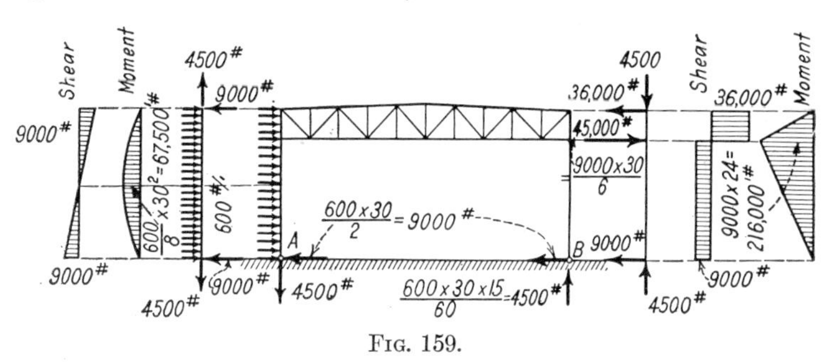

FIG. 159.

moment diagrams for the truss and calculate the stress in a few of its members. The actual distribution of shear between the windward and leeward columns depends on the action (elastic or inelastic) of the foundations as well as on the elasticity of the members of the bent, and as little is known about the former an analysis based on the latter may not in some cases be much more

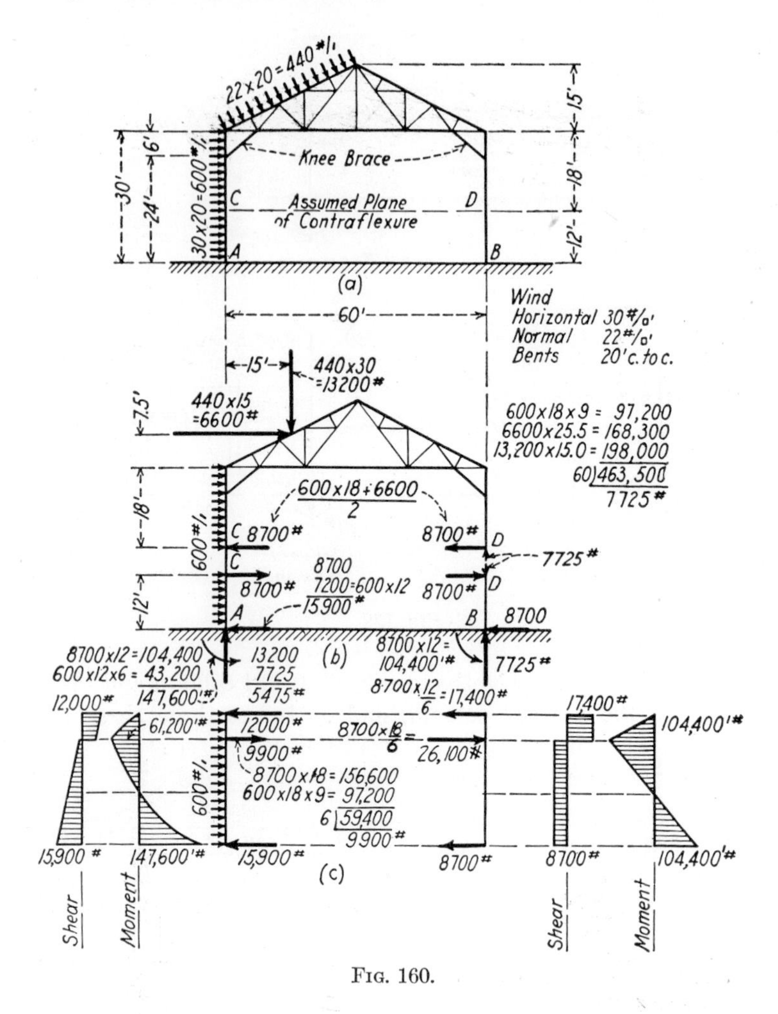

Fig. 160.

accurate than an estimate based on assumptions such as have been used above.

135. Bent with Knee Brace.—In Fig. 160 (*a*) there is shown a bent similar to those previously considered but having a pitched roof instead of being practically flat. In such bents the lateral stability is generally increased by means of **knee braces** connecting to the columns and the truss as shown. In (*b*) and (*c*) the complete analysis for the columns is given, based on an assumed plane of contra-flexure, located as shown, and on the assumption that shear on this plane is divided equally between the columns. The stress in the knee braces and in several members of the truss should be calculated by the student. In calculating stresses in members of the truss which are on the windward side of the center line, it should be kept in mind that although the total wind load normal to the roof surface may be resolved into two components (as shown in (*b*)) when dealing with the columns and knee braces, this must not be done when computing stresses in the truss members mentioned.

136. Multiple-story Bent.—In Fig. 161 (*a*) is shown a three-story single-aisle bent for an industrial building. The wind stresses in such cases may be estimated in the same manner as for a single-story building, except that it is necessary to assume a plane of contra-flexure in each story as is indicated in the figure. It is usual in approximate analyses to assume the shear on each plane of contra-flexure divided equally between the columns cut by that plane. The calculation of shears and moments in the columns then follows as directly as for a single-story bent. The moment diagrams for the columns are given in (*b*) of Fig. 161, the shear and moment diagrams for the upper floor girder are given in (*c*); and in (*d*), the tabulated calculations for shear and moment in the columns. The calculation given for moment at the top of the windward column in the top story is for a section at the bottom of the truss; the maximum for this part of the column occurs 6 in. below the truss, and its magnitude, 12,675 ft.-lb., is shown on the moment diagram in (*b*).

It is usual in the calculation of wind stresses in multi-story bents to disregard the depth of the floors, treat the girders as a line having no depth, and call the distance from the top of one floor to the top of the floor above the story height. In this problem, however, the calculations are given for floor depths of 5 ft., and the moment diagrams for the columns are shown extending from the top of any floor to the under side of the girder in the floor above. The student will do well to recalculate the problem just discussed, ignoring floor depth and calling floor to floor distance the story height. The first two stories will then be 20 ft each and the top story 14 ft. from the floor to the under side of the truss; the planes of contra-flexure should of course be taken at the middle of the story height.

It is also customary in estimating wind stresses in high buildings to assume that the wind pressure is delivered to the bents as

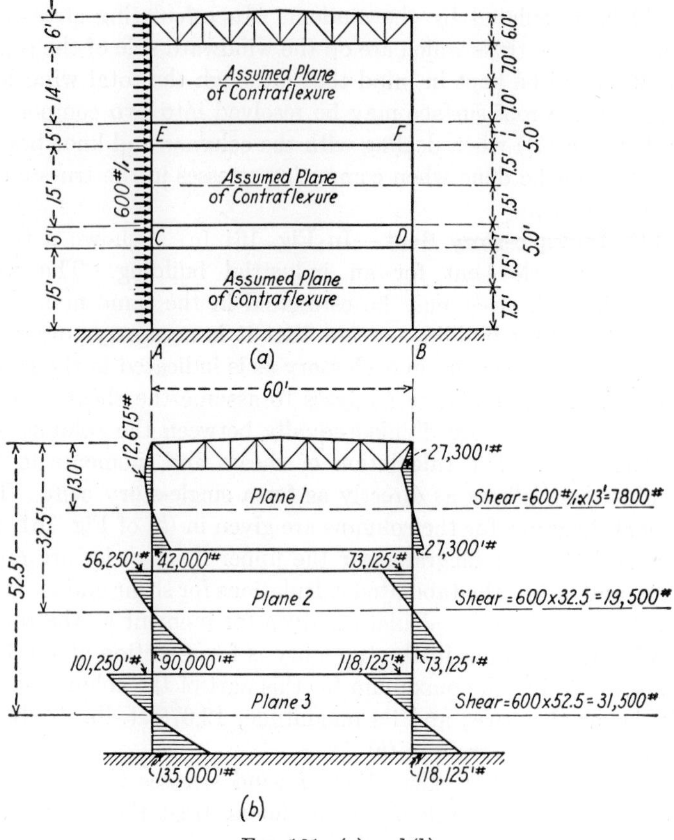

FIG. 161. (*a*) *and* (*b*)

a series of concentrated loads applied at the floor lines, instead of a uniformly distributed load applied along the full height of the columns. This is equivalent to treating the wall construction as a series of vertical beams having reactions at the floor lines, and the floors as horizontal beams which transmit these loads to the columns. The wall construction for most office buildings is such

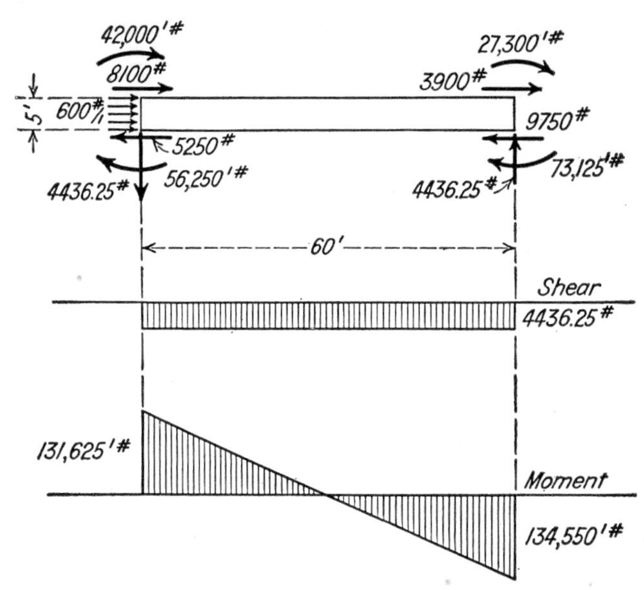

Shear and Moment Diagrams for Third Floor Girder *EF*

(*c*)

Plane	*Shear*	*Moment*		
		Leeward Column Top and Bottom	*Windward Column*	
			Top	*Bottom*
1	600 × 13 = 7800# × ½ = 3900#/col.	3900 × 7 = 27,300'#	7 × 3900 = 27,300 $7 \times 600 \times \frac{7}{2} =$ 14,700 *12,600'#	7 × 3900 = 27,300 $7 \times 600 \times \frac{7}{2} =$ 14,700 42,000'#
2	600 × 32.5 = 19,500# × ½ = 9750#/col.	9750 × 7.5 = 73,125'#	7.5 × 9750 = 73,125 $7.5 \times 600 \times \frac{7.5}{2} =$ 16,875 56,250'#	7.5 × 9750 = 73,125 $7.5 \times 600 \times \frac{7.5}{2} =$ 16,875 90,000'#
3	600 × 52.5 = 31,500# × ½ = 15,750#/col.	15,750 × 7.5 = 118,125'#	7.5 × 15,750 = 118,125'# $7.5 \times 600 \times \frac{7.5}{2} =$ 16,875 101,250'#	7.5 × 15,750 = 118,125 $7.5 \times 600 \times \frac{7.5}{2} =$ 16,875 135,000'#

* *At bottom of truss.*

(*d*)

Fig. 161. (*c*) *and* (*d*)

that this practice is probably a fairly accurate representation of the action of the wind pressure on such buildings. The greater story heights and different wall construction generally used in industrial buildings make it desirable to treat the wind loads on these as uniformly distributed along the columns, as has been done in the examples presented above.

137. Application to High Buildings.—The general method of attack used in the analysis of the three-story bent of Fig. 161 has been very widely used, in an extended form, in the analysis of wind stresses in high office buildings. The difference in procedure results from the fact that office buildings usually are composed of several relatively narrow aisles, instead of a single wide aisle. In such cases the modification used is simply to treat each aisle as though it were independent, divide the total load equally among the aisles, and then combine algebraically the resulting shears, moments and stresses in those members which are common to two aisles.

The application of this method is illustrated in the analysis of a ten-story building in Figs. 162, 163 and 164. In Fig. 162 (*a*) is shown one bent of the building, which has a width of three aisles of 20 ft. each with story heights as shown. At the left of the figure are shown the concentrated loads at the floor levels which result from the assumed wind pressure and bent spacing (noted in Fig. 162) when the walls and floors are considered to act as stated in Art. 136. In (*b*) of Fig. 162 the three aisles are shown as separate structures with the total loads shown in (*a*) equally divided among them. The same procedure used for the three-story bent in Art. 136 and Fig. 161 is then applied to each aisle and the shears and moments calculated for the columns and girder in each story. The results of these calculations are shown in Fig. 163, the portions relating to a single aisle and to two aisles combined being indicated. Keeping in mind the simplifying assumptions made (viz.: there is a plane of contra-flexure at the mid-height of each story and the total shear on this plane is divided equally between the two columns of the aisle), the student should have no difficulty in obtaining the results shown for the single aisle.

To show the effect of combining the single aisles Fig. 164 has been drawn showing the fifth floor and the columns between the planes of contra-flexure just above and below. In (*a*) the three aisles are shown separately with the forces and moments acting on the members of each. In (*b*) the three aisles are combined and the resulting forces and moments shown. Further explanation seems unnecessary, but it may be well to call attention to the fact

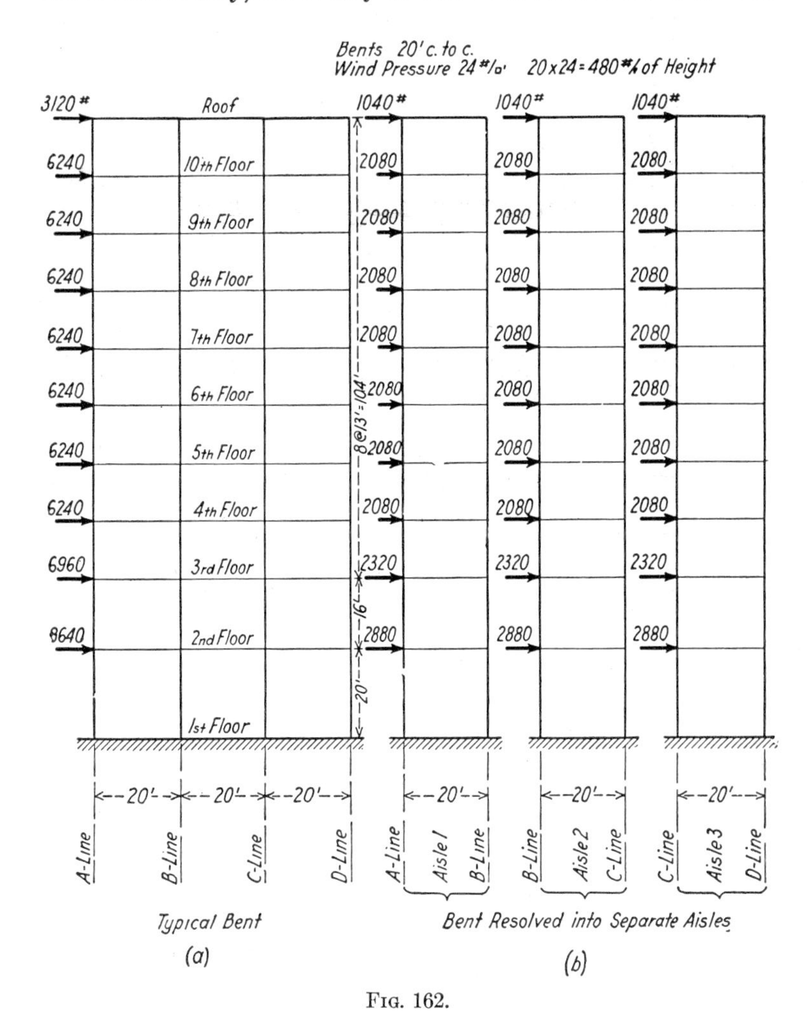

FIG. 162.

that the *B* line column in aisle 1 is in compression whereas the *B* line column in aisle 2 is subjected to tension of equal magnitude.

The same is true of the *C* line column which occurs in aisles 2 and 3. When the separate aisles are combined the compression in the B column of aisle 1 neutralizes the equal tension in the B column of aisle 2 resulting in no direct stress in the B column of the combined bent, and this of course is also true of the C column. As a consequence of the simplifying assumptions made, we find direct stress only in the exterior columns. The magnitude of this

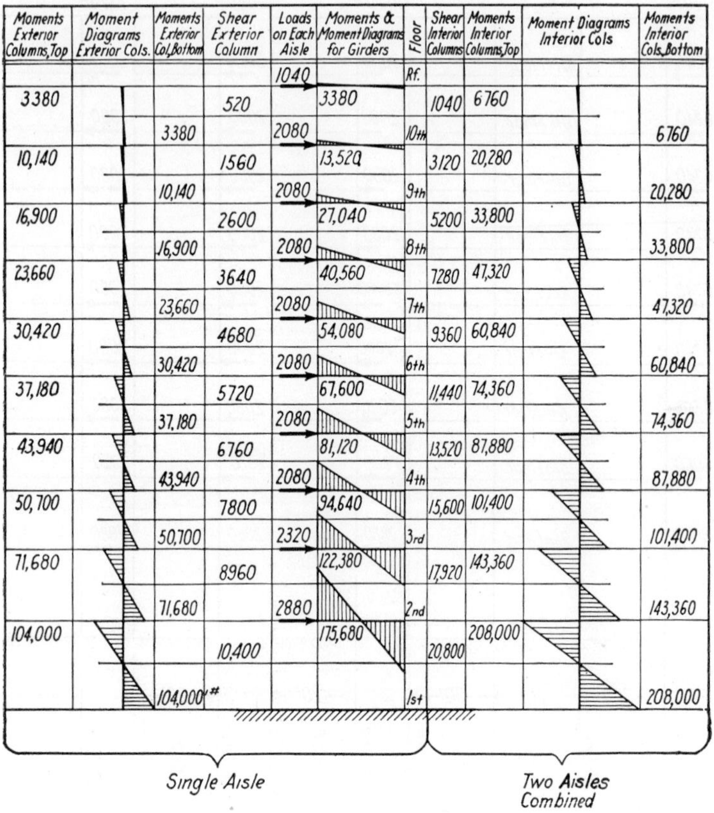

Moments Exterior Columns, Top	Moment Diagrams Exterior Cols.	Moments Exterior Col, Bottom	Shear Exterior Column	Loads on Each Aisle	Moments & Moment Diagrams for Girders	Floor	Shear Interior Columns	Moments Interior Columns, Top	Moment Diagrams Interior Cols	Moments Interior Cols, Bottom
				1040		Rf.				
3380			520		3380		1040	6760		
		3380		2080		10th				6760
10,140			1560		13,520		3120	20,280		
		10,140		2080		9th				20,280
16,900			2600		27,040		5200	33,800		
		16,900		2080		8th				33,800
23,660			3640		40,560		7280	47,320		
		23,660		2080		7th				47,320
30,420			4680		54,080		9360	60,840		
		30,420		2080		6th				60,840
37,180			5720		67,600		11,440	74,360		
		37,180		2080		5th				74,360
43,940			6760		81,120		13,520	87,880		
		43,940		2080		4th				87,880
50,700			7800		94,640		15,600	101,400		
		50,700		2320		3rd				101,400
71,680			8960		122,380		17,920	143,360		
		71,680		2880		2nd				143,360
104,000			10,400		175,680		20,800	208,000		
		104,000'#				1st				208,000

Single Aisle — Two Aisles Combined

FIG. 163.

direct stress in any story may be found, for the single aisle, by calculating the moment about the plane of contra-flexure in that story of all the forces acting on the aisle above the plane and dividing this moment by the horizontal distance between the aisle columns. This stress may also be found from the bent as a whole by taking moments about the same plane of contra-flexure of all the forces acting on the bent as a whole above this plane, and dividing the moment by the horizontal distance between the *exterior* columns of the bent.

The popularity of this method of estimating wind stresses is partly due to its simplicity and to the fact that the calculations necessary may be reduced to tabular form and very rapidly carried out as a routine procedure. Many engineers have developed forms for such computations; in fact, it may be not far from true

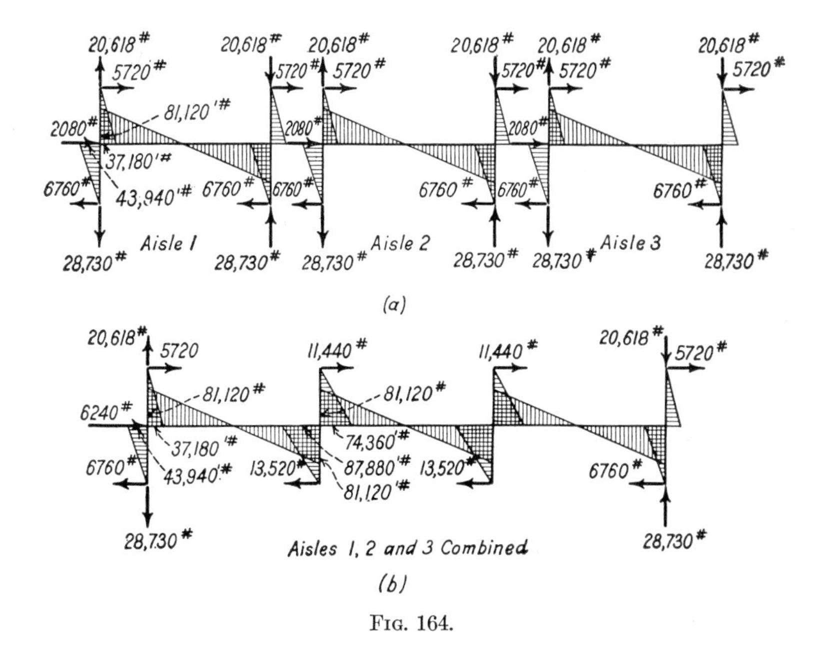

FIG. 164.

to say that every computer dealing with such problems has devised his own form, and in Fig. 165 is given, in a form the authors find convenient, the complete calculations for the bent discussed above. The construction of the table should be clear if studied in connection with Figs. 162, 163, and 164.

138. Smith's Method.—The method of analysis just described coincides with that developed by Albert Smith, formerly professor of structural engineering in Purdue University. In an address before the Western Society of Engineers, Professor Smith described wind stress studies which he had made, employing theoretically

Floor Level	Story Height	Number of Columns	Wind Load	Total Shear	Shear in Exterior Column		One-half Story Height	Moment in Exterior Column	Shear in Interior Column		One-half Story Height	Moment in Interior Column	Girder Moments	Direct Stress in Exterior Columns, Pounds
					Increment	Total			Increment	Total				
Roof	13.0	4	3120	3,120	520	520	6.5	3,380	1040	1040	6.5	6,760	3,380	338
10th	13.0	4	6240	9,360	1040	1560	6.5	10,140	2080	3120	6.5	20,280	13,520	1,690
9th	13.0	4	6240	15,600	1040	2600	6.5	16,900	2080	5200	6.5	33,800	27,040	4,394
8th	13.0	4	6240	21,840	1040	3640	6.5	23,660	2080	7280	6.5	47,320	40,560	8,450
7th	13.0	4	6240	28,080	1040	4680	6.5	30,420	2080	9360	6.5	60,840	54,080	13,858
6th	13.0	4	6240	34,320	1040	5720	6.5	37,180	2080	11,440	6.5	74,360	67,600	20,618
5th	13.0	4	6240	40,560	1040	6760	6.5	43,940	2080	13,520	6.5	87,880	81,120	28,730
4th	13.0	4	6240	46,800	1040	7800	6.5	50,700	2080	15,600	6.5	101,400	94,640	38,194
3rd	16.0	4	6960	53,760	1160	8960	8.0	71,680	2320	17,920	8.0	143,360	122,380	50,432
2nd	20.0	4	8640	62,400	1440	10,400	10.0	104,000	2880	20,800	10.0	208,000	175,680	68,000
1st														

Fig. 165.

exact methods of calculation, and presented an approximate method employing the following assumptions: [1]

1. The point of contra-flexure of each column is at mid-height of the story.
2. The point of contra-flexure of each girder is at its mid-length.
3. The shears on the internal columns are equal, and the shear on each external column is equal to one-half the shear on an internal column.

Although stated in a slightly different manner, it should be clear that these assumptions lead to exactly the same solution as is given above.

139. Relation to Statics.—The authors' primary interest in the problem of wind stresses, so far as it concerns this text, is as an application of the laws of statics after the necessary simplifying assumptions have been made. The student should be very careful, in studying the discussions and illustrative examples, to be very sure that he understands clearly *why* simplifying assumptions are necessary, *what* the assumptions are, which parts of the analysis rest on such assumptions, and which parts are a necessary consequence of the laws of statics.

140. Stresses in Bridges Due to Lateral Forces.—Figure 166 shows diagrammatically an elevation of a single-track through railroad bridge, a plan of its top lateral bracing truss, and a plan of its bottom lateral bracing truss. The function of lateral bracing trusses, as the name implies, is to resist forces transverse to the axis of the structure. These forces, as previously stated, are the result of the action of wind on the structure and on the train, and also lateral vibration caused by swaying of the locomotive and train.

The pressure of the wind on the structure itself is delivered to the lateral trusses at the panel points by the vertical truss members acting as beams, e.g., the diagonal U_2L_3 of the main truss when pressed against by the wind must have reactions at U_2 and at L_3, and presumably each reaction is equal to one-half the total wind force against the diagonal. The members U_1U_2, U_2U_3, and U_2L_2 must also contribute to a horizontal load at U_2 which the top lateral truss must resist; and in a similar manner L_2L_3, L_3L_4, and U_3L_3, as well as U_2L_3, contribute to a horizontal load at L_3 which the bottom lateral truss must resist. Wind pressure against

[1] *Journal Western Society of Engineers*, Vol. 20, No. 4, p. 341.

the floor system of the truss evidently must be resisted by the lateral truss to which the floor connects — the bottom lateral truss in this case and in other through bridges. Wind pressure against the train must be resisted by the action of the wheels on the track which in turn is supported by the floor system, and thus this force also is finally resisted by the bottom lateral truss in through bridges.

The determination of the magnitude of the loads to which the lateral trusses are finally subjected from these various sources

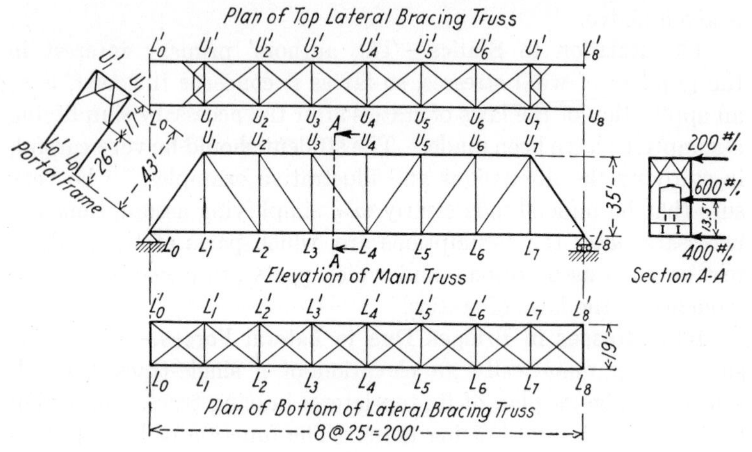

FIG. 166.

requires a knowledge of the exposed area of the truss members, floor system, and train, as well as the amount of pressure to be expected from the wind and a reasonable estimate of the effect of lateral vibration from nosing and swaying. The exposed area of the structure can be determined accurately only after its design, and the wind pressure and lateral effect of the train are generally somewhat arbitrarily fixed in accordance with prevailing practice.

141. Illustrative Example.—For the purposes of this discussion the lateral forces will be assumed as follows:

Top lateral truss: 200 lb. per lin. ft.

Bottom lateral truss: 400 lb. per lin. ft. (includes wind on floor).

Wind on train and effect of lateral vibration: 600 lb. per lin. ft. applied 7 ft. above top of rail.

In accordance with most specifications for design these will be treated as *moving* loads.

The top lateral truss shown in plan in Fig. 166 is a complete truss only between the top chord panel points U_1 and U_7. Beyond these points the diagonals must be omitted to allow the clearance necessary for the passage of the train. The top lateral truss may be treated as extending from U_1 to U_7, having at these points its reactions which are provided by rigid frames consisting of the end posts of the vertical trusses and portal frames between them as shown in Fig. 166. The reactions of the lateral truss at the tops of the portal frames are transferred to the masonry support by the ability of the end posts to resist transverse forces in bending. The top chords of the main trusses serve also as chords in the lateral truss, the only additional members necessary to form the lateral truss being the diagonals and the struts. The struts are the members U'_2U_2, U'_3U_3, and so on.

The top lateral truss, as it is shown in Fig. 166, is statically indeterminate with respect to inner stresses, i.e., there are too many members to permit the calculation of the stresses by means of the laws of statics. The diagonals in such a truss, however, are likely to be so slender as to be incapable of resisting compression, and it may be assumed that those which would be in compression for a given loading are not acting, the other diagonals, which of course are in tension, resisting the shear. Thus for the lateral loads applied as in Fig. 167 the top lateral truss consists of the members shown in full lines, the diagonals in dotted lines being out of action. For loads in the opposite direction the dotted diagonals come into action, in tension, and the others are considered as out of action.

If the wind loads are considered as moving loads the maximum stresses in the diagonals and struts of the lateral truss will occur for the position of the loads producing maximum shear in the panel concerned, e.g., maximum stress in U'_2U_3 will occur when the shear in panel $U'_2U'_3$ is a maximum, and of course the strut U'_3U_3 has maximum stress at the same time. The wind stresses are not sufficiently important (nor is our knowledge of wind pressures sufficiently accurate) to justify precise computations; and it is usual to use the conventional full panel load method described in Chapter IV. In Fig. 168 there is shown a plan of the top lateral truss supported at U'_1 and U'_7. The index stresses are written on the bars for full loading, and below the sketch the calculations for stress in the diagonals and struts are given, using the full panel load method. Since the truss is symmetrical it is only necessary to calculate the stresses in one half.

The bottom lateral truss may be treated in the same manner as the top lateral truss, if its diagonals are too slender to resist compression. However, the diagonals of the bottom bracing truss are usually heavier, because of larger forces acting at the floor line, and stiffer not only because of their greater section but

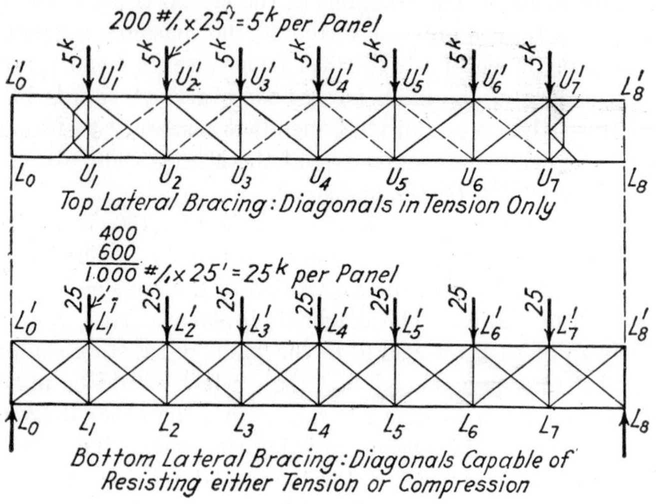

FIG. 167.

also because they are often supported by connections to the stringers. Under these conditions the diagonals may be stiff enough to resist compression. The truss then is in fact statically indeterminate, but the secondary importance of its stresses and our inadequate knowledge of wind forces and lateral vibration do not justify an analysis based on the elastic properties, as a design procedure. It is therefore necessary to make some simplifying assumptions to enable the computer to estimate the stresses by application of the laws of statics. The usual assumption is that the shear in any panel is resisted equally by the two diagonals (one acting in tension and the other in compression), and this gives the necessary additional information to enable the calculation of all stresses.

In Fig. 169 the bottom lateral truss is shown fully loaded for maximum chord stresses. The calculations for chord stresses for this condition of loading and the calculations for diagonal stresses, using the conventional full panel load method, are given below the sketch. Stresses in the struts have not been shown. The struts in the bracing truss between the chords at which the floor is located are generally the floorbeams, and the stresses to which they are subjected as members of the bracing truss are insignificant in most cases. These stresses may be easily determined, however, and the student should calculate them in a few cases as

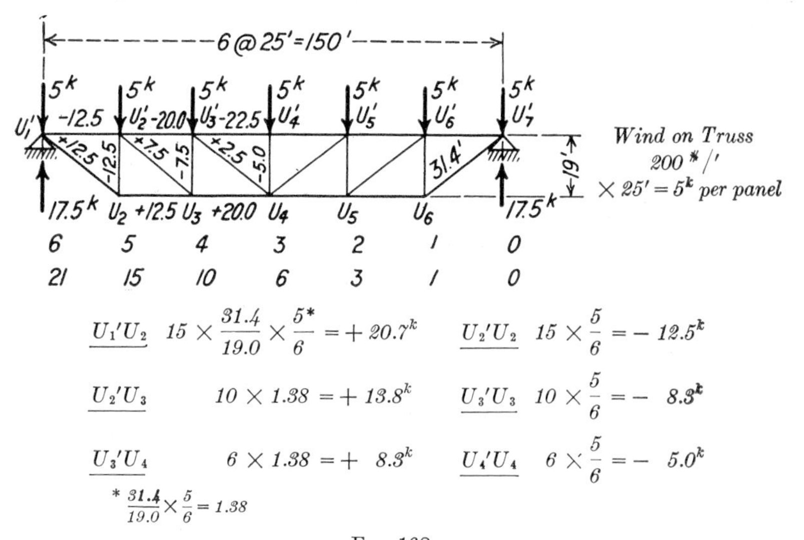

Fig. 168.

an exercise in statics. It may be well to note that in calculating chord stresses a section is passed through the panel in which the chord in question occurs and moments taken about the intersection of the diagonals. A little study should show that, if the shear in a panel is divided equally between the diagonals therein, the stresses in the chords of the panel must be equal and opposite, and may be determined by dividing the bending moment about the intersection of the diagonals by the perpendicular distance between the chords. The diagonal and chord stresses are given as plus or minus since the lateral forces may act in either direction.

142. Portal Frame Stresses.—As stated in Art. 141, the top lateral bracing truss reacts against the portal frame at the top, and this reaction must be transferred to the ground by the ability

Wind on Truss and Floor = 400 #/′
Wind on Train, and Lat. Vibration = 600

1000 #/′
×25′ = 25^k *per panel*

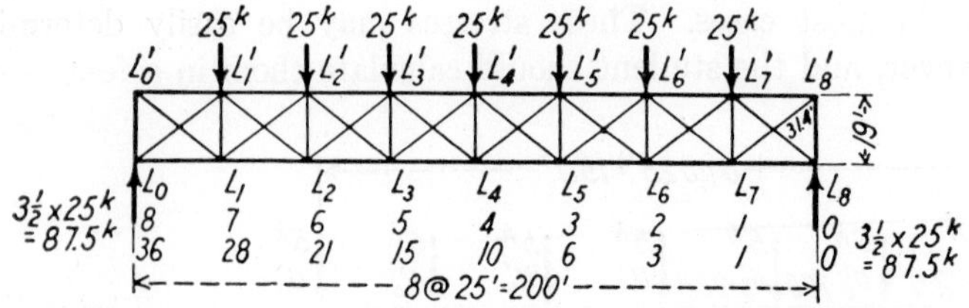

$L_0'L_1'$ or L_0L_1

$$87.5 \times \frac{12.5}{19.0} = \pm\ 57.6^k$$

$L_1'L_2'$ or L_1L_2

$87.5 \times 37.5 = 3280$
$25.0 \times 12.5 = 313$
2967
$\div 19.0 = \pm 156.0^k$

$L_2'L_3'$ or L_2L_3

$87.5 \times 62.5 = 5470$
$2 \times 25.0 \times 25.0 = 1250$
4220
$\div 19.0 = \pm 222^k$

$L_3'L_4'$ or L_3L_4

$87.5 \times 87.5 = 7650$
$3 \times 25.0 \times 37.5 = 2810$
4840
$\div 19.0 = \pm 255^k$

$$\frac{1}{2} \times \frac{25}{8} \times \frac{31.4}{19.0} = 2.58$$

$L_0'L_1$ or $L_1'L_0$

$$28 \times \frac{1}{2} \times \frac{25}{8} \times \frac{31.4}{19.0} = \pm 72.4^k$$

$L_1'L_2$ or $L_2'L_1$

$21.0 \times 2.58 = \pm 54.3^k$

$L_2'L_3$ or $L_3'L_2$

$15.0 \times 2.58 = \pm 38.8^k$

$L_3'L_4$ or $L_4'L_3$

$10.0 \times 2.58 = \pm 25.8^k$

FIG. 169.

of the frame to resist transverse forces. Evidently the portal frame as shown in Fig. 166 is an indeterminate structure very similar to the industrial building bents discussed before. The end posts of the main trusses, forming the columns of the portal frame, are subjected to bending and direct stress in resisting the lateral truss reaction, in addition to their stresses as members of

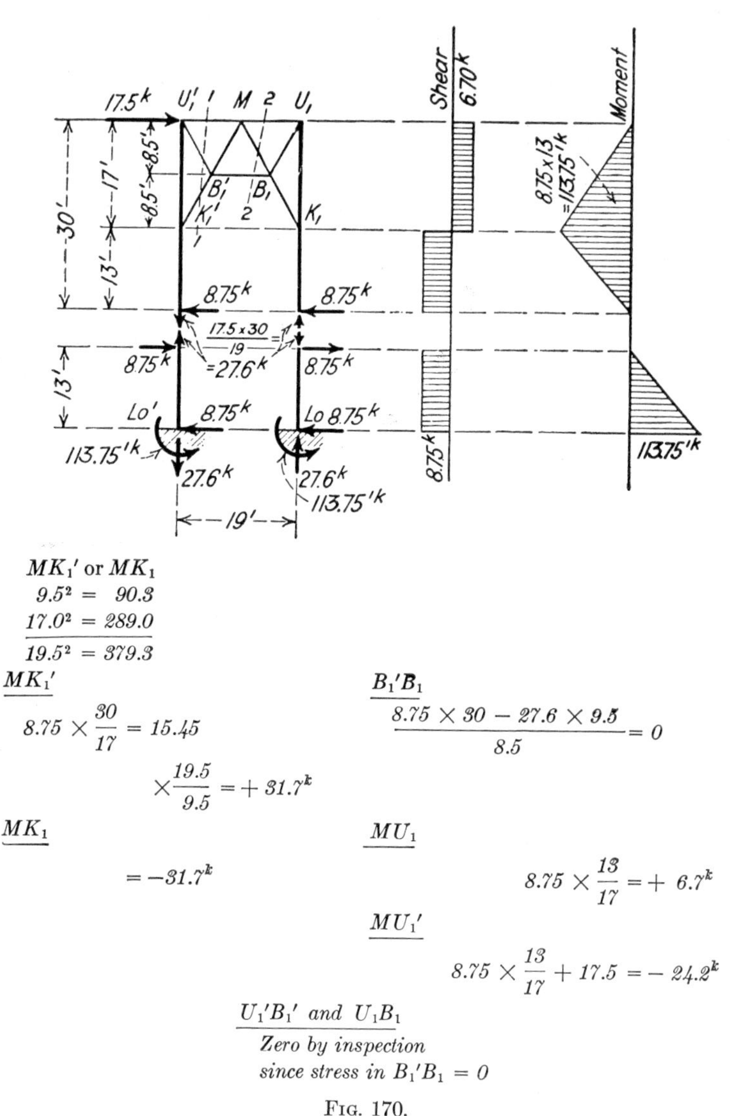

Fig. 170.

the main trusses. If the bottoms of the end posts may be considered as fixed in direction in the plane of the portal bent there are six unknown reactions. These reactions are clearly of the same kind as those on the industrial building bent, and the simplifying assumptions made are the same as in that problem. A plane of contra-flexure is assumed, generally half-way between the bottom of the portal knee brace and the bottom of the post,

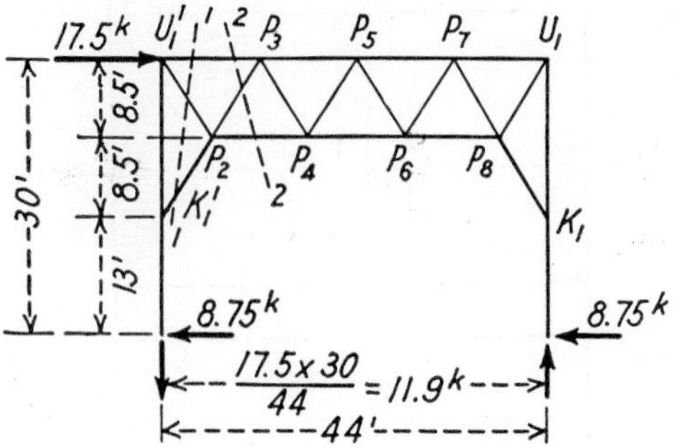

All portal diagonals

$5.5^2 = 30.25$

$8.5^2 = 72.25$

$10.13^2 = 102.50$

$\underline{P_2K_1'}$ $8.75 \times \frac{30.0}{17.0} = 15.45$

$\times \frac{10.13}{5.5} = +28.4^k$

$\underline{U_1'P_3}$

$8.75 \times 21.5 = 188.0$

$17.50 \times 8.5 = 148.8$

336.8

$11.9 \times 5.5 = 65.5$

$271.3'^k$

$\div 8.5' = -31.9^k$

$\underline{U_1'P_2}$

$15.45 \times \frac{8.5}{5.5} = 23.9$

$\frac{11.9}{12.0}$

$\times \frac{10.13}{8.5} = +14.3^k$

$\underline{P_2P_4}$

$8.75 \times 30.0 = 262.5$

$11.90 \times 11.0 = 130.9$

$131.6'^k$

$\div 8.5' = +15.5^k$

FIG. 171.

and the shear on that plane assumed to be divided equally between the two end posts. Having made these assumptions the remainder of the analysis follows exactly the reasoning applied to the building bent, and in Fig. 170 will be found the complete calculations. The student's attention should be called to the fact that although the stress in $U'_1B'_1$ is zero it is not correct to pass a section around the joint U'_1 and say that the stress in U'_1M is equal and opposite to the 17.5^k load at that joint. Why not?

In Fig. 171 will be found the calculations for some of the members in the portal frame for a wider bridge. Only the part above the assumed plane of contra-flexure is shown.

143. "Portal Effect" in Bottom Chord of Main Truss.—It will be noticed that in analyzing the portal frame in Fig. 170 a direct stress of 27.6^k was found in the columns $U'_1L'_0$ and U_1L_0, tension in the windward column and compression in the leeward. If the student will picture in his mind the complete top lateral truss separated from the rest of the structure and supported by the two portal frames, he will see at once that the bottom ends of the portal frame columns must have horizontal reactions. Since one end of the structure is supported on rollers, it should be clear that this horizontal reaction must be furnished by the bottom chord of the main truss, and in magnitude it must be equal to the horizontal component of the direct stress in the column of the portal frame. In the frame in Fig. 170 its magnitude is:

$$27.6 \times \frac{25.0}{43.0} = 16.1^k$$

This must be constant throughout the bottom chord of the main truss and is evidently tension in the leeward chord and compression in the windward. Figure 172 is an isometric sketch showing the top lateral bracing truss and the two portal frames. The student should see clearly that there must be a constant stress throughout the bottom chords L_0L_8 and $L'_0L'_8$ to resist the components of the end post stresses parallel to them.

144. Overturning Effect of Wind on Train.—In section A–A, Fig. 166, there is shown the 600 lb. per lin. ft. lateral force assumed to represent wind on the side of the train plus the effect of lateral vibration. As stated before, this force is assumed to act 7 ft. above the top of the rail, which for this structure places the force about 13.5 ft. above the center of the bottom chord. It is clear that this force on the side of the train tends to tip it over about the leeward wheels, thus causing an increase of the load on these and a relief of the load on the windward wheels, which in turn produces an increase in the downward load on the leeward main truss, and a relief of the downward load on the windward main truss. The amount of this increase in downward load on the leeward truss must be:

$$600 \text{ lb. per ft.} \times \frac{13.5}{19.0} = 426 \text{ lb. per ft.}$$

The effect of this readjustment of the downward load is not significant in the top chord and web system of the leeward truss (because of an increase in permissible fiber stress when wind stresses are included) or in any member of the windward truss. Its effect is

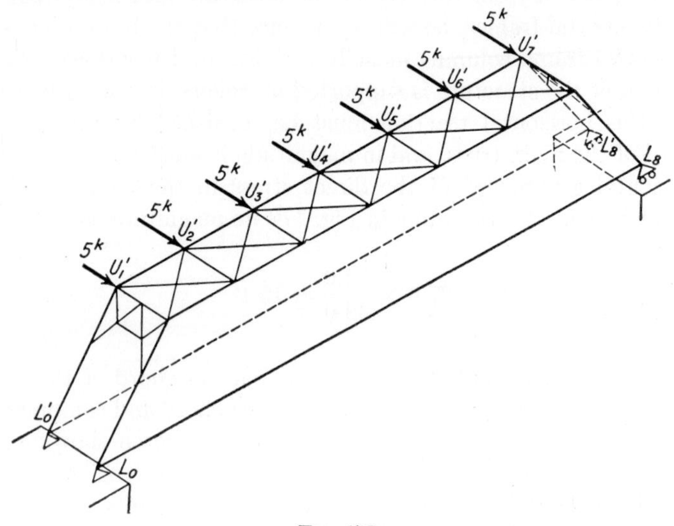

Fig. 172.

important, however, in the bottom chord and end posts of the leeward truss because in these members it produces stress of the same kind as the lateral and vertical forces. In the end posts of the leeward main truss, lateral forces on the top lateral truss and the overturning tendency of the wind on the train both produce compression, and the former also produces bending in the member. In the bottom chord of the leeward main truss, wind on the top lateral truss produces tension through the action of the portal frame, wind on the bottom bracing truss produces tension through the action of the lateral truss, and wind on the train produces tension because of its downward effect on the vertical truss.

The total effect of lateral forces on the end posts then is as follows:

Portal frame $= - 27.6^k$ and 113.8 ft.-kips. (See Fig. 170.)

Overturning

$$426 \text{ lb. per ft.} \times 25 \times \frac{7}{2} \times \frac{43.0}{35.0} = - 45.8$$

$- 73.4^k$ and 113.8 ft.-kips.

And the total effect of lateral forces on the leeward main truss chord L_3L_4 is as follows:

Stress as a member in the lateral truss $= + 255^k$ (See Fig. 169.)

Portal frame effect, $27.6 \times \frac{25.0}{43.0} = + 16$

Overturning, $\frac{426}{2} \times 75 \times 125 \times \frac{1}{35} = + 57$

$+ 328^k$

145. Effect of Lateral Forces on Non-parallel Chord Trusses.— In addition to the effects of lateral forces already discussed, non-parallel chord trusses are stressed through the changing inclination of the plane of the top lateral truss.

Figure 173 (*a*) shows a plan of the top lateral bracing truss for a structure the main trusses of which are shown in elevation in Fig. 173, (*b*) and (*c*). When projected onto a horizontal plane the top lateral truss for this structure is identical with the top lateral truss for the structure in Fig. 166; and a little reflection should make it clear that the stresses may be correctly, and most easily, found for the former by calculating those for the latter and multiplying the stress for any member thus determined by the ratio of its true length to its horizontal projection — the correction, as the student will find, is very small and not necessary unless the main truss chords have large inclinations with the horizontal.

If a section parallel to the main trusses is passed between them cutting all web members of the top lateral truss, and the stresses in the cut members resolved into horizontal, vertical, and normal components acting at the panel points of the main truss, there will then be vertical and horizontal loads in the plane of the main trusses at these points, as shown in (*b*) and (*c*) of Fig. 173, and of course components normal to the plane of the paper. The horizontal and vertical loads produce stresses in the various members of the main truss in addition to those already discussed. In long-

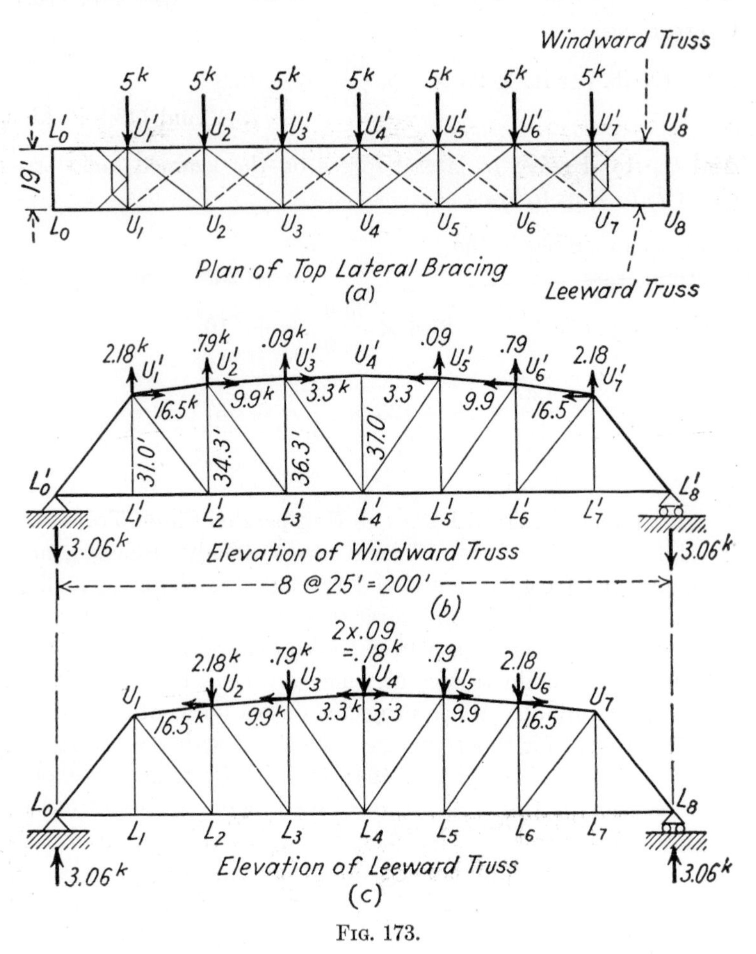

Fig. 173.

span single-track bridges, with steep inclinations for the top chords, these stresses may be appreciable, and in arches with high rise they become important, but for ordinary bridges they are small, and seldom, if ever, calculated. Some idea of their magnitude may be obtained by studying the loads produced on this structure by the top lateral system. The index stresses in Fig. 168 are evidently the correct index stresses for the horizontal projection of the truss considered here (for full loading) and are made use of in the following calculations:

Horizontal Components	Vertical Components
$U'_1U_2\ \frac{25}{19} \times 12.5 = 16.5^k$	$U'_1U_2\ 16.5 \times \frac{3.3}{25.0} = 2.18^k$
$U'_2U_3\ \frac{25}{19} \times 7.5 = 9.9^k$	$U'_2U_3\ 9.9 \times \frac{2.0}{25.0} = .79^k$
$U'_3U_4\ \frac{25}{19} \times 2.5 = 3.3^k$	$U'_3U_4\ 3.3 \times \frac{0.7}{25.0} = .09^k$

From these we may write at once the panel loads shown in (*b*) and (*c*) of Fig. 173. These are rather small loads, and it seems clear that the stresses produced in the truss will be inappreciable in comparison with those resulting from other forces. In the bottom chord of the leeward truss, however, the stresses produced are of the same sign as the other stresses produced by the lateral forces, and in order to get some notion of the relative values, the stress in L_3L_4 is calculated below.

L_3L_4

$3.06^k \times 75 \text{ ft.} = 229 \text{ ft.-kips}$

$16.5^k \times 2 \text{ ft.} = 33$

262 ft.-kips

$2.18^k \times 25 \text{ ft.} = 55$

$207 \text{ ft.-kips} \div 36.3 \text{ ft.} = 5.7^k$

The other stresses in this member due to lateral forces will be nearly the same as found in Art. 144 for a parallel chord truss of similar dimensions, i.e., about 328^k.

146. Stresses Due to Longitudinal Forces.—The most important longitudinal forces are the accelerating and braking forces resulting from starting or stopping trains or other loads on a structure. The stresses resulting from them are not severe in ordinary truss bridges, but may become important in long-span structures and are always important in high steel trestles. There are no new principles involved and only a brief discussion follows.

Figure 174 shows the truss of Fig. 166 with E–60 loads in the proper position for maximum stress in $L_6L_7L_8$. The longitudinal force is assumed in accordance with the 1923 Am. Soc. C. E. Specifications for Steel Railway Bridge Superstructure [2]— 20 per cent of the weight on the drivers and 10 per cent of the weight of the rest of the train. Although not specifically required by these specifications, the longitudinal force is assumed as acting 6 ft. above the top of the rail, as is usual in bridge design. The calculations are practically self-explanatory and no comment is necessary, except to state that in calculating the stress in L_6L_7 it was assumed in both cases that the friction from all the wheels in panels 6–7 and 7–8 acted to the right of the section passed in making the calculations. It is evidently impossible to determine definitely where the longitudinal force is transferred into the structure; in fact, we are not at all certain as to how much of the longitudinal force is resisted by the structure itself or how much is transferred by the track to the embankment or roadbed at either end of the bridge.

Examination of the figure and calculations in Fig. 174 should make it clear that stresses from longitudinal forces, even under the most unfavorable circumstances, will not be large in an ordinary bridge such as above. They are often neglected, but the designer should never make the mistake of dismissing them as negligible without investigation unless he knows from previous experience with structures similar to the one under consideration that such is the case.

In this connection the student is cautioned against the common error of adding stresses which cannot occur simultaneously, e.g., in investigating the importance of stresses from longitudinal forces, the maximum possible stress from these forces, in a particular member, should not be added to its maximum live load stress unless the two occur for the same position of the loads. This is true, of course, for all kinds of loading. Sometimes it is hard to decide whether *possible* combinations of loading are sufficiently *probable* to justify considering them as occurring simultaneously.

147. Steel Trestle.—As a final example of the application of the laws of statics in dealing with lateral and longitudinal forces, the steel trestle shown in Fig. 175 will be briefly considered. The

[2] *Transactions Am. Soc. C. E.*, Vol. 86, p. 478.

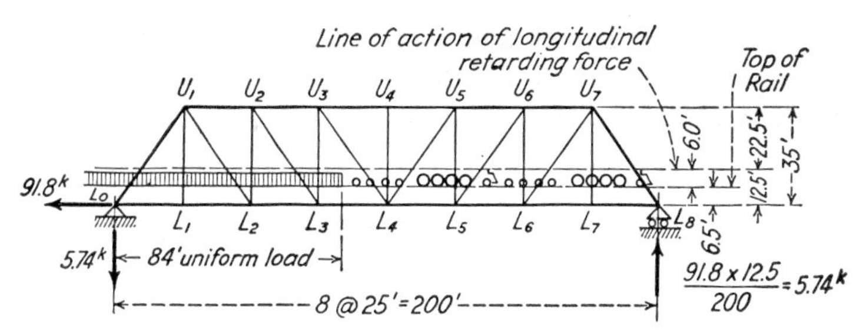

Load on drivers (1 rail) $= 240^k$, @ $20\% = 48^k$ *longitudinal*
Load on rest of locomotive $= 186^k$, @ $10\% = 18.6$
Unif. load $84 \times 3 = \underline{252^k}$, @ $10\% = \underline{25.2}$
678^k 91.8^k *longitudinal*

120^k @ $20\% = 24.0^k$
54 @ $10\% = \underline{5.4}$
29.4^k

<u>L_6L_7</u>

$5.74 \times 25.0 = 143.5$
$29.4 \times 22.5 = \underline{662.0}$
805.5
$\div 35.0 = +23.0^k$

<u>U_7L_8</u>

$$29.4 \times \frac{12.5}{25.0} = 14.7^k \downarrow \text{end floorbeam reaction}$$
$\underline{5.74}$
8.96
$$\times \frac{43.0}{35.0} = +11.0^k$$

As shown above

<u>L_6L_7</u>

$5.74 \times 25.0 = 143.5$
$29.4 \times 22.5 = \underline{662.0}$
805.5 91.8
$\div 35.0 = \underline{23.0}$
$+68.8^k$

<u>U_7L_8</u>

$$29.4 \times \frac{12.5}{25.0} = 14.7^k \uparrow \text{end floorbeam reaction}$$
$\underline{5.74}$
8.96
$$\times \frac{43.0}{35.0} = -11.0^k$$

Rollers under left end. Train in position shown above and backing on from right.

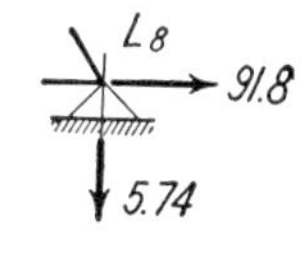

FIG. 174.

requirements for lateral and longitudinal forces given in the "General Specifications for Steel Railway Bridges" of the American Railway Engineering Association, May, **1931**, edition,

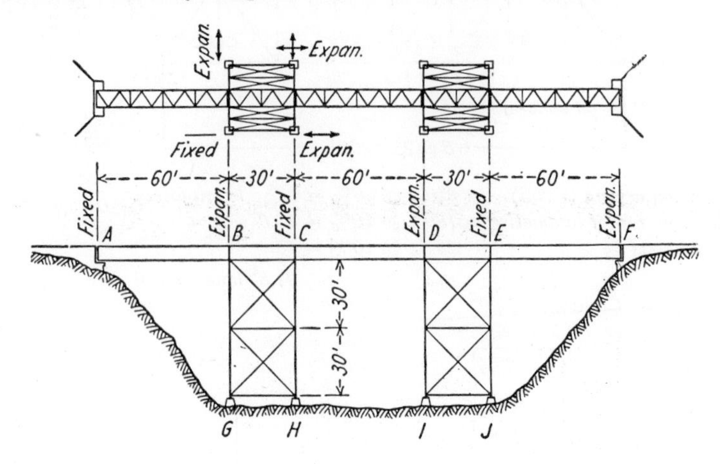

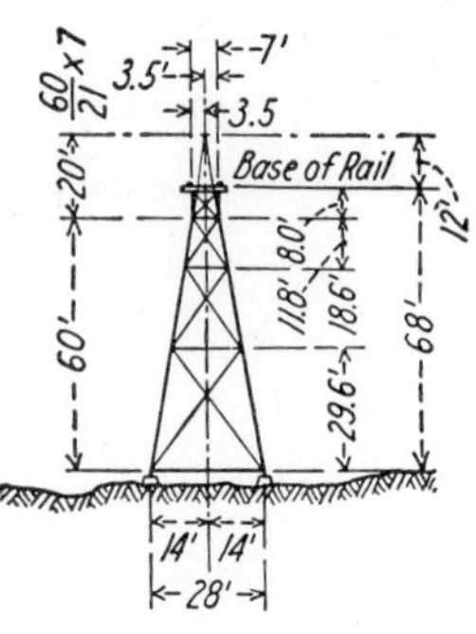

FIG. 175.

will be used in this case, slightly modified for longitudinal forces. These result substantially in the following:

Side of train 8 ft. above rail	300 lb. per ft. for wind
Base of rail	400 lb. per ft. for swaying of train 200 lb. per ft. for wind on girder and track
Bottom flange	180 lb. per ft. for wind on girder
Tower posts, etc.	30 lb. per sq. ft. on $1\frac{1}{2}$ times exposed area

Longitudinal forces: 20 per cent of driver loads, 10 per cent of rest

which give the concentrations shown in Fig. 176, when the loads are in the position indicated backing on the span from the left. This is an illustration of the matter mentioned in the previous

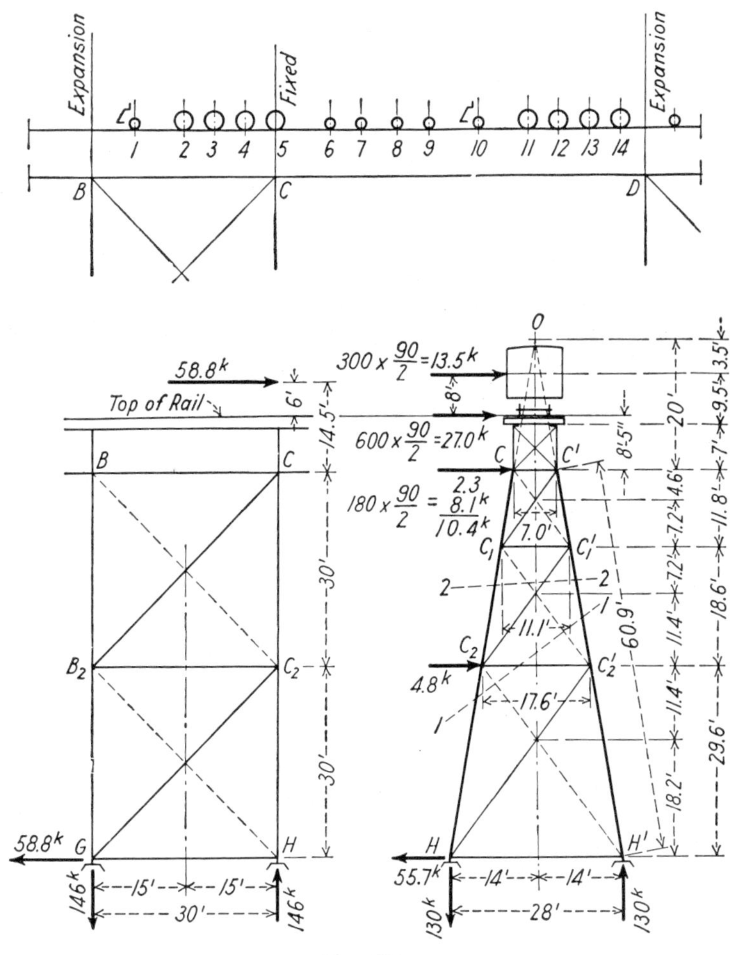

Fig. 176.

article. Is the *probability* of the brakes being suddenly applied, when a train *backing* across the structure is in the position indicated, sufficiently great to justify adding the resulting stresses to maximum live load and impact stresses?

The reactions shown in Fig. 176 are for the tower loaded as

shown and its bases arranged for expansion as shown in the plan in Fig. 175. The calculations for these reactions and for typical members accompany Fig. 176. The diagonals shown dotted are presumed to be out of action. If the diagonals are stiff enough to resist compression the assumption of equal and opposite stress may be made and the calculations made accordingly.

Reactions on Transverse Bent CC′ H′ H:

$$\begin{array}{rl} 4.8^k \times 29.6 = & 142 \\ 10.4 \times 60.0 = & 624 \\ 27.0 \times 68.5 = & 1850 \\ 13.5 \times 76.5 = & \underline{1032} \\ \overline{55.7} & 3648 \div 28 = \end{array}$$

130^k ↑ at H'
130^k ↓ and **55.7**^{k} ← at H

Reactions on Longitudinal Bent BCHG·

$$58.8 \times \frac{74.5}{30.0} =$$ **146**^{k} ↑ at H

146^k ↓ and **58.8**^{k} ← at G

Stresses in Typical Members of Bents—Lateral Forces:

$C'_1C'_2$

$$\begin{array}{rl} 10.4^k \times 30.4 = & 316 \\ 27.0 \times 38.9 = & 1050 \\ 13.5 \times 46.9 = & \underline{634} \\ & 2000 \div 17.6 = 113.8 \end{array}$$

$$\times \frac{60.9}{60.0} =$$ **115.2**^{k} comp.

$C_2C'_2$

$$\begin{array}{rl} 13.5 \times 3.5 = & 47.3 \\ 27.0 \times 11.5 = & 311 \\ 10.4 \times 20.0 = & \underline{208} \\ & 566.3 \div 50.4 = 11.2 \\ & \qquad\qquad\quad \underline{4.8} \\ & \qquad\qquad\quad 16.0 \end{array}$$

= **16.0**^{k} comp.

C'_1C_2

$$\begin{array}{rl} 13.5 \times 3.5 = & 47.3 \\ 27.0 \times 11.5 = & 311 \\ 10.4 \times 20.0 = & \underline{208} \\ & 566.3 \div 39.0 = 14.5 \end{array}$$

$$\times \frac{23.5}{14.4} =$$ **23.7**^{k} tension

Stresses in Typical Members of Bents—Longitudinal Forces:

$\underline{CC_2}$	$58.8 \times \frac{44.5}{30.0}$	$= \mathbf{87.3^k}$ comp.
$\underline{B_2C_2}$	By inspection	$= \mathbf{58.8^k}$ comp.
$\underline{CB_2}$	$58.8 \times \frac{42.8}{30.0}$	$= \mathbf{83.9^k}$ tension

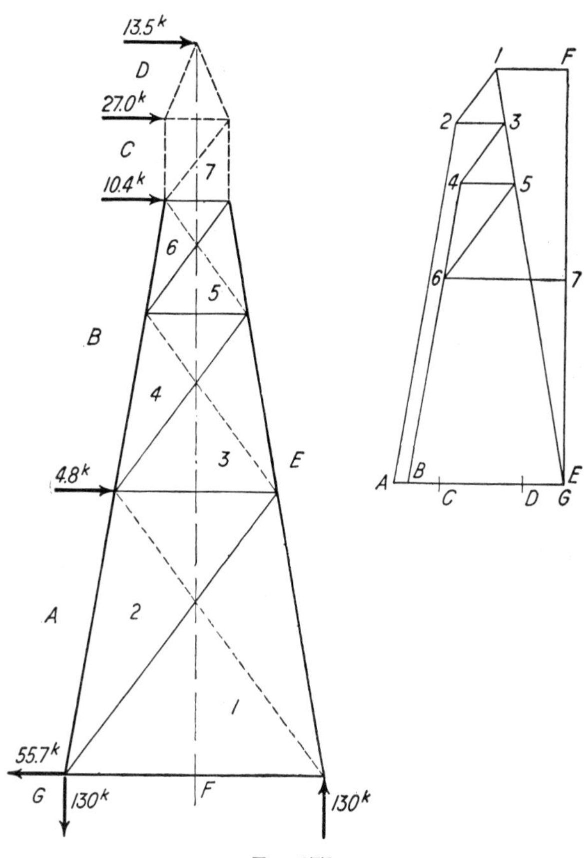

Fig. 177.

Graphical calculation of the stresses in the transverse bent will be found very convenient, and in Fig. 177 is shown a complete graphical solution. The dotted lines shown above the bent form a substitute framework to replace the girders and train on which the 27.0^k and 13.5^k forces are really acting. It is not necessary to use this framework if the effect of the forces above the bent is calculated and introduced at the top. The forces which must be applied at the top of the bent to replace the effect of the girder spans and train are calculated below.

$$27.0 \times \frac{8.5}{7.0} = 32.8$$

$$\begin{array}{ll} 13.5 \times \frac{16.5}{7.0} & = 31.8 \\ \hline 40.5^k & \quad 64.6^k \end{array}$$

A force of 40.5^k must be added to B–C, a vertical force of 64.6^k acting up placed at the top of the column B–6, and a vertical force of 64.6^k acting down placed at the top of E–5.

148. Centrifugal Force.—Bridges must sometimes be built on curves, and when this is done centrifugal force may become a very important factor. The amount of centrifugal force generally considered was given in Chapter I, and its magnitude having been estimated it is treated exactly as any other lateral force. It is usually specified that it is to be considered acting a certain distance above the rail (6 ft. being most common), in spite of the fact that the track always has superelevation on the curve. Consequently calculations involving centrifugal force must include the effect of a considerable overturning moment on the train, which of course results in an increase in the downward load on the trusses or girders on the outside of the curve and a relief of downward load on those on the inside. The bottom chord of the outside truss for a through bridge on a curve will have its stress increased as a member of the bottom lateral truss which resists the centrifugal force, as well as through the increase in downward load resulting from the overturning tendency, and may require a considerable increase in section.

Calculations of stress resulting from centrifugal force are simple and direct in themselves, but a condition which tends to complicate the entire analysis for a bridge on a curve is the fact that the structure itself must be straight. Since the trusses or girders must be straight and the track curved, it is clear that the distance from the center-line of track to either truss is constantly changing, and of course the proportion of the load carried by one truss or the other must also change continuously as the load moves across the bridge. This difficulty may generally be overcome by making an approximate allowance for the increase in the proportion of load carried by a truss as the track curves toward it, but sometimes it becomes necessary to draw influence lines for stress in the various members. Although the calculations may become tedious there are no new principles involved, and the student is fully prepared for such a problem if he thoroughly understands the previous discussions.

PROBLEMS

250. Given the bent in the figure subjected to the loads shown. Assume a plane of contra-flexure 15 ft. above the ground.

(*a*) Calculate the reactions at A and D.
(*b*) Draw the shear and moment diagrams for the columns AB and CD.
(*c*) Calculate the stress in bars a, b, c, and d.

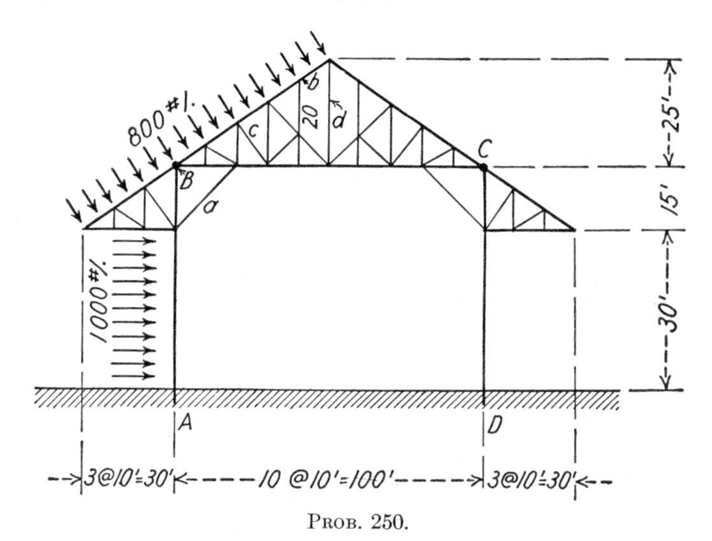

Prob. 250.

251. Same as Problem 250 but a plane of contra-flexure 10 ft. above the ground.

252. Same as Problem 250 but hinged column bases and:

(*a*) Total horizontal force divided equally between the column bases.
(*b*) Total horizontal force divided five-eighths to windward and three-eighths to leeward columns.

253. The same bent as for Problem 250 except that: Column AB is 20 ft. from ground to bottom of knee brace; Column CD is 40 ft. from ground to bottom of knee brace. With wind from the left assume a point of contra-flexure halfway between the foot of the knee brace and the ground for each column. Assume that the shear above the point of contra-flexure for the windward column is divided 20 per cent to column AB and 80 per cent to column CD. Calculate the quantities called for in Problem 250.

254. Same as Problem 253 but with wind from the right.

255. Given a 20-story building having a width of three aisles of 22 ft. each and story heights as follows:

First:	20 ft.
Second:	16 ft.
Third and the rest:	12 ft.

The wind load is 600 lb. per ft. of height.

(*a*) Calculate the shears and moments for the columns in the fifth and sixth stories.

(*b*) Draw the shear and moment diagrams for these columns and also the girders between them.

(*c*) Calculate the direct stress in the columns in the fifth and sixth stories. Use Smith's method as outlined in the text.

256. Calculate the stresses in the top lateral system of the plate girder span shown for Problem 114, p. 146. The lateral load is 1200 lb. per ft. Use the approximate full panel load method assuming that there are verticals at each panel point of the truss.

257. If the effect of wind and lateral vibration is assumed to be 600 lb. per ft. applied 8 ft. above the rail, what is the resulting vertical moment in the leeward girder of the span shown in Problem 114, p. 146?

258. The following wind and lateral vibration loads act on the truss in Problem 157, p. 199:

Top chord,	180 lb. per ft.	
Bottom chord,	540 lb. per ft.	
Train,	600 lb. per ft.	13 ft. 0 in. above the bottom chord.

All taken as moving loads. The trusses are 18 ft. 6 in. center to center. The portal knee braces connect 16 ft. 0 in. below U_1 and U_5 measured along the end posts. The lateral systems are arranged as those shown in Fig. 166. Calculate the stresses due to the lateral loads in the bars L_2L_3; U_2U_3; U_1L_0; and U_2L_3.

259. The following wind and lateral vibration loads act on the truss in Problem 160, p. 201.

Top chord,	360 lb. per ft.	
Bottom chord,	900 lb. per ft.	
Train,	600 lb. per ft.	14 ft. 0 in. above the bottom chord.

All taken as moving loads. The trusses are 20 ft. 0 in. center to center. The portal knee braces connect 13 ft. 6 in. below U_1 and U_9 measured along the end posts. The lateral systems are arranged in a manner similar to those in Fig. 166. Calculate the stresses due to the lateral loads in the bars U_4U_5; L_4L_5; U_1L_0; and U_3L_4.

260. Given the wind loads stated in Problem 259. Calculate the stress in bars *a*, *b*, *c*, *d*, and *e* of the bent shown in Problem 160, p. 201.

261. Make a complete graphical solution of the stresses in the bent of Problem 160, p. 201, due to the loads stated in Problem 259.

PART TWO

INTRODUCTION TO STATICALLY INDETERMINATE STRUCTURES

CHAPTER X

BEAMS AND FRAMES

149. The introduction to this book contains the statement that during the analysis and design of a bridge, building frame, or other structure the engineer is continually confronted with the necessity for calculating the reactions, shears, bending moments, and stresses produced by the applied loads. It was stated, also, that in making such calculations the laws of statics are the fundamental and most important tools of the structural engineer, and that the student of structural theory should secure a mastery of these tools so complete that their correct use becomes a matter of second nature. The purpose of the preceding chapters has been to aid and guide the student in the thorough and painstaking study which is an inescapable prerequisite to such mastery.

In addition to a complete working mastery of the laws of statics, the modern engineer must obtain a thorough understanding of the principles underlying the analysis of structures more complex than those considered in the preceding chapters as was suggested in the original preface and in Art. 2—structures in which the laws of statics must be supplemented by a study of the deformations produced by the applied loads. It is the purpose of this and the succeeding chapter to present the fundamental principles useful in the study of such structures and to illustrate their application in simple cases. Although the engineer who specializes in higher structures must extend his intellectual equipment beyond the material presented here, a thorough mastery of this material will enable him to understand and use intelligently the information contained in treatises devoted exclusively to such structures.

150. Statical Indetermination.—A definition of *statically indeterminate* structures and some discussion of their characteristics may be found in Arts. 22, 23, and 24. In discussing statically indeterminate structures it is frequently convenient to refer to the *degree* of indetermination. The degree of indetermination indicates the number of unknowns which must be determined from a consideration of the elastic distortions (or inelastic, if known) of the structure in addition to those which may be determined from statics. For example, the structure shown at (m) in Fig. 25 is said to be indeterminate to the *first degree* since four independent relations are necessary to calculate its reactions, only three of which are furnished by the laws of statics. Similarly the structure in Fig. 25 (o) is indeterminate to the *third degree*, and that in Fig. 25 (p) is indeterminate to the *second degree.* Structures which are statically indeterminate *internally* are usually said to contain *redundant* bars, and it should be clear that such a structure containing one redundant bar is statically indeterminate internally to the first degree, one containing two redundant bars is statically indeterminate internally to the second degree, and so on.

151. Methods of Analysis.—Some text-books devoted exclusively to the study of statically indeterminate structures list and discuss a number of "methods" of analysis for such structures, some applicable to the general problem and others particularly adapted to certain types. The methods of work, of virtual work, of least work, of slope deflection, of elastic energy, of conjugate points, of moment distribution, of column analogy, of angle changes, of elastic weights, and of systematic relaxation of constraints are some "methods" frequently discussed, and it may be noted that the publications of technical societies contain innumerable amplifications, modifications, extensions, and subdivisions.

In a very broad sense one may say that there is only one way to analyze a statically indeterminate structure and that is to determine by some means a sufficient number of unknowns (reactions, shears, bending moments, or stresses) so that they, in combination with the laws of statics, will make possible a complete analysis of the structure. The means used to determine the necessary number of unknowns form the bases of the various methods mentioned.

Many of the various methods of analysis are rather closely related, and, speaking in a somewhat less broad sense than in the preceding paragraph, it may be fair to say they all fall into one of two general groups depending on the line of attack:

1. Those which depend fundamentally on making the statically indeterminate structure statically determinate and stable and calculating the forces or moments, or both, necessary to restore the structure to its original condition—the moments or forces, or both, thus calculated, in combination with the laws of statics, make possible a complete analysis of the structure.

2. Those which depend fundamentally on making all joints or supports absolutely rigid and calculating corrections to the fixed-end moments as the various joints are allowed to adjust themselves to consistency with the original condition of the structure.

Although the technique of application may sometimes obscure the actual procedure, a majority of the methods may be said to fall into the first group. Moment distribution is the outstanding example of the second group.

152. The development of the principles underlying each general method of attack and illustrative applications will be presented in detail later. However, their fundamental procedures and differences may be qualitatively illustrated by reference to Fig. 178. At (*a*) is shown the structure to be analyzed. The student will note at once that there is one more unknown than can be determined from the laws of statics and that it is necessary therefore to calculate one unknown (reaction, shear, or moment) by some other means.

Making use of the first fundamental procedure stated above, we may evidently make the structure statically determinate and stable by removing the right support. It seems clear that the right end will then sag down through the distance Δ_B, as shown at (*b*) in Fig. 178. If we now apply an upward force, R_B, at the right end, large enough to push that end back to the position it came from, the structure will be restored to its original condition. If we can calculate the magnitude of the force R_B, we will have found the right reaction and can complete the analysis by statics.

The structure may also be made statically determinate and stable by introducing a hinge at A as shown in (*d*), Fig. 178. The beam will then deflect in the manner shown, and the tangent to the elastic line at A will rotate through some angle θ_A as shown. If we now apply a moment at the left end, M_A, large enough to rotate that end of the beam through the angle θ_A, that is, to bring the tangent to the elastic line back to the horizontal as at (*e*), the beam will have been restored to its original condition. If we can calculate the magnitude of the moment M_A, we will have found one unknown reaction and can complete the analysis by statics.

We may also deal with this problem by the second fundamental procedure. Following this line of attack, the right end of the beam is fixed in position and the structure is then in the condition shown

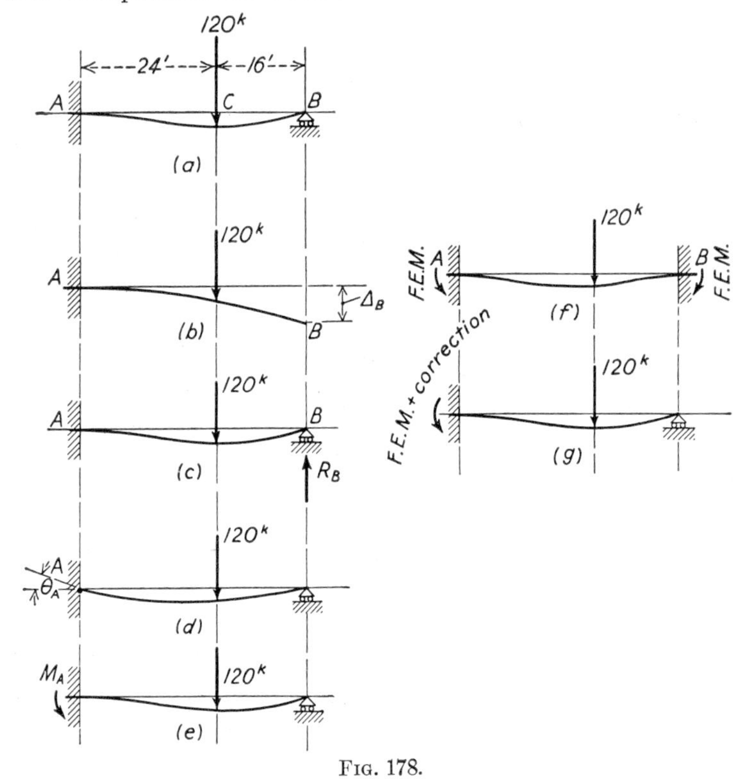

FIG. 178.

at (*f*) in Fig. 178. The moments at the ends, that is, the *fixed-end moments*, are easily calculated by principles which will be developed later. If we now release the restraining moment at the support *B*, i.e., allow it to adjust itself to consistency with the original condition of the structure, that end of the beam will rotate until there is no bending moment there and in doing so will cause a *change* in the bending moment at the end *A*. If we can calculate this change or correction to the fixed-end moment at *A* we will know the final moment there, will have found one unknown, and can of course complete the analysis by statics.

The process described in the preceding paragraph is the basic procedure in the method of analysis, known as "moment distribution," developed by Professor Hardy Cross. The student will find this to be one of the most powerful and versatile tools of structural analysis (if not the most powerful and versatile) ever developed.

153. Angle Changes.—In the analysis of statically indeterminate structures a thorough understanding and facility in the use of the principles underlying the calculation of deflections and angle changes or rotations of beams are of great importance. In fact, one may be justified in saying that these principles are to indeterminate structures as the principles of statics are to determinate structures. As previously intimated there are several approaches to the problem, but the authors so greatly prefer the geometric conception that it will receive major emphasis in this book.

Before discussing the calculation of deflections and angle changes or rotations of practical beams, it is important to consider a purely geometrical problem; the calculation of the departures and slope changes in a straight line which is subjected to a series of very small [1] bends or changes in direction.

The straight line X–X, shown at (a) in Fig. 179, is presumed to be bent through the very small angles θ_1, θ_2, and θ_3 at points C, D, and E, respectively. At (b) in the same figure is shown the resulting condition of the line. If any two points on the original straight line, say points A and B, are chosen as reference points the departure of any point between them from a line through A and B, or the slope of the bent line, relative to A–B, at any such point, may be readily calculated by purely geometrical procedures. For example, suppose that we wish to find the departure of point p from a reference line through A and B and the slope of the bent line at point p, with respect to the same reference. The departure of point p is the distance $pp_1 = \Delta_p$ in Fig. 179 (c), and evidently:

$$pp_1 = \Delta_p = pp_3 - (p_2p_3 + p_1p_2)$$

[1] The magnitude of the angle changes which may be expected in the practical loaded beam will be discussed later. For the present it is sufficient to define a *very small angle* as one in which the differences between the angle, the sine, and the tangent are negligible quantities. The student will do well to determine definitely the magnitude of angles which may be dealt with by the methods considered here, with sufficient accuracy for practical purposes.

Since we are dealing with *very small angles*, we may say that:

$$pp_3 = p_a\alpha$$

$$p_2p_3 = p_c\theta_1$$

$$p_1p_2 = p_d\theta_2$$

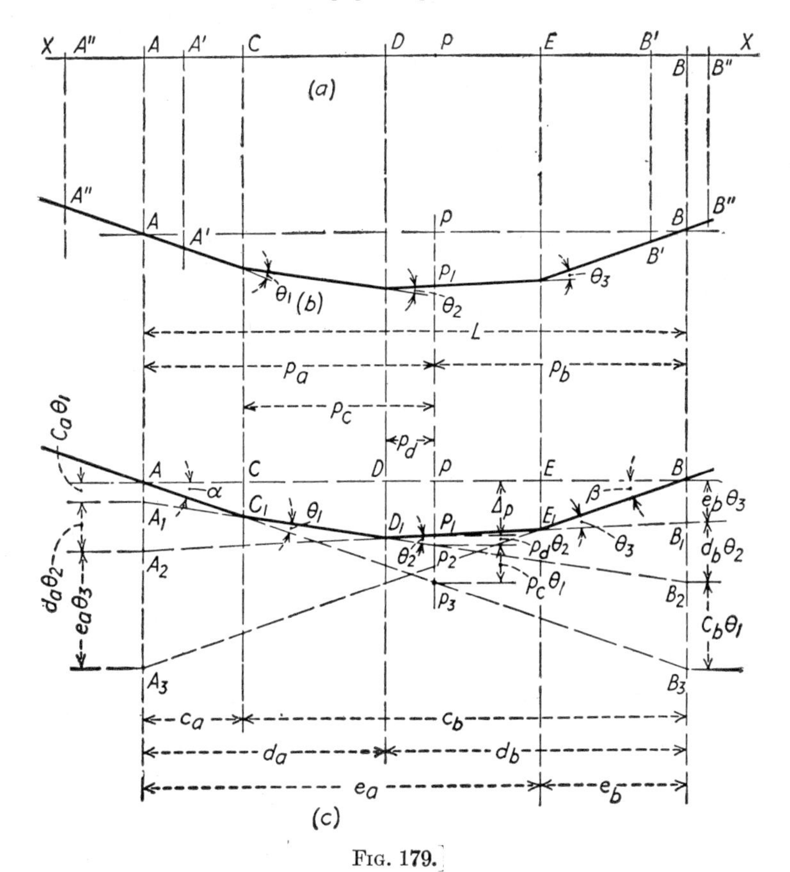

FIG. 179.

Also

$$\alpha = \frac{BB_1 + B_1B_2 + B_2B_3}{L} = \frac{e_b\theta_3 + d_b\theta_2 + c_b\theta_1}{L}$$

Therefore

$$pp_1 = \Delta_p = p_a\frac{(e_b\theta_3 + d_b\theta_2 + c_b\theta_1)}{L} - p_c\theta_1 - p_d\theta_2$$

Similarly the slope of the line at p may be found as:

$$\theta_p = \alpha - (\theta_1 + \theta_2) = \frac{e_b\theta_3 + d_b\theta_2 + c_b\theta_1}{L} - (\theta_1 + \theta_2)$$

The student will immediately recognize the form of the above calculations for Δ_p and θ_p and realize that, if he calculated the bending moment and shear at p in the beam shown in Fig. 180, he would obtain identical results. Furthermore, it will be clear that

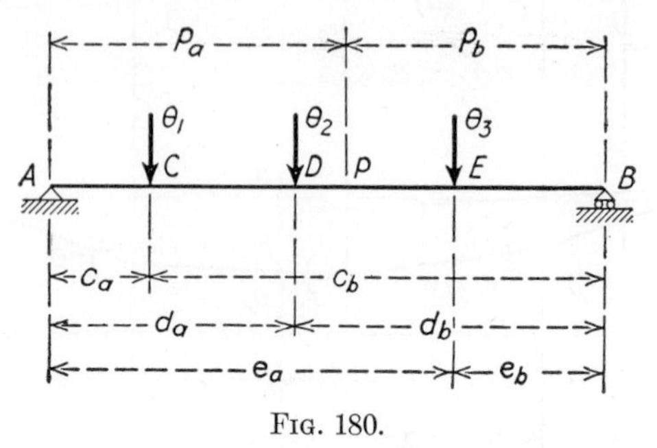

FIG. 180.

had points of reference been chosen, such as $A'B'$ or $A''B''$, Fig. 179 (*a*) and (*b*), exactly the same procedure would have been followed and results identical in form obtained. We may then make the following general statements:

(1) If a point *p* on a line, originally straight, lies between any other two points on the same line, say *A* and *B*, its departure from a straight line through *A* and *B* may be found as the bending moment at *p* on a beam simply supported at *A* and *B* and loaded with the angle changes that occur between *A* and *B*.

(2) The slope of the bent line at *p* referred to the line *A–B* may be found as the shear at *p* on a beam simply supported at *A* and *B* and loaded with the angle changes that occur between *A* and *B*.

Referring to Fig. 181 (*a*), the straight line X–X is presumed to be bent through the very small angles θ_1, θ_2, and θ_3 at points C, D, and E, respectively. Assume now that we wish to calculate the departure of some point in the original line, say p, from the slope of the line at A, and the change in slope of the bent line at p from the slope of the line at A. The figure shows the result clearly.

The departure of p from the slope of the line at A is $pp_3 = \Delta_p$, and we may write at once:

$$pp_3 = \Delta_p = c_p\theta_1 + d_p\theta_2 + e_p\theta_3$$

The change in slope of the line at p from the slope of the line at A is evidently

$$\theta_p = \theta_1 + \theta_2 + \theta_3$$

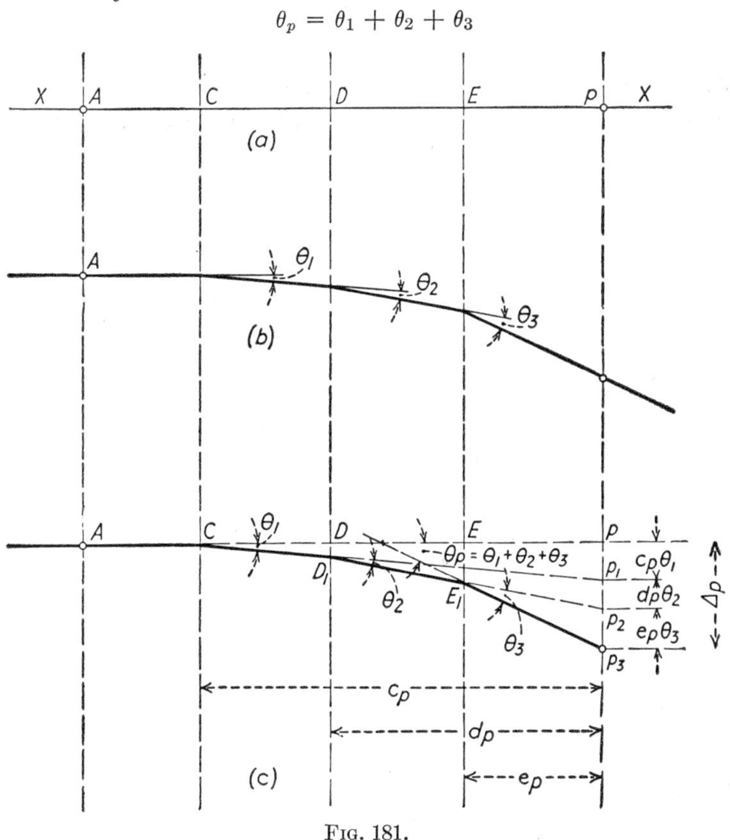

FIG. 181.

Examination of Fig. 181 will clearly show the validity of the following general statements:

(3) The departure of any point p in an originally straight line from the slope at any other point in that line, such as A, is equal to the statical moment *about* p of all the angle changes between p and A.

(4) Thc change in slope of a bent line at any point *p* from the slope at any other point *A* is equal to the sum of the angle changes between *p* and *A*.

It should be emphasized that the reference points and reference lines mentioned in the general statements just presented may themselves change in position or direction; that is, in general statements (**1**) and (**2**) the reference points A and B may move from their original positions and the reference line A–B may change from its original direction. However, the departure, normal to the reference line A–B, of any point between its extremes, such as p, or the slope of the bent line at any point, such as p, referred to the line A–B, may still be found from the general principles stated. Similarly movement of the reference point A or rotation of the slope of the reference line at A does not affect the validity of the general statements (**3**) and (**4**).

The four general statements just presented, set in bold-faced type, are of fundamental importance. They should be carefully memorized and studied until they are clearly and thoroughly understood. It should be particularly impressed on the mind that they are principles of *geometry*. As an aid to the memory they are stated in terms of everyday familiarity to the structural engineer, but they are not in any sense dependent on the principles of structural analysis for their validity.

154. Angle Changes in Loaded Beams.—Consider a beam loaded in any manner, for example as in Fig. 182 (a): The beam is assumed to be homogeneous, not necessarily rectangular but symmetrical about a vertical axis through the centroid of its cross section. Imagine the unloaded beam divided into a series of sections, rectangular in elevation and very short in length, ds, such as $CDEF$ in Fig. 182 (a). These sections or blocks are assumed to be *very short* in length although necessarily illustrated diagrammatically as of appreciable length as in Fig. 182. Under the action of loads on the beam as at (a), Fig. 182, the upper fibers of the beam shorten and the lower fibers lengthen. If we accept the conventional hypothesis that flexural stress and strain are proportional to the distance from the neutral axis, a block such as $CDEF$, rectangular before loading, deforms under load as shown by the dotted lines in (b), Fig. 182. If the section is taken so short that

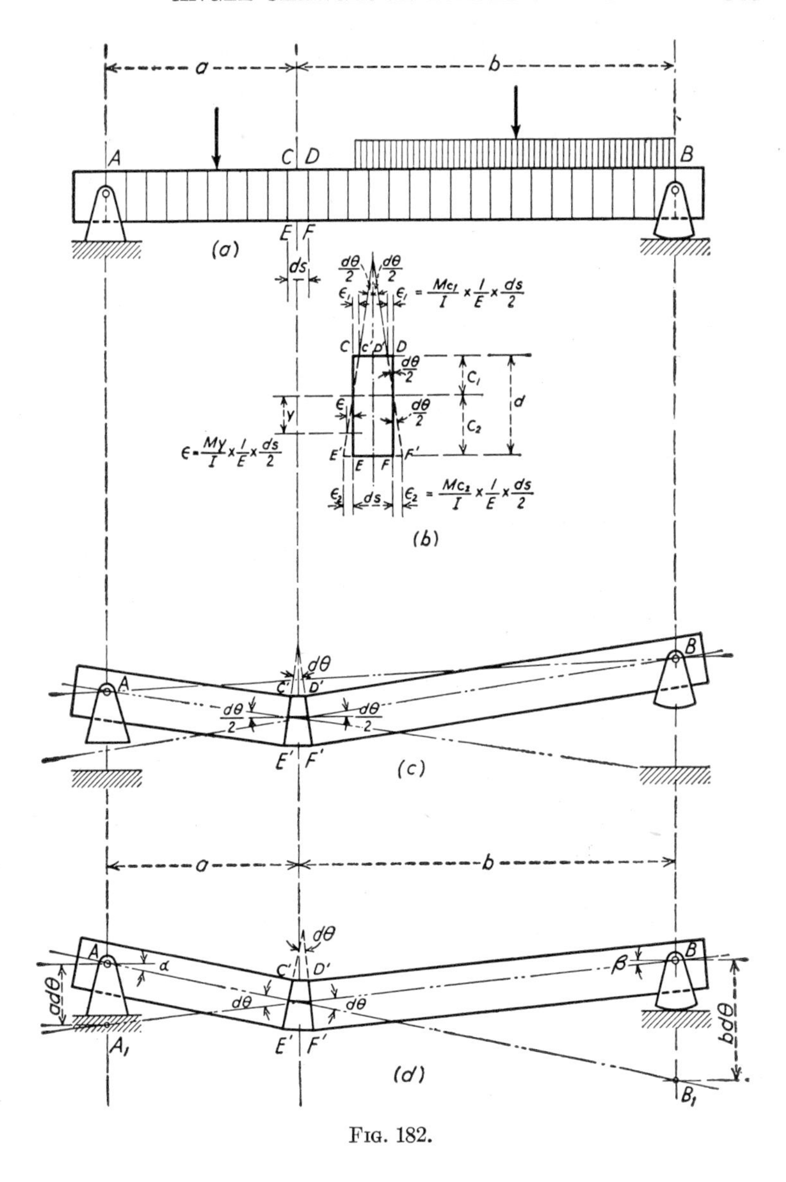

FIG. 182.

we may disregard any change in bending moment from one face to the other, the side CE rotates through the angle $\frac{d\theta}{2}$ into the position $C'E'$ and the side DF through the same angle into the position $D'F'$. Using the notation on the figure, evidently:

$$\frac{d\theta}{2} = \frac{\epsilon}{y} = \frac{\epsilon_1}{c_1} = \frac{\epsilon_2}{c_2} = \frac{My}{EI}\frac{ds}{2y} = \frac{Mc_1}{EI}\cdot\frac{ds}{2c_1} = \frac{Mc_2}{EI}\cdot\frac{ds}{2c_2} = \frac{Mds}{2EI}$$

and

$$d\theta = 2 \times \frac{d\theta}{2} = \frac{Mds}{EI}.$$

That is, we may say that as a result of loads on the beam the vertical sides of a rectangular block, such as $CDEF$ in (*a*), Fig. 182, deform relative to each other through a *very small angle*

$$d\theta = \frac{\text{Bending moment} \times \text{Length of block}}{\text{Modulus of elasticity} \times \text{Moment of inertia}}$$

155. Effect of Angle Changes on Loaded Beams.—Referring again to the beam in Fig. 182, assume for the present that only the block $CDEF$ deforms under load, and that this block takes the form $C'D'E'F'$ shown at (*b*). If we imagine that the block $C'D'E'F'$ is held against movement the left end of the beam must rise from its support in order to remain at right angles to the face $C'E'$, and similarly the right side, in order to remain normal to the face $D'F'$, must extend up and to the right as shown in (*c*) of Fig. 182. Actually of course the left and right ends must remain on their supports, and if the ends are brought down from the positions shown at (*c*) to their proper positions the beam will be in the condition shown at (*d*). Since the length of the block $CDEF$, ds, is presumed to be very small the student will recognize at once that the axis of the beam is a line bent, at the center of the block $CDEF$, through a very small angle $d\theta$, and that the departure of any point on that axis from a line through A and B may be found by purely geometrical means as in Art. 153. Furthermore, the deformation of any other block produces a similar angle change or bend at its center. Thus the departure of any point on the axis from a line through A and B may be found as the bending moment at that point on a beam simply supported at A and B and loaded with the angle changes occurring in all the blocks between A and B, in accordance with the general principle stated under (1) in Art. 153.

Since the angle change on a block is equal to the bending moment (resulting from external loads) at its center multiplied by its length and divided by EI, it seems clear that when we load the beam at the center of a block with the angle change between the faces of that block we are really applying the area of the moment diagram (divided by EI) just above the block as a load. Thus, when we have taken account of all the blocks between A and B, we have applied to the beam the entire moment diagram divided by EI.

It is now possible to rewrite the general statements of Art. 153 in terms directly applicable to loaded beams. In these rewritten statements it will be convenient to use terms defined as follows:

M-diagram = the bending-moment diagram resulting from the external forces.

E = the modulus of elasticity.

I = the moment of inertia of the cross section of the beam.

$\frac{M}{EI}$-diagram = the diagram resulting when every ordinate to the bending-moment diagram resulting from the external forces is divided by the corresponding value of EI.

(1A) If a point p on the axis of a beam originally straight lies between any other two points on the same axis, say A and B, its departure from a straight line through A and B may be found as the bending moment at p on a beam simply supported at A and B and loaded normal to the reference line with that portion of the M-diagram between A and B, divided by EI, when E and I are constant between A and B; if E and I are not constant in value the departure may be found as the bending moment when the beam is loaded with that portion of the $\frac{M}{EI}$-diagram between A and B.

(2A) The slope of the deformed beam axis at any point p referred to the line A–B may be found as the shear at p on a beam simply supported at A and B and loaded normal to the reference line with that portion of the M-diagram between A and B, divided by EI, when E and I are constant between A and B; if E and I are not constant the slope may be found as the shear at p when the beam is loaded with the $\frac{M}{EI}$-diagram between A and B.

(3A) The departure of any point p on the axis of an originally straight beam from the tangent at any other point on that axis, such as A, is equal to the statical moment *about* p of the M-diagram between p and A, divided by EI, if E and I are constant between the points; if E and I are not constant the departure may be found as the statical moment *about* p of the $\frac{M}{EI}$-diagram between p and A.

(4A) The change in slope of the axis of a loaded beam at any point p from the tangent at any other point A is equal to the area of the M-diagram between p and A, divided by EI, if E and I are constant between p and A; if E and I are not constant the change in slope is equal to the area of the $\frac{M}{EI}$-diagram between p and A.[2]

Using the following additional definitions of terms:

Δ_p^{AB} = departure of point p from a line through A and B,
θ_p^{AB} = slope of line (or axis) at point p referred to a line through A and B,

[2] The general principles just stated are frequently referred to as the "moment-area theorems." The statements (3A) and (4A) are identical in principle with the theorems generally credited to Professor Charles E. Greene, who, according to a paper by Professor A. E. Greene in the *Michigan Technic* of June, 1910, Vol. 23, No. 2, pages 21–34, discovered and began to teach them at the University of Michigan in 1873. The general statements (1A) and (2A) apparently were not used by Professor Greene, and some American writers do not include them in the moment-area theorems, although they may be deduced readily therefrom. Writers who do not regard these principles as moment-area theorems frequently designate them by the term "method of elastic weights." They are generally credited to Professor Otto Mohr.

These general principles may be derived in several different ways, but as previously stated the purely geometric approach seems distinctly preferable, and it may be noted in passing that when considered from this point of view there seems to be less reason for differentiating between the principles. The authors would suggest that the student think of these general principles as *principles of the geometry of small-angle changes*, and if he must apply the term "method" to them that he consider them collectively as the method of computing slope changes and deflections by angle changes. However, it is of course necessary and proper that the student relate these principles to the discussions in text-books and articles devoted entirely to the subject of indeterminate structures, and for that reason he should become familiar with the terminology commonly employed.

$\Delta_p^{\text{Tan } A}$ = departure of point p from a tangent at A,
$\theta_p^{\text{Tan } A}$ = slope of line (or axis) at point p referred to a tangent at A,

these general statements may be written in abbreviated form as follows:

$$\Delta_p^{AB} = \frac{1}{EI}\left[\begin{array}{l}\text{Bending moment at } p \text{ due to } M\text{-diagram between} \\ A \text{ and } B \text{ applied as load on simple beam } AB\end{array}\right]$$

if E and I are constant between A and B. If not,

$$= \left[\begin{array}{l}\text{Bending moment at } p \text{ due to } \dfrac{M}{EI}\text{-diagram between} \\ A \text{ and } B \text{ applied as load on simple beam } AB.\end{array}\right]$$

$$\theta_p^{AB} = \frac{1}{EI}\left[\begin{array}{l}\text{Shear at } p \text{ due to } M\text{-diagram between } A \text{ and} \\ B \text{ applied on simple beam } AB \text{ as a load}\end{array}\right]$$

if E and I are constant between A and B. If not,

$$= \left[\begin{array}{l}\text{Shear at } p \text{ due to } \dfrac{M}{EI}\text{-diagram between } A \text{ and } B \\ \text{applied as load on simple beam } AB.\end{array}\right]$$

$$\Delta_p^{\text{Tan } A} = \frac{1}{EI}\left[\begin{array}{l}\text{Statical moment } \textit{about } p \text{ of } M\text{-diagram between} \\ p \text{ and } A.\end{array}\right]$$

if E and I are constant between p and A. If not,

$$= \left[\begin{array}{l}\text{Statical moment } \textit{about } p \text{ of } \dfrac{M}{EI}\text{-diagram between } p \\ \text{and } A.\end{array}\right]$$

$$\theta_p^{\text{Tan } A} = \frac{1}{EI}\left[\text{Area of } M\text{-diagram between } p \text{ and } A.\right]$$

if E and I are constant between p and A. If not,

$$= \left[\text{Area of } \frac{M}{EI}\text{-diagram between } p \text{ and } A.\right]$$

It should be obvious that if either E or I is constant and the other variable, within the limits of consideration, the constant factor may be kept outside the bracket, and the moment diagram, divided by the varying factor, may be placed within the bracket, i.e., the $\frac{M}{I}$ -diagram or $\frac{M}{E}$ -diagram may be placed within the bracket instead of the $\frac{M}{EI}$ -diagram.

156. Applications in Calculating Beam Deflections and Slopes. —We may now illustrate the application of the general principles stated in the preceding article in the calculation of deflections and changes in slope in a few simple cases with which the student is familiar through his study of the mechanics of materials.

Consider first the simply supported beam, having constant moment of inertia, and supporting a concentrated load at the center, shown in Fig. 183 (*a*). The bending-moment diagram is shown at (*b*) in Fig. 183. At (*c*) the bending-moment diagram is shown applied as a load on a simple beam supported at A and B in accordance with the principle stated in (**1A**). At (*d*) and (*e*) are shown the shear and bending-moment diagrams due to the loading shown at (*c*). In accordance with the principles stated in (**1A**) and (**1B**) if the ordinates to these diagrams are divided by EI, the values obtained from (*e*) will be the deflections of the beam referred to the line AB and the values obtained from (*d*) will be the changes in slope of the neutral axis (elastic line) referred to the line AB.

Thus we find that the center deflection is:

$$\Delta_5^{AB} = \frac{125}{6000} PL^3 \times \frac{1}{EI} = \frac{1}{48} \frac{PL^3}{EI}$$

and the change in slope of the neutral axis at the left end, *0*, is:

$$\theta_0^{AB} = \frac{25}{400} PL^2 \times \frac{1}{EI} = \frac{1}{16} \frac{PL^2}{EI}$$

values which the student presumably has found previously in his study of the mechanics of materials. The deflection or change in slope at any other point may be obtained in a similar manner.

The units involved in these statements should be carefully noted and *consistent* values used in all cases. The quantities E and I are generally given in terms of inch units; i.e., E is usually stated as so many pounds per square inch, or kips per square inch, and I as so many inches to the fourth power. When E and I are stated in inch units the deflection is normally calculated in

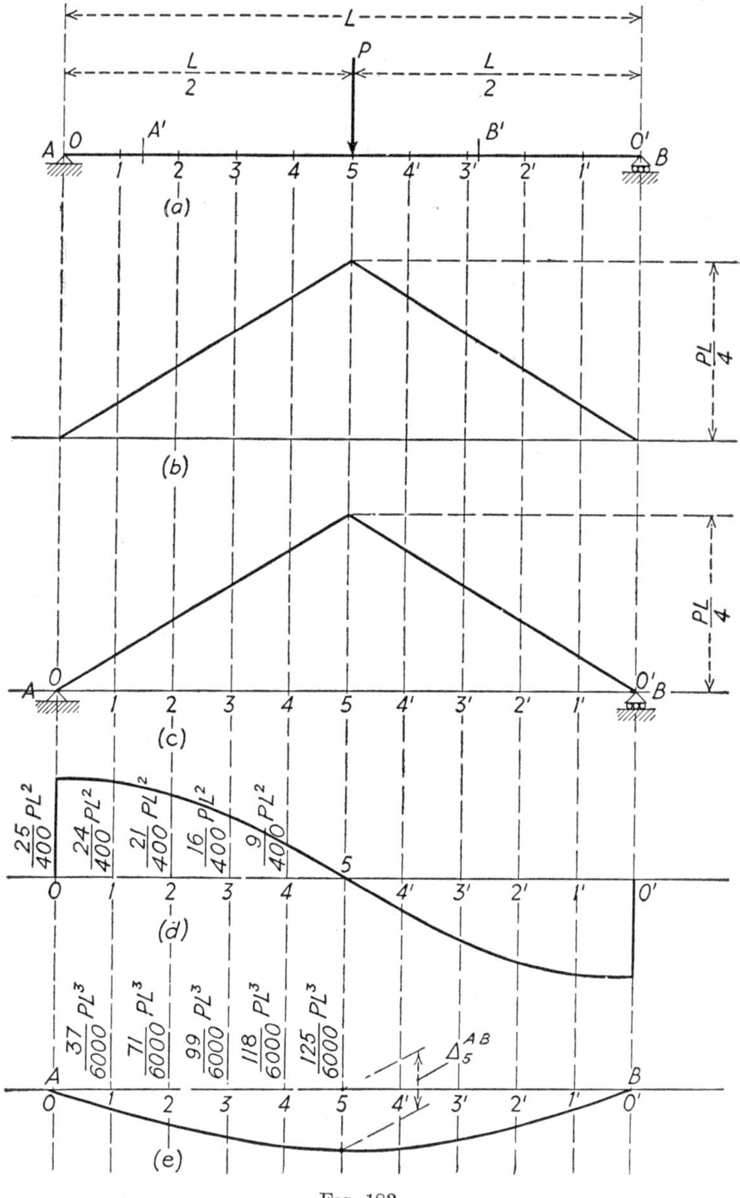
L
P
L/2
L/2
A
0
A'
B'
0'
B
1
2
3
4
5
4'
3'
2'
1'
(a)
PL/4
(b)
(c)
25/400 PL²
24/400 PL²
21/400 PL²
16/400 PL²
9/400 PL²
(d)
37/6000 PL³
71/6000 PL³
99/6000 PL³
118/6000 PL³
125/6000 PL³
Δ₅^AB
(e)

FIG. 183.

inches, and the dimension L should be in inches, or if used in feet the result must be multiplied by 12^3. Obviously the load P and the constant E must be in consistent units: P in pounds and E in pounds per square inch, or P in kips and E in kips per square inch.

A second illustration is given in Fig. 184, a simple beam supporting a uniformly distributed load of w pounds per foot. The arrangement is exactly the same as in Fig. 183; the only comment the authors wish to make is that the center deflection is

$$\Delta_5^{AB} = \frac{3125}{240{,}000} wL^4 \times \frac{1}{EI} = \frac{5}{384} \frac{wL^4}{EI}$$

and the change in slope at the left end, 0,

$$\theta_o^{AB} = \frac{125}{3000} wL^3 \times \frac{1}{EI} = \frac{1}{24} \frac{wL^3}{EI}$$

in each case referred to the line AB. These are familiar results.

The applications of the fundamental principles given in Figs. 183 and 184 are shown in considerable detail for the sake of clearness. Such detail is not necessary in the normal use of these principles, as will appear in later applications.

Changes in slope and deflections of beams are generally calculated with reference to a line through the supports, but the principles stated are applicable to any reference line and illustrations of such applications are presented in Fig. 185. It is assumed that the deflection of point 5 is wanted in each of the beams shown in Figs. 183 and 184, referred in each case to a line through A' and B'. In accordance with the principle stated, a simple beam supported at A' and B' is loaded with that portion of the moment diagram between A' and B', and the deflection at 5 found as the bending moment at 5 divided by EI. Figure 185 (*a*) shows the portion of the moment diagram between A' and B' for the beam of Fig. 183, and (*b*) shows the deflection diagram referred to the line $A'B'$. The same data for the beam in Fig. 184 are shown in (*c*) and (*d*) of Fig. 185.

Illustrations of the theorems stated in (**3A**) and (**4A**) are given in Fig. 186. At (*a*) is shown a cantilever beam loaded at one end; at (*b*) is shown the bending-moment diagram; and at (*c*) the deflected beam with the departure and rotation at F, referred to

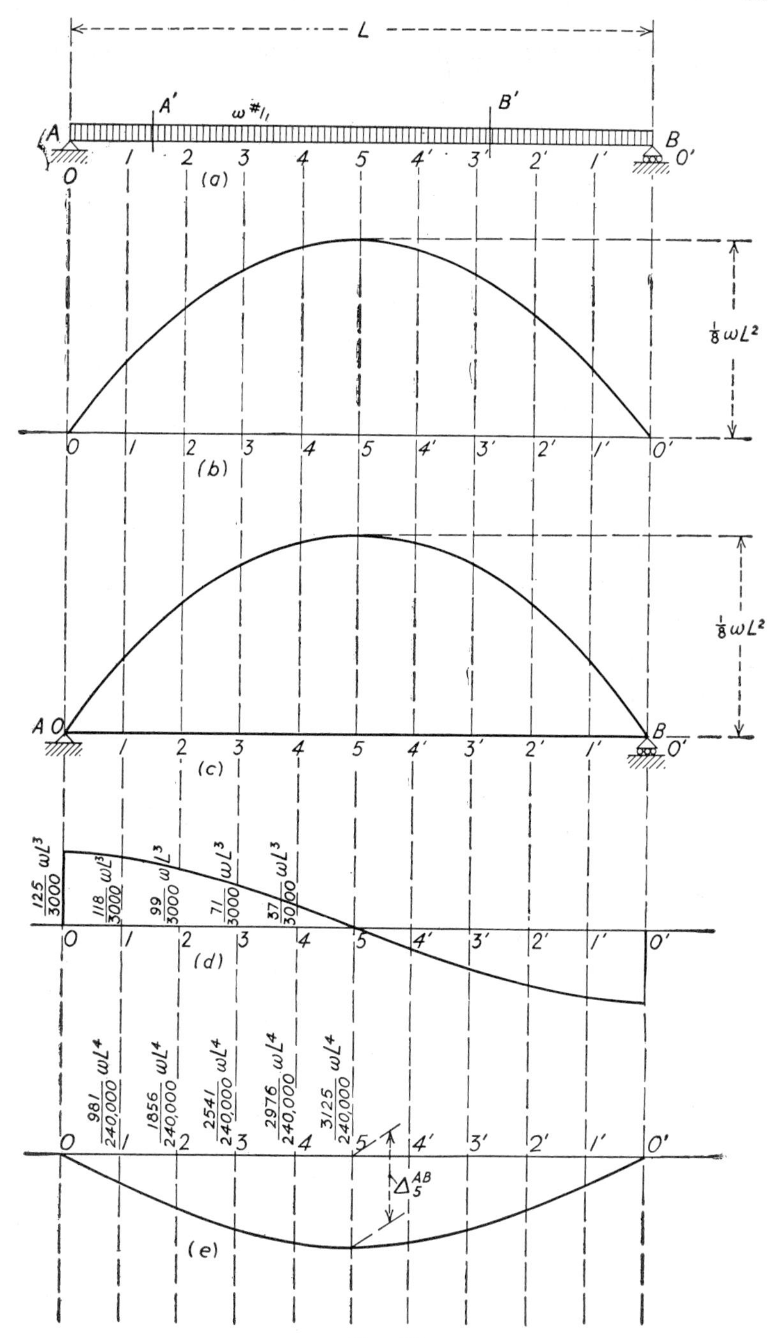
L
A'
B'
w #/l
A
B
0
1
2
3
4
5
4'
3'
2'
1'
0'
(a)
(b)
(c)
(d)
(e)
1/8 wL²
125/3000 wL³
118/3000 wL³
99/3000 wL³
71/3000 wL³
37/3000 wL³
981/240,000 wL⁴
1856/240,000 wL⁴
2541/240,000 wL⁴
2976/240,000 wL⁴
3125/240,000 wL⁴
Δ5 AB

FIG. 184.

the tangent at A, indicated. Application of the general statements gives the following:

$$\Delta_F^{\text{Tan } A} = PL \times \frac{L}{2} \times \frac{2}{3} L \times \frac{1}{EI} = \frac{1}{3} \frac{PL^3}{EI}$$

and

$$\theta_F^{\text{Tan } A} = PL \times \frac{L}{2} \times \frac{1}{EI} = \frac{1}{2} \frac{PL^2}{EI}$$

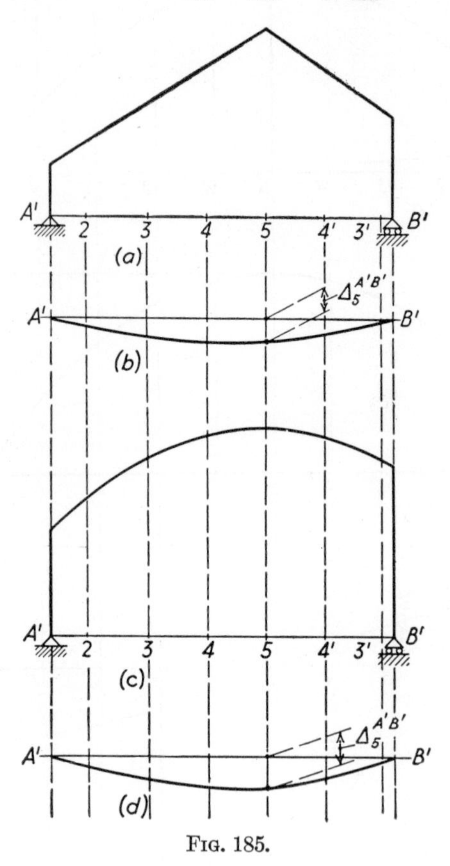

Fig. 185.

It should be clear that deflection and rotation of *any* point referred to the tangent at *any other point* may be found by the same procedure. Illustrations are given in (*d*) and (*e*) of Fig. 186, which show the bending-moment diagram between F' and A and the deflection and rotation of F' referred to the tangent at A; also, in

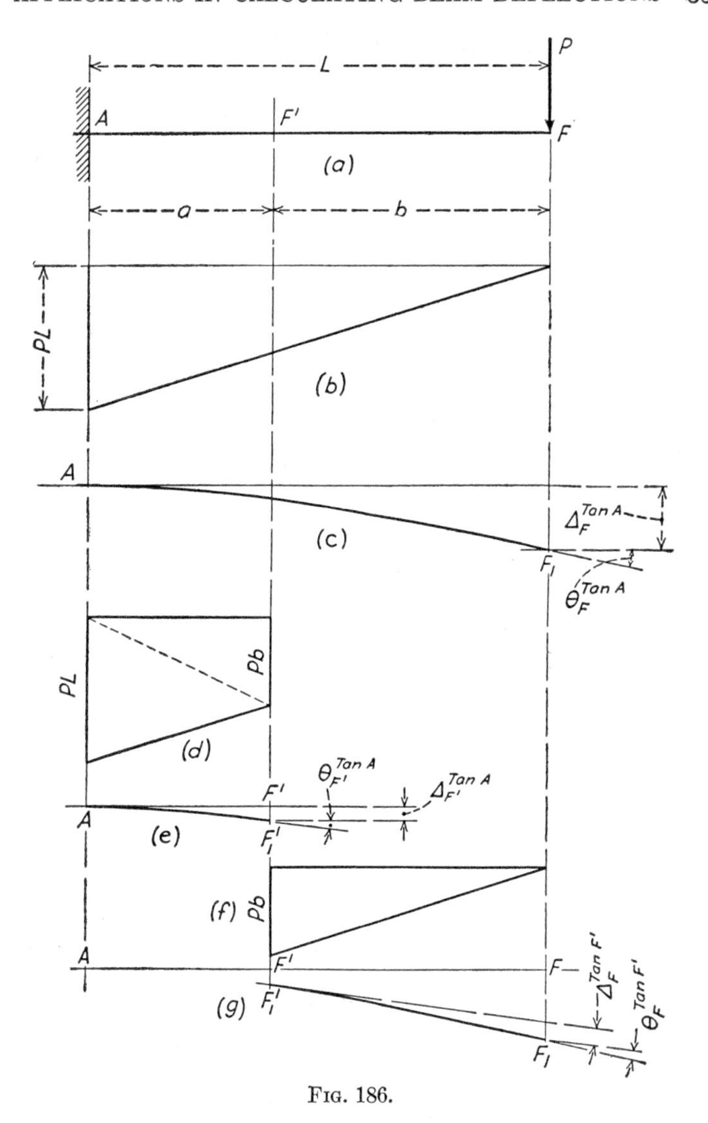

FIG. 186.

(f) and (g), which show the bending-moment diagram between F and F' and the deflection and rotation of F referred to the tangent at F'. Application of the general theorems gives at once:

$$\Delta_{F'}{}^{\text{Tan } A} = \left[PL \times \frac{a}{2} \times \frac{2}{3}a + Pb \times \frac{a}{2} \times \frac{1}{3}a\right]\frac{1}{EI} = \frac{1}{6}\frac{Pa^2}{EI}(2L + b)$$

$$\theta_{F'}^{\text{Tan } A} = \left[PL \times \frac{a}{2} + Pb \times \frac{a}{2}\right]\frac{1}{EI} = \frac{1}{2}\frac{Pa}{EI}(L + b)$$

$$\Delta_F^{\text{Tan } F'} = Pb \times \frac{b}{2} \times \frac{2}{3}b \times \frac{1}{EI} = \frac{1}{3}\frac{Pb^3}{EI}$$

$$\theta_F^{\text{Tan } F'} = Pb \times \frac{b}{2} \times \frac{1}{EI} = \frac{1}{2}\frac{Pb^2}{EI}$$

The preceding illustrations were based on prismatic beams, i.e., beams in which the section and moment of inertia are constant throughout the length. The use of the fundamental principles in connection with beams in which the moment of inertia is not constant is illustrated in Figs. 187 and 188. In Fig. 187 the loaded beam is shown at (*a*), the bending-moment diagram at (*b*), the $\frac{M}{I}$-diagram at (*c*), and the deflected neutral axis at (*d*). Similar data are shown for a cantilever beam in Fig. 188. It should be clear that the deflection at any point of the beam in Fig. 187 (*a*) may be found as the bending moment at that point due to the $\frac{M}{I}$-diagram loading shown at (*c*), Fig. 187, divided by E, and correspondingly the change in slope at any point the shear at that point due to the $\frac{M}{I}$-diagram as a load divided by E. Comment on the cantilever beam of Fig. 188 seems unnecessary.

One other illustrative example may be worth while, the fixed-end beam supporting a single concentrated load at the center shown in Fig. 189 (*a*). The bending-moment diagram is shown at (*b*); the moment diagram, i.e., the angle changes, applied as a load on a simple beam supported at A and B, at (*c*); the shear diagram resulting from that loading is shown at (*d*); and the moment diagram resulting from the loading at (*c*) is shown at (*e*). It should be clear that the ordinates to the diagram at (*e*) divided by EI will be the deflections, and the ordinates to the diagram at (*d*) divided by EI the changes in slope of the neutral axis, or elastic line, referred to A–B, at the various points on the axis.

The student should note that the loading shown at (*c*) in Fig. 189 may be replaced by the two loading diagrams shown at (*a*) and (*b*) of Fig. 190; obviously when combined as in (*c*) the result

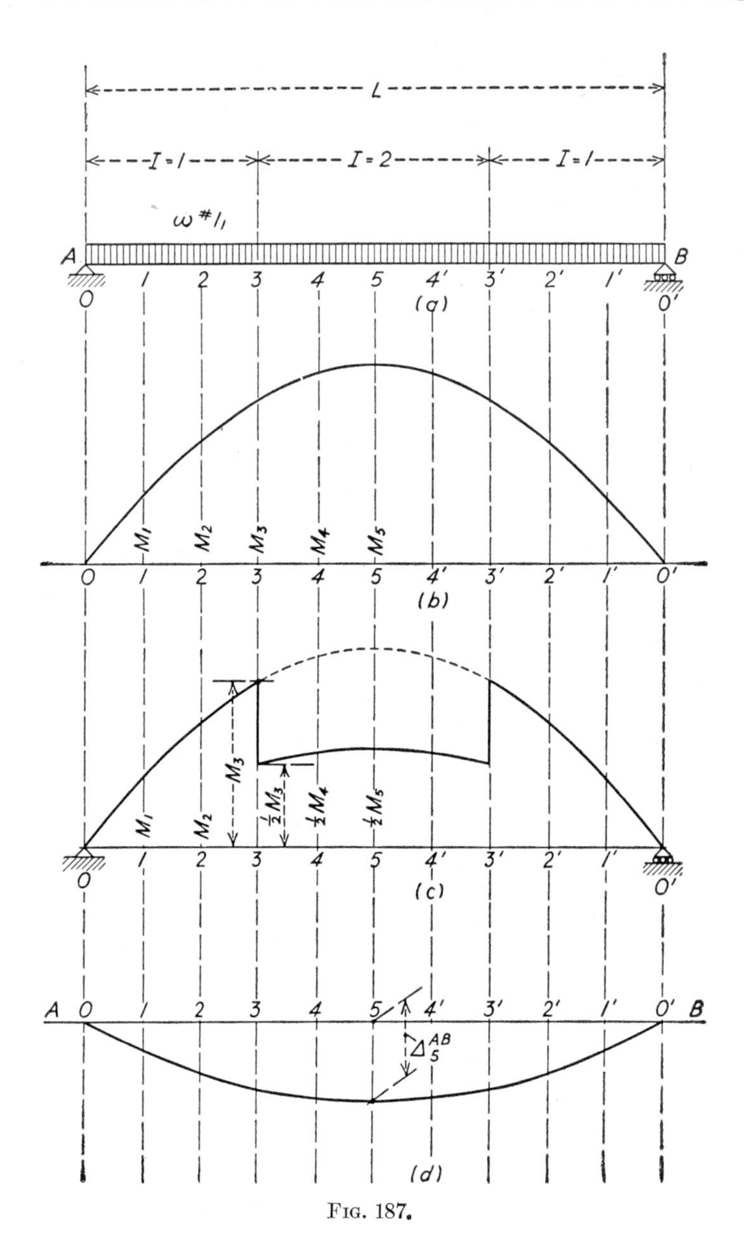

FIG. 187.

is identical with that at (*c*) of Fig. 189. It is frequently, if not usually, more convenient to deal with the bending-moment diagrams for beams with negative moments at the supports in that manner, i.e., to treat the moment diagram as composed of two

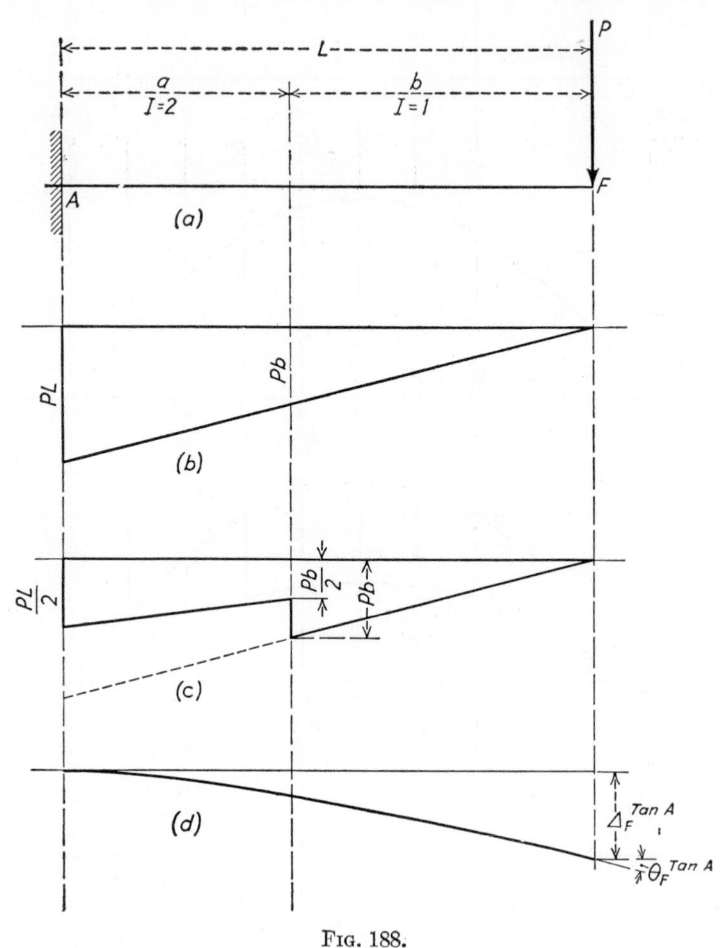

Fig. 188.

parts, the simple beam moment diagram which would exist if there were no end moments and the moment diagram which would result from application of the end moments only. This is particularly true when the end moments are unequal, or when there is dissymmetry from some other cause.

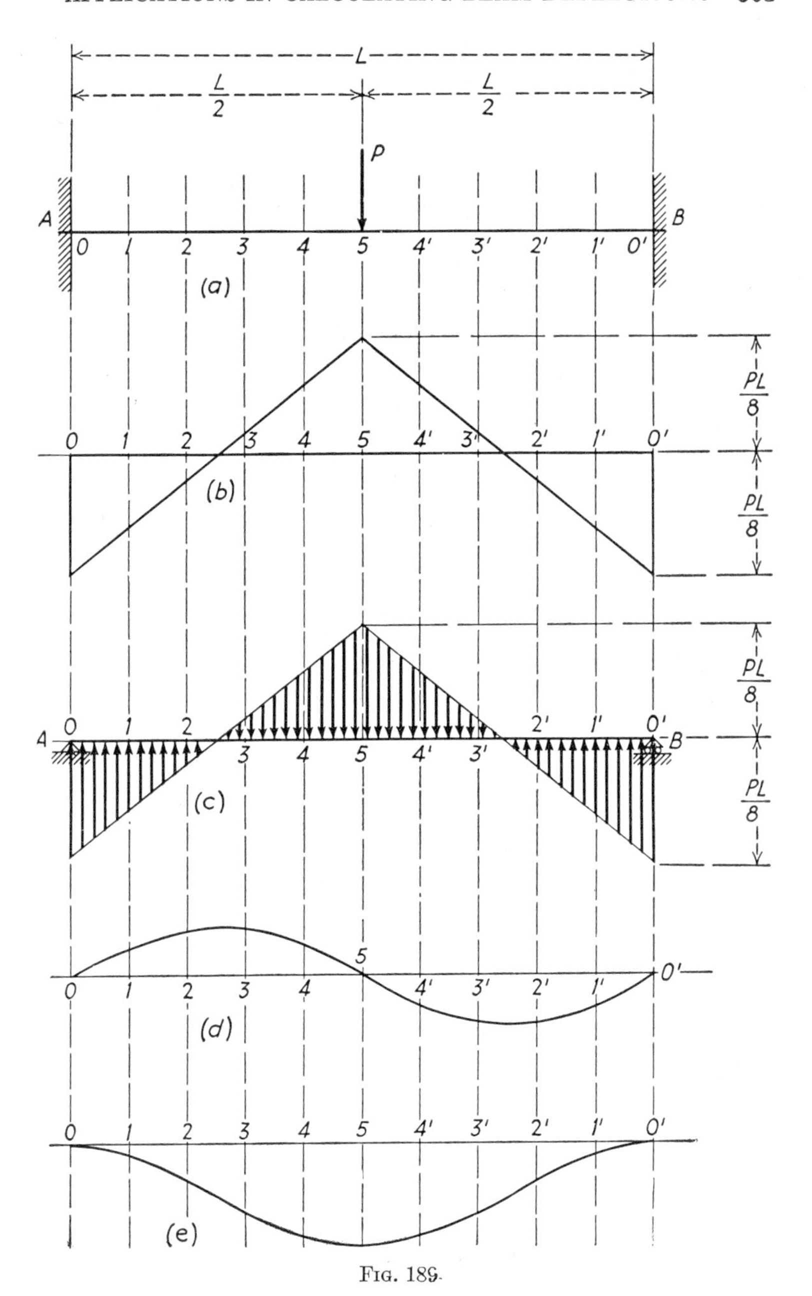

FIG. 189.

157. Numerical Examples.—The general discussion of the preceding article is illustrated here with a few examples showing the calculation of actual deflections and rotations.

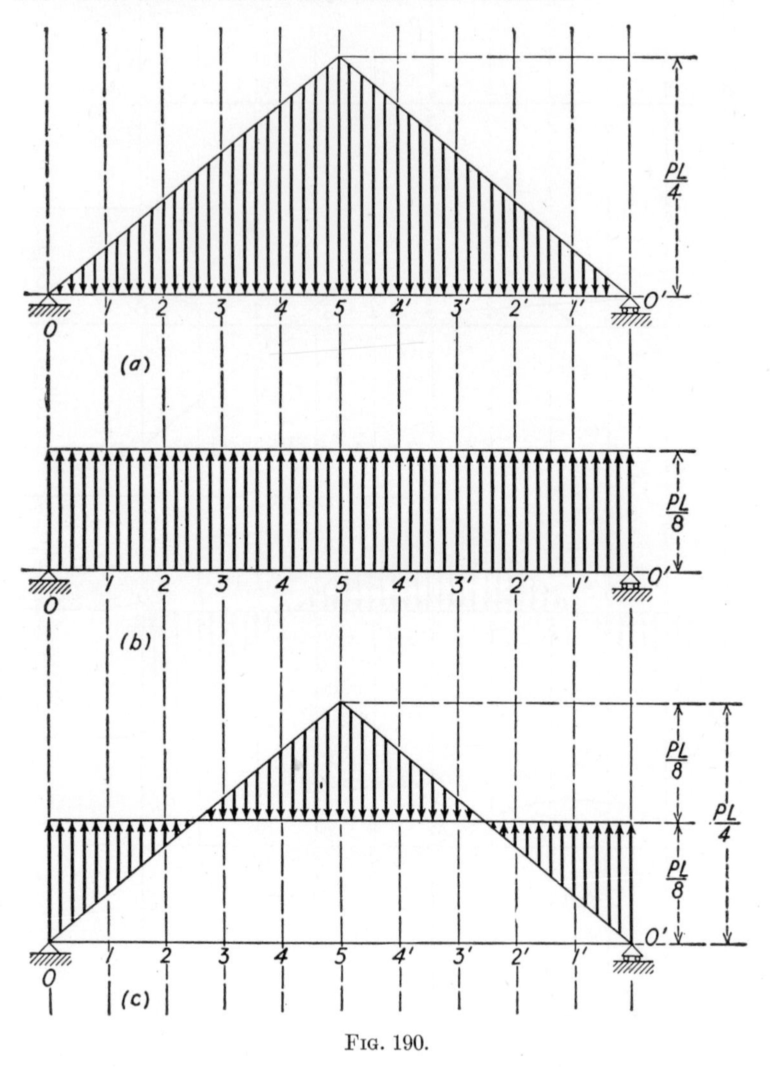

FIG. 190.

Figure 191 (a) shows diagrammatically a beam supporting a uniformly distributed load and the deflected shape of the elastic line. The general relations developed on pages 356 and 357 may be applied to find the center deflection and the change in slope at the end.

$$\Delta_5^{AB} = \frac{5}{384} \times \frac{4 \times 40}{30{,}000} \times \frac{480 \times 480 \times 480}{8147.6} = 0.943 \text{ in.}$$

$$\theta_o^{AB} = \frac{1}{24} \times \frac{4 \times 40 \times 480 \times 480}{30{,}000 \times 8147.6} = 0.006284 \text{ radian}$$

$$= 0.006284 \times \frac{180}{\pi} = 0.360° = 0° \, 21' \, 36''$$

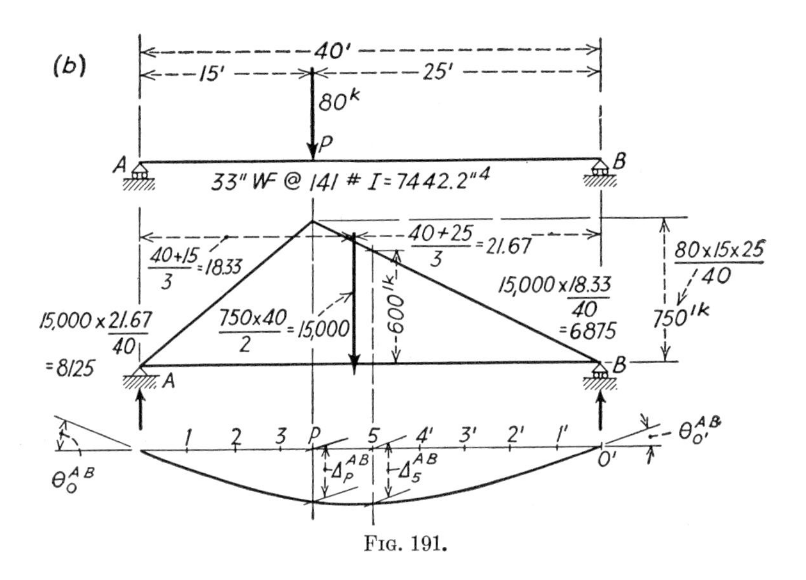

Fig. 191.

The reader should note particularly the amount of change in slope at the end, and the angle between the tangents at the ends of the deflected beam, and reflect on the statement made in the footnote on page 344.[3]

A beam supporting an unsymmetrical concentrated load is shown at (*b*), Fig. 191, together with its moment diagram applied

[3] It may be well to give further emphasis to this matter, and attention is called to the relation developed on pages 356 and 357, which may be written

$$\theta_o^{AB} = \frac{1}{24}\frac{wL^3}{EI} = \frac{1}{8}\frac{wL^2 \times c}{I} \times \frac{1}{3}\frac{L}{Ec}$$

since $\frac{1}{8}\frac{wL^2}{I}c = \frac{Mc}{I} = s$, we may write

$$\theta_o^{AB} = \frac{1}{3}\frac{sL}{Ec}$$

or for a symmetrical beam, since $c = \frac{d}{2}$, $\theta_o^{AB} = \frac{2}{3}\frac{sL}{Ed}$.

In this expression, s is the maximum fiber stress at the center of a span supporting a uniform load, L is the length of the span, d the depth of the beam, and E the modulus of elasticity. For ordinary structural steel the value of s will rarely exceed about 26 kips per sq. in., even for greatly overloaded structures, and the ratio L/d will generally lie between 10 and 20. However, in order to get some notion of the maximum possible angle of rotation, assume that the beam in question is composed of an alloy steel leaving a yield-point stress of 50 kips per sq. in. and that the stress is 90 per cent of the yield-point stress; also assume that L/d has the very improbable value of 50.

Then

$$\theta_o^{AB} = \frac{2}{3} \times \frac{45 \times 50}{30{,}000} = .050 \text{ radian}$$

or

$$\frac{50}{1000} \times \frac{180}{\pi} = 2.8648° = 2° \ 51' \ 53''$$

The comparison between the angle, the sine, and the tangent is as follows:

$$\text{angle} = .05000 = .0500$$

$$\text{sine} = .04998 = .0500$$

$$\text{tangent} = .05004 = .0500$$

which means that for conditions of stress and ratio of length to depth so extreme as to be absurd the change in slope is so small that the difference between the angle, the sine, and the tangent is only a little over 1 part in 1000 —a difference which is meaningless in such calculations as are contemplated here.

as a load on a simple beam supported at A and B, and the deflected elastic line. From the data in the figure we may write at once:

$$\Delta_5{}^{AB} = 6875 \times 20 = 137{,}500$$

$$600 \times \frac{20}{2} \times \frac{20}{3} = \underline{40{,}000}$$

$$97{,}500 \times \frac{1728}{30{,}000 \times 7442.2} = 0.755 \text{ in.}$$

$$\Delta_P{}^{AB} = 8125 \times 15 = 121{,}875$$

$$750 \times \frac{15}{2} \times \frac{15}{3} = \underline{28{,}125}$$

$$93{,}750 \times \frac{1728}{30{,}000 \times 7442.2} = 0.726 \text{ in.}$$

$$\theta_o{}^{AB} = \frac{8125 \times 144}{30{,}000 \times 7442.2} = 0.00524 \text{ radian} = 0^\circ\ 18'\ 1''$$

$$\theta_{o'}{}^{AB} = \frac{6875 \times 144}{30{,}000 \times 7442.2} = 0.00443 \text{ radian} = 0^\circ\ 15'\ 14''$$

Figure 192 shows a beam with overhanging ends; the bending-moment diagram; the deflected elastic line, drawn to a greatly exaggerated scale; and the calculation of the deflection of the ends, and of the center of the beam. The calculations for deflections show direct numerical application of the principles stated in bold-faced type on pages 351 and 352.

It may be desirable to explain in some detail the calculations in this case. The computations for the deflection of point C, referred to line BD, are headed $\Delta_C{}^{BD}$. Since E and I are constant the angle changes are directly proportional to the bending moments and the calculations show the determination of the bending moment at C due to the moment diagram **between B and D** applied on the line BD as a beam simply supported at B and D. The moment diagram is as shown at (*b*) in Fig. 192, but as a matter of convenience in calculation it is dealt with in two parts as suggested in connection with Figs. 189 and 190. Thus the calculation:

$$800 \times \tfrac{40}{2} \times \tfrac{1}{2} = 8000, \times 20 = 160{,}000$$

$$800 \times \tfrac{20}{2} \times \tfrac{20}{3} = \underline{53{,}333}$$

$$106{,}667$$

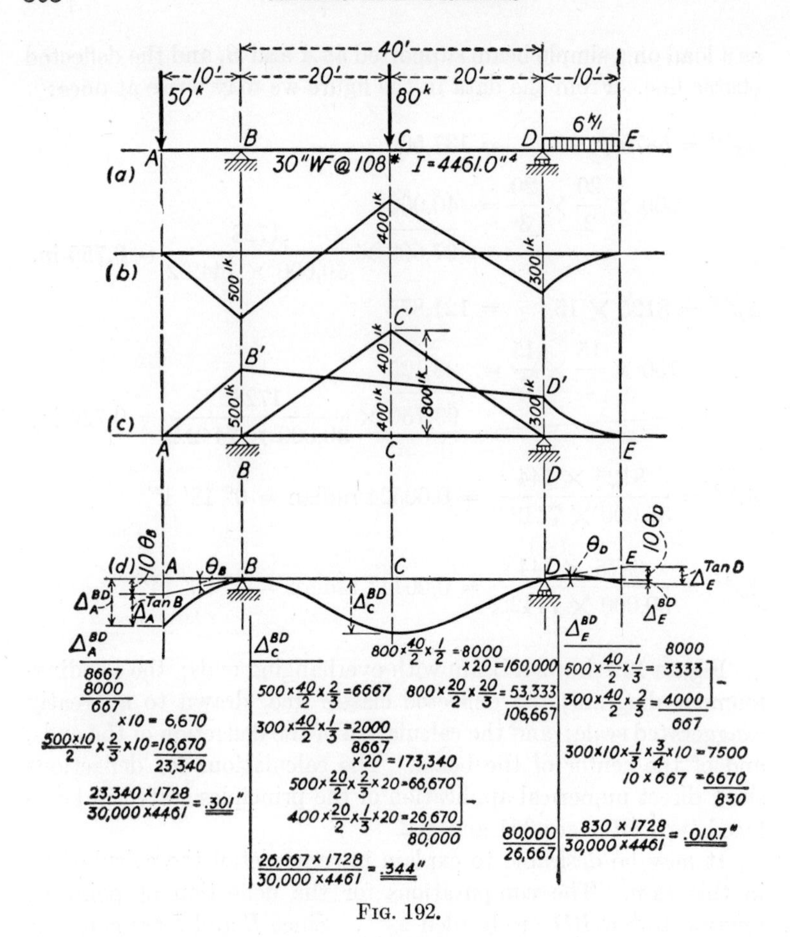

FIG. 192.

is the bending moment at C due to the simple beam moment diagram, $BC'D$, applied as a load on BD, and the calculation:

$$500 \times \tfrac{40}{2} \times \tfrac{2}{3} = 6667$$

$$300 \times \tfrac{40}{2} \times \tfrac{1}{3} = 2000$$

$$8667 \times 20 = 173{,}340$$

$$\left.\begin{aligned} 500 \times \tfrac{20}{2} \times \tfrac{2}{3} \times 20 &= 66{,}670 \\ 400 \times \tfrac{20}{2} \times \tfrac{1}{3} \times 20 &= 26{,}670 \end{aligned}\right] -$$

$$80{,}000$$

is the bending moment at C due to the diagram $BB'D'D$ applied to BD as a load. Of course the algebraic sum of these quantities:

$$\begin{array}{r} 106{,}667 \\ 80{,}000 \\ \hline 26{,}667 \end{array}$$

is EI times the deflection of point C, referred to the line BD, in feet. To get the actual deflection of C in inches we must of course multiply by 12^3 and divide by E and I in inch units. Therefore:

$$\Delta_C^{BD} = \frac{26{,}667 \times 1728}{30{,}000 \times 4461} = 0.344 \text{ in.}$$

Deflection of point A is made up of two parts, deflection due to rotation of the tangent to the elastic line at B, and departure from the tangent due to angle changes between A and B. The calculations for deflection of point A are headed Δ_A^{BD} in Fig. 192 (d). The computation

$$\begin{array}{l} 8667 \\ 8000 \\ \hline 667 \times 10 = 6670 \end{array}$$

gives the deflection due to rotation of the tangent to the elastic line at B, and $\frac{500 \times 10}{2} \times \frac{2}{3} \times 10 = 16{,}670$, the departure from the tangent due to angle changes between A and B. The sum 23,340 is then EI times the deflection of A referred to BD in feet and the deflection in inches

$$\frac{23{,}340 \times 1728}{30{,}000 \times 4461} = 0.301 \text{ in.}$$

In studying the deflection of point E it should be noted that rotation of the tangent to the elastic line at D lifts E *above* the reference line B, while departure from the tangent, due to angle changes between E and D, brings the final position of E to slightly below the reference line BD.

The student should observe in studying these calculations that there has been no attempt to use a formal sign convention. In all calculations in structural analysis the authors believe it preferable to form a mental picture (aided by actual sketches when necessary) of the *action* of the structure and to determine the direction of a force, rotation, or movement from that picture rather than from dependence on a formal sign convention. Thus in the calculations for deflection of point C it is easy to see mentally that the angle changes represented by the moment diagram $BC'D$, Fig. 192 (c), must cause the beam to bend *down* between B and D, while the angle changes represented by the moment diagram $BB'D'D$ would cause it to bend *up*. Consequently, without any formal use of signs the movement of C due the latter angle changes is subtracted from the movement due to the former. In the same way, in making calculations for the movements of points A and E quantities are added or subtracted in accordance with a mental picture of the physical action of the structure. It is the authors' opinion that adherence to this procedure will develop a better understanding of fundamental principles, a clearer picture of structural action, and a better sense of proportion, and in addition reduce the probability of error.

158. Application to Indeterminate Structures.—The calculation of actual deflections and rotations in structural design is not so frequent as the calculation of relative hypothetical deflections or rotations as an aid in analyzing indeterminate structures.

The general method of attack on such problems was outlined in Art. 152 and now may be illustrated by the solution of a number of concrete cases. Many of these problems can be solved more simply by methods other than those used here, and simpler solutions will be presented later in several cases, but the immediate purpose is to illustrate and fix in the mind of the student the all-important fundamental principles.

159. The supported cantilever beam shown in Fig. 193 (a) is assumed to have constant moment of inertia and to be loaded as shown.

The structure is evidently indeterminate to the first degree, and one unknown quantity must be determined from the geometry of continuity.

This is the same beam shown in Fig. 178 and discussed in general terms in Art. 152, and the calculations for determination of the right reaction by the fundamental procedure suggested there are shown in the figure. The only comment which seems necessary is to call attention to the term δ_B, which is the amount that a unit vertical reaction will move the end B. If the amount which the right end deflects when the support is removed, and the amount that a unit reaction will push that end up, are known, it seems

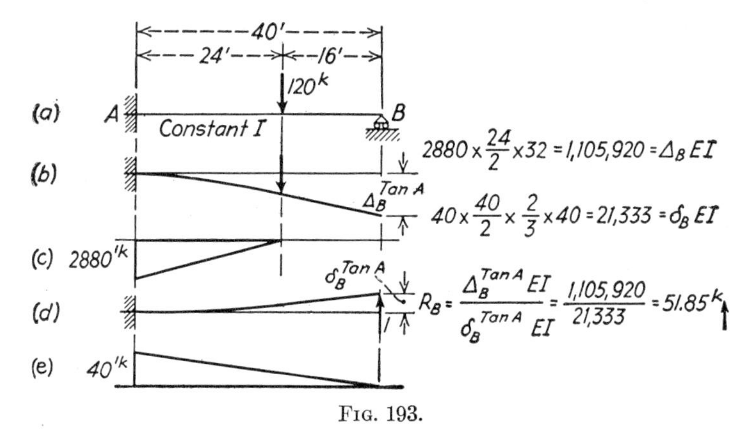

FIG. 193.

clear that the reaction required to restore the end B to its original position is the ratio of these movements as indicated in the figure.

It was also pointed out in Art. 152 that instead of removing the right support the problem may also be solved by introducing a

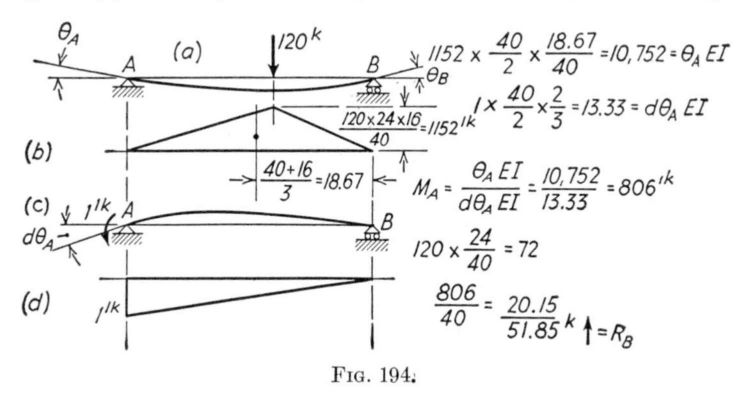

FIG. 194.

hinge at A, calculating the resulting rotation and the moment necessary to restore the rotated end to its horizontal position. Solution by this method is shown by the calculations in Fig. 194. Here also the only comment which seems necessary is to call attention to the quantity $d\theta_A$, which is the amount that a unit moment will rotate the end of the beam. Clearly, if the hinged end rotates through the angle θ_A and a *unit* moment can produce a rotation $d\theta_A$ the moment necessary to rotate the end back to its original position is $M_A = \dfrac{\theta_A}{d\theta_A}$.

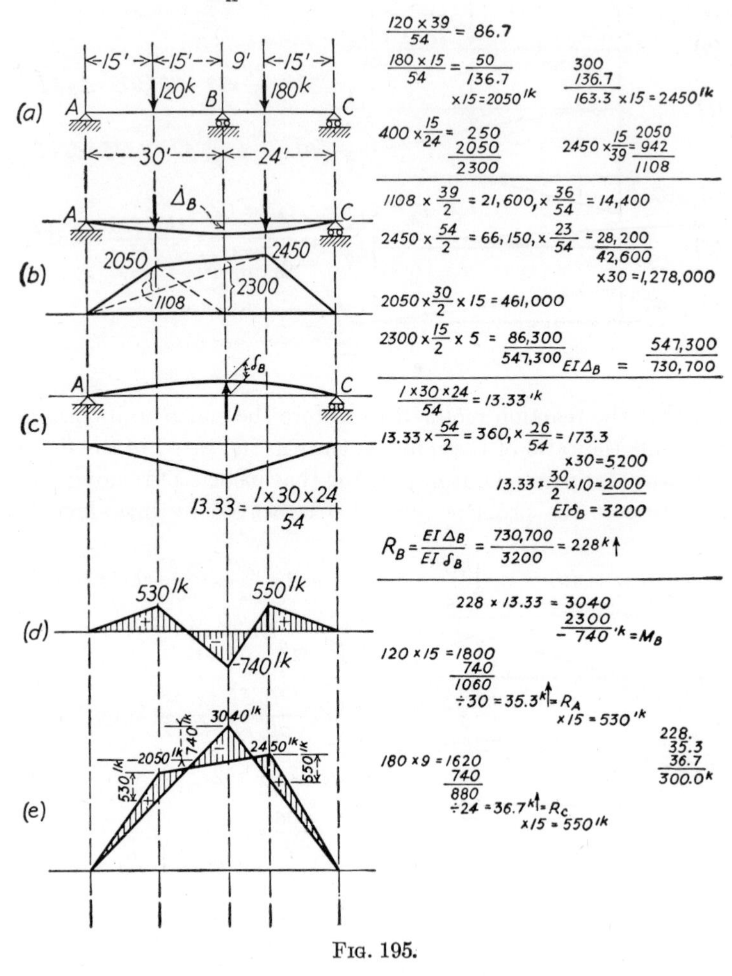

Fig. 195.

160. A two-span continuous beam is shown in Fig. 195 (*a*). It is assumed to have constant moment of inertia. The structure is indeterminate to the first degree and may be made determinate and stable in one of several ways. The procedure followed in the calculations shown in the figure was to remove the support at B and determine the reaction necessary to return the point B to its original position. The deflected elastic line and the moment diagram when the support at B has been removed are shown at (*b*), Fig. 195, and at (*c*) are shown the deflected elastic line and moment diagram due to a unit reaction acting at B. The magnitude of the reaction at B having been found, the remainder of the problem is

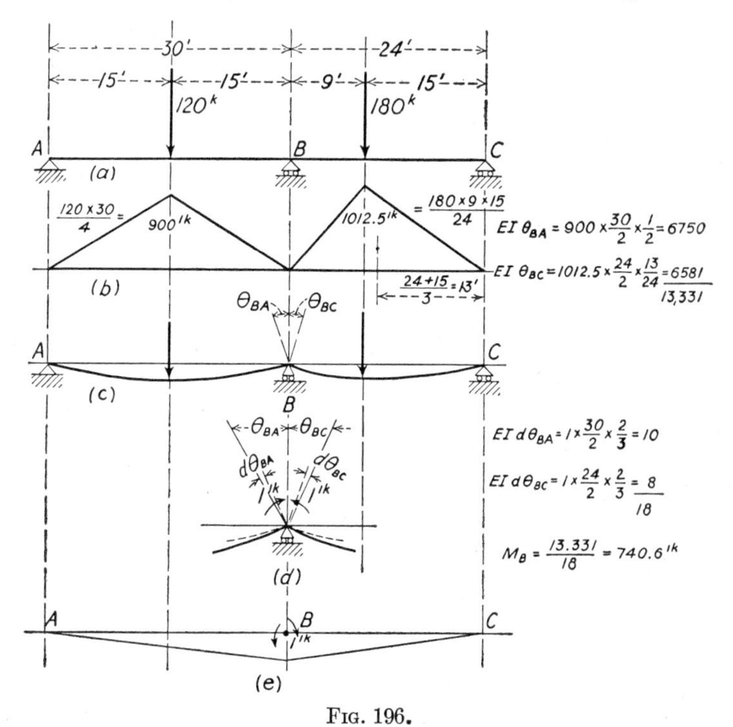

FIG. 196.

one in statics. The moment diagram for the continuous beam has been drawn in (*d*), Fig. 195, and at (*e*) has been shown the determination of the moment diagram for the continuous structure by combining the simple beam moment diagram of (*b*) with the moment diagram resulting from the reaction of 228^k acting up at B.

161. As stated in the previous paragraph there are several ways of making the structure of Fig. 195 (*a*) statically determinate and stable. One way which leads to rather simple calculations is shown in Fig. 196. A hinge introduced at B results in two simply supported spans with moment diagrams as shown in (*b*) and deflected elastic lines as shown at (*c*). The normal to the elastic line at B in the span BA rotates through the angle θ_{BA} as shown in Fig. 196 (*c*), and the normal to the elastic line at B in the span BC rotates through the angle θ_{BC}. In order to restore continuity at B it is necessary to apply a clockwise moment at the B end of span BA and an equal counter-clockwise moment at the B end of span BC sufficient in magnitude to bring the normals to the elastic lines to coincidence.

A unit moment at the B end of span BA rotates the normal through the angle $d\theta_{BA}$, and a unit moment at the B end of span BC rotates its normal through the angle $d\theta_{BC}$ as shown at (*d*) in Fig. 196. It follows at once that the moment necessary to restore the normals to coincidence must be of such magnitude that

$$M(d\theta_{BA} + d\theta_{BC}) = \theta_{BA} + \theta_{BC}$$

and

$$M = \frac{\theta_{BA} + \theta_{BC}}{d\theta_{BA} + d\theta_{BC}}$$

The calculations are shown in the figure and need no further comment.

It will be noted that the values of modulus of elasticity and moment of inertia had no bearing on the calculations in Arts. 159, 160, and 161 and could have been omitted entirely. When dealing with problems such as discussed in these articles the physical constants E and I may be omitted from the calculations if they are constant throughout the beam. It is of the greatest importance, however, to see clearly in every problem the exact significance of the physical constants E and I and to make certain that they are not omitted in some case in which such omission is not permissible. The problem presented in the next article is one illustration of the point.

162. The supported cantilever beam shown in Fig. 197 (*a*) is indeterminate to the first degree. It may be made determinate and stable by removing the support B. The one fact necessary to a solution, in addition to the laws of statics, may then be obtained by calculating the reaction at B required to restore the support to its original level. The calculations and explanatory sketches are shown in Fig. 197 (*a*) to (*c*) inclusive, and in (*d*) is shown the bending-moment diagram.

The calculations follow precisely those of Art. 159, and the student will note that the quantities E and I are merely "understood," and do not actually appear in the calculations. It should be clear that the quantity 1,866,600 is merely *proportional* to the

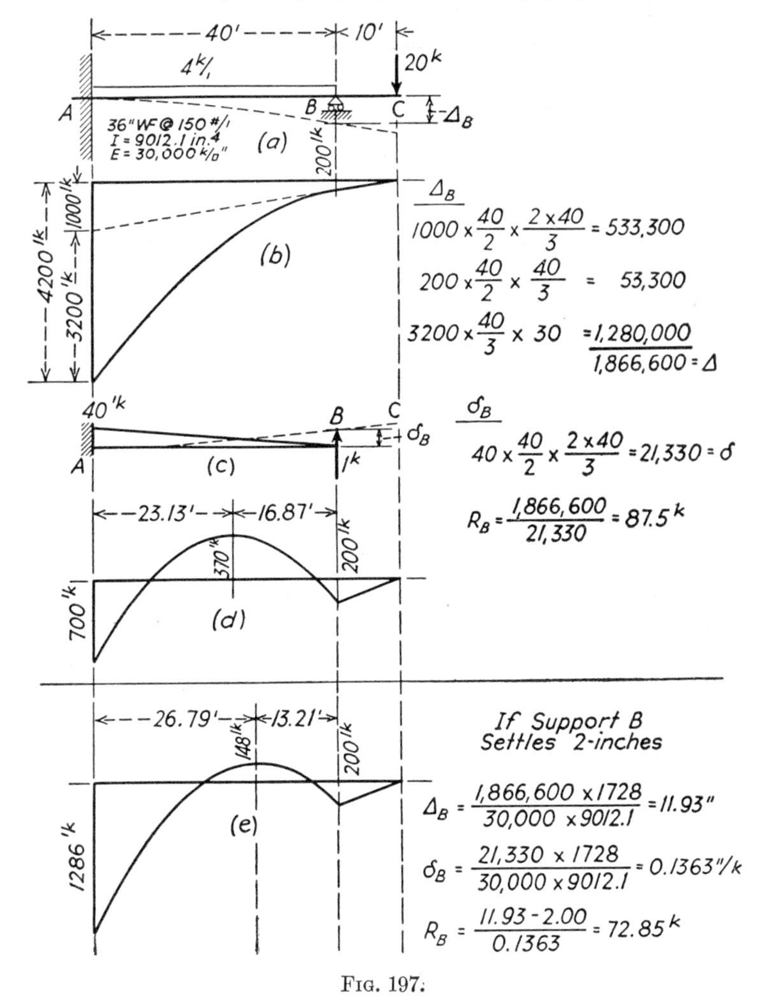

FIG. 197.

deflection Δ_B, and similarly the quantity 21,330 is merely *proportional* to the distance through which a unit reaction can lift the support B. Since the proportionality factor is the same in each case and since the reaction R_B is the ratio of these quantities it seems evident that the proportionality factor cancels and need not be introduced.

Assume, however, that the support B settles a known amount, say 2 in. It will then be necessary to know exactly how much the point B deflects when that support is removed, and to know exactly how much a unit reaction can lift the support. In that event the actual values of the physical constants E and I must be introduced into the solution. The necessary additional calculations and the resultant moment diagram are shown in Fig. 197 (*e*). The reader should note that, when the reaction which would exist at support B if no settlement occurred has been found, the problem with settlement could have been solved simply by calculating the relief of this reaction caused by settlement.

$$\text{Relief of } R_B = \frac{2}{0.1363} = \underline{\underline{14.65^k}}$$

then

$$R_B = 87.50 - 14.65 = \underline{\underline{72.85^k}}$$

163. Elastic Support.—As an additional illustration of a case in which physical constants may not be ignored the problem of Fig. 198 is presented. Here the same beam previously discussed is assumed to be supported by a wire rope attached at B. The area of the rope and its effective modulus of elasticity are stated. The calculations to determine the magnitude of the pull in the rope are given in the figure, the previously calculated data taken from Fig. 197 being utilized.

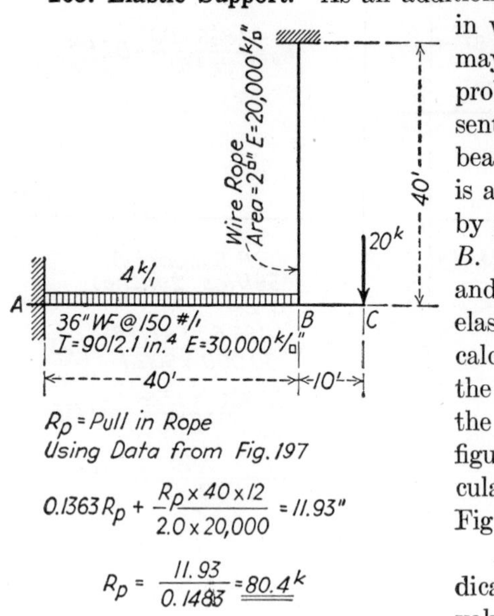

Fig. 198.

A little reflection will indicate that here the actual values of the moment of inertia of the beam and the area of the rope must be introduced into the calculations, but that only *relative* values of the moduli of elasticity would be needed if the calculations were made independently of previously computed results. The relation involving R_p used in Fig. 198 could be written:

$$\frac{1{,}866{,}600 \times 1728}{30{,}000 \times 9012.1} = \frac{R_p \times 21{,}330 \times 1728}{30{,}000 \times 9012.1} + \frac{R_p \times 40 \times 12}{2.0 \times 20{,}000}$$

In this relation it is clear that the modulus of elasticity for the rope could be taken as 1.0 and that of the beam as 1.5 (relative values), and the statement would then be:

$$\frac{1{,}866{,}600 \times 1728}{1.5 \times 9012.1} = \frac{R_p \times 21{,}330 \times 1728}{1.5 \times 9012.1} + \frac{R_p \times 40 \times 12}{2.0 \times 1.0}$$

Clearly these two statements lead to identical results.

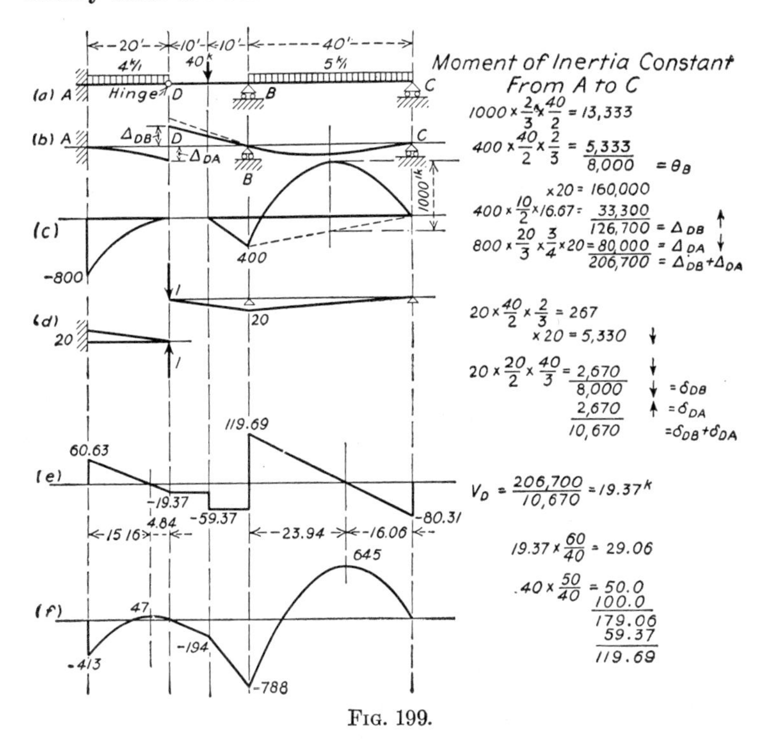

FIG. 199.

164. In the structure shown in Fig. 199 there are five unknowns to be determined for a complete solution. Since there are three equations of statics and the additional condition of no bending moment at the hinge evidently one fact must be determined from the elastic properties of the structure. Several methods of solution are possible. The solution for which calculations are shown in Fig. 199 is based on making the structure determinate and stable by disconnecting the hinge at D, converting the structure into a cantilever beam AD and a beam, DBC, with an overhanging end. The point D on the cantilever AD then deflects downward and the same point on the beam DBC moves upward as shown at (*b*), Fig. 199. The analysis is based on calculating the amount of separation of these ends and the force required to bring them together—that force being the reaction on the hinge and furnishing the additional fact necessary to complete the solution by statics. The calculations are shown in Fig. 199; it should be noted that the physical constants E and I are merely "understood" and do not appear in the work. The force acting on the hinge having been found, the analysis was completed by the application of the principles of statics, and the shear and moment diagrams are shown at (*e*) and (*f*), Fig. 199.

The student should assume that the moment of inertia of the part DBC is twice that of the part AD and recalculate the shear and moment diagrams.

165. Three-span Beam.—The structure shown at (*a*) in Fig. 200 is indeterminate to the second degree and may be made statically determinate and stable in one of several ways: by removing any two supports; by introducing hinges at B and C; or by introducing a hinge at either B or C and removing one support, in which event the support must be chosen so that its removal will not result in instability of any part of the structure.

The solution for which calculations are shown in the figure is based on the introduction of hinges at B and C. At (*b*) in Fig. 200 are shown the deflected shape and moment diagrams for the structure thus made statically determinate, and at (*c*) are shown the deflected shapes and moment diagrams which result from applying unit moments first on the hinge at B and second on the hinge at C as indicated by the arrows. The normals to the elastic lines of the three determinate beams separate under load as indicated: those at B by an amount equal to $\theta_{AB} + \theta_{BC}$ and those at C by an amount equal to $\theta_{CB} + \theta_{CD}$. There is no such separation in the continuous structure, and the solution of the problem requires the determination of the moments necessary at B and at C to restore the normals at each support to coincidence. Since a moment applied on each side of the hinge at B produces rotation of a normal at C, and vice versa, it is clear that a complete expression involving only the moment at one hinge cannot be written; in other words, since there are two unknowns to be determined we must have two independent relations involving those unknowns.

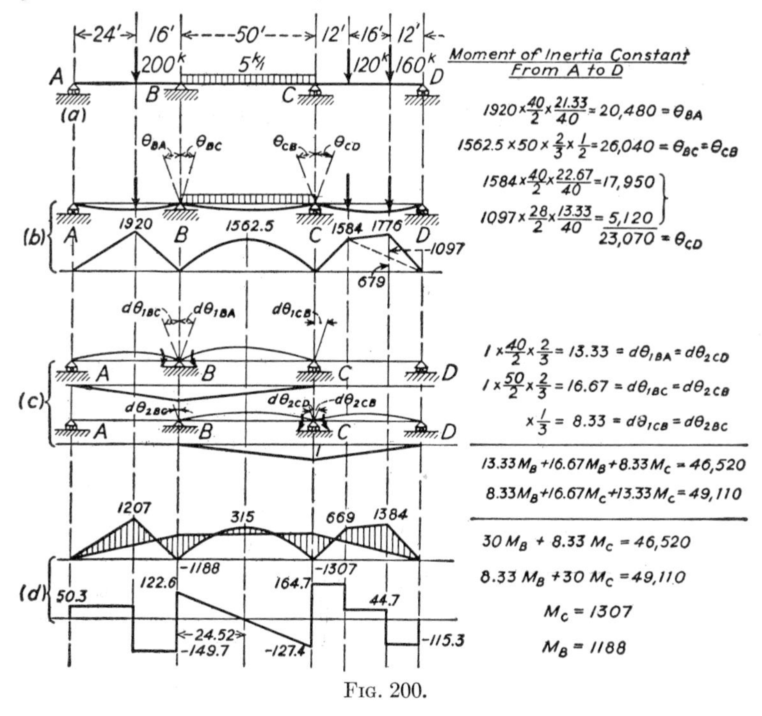

FIG. 200.

At the risk of seeming tedious it is desirable to point out again that since E and I are constant throughout the structure their values do not influence the result and in the calculations shown in the figure these quantities are "understood" and do not appear. Thus in the first statement in the calculations:

$$1920 \times \frac{40}{2} \times \frac{21.33}{40} = 20{,}480 = \theta_{BA}$$

it is understood that literally the statement should read:

$$\frac{1}{EI} \times 1920 \times \frac{40}{2} \times \frac{21.33}{40} = \frac{20{,}480}{EI} = \theta_{BA}$$

but since the values of E and I do not affect the result they may be thought of as each having a value of 1 and omitted from the calculations. Although it seems permissible to do this to avoid a continuous writing of factors which do not affect the result the

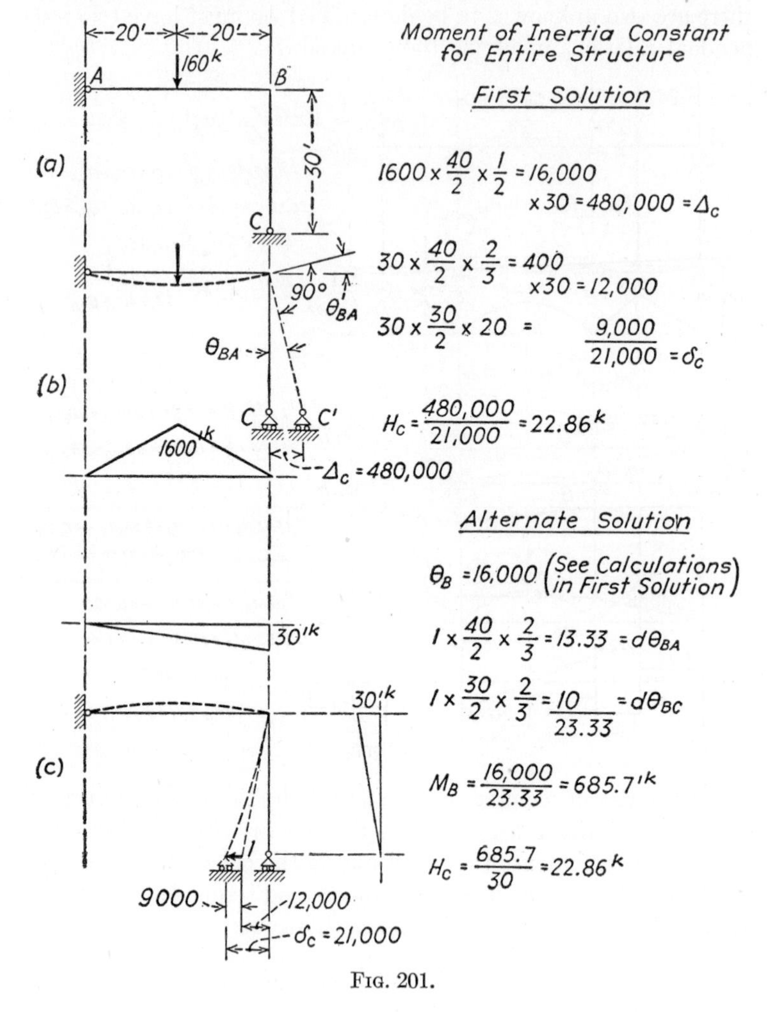

Fig. 201.

student should be constantly on the alert to avoid the error of making the omission when the result would be affected.

166. The angle frame shown in Fig. 201 (a) is indeterminate to the first degree, and two obvious ways of making the structure determinate are to put the right support at C on rollers or to introduce a hinge at B.

If the structure is made determinate by putting the right end on rollers it will assume the deflected shape indicated by dotted lines in (*b*), Fig. 201, point C moving out to C' through the distance Δ_c. If a unit horizontal reaction will move the point C through a distance δ_c, evidently the force necessary to restore the deflected structure to its original position may be found as

$$H_C = \frac{\Delta_C}{\delta_C}$$

and its calculation will make possible the analysis of the frame by statics. Calculations for H_c are shown in the figure.

An alternate solution may be made by introducing a hinge at B and calculating the moment necessary to restore continuity at the hinge. Calculations for this method of solution are given in Fig. 201 but without explanatory sketches which the student should provide.

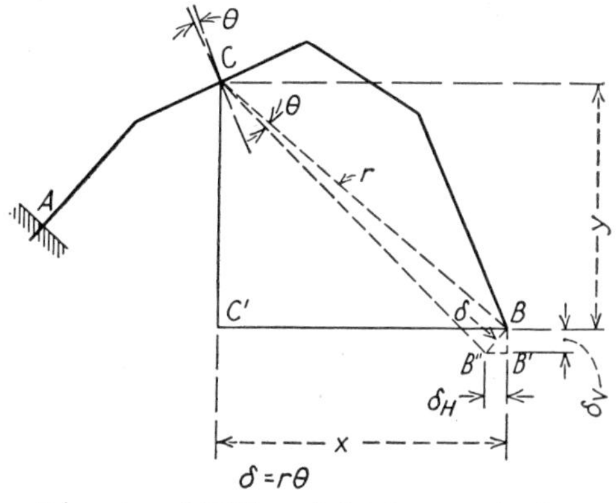

Fig. 202.

167. In dealing with such structures as the one just considered and some analyzed in later problems it may be convenient, though not necessary, to make use of an extension of the general principle stated under **(3A)** on page 352.

The irregular cantilever beam ACB, Fig. 202, is subjected to a *small* angle change θ at C, and we wish to evaluate the movement of the point B due to that angle change. Evidently the point B moves to B'', and the horizontal and vertical components of that movement may be found as indicated in the figure. A little reflection will show the truth of the following general statement: The movement in a given direction of any point B on any beam, due to a small angle change, θ, at some other point, C, on the beam, is equal to the angle change θ times the distance from B to C measured perpendicular to the given direction of movement. This statement is of great importance; it should be carefully memorized and studied until it is thoroughly understood.

It should be clear that the movement due to a number of angle changes is equal to the sum of the movements due to the individual angle changes.

Although primarily developed for irregular fixed-end beams or bents the principle may be applied to similar hinged-end beams or bents if the results are corrected to allow for the necessary rotation of the hinged ends. For example, referring again to the angle frame of Fig. 201, imagine that the angle changes proportional to the moment diagram at (b) take place but that the frame is not allowed to turn about the hinge at A. In accordance with the principle just stated the end C would then have horizontal and vertical movements of:

$$1600 \times \frac{40}{2} = 32{,}000$$
$$\times\ 30 = 960{,}000 \text{ horizontal}$$
$$\times\ 20 = 640{,}000 \text{ vertical}$$

Actually, of course, the vertical movement of C cannot take place under the conditions of support shown at (b) in the figure. Therefore to restore the structure to a position consistent with the conditions shown it must be rotated around the hinge at A until C reaches the proper level; i.e., it must be rotated until C has moved downward through the distance 640,000. In moving downward, however, C moves horizontally to the left, and the horizontal movement found above must be combined therewith. The net movement of C is then

$$1600 \times \frac{40}{2} = 32{,}000$$
$$\times\ 30 = 960{,}000$$
$$640{,}000 \times \frac{30}{40} \qquad = 480{,}000$$
$$\overline{480{,}000}$$

When the hinges are on the same level, as in Fig. 203, rotation about the hinge at one end through a *very small angle* produces no horizontal movement of the other end.

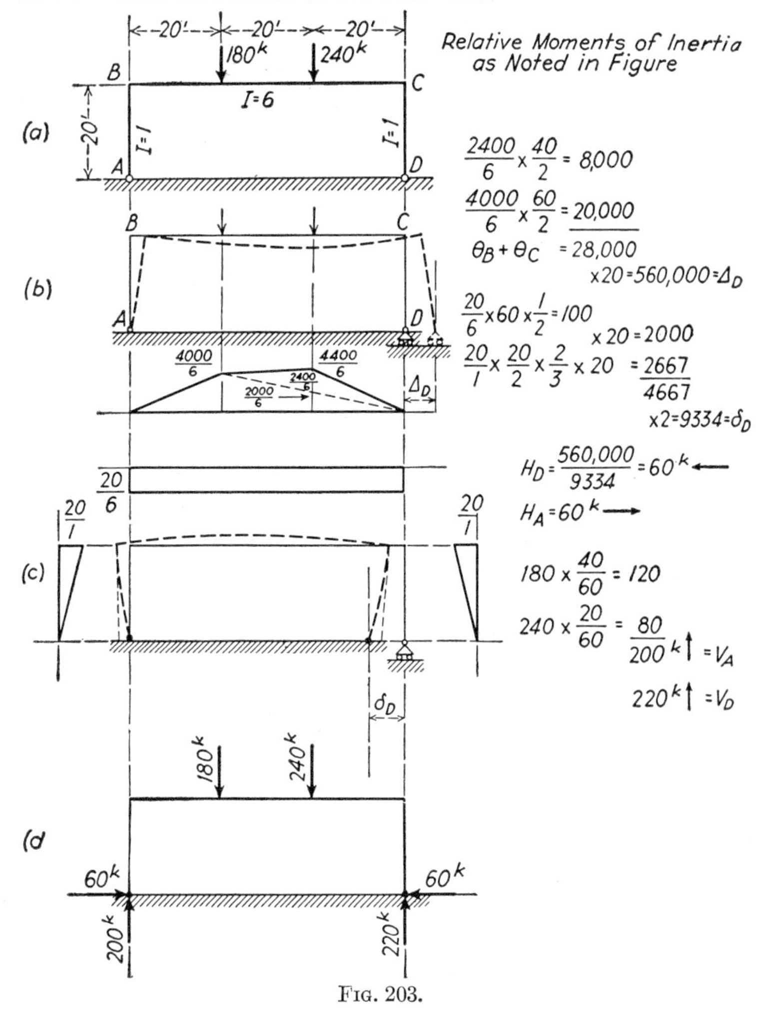

FIG. 203.

168. Two-hinged Bent.—If the student has grasped the general principle of the preceding article he is prepared to follow the calculations for the structure of Fig. 203. The structure is indeterminate to the first degree and may be made determinate and stable by placing the right reaction on rollers. The calculations for the horizontal reactions are based on determining the distance that the right end of the determinate structure moves in a horizontal direction and the force required to push the end back to its original position. That force, of course, is the horizontal reaction. The only comment which seems necessary is to call attention to the fact that the moment of inertia of the horizontal member of the frame is six times that of the columns. The relative values of I must be introduced into the calculations. This has been done through the use of $\frac{M}{I}$-diagrams as indicated at (*b*) and (*c*) in Fig. 203. The forces acting on the structure are shown in Fig. 203 (*d*), and the analysis may be completed by statics.

The student will do well to assume that the moment of inertia of the columns is 10,000 in.^{4} each and that of the girder 60,000 in.^{4}, set up the analysis using these values, and demonstrate that the result is exactly the same as when *relative* values of 1 and 6 are used, as in the figure. It will also be profitable to assume that E for the columns is 10,000 kips per sq. in., for the girder 30,000 kips per sq. in., and reanalyze the structure setting up the analysis using actual values of E and *relative* values of E.

169. The structure shown in Fig. 204 is similar to that shown in Fig. 203, and may be made determinate and stable by the same device, i.e., placing the support at D on rollers. The calculations are shown in the figure and are broken down in detail to show as clearly as possible the action of the structure under the assumed conditions: at (*b*) in the figure is shown the deformed determinate structure and its moment diagrams; at (*c*) the determinate structure under the action of a unit horizontal reaction; at (*d*) the reactions and moment diagrams for the original structure. The calculations seem self-explanatory.

The student should note that the use of the principle stated in Art. 167 leads to the following calculations:

$$\Delta_D = \begin{cases} \frac{2250}{6} \times 60 \times \frac{2}{3} \times 20 = 300{,}000 \\ \frac{200}{6} \times \frac{60}{2} \times 20 = 20{,}000 \\ \frac{200}{2} \times 10 \times 15 = 15{,}000 \\ \frac{200}{2} \times \frac{10}{2} \times \frac{2}{3} \times 10 = 3{,}330 \\ \hline \qquad 338{,}330 \end{cases}$$

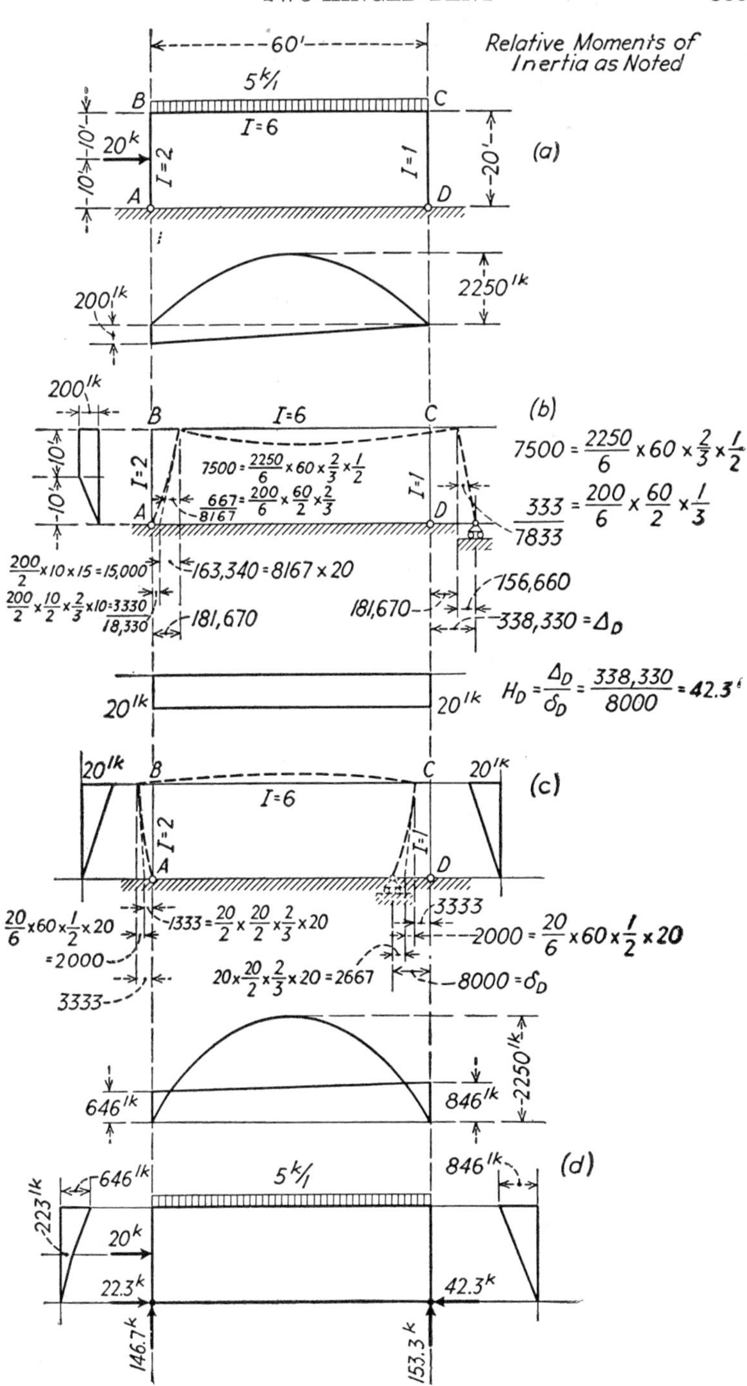

Relative Moments of Inertia as Noted
60'
5k/1
B
C
I=6
20k
I=2
I=1
A
D
10'
20'
(a)
2250'k
200'k
(b)
7500 = 2250/6 × 60 × 2/3 × 1/2
333 = 200/6 × 60/2 × 1/3
7833
667 = 200/6 × 60/2 × 2/3
8167
200/2 × 10 × 15 = 15,000
200/2 × 10/2 × 2/3 × 10 = 3330
18,330
163,340 = 8167 × 20
181,670
156,660
338,330 = Δ_D
H_D = Δ_D/δ_D = 338,330/8000 = 42.3
20'k
(c)
1333 = 20/2 × 20/2 × 2/3 × 20
20/6 × 60 × 1/2 × 20 = 2000
3333
2000 = 20/6 × 60 × 1/2 × 20
20 × 20/2 × 2/3 × 20 = 2667
8000 = δ_D
646'k
846'k
(d)
223'k
22.3k
42.3k
146.7k
153.3k

FIG. 204.

$$\delta_D = \begin{cases} \frac{20}{6} \times 60 \times 20 & = \quad 4000 \\ \frac{20}{2} \times \frac{20}{2} \times \frac{2}{3} \times 20 & = \quad 1333 \\ \frac{20}{1} \times \frac{20}{2} \times \frac{2}{3} \times 20 & = \quad \underline{2667} \\ & \quad\;\; 8000 \end{cases}$$

$$H_D = \frac{338{,}330}{8000} = \underline{\underline{42.3^k}}$$

and should carefully relate them to the detailed analysis shown in the figure.

170. Fixed-end Moments—The fixed-end beam subjected to a single concentrated load, such as is shown in Fig. 205, has an importance in later development somewhat out of proportion to the simplicity of the analysis of a particular case. For that reason the analysis given in the figure is shown in great detail.

In addition to making certain that he clearly understands the calculations in Fig. 205, the student should verify the general statement indicated in Fig. 206 and carefully memorize it in the following form:

> **In a fixed-end beam supporting a single concentrated load that divides the span into two segments, the moment at the near end is equal to the simple beam moment under the load times the far segment divided by the span length.**

The use of this principle makes possible the calculation of the fixed-end moments for a beam subjected to any system of loading.

An illustration of the general utility of the principle is given in Fig. 207. At (*a*) in that figure is shown a beam fixed at the ends and loaded with a uniform load of w pounds per foot. Statements for determination of the fixed-end moments by simple integration based on the above principle are written under the figure. In these statements wdx is evidently the load at any distance x from A, while

$$wdx \cdot x \frac{(L - x)}{L}$$

is the bending moment under that load when the beam is simply supported at A and B. This simple beam moment multiplied by the appropriate ratio is the fixed-end moment at the end in ques-

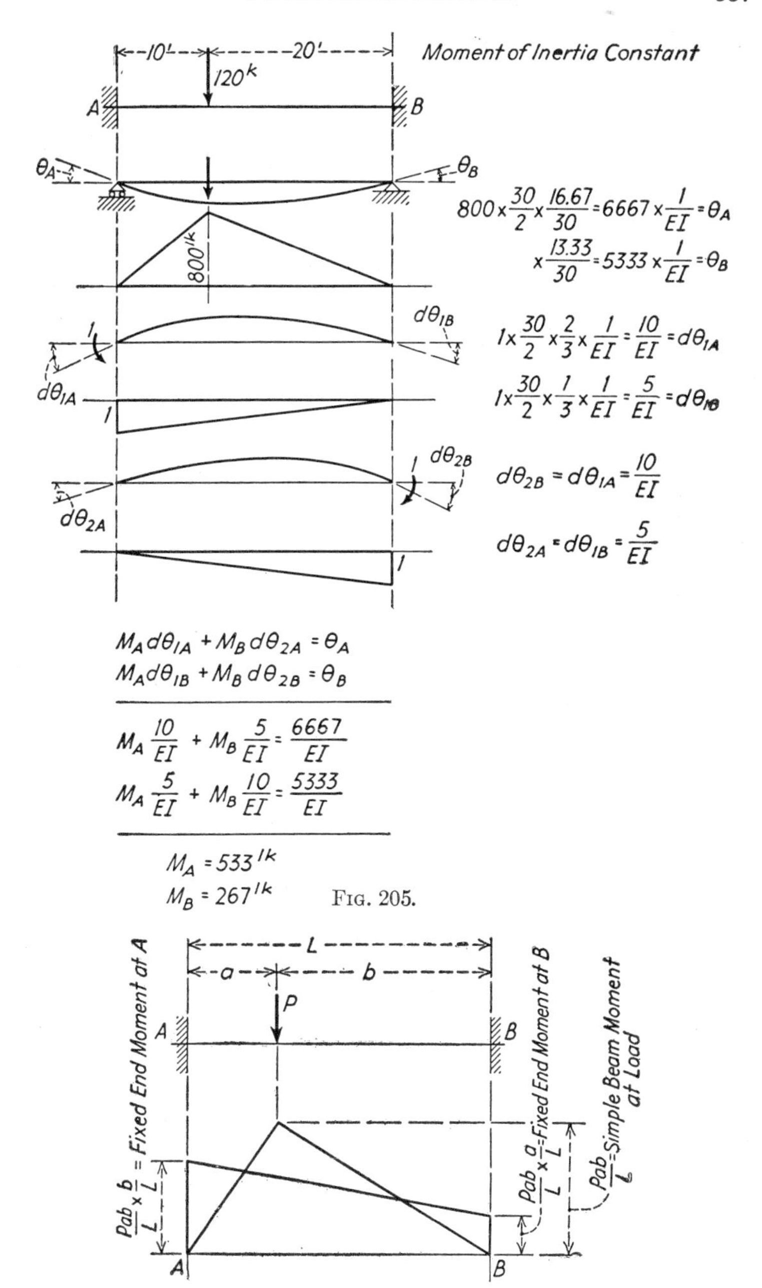

FIG. 205.

FIG. 206.

tion for the load wdx, and integrating this resulting expression for all values of x of course gives the fixed-end moment for the entire load.

Another illustration is given at (*b*) in the same figure. In the statements under the figure the quantity

$$\frac{x}{L} wdx$$

is the load at any distance x from the end A. The other terms are as before, and the result is self-explanatory.

It should be clear that by similar procedures the principle under discussion will enable the simple calculation of fixed-end moments for any combination of distributed and concentrated loads.

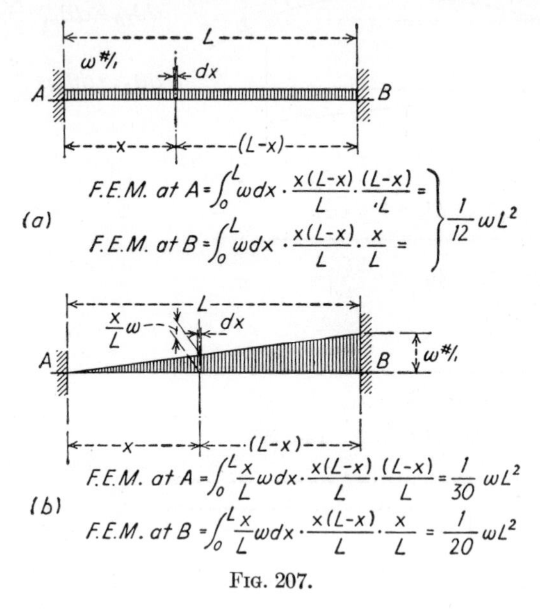

L
w #/,
dx
A
B
x
(L-x)
F.E.M. at A = ∫₀ᴸ wdx · x(L-x)/L · (L-x)/L =
F.E.M. at B = ∫₀ᴸ wdx · x(L-x)/L · x/L =
1/12 wL²
(a)
x/L w
w #/,
F.E.M. at A = ∫₀ᴸ x/L wdx · x(L-x)/L · (L-x)/L = 1/30 wL²
(b)
F.E.M. at B = ∫₀ᴸ x/L wdx · x(L-x)/L · x/L = 1/20 wL²

FIG. 207.

171. The two-span beam shown in Fig. 208 presents no new problem or principle but requires the determination of three unknowns from the geometry of continuity. The structure has been made determinate by placing a hinge at each support, and at (*a*) in the figure the deflected determinate structure and its moment diagram are shown. At the right of (*a*) are shown the calculations for the end rotations of the determinate structure

At (*b*) and (*c*) are shown the deflected elastic lines and the corresponding moment diagrams resulting from the application of unit couples, m_1 at the A end of AB, m_2 at the C end of BC, m_3 at the B end of AB, and m_4 at the B end of BC. The calculations are shown in detail as this problem will be used later to introduce moment distribution.

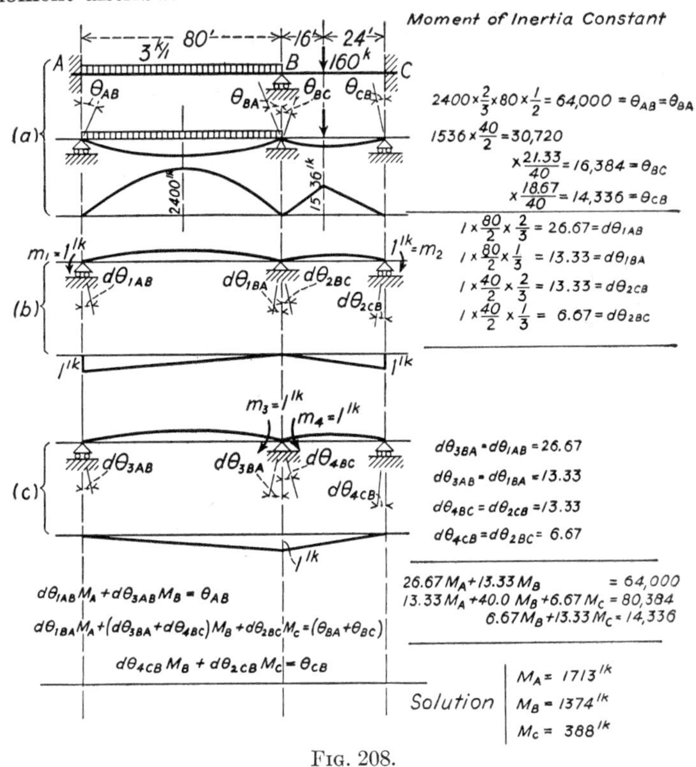

FIG. 208.

172. In Figs. 209, 210, and 211 are shown solutions of two problems, each involving the determination of three unknowns from a consideration of the geometry of continuity.

In Fig. 209 are shown the calculations for a solution based on making the structure determinate and stable by completely removing the support at D, calculating the horizontal and vertical movements and rotation of that end and then determining the horizontal and vertical forces and the bending moment which must be applied there to restore the end D to its original position.

In Fig. 210 the bent dealt with in Fig. 209 is analyzed by making the structure determinate and stable by placing end D on rollers and introducing a hinge at A; calculating the horizontal movement and rotation at D, and the rotation at A; and then determining the horizontal force at D, and the bending moments

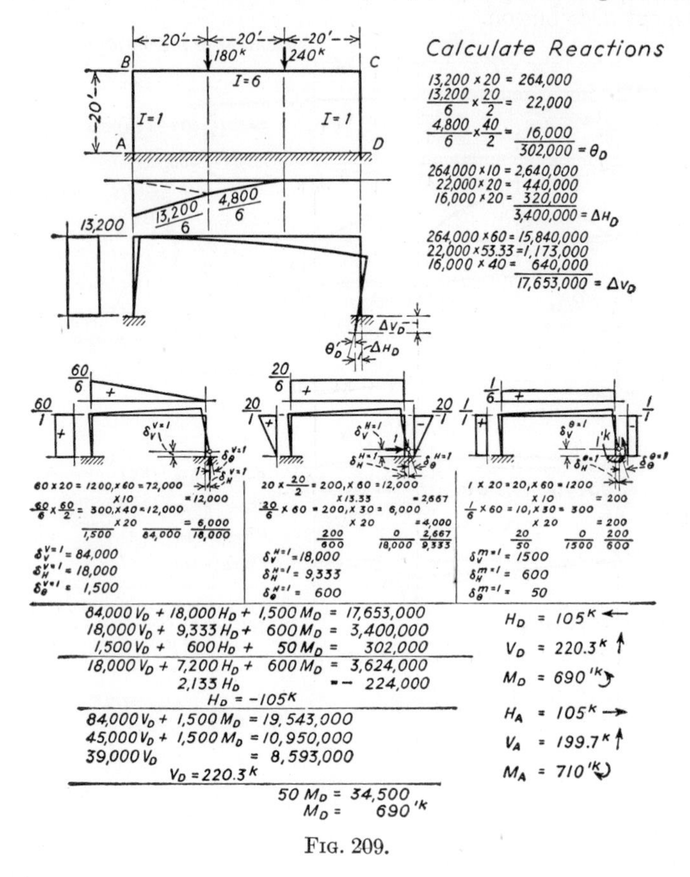

FIG. 209.

at A and D necessary to restore these ends to their original positions.

The structure shown in Fig. 211 was made determinate and stable by removing the support at F and putting the support at D on rollers. It was analyzed by calculating the horizontal and vertical movements at F and the horizontal movement at D, and then determining the horizontal and vertical forces at F and the horizontal force at D necessary to restore these points to their original positions.

The calculations are shown in detail in Figs. 209, 210, and 211

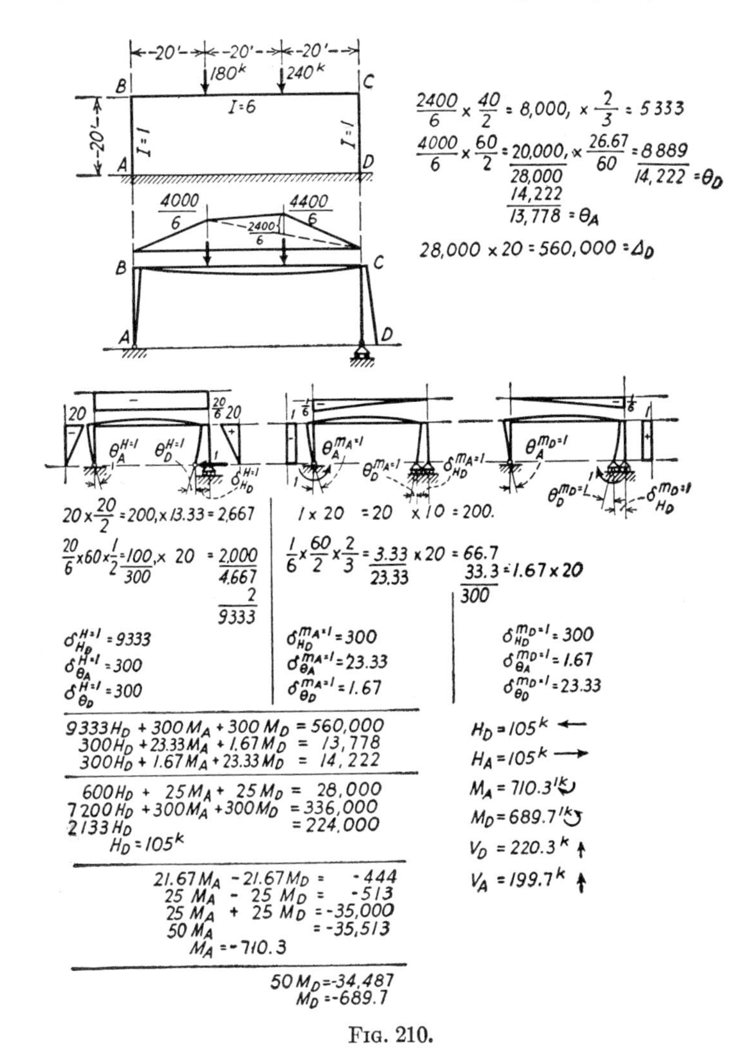

FIG. 210.

with explanatory sketches, and they follow the methods already discussed fully. No additional comment seems necessary except to call attention to the notation used. In Fig. 209, only the point

D is allowed to move, and since all calculations refer to that point no defining subscripts are necessary in the notation. Thus:

$\delta_V{}^{V=1}$ is the vertical movement of D due to a unit force acting vertically on D.

$\delta_H{}^{V=1}$ is the horizontal movement of D due to a unit force acting vertically on D.

$\delta_\theta{}^{V=1}$ is the rotation of D due to a unit force acting vertically on D.

Similarly:

$\delta_V{}^{H=1}$ is the vertical movement of D due to a unit force acting horizontally on D.

and

$\delta_H{}^{m=1}$ is the horizontal movement of D due to a unit couple acting on D.

The basis for the notation is that: the subscript indicates the nature of the movement, V for vertical, H for horizontal, and θ for rotation; while the superscript indicates the nature and magnitude of the force producing movement, $V = 1$ a unit vertical force, $H = 1$ a unit horizontal force, and $m = 1$ a unit moment or couple.

The notation in Figs. 210 and 211 has the same basis, but since movements of two points are permitted designation of the point in question is necessary, and such designation is made by a defining subscript added to the existing subscript or superscript. Thus (Fig. 211):

$\delta_{V_F}{}^{H_F=1}$ is the vertical movement of point F due to a unit force acting horizontally on F

while (Fig. 211)

$\delta_{H_D}{}^{V_F=1}$ indicates the horizontal movement of point D due to a unit force acting vertically on F

and (Fig. 210)

$\delta_{\theta_A}{}^{m_D=1}$ indicates the rotation of point A due to a unit moment or couple acting on point D.

With this explanation of the notation used, the student should be able to follow the calculations without difficulty if he has obtained a proper grasp of the principles discussed.

173. Moment Distribution. Introductory Relations.—Before proceeding with a discussion of moment distribution, it is desirable

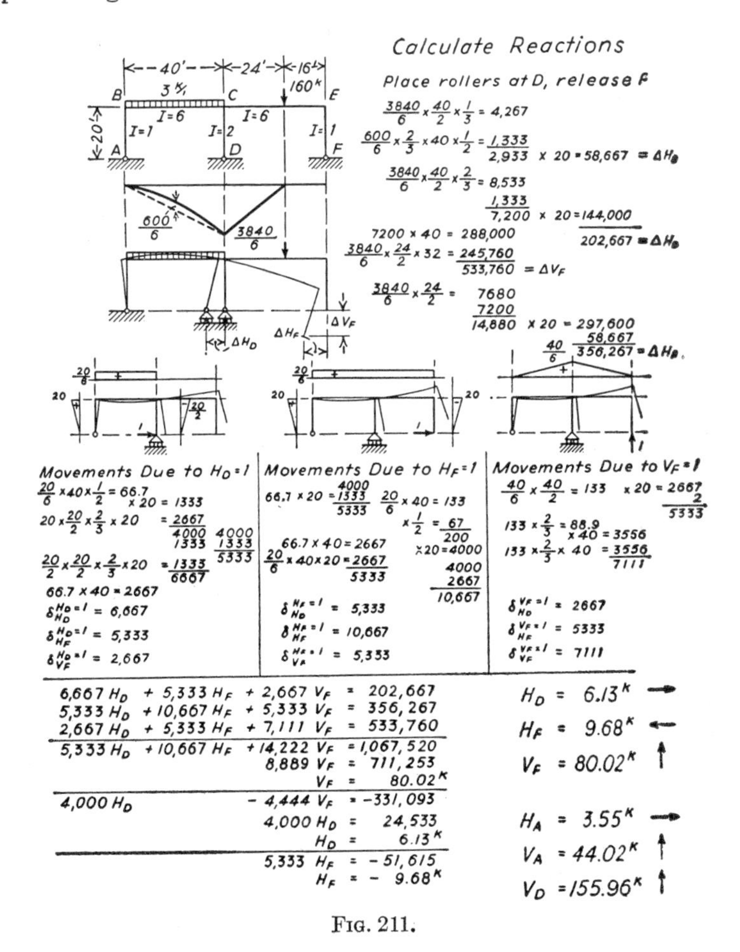

FIG. 211.

to establish some fundamental relations for **prismatic beams.**

Study of Fig. 212 (b) will show the following relations:

$$\theta_{AB}' = \frac{ML}{2EI} \times \frac{2}{3} = \frac{1}{3}\frac{ML}{EI}$$

$$\theta_{BA}' = \frac{ML}{2EI} \times \frac{1}{3} = \frac{1}{6}\frac{ML}{EI}$$

Similarly from (c)

$$\theta_{AB}'' = \frac{1}{6}\frac{M'L}{EI}$$

$$\theta_{BA}'' = \frac{1}{3}\frac{M'L}{EI}$$

If the moment M' has a magnitude such that $\theta_{BA}'' = \theta_{BA}'$, evidently we may combine (b) and (c), Fig. 212 and obtain the beam

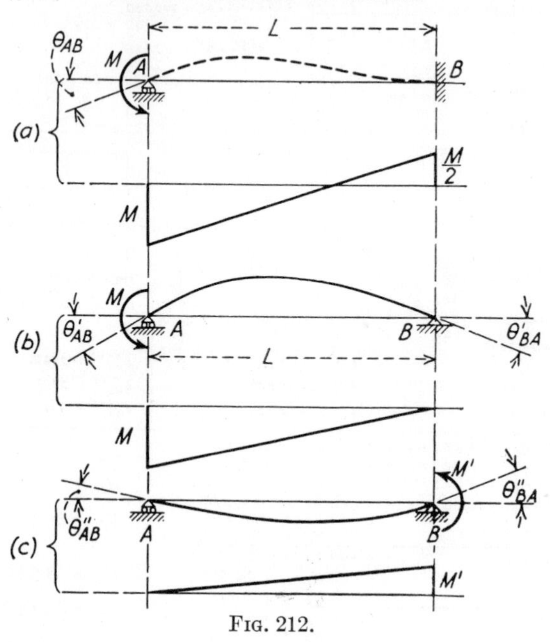

FIG. 212.

shown at (a). The necessary magnitude of M' is given by the relations just stated,

$$\theta_{BA}'' = \theta_{BA}'$$

Therefore

$$\frac{1}{3}\frac{M'L}{EI} = \frac{1}{6}\frac{ML}{EI}$$

and

$$M' = \frac{M}{2}$$

Reference to a sketch of the deflected elastic line will show by inspection that these moments must be opposite in sign no matter which way the moment at A acts—a result which will be obtained mathematically by the consistent use of a sign convention. The authors prefer to avoid the use of sign conventions when inspection of the structure will indicate the result.

Further study of Fig. 212 will show that:

$$\theta_{AB} = \theta_{AB}' - \theta_{AB}'' = \frac{ML}{3EI} - \frac{1}{6}\frac{M'L}{EI} = \frac{ML}{3EI} - \frac{ML}{12EI} = \frac{ML}{4EI}$$

Therefore

$$M = \frac{4EI}{L}\theta_{AB}$$

also, from (b),

$$M = \frac{3EI}{L}\theta_{AB}'$$

We may now state three important relations for prismatic beams:

(1) A moment which rotates the near end of a prismatic beam without translation, the far end being fixed, will produce a moment at the far end of one-half its magnitude and opposite in sign.

In moment distribution the moment produced at the far end by rotation of the near end of a beam is called the "carry-over moment." The ratio of the moment produced at the far end to the moment produced at the near end by rotation of the near end is called the "carry-over factor," i.e.,

$$\textbf{Carry-over factor} = \frac{\left(\begin{array}{c}\text{Moment at far end produced}\\ \text{by rotation of near end}\end{array}\right)}{\left(\begin{array}{c}\text{Moment at near end produced}\\ \text{by rotation of near end}\end{array}\right)}$$

The carry-over factor is always one-half for straight prismatic beams, and may be considered as negative since the carry-over moment for straight beams is always opposite in sign to that of the moment at the near end.

(2) The moment required to rotate the near end of a prismatic beam through *a unit angle* without translation, the far end being fixed, is

$$m = \frac{4EI}{L}$$

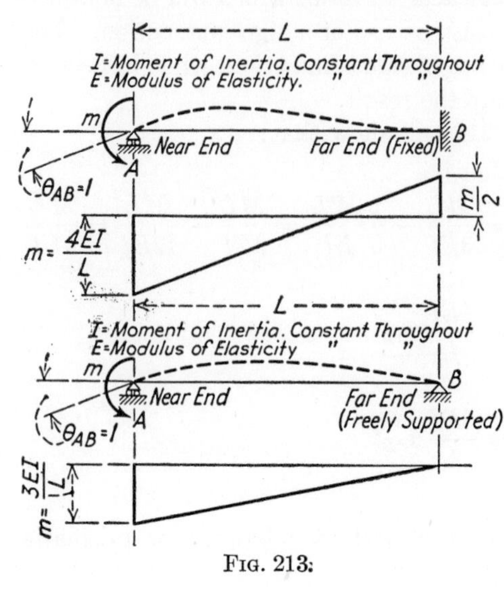

FIG. 213.

(3) The moment required to rotate the near end of a prismatic beam through *a unit angle* without translation, the far end being freely supported, is:

$$m = \frac{3EI}{L}$$

These relations are illustrated in Fig. 213. They should be carefully memorized and studied until the reader thoroughly understands them and is able to develop them without reference to the text.

A relation of equal importance concerning a series of members meeting at a common joint may be developed from those just stated and from a study of Fig. 214. Five members, marked (1) to (5) inclusive, are connected at their common intersection A so rigidly that any rotation of the joint causes an equal rotation of each connected member. If a moment, m, is applied to the joint A, evidently each member in the assembly will resist the tendency for the joint to rotate. If the moment m applied to the joint is of such a magnitude that it rotates the joint (and therefore the A end of

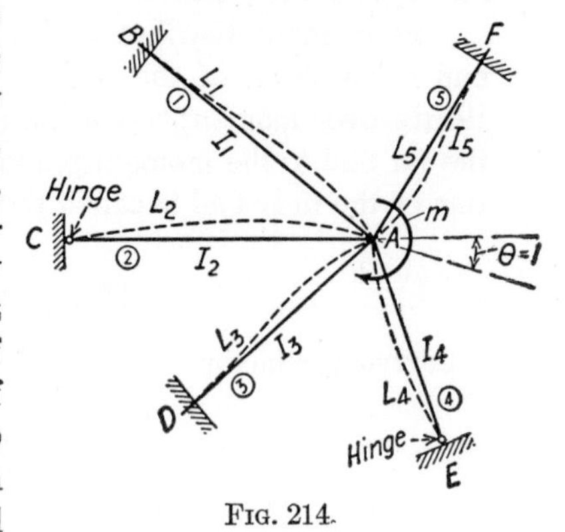

FIG. 214.

each connected member) through a *unit angle,* we may say at once from (2) and (3):

$$m_1 = \text{resistance to rotation of member (1)} = 4\frac{E_1 I_1}{L_1}$$

$$m_2 = \text{'' '' '' '' '' (2)} = 3\frac{E_2 I_2}{L_2}$$

$$m_3 = \text{'' '' '' '' '' (3)} = 4\frac{E_3 I_3}{L_3}$$

$$m_4 = \text{'' '' '' '' '' (4)} = 3\frac{E_4 I_4}{L_4}$$

$$m_5 = \text{'' '' '' '' '' (5)} = 4\frac{E_5 I_5}{L_5}$$

From statics, $m = m_1 + m_2 + m_3 + m_4 + m_5$. If a moment of $2m$ were applied to the joint, evidently the moments at the A ends of the connected members would be $2m_1$, $2m_2$, $2m_3$, and so on, or in general if any moment, M, were applied to the joint the moments at the A ends of the connected members would be

$$M_1 = \frac{M}{m} \times m_1 = \left(\frac{m_1}{m}\right) \times M$$

$$M_2 = \frac{M}{m} \times m_2 = \left(\frac{m_2}{m}\right) \times M$$

$$M_3 = \frac{M}{m} \times m_3 = \left(\frac{m_3}{m}\right) \times M$$

etc.

i.e., any moment applied to the joint will be distributed among the members in proportion to the quantities m_1, m_2, m_3, etc. If we now introduce the following *definition*:

> **The stiffness of a member is the moment required to rotate the end we are considering through a unit angle, without translation of either end,**

we may make the general statement:

> **A moment which tends to rotate a joint without translation will be divided among the connecting members in proportion to their respective stiffnesses.**

As an illustration of the application of this principle, assume the following data for the members in Fig. 214.

Member	Length	Moments of Inertia	Modulus of Elasticity	Stiffness
(1)	$35'-\ 8''=428''$	800 in.^{4}	30,000 $k/\square''$	$\frac{4\times1\times800}{428''}=7.48$
(2)	$37'-10''=454''$	960 in.^{4}	"	$\frac{3\times1\times960}{454''}=6.34$
(3)	$29'-\ 9''=357''$	694 in.^{4}	"	$\frac{4\times1\times694}{357''}=7.78$
(4)	$25'-10''=310''$	398 in.^{4}	"	$\frac{3\times1\times398}{310''}=3.85$
(5)	$25'-\ 2''=302''$	590 in.^{4}	"	$\frac{4\times1\times590}{302''}=7.81$
				33.26

If a moment of 1600 ft.-kips tends to rotate the joint at A the moment will be distributed among the connecting members as follows:

Member	Moment
(1)	$\frac{7.48}{33.26}\times1600=$ 360 ft.-kips
(2)	$\frac{6.34}{33.26}\times1600=$ 305 ft.-kips
(3)	$\frac{7.78}{33.26}\times1600=$ 374 ft.-kips
(4)	$\frac{3.85}{33.26}\times1600=$ 185 ft.-kips
(5)	$\frac{7.81}{33.26}\times1600=$ 376 ft.-kips
	1600 ft.-kips

The units used in the calculations just presented and the fact that the value of the modulus of elasticity was taken as 1 should be carefully noted. It seems clear that the actual value of the modulus of elasticity will not affect the result since it was assumed to be the same for all members. It is also important for the student to see clearly that *relative* values of moment of inertia and lengths in feet could have been used in the calculations without affecting the result. In the great majority of problems the engineer is interested only in *relative* rather than actual stiffnesses, and the values for stiffness just computed are in reality only relative since the modulus of elasticity was taken as unity in the calculations.

As a matter of fact, when the modulus of elasticity is the same for all members meeting at a joint, it may be (and usually is) omitted from calculations for stiffness. It may be worth while to show calculations for stiffnesses and distribution of moment for the above joint using lengths in feet, relative values of moment of inertia, and omitting E. It should be clear that all the stiffnesses computed here may be multiplied by some constant factor if doing so leads to more convenient values. This is often done.

Member	Length, ft.	Relative I	Relative Stiffness	Distributed Moment
(1)	35.67	2.01	$\frac{4 \times 2.01}{35.67} = 0.225$	$\frac{0.225}{1.001} \times 1600 = 360$
(2)	37.83	2.41	$\frac{3 \times 2.41}{37.83} = 0.191$	$\frac{0.191}{1.001} \times 1600 = 305$
(3)	29.75	1.74	$\frac{4 \times 1.74}{29.75} = 0.234$	$\frac{0.234}{1.001} \times 1600 = 374$
(4)	25 83	1.00	$\frac{3 \times 1.00}{25.83} = 0.116$	$\frac{0.116}{1.001} \times 1600 = 185$
(5)	25.17	1.48	$\frac{4 \times 1.48}{25.17} = 0.235$	$\frac{0.235}{1.001} \times 1600 = 376$
			1.001	1600

174. Moment Distribution. Fundamental Procedure.—The fundamental relations presented in the preceding article are the basic tools of moment distribution, and their use in analysis will be illustrated by reconsidering the structure for which a solution was presented in Fig. 208.

The structure is redrawn without loads at (*a*), Fig. 215. Imagine now that the freely supported joint at B is held against rotation, and apply the loads shown at (*b*) in the figure. Since

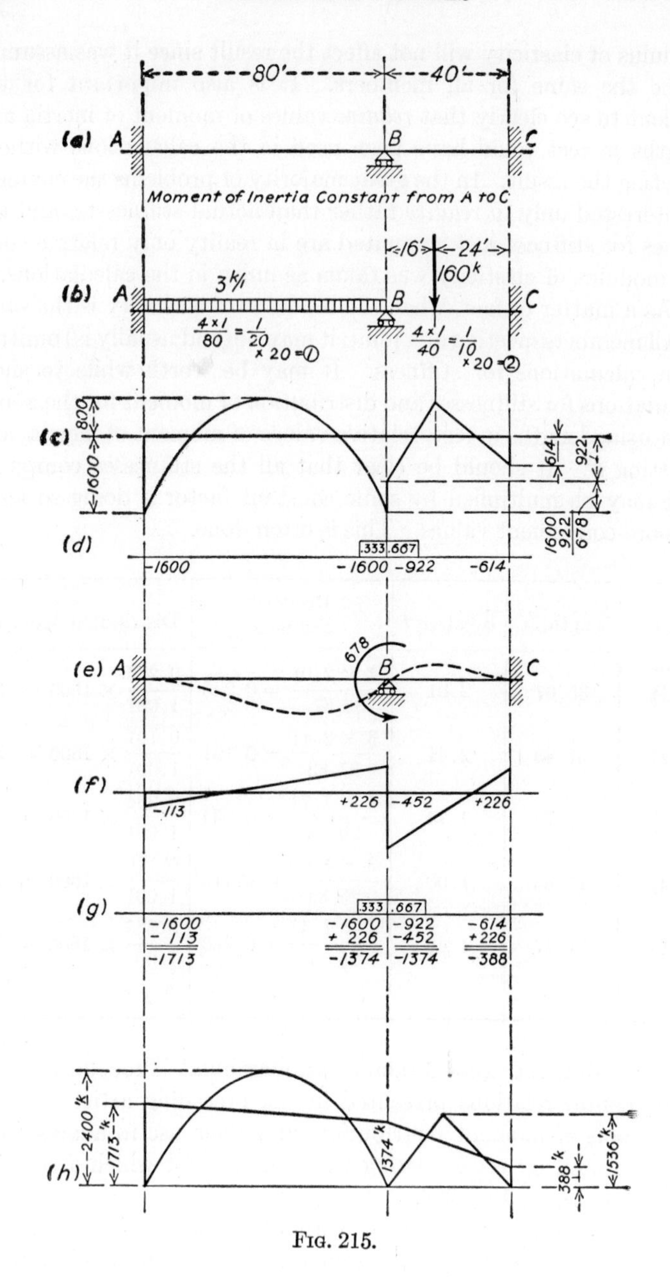
80'
40'
(a) A
B
C
Moment of Inertia Constant from A to C
16'
24'
160k
(b) A
3k/1
B
C
4×1/80 = 1/20 ×20 = ①
4×1/40 = 1/10 ×20 = ②
800
(c)
1600
614
922
1600
922
678
(d)
.333 .667
-1600
-1600 -922
-614
678
(e) A
B
C
(f)
-113
+226 -452
+226
(g)
.333 .667
-1600
- 113
-1713
-1600
+ 226
-1374
-922
-452
-1374
-614
+226
-388
-2400'k
-1713'k
1374'k
388'k
1536'k
(h)

FIG. 215.

the joint B is being held against rotation the moments shown by the moment diagram at (*c*) will result. The **fixed-end moments** shown at (*d*) may be calculated from the principle discussed in Art. 170. It is clear that if the joint B were not being held it would rotate counter-clockwise since there is a moment of 1600 ft.-kips tending to turn the joint counter-clockwise and a moment of only 922 ft.-kips tending to turn it clockwise—the difference 678 ft.-kips is called the "unbalanced moment" on the joint, tending to rotate it counter-clockwise. According to the principle stated in the previous article if we release the joint it will rotate counter-clockwise and the unbalanced moment will be distributed between the two connecting members in proportion to their stiffnesses. The calculations for the relative stiffnesses are shown under the beam in (*b*), and it should be noted that since I is constant throughout it was taken as 1, E was omitted, and the results were multiplied by 20 as a matter of convenience, giving relative stiffnesses of ① and ② for AB and BC, respectively.

Attention is called to the factors 0.333 and 0.667 shown in rectangles just above the joint B in (*d*) and (*g*) in the figure. These are the distribution factors; i.e., they indicate that a moment which tends to rotate joint B will be distributed $\frac{1}{3}$ to BA and $\frac{2}{3}$ to BC. Their determination is obvious since the stiffness of BA was found to be 1, and that of BC, 2. It is usually convenient to write these distribution factors on the diagram, and generally they will be used in the analyses which follow.

If the restraint which is holding joint B against rotation is now released the unbalanced moment of 678 ft.-kips will rotate the joint counter-clockwise, producing the deformation shown at (*e*) in the figure and the moments shown at (*f*). If the moments shown at (*f*) are added to the fixed-end moments shown at (*c*) and (*d*), the result will be as shown at (*g*). The joint B is now balanced and the moments at A, B, and C are the same as found in the previous solution of Fig. 208. The solution of the problem by moment distribution is shown in great detail in Fig. 215 for explanatory purposes. After the student has grasped the procedure he will realize that (*b*) and (*g*) from the figure constitute a complete solution, and should contrast it with the solution in Fig. 208. The final moment diagram shown in (*h*), if required, would be common to each solution.

The sign convention used is that used throughout the text (see Art. 37): positive moment is that which produces compression in the top fibers of the member, and negative moment that which produces tension in the top fibers; horizontal members are regarded from the bottom and vertical members from the right-hand side of the calculation sheet.

175. The supported cantilever beam analyzed in Figs. 193 and 194 is reanalyzed by moment distribution in Fig. 216. It is first assumed that the end B is restrained against rotation and the fixed-end moments shown at (b) calculated. The moment of 691 ft.-kips at B is then allowed to rotate the joint, producing the situation shown at (c) and (d). Finally (b) and (d) are added together, securing the final result shown at (e). It should be noted that (a) and (e) in reality constitute a complete solution. Attention is called to the fact that a calculation of stiffness is not necessary since only one member is involved.

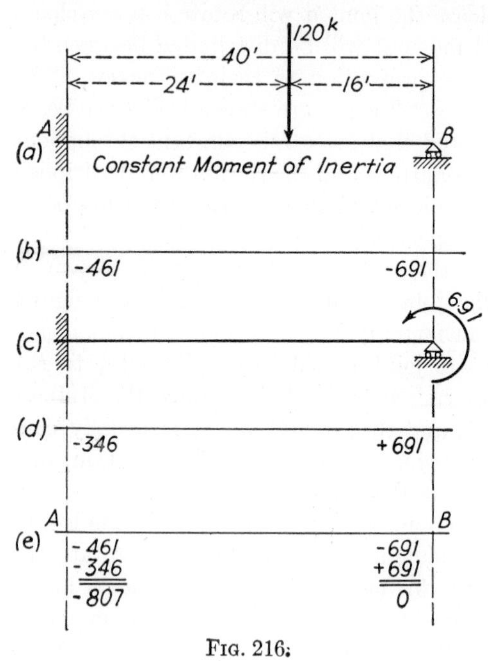

Fig. 216.

The simplicity of this solution is obvious and it will be used frequently to calculate the fixed-end moments in beams which have one end freely supported while the other is assumed to be held temporarily against rotation.

176. The two-span beam analyzed in Figs. 195 and 196 by two different procedures is solved by moment distribution in Fig. 217. The distribution factors 0.444 and 0.556 are calculated and shown in the figure, indicating that 44.4 per cent of the unbalanced moment of 148 ft.-kips at joint B is distributed to BA and 55.6 per cent to BC. The fixed-end moments of 675 ft.-kips and

823 ft.-kips were calculated by the procedure noted in the previous article.

177. The supported cantilever beam shown and analyzed in Fig. 218 is presented to illustrate the influence of an overhanging end on moment distribution. As usual it is first assumed that

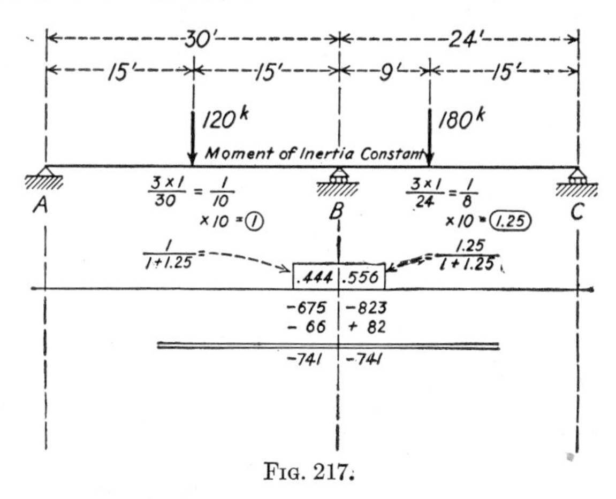

FIG. 217.

joint B is restrained against rotation and the fixed-end moments calculated. There is then an unbalanced moment of 350 ft.-kips at joint B tending to produce clockwise rotation. This unbalanced moment will be distributed among the connecting members in

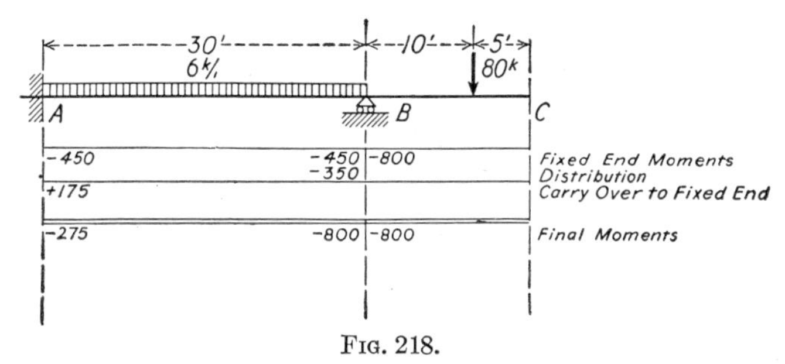

FIG. 218.

proportion to their stiffnesses as soon as the restraint at joint B is released. The only question is regarding the stiffness of the cantilever end BC. Applying the definition of stiffness we see at once that BC has zero stiffness; i.e., if we apply a moment at the B end of BC, the member has no resistance to rotation and therefore no moment is required to rotate the end we are considering through a unit angle. Consequently when the restraint at joint B is released the entire unbalanced moment of 350 ft.-kips must be distributed to BA as shown.

178. The angle frame analyzed by two different procedures in Fig. 201 is reanalyzed by moment distribution in Fig. 219. The calculations for relative stiffnesses and distribution factors are

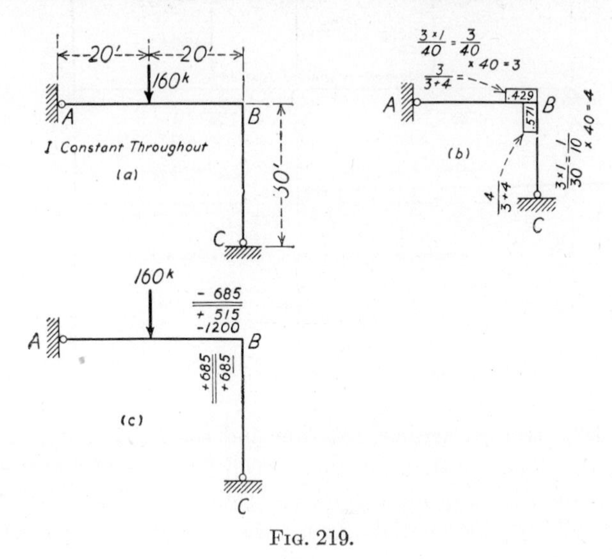

Fig. 219.

shown at (*b*) in the figure, and the fixed-end moment, distribution, and final result at (*c*).

When vertical and horizontal members occur together in a frame the arrangement of calculations in moment distribution is important from the standpoint of clarity. Many arrangements have been suggested, but the authors prefer that first used by Professor Cross in his original paper.[4] In that arrangement fixed-end moments are written parallel to the member to which they relate, immediately below the left end and immediately above the right end. Horizontal members are viewed from the bottom and vertical members from the right-hand side of the calculation sheet. Successive corrections are written parallel to the fixed-end mo-

[4] "Analysis of Continuous Frames by Distributing Fixed-End Moments," by Hardy Cross, *Trans. Am. Soc. C. E.*, Vol. 96 (1932), page 1.

ments and outward from the beam. This arrangement was followed in Fig. 219 and will be used in succeeding problems with vertical members.

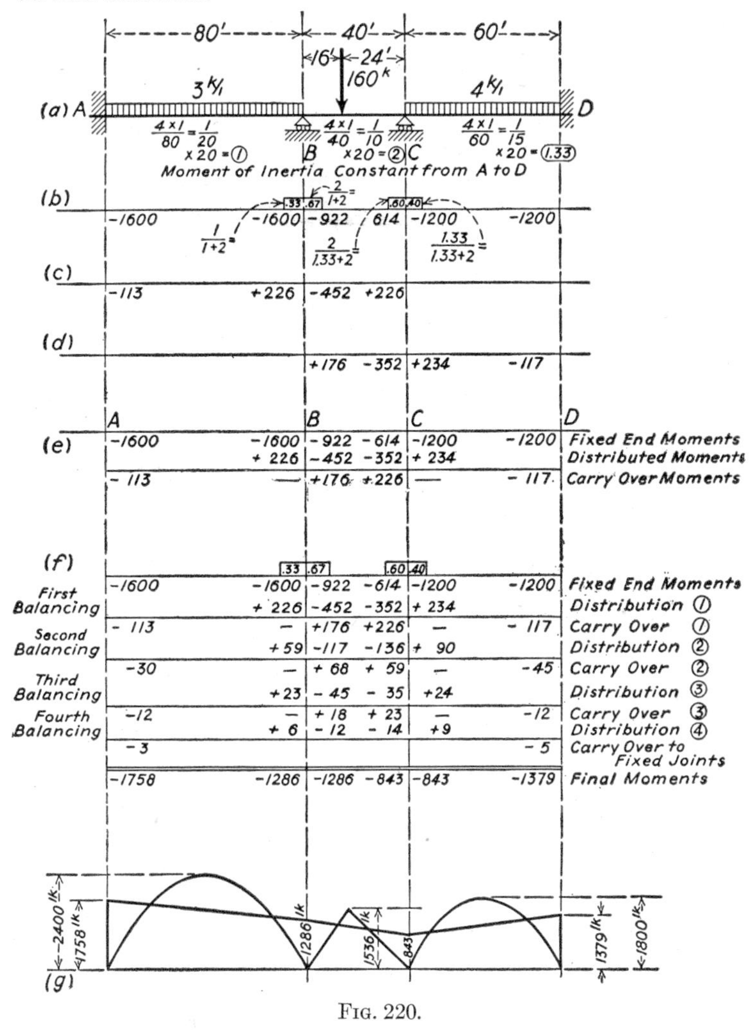

FIG. 220.

179. Multiple Distribution.—The examples of moment distribution so far presented have been such that only a single distribution has been necessary for a complete solution, i.e., they have been structures in which only one joint had to be balanced. Structures in which two or more joints must be balanced generally require several cycles of distribution. The number of cycles necessary depends on the precision required for the result.

The structure shown in Fig. 220 has two joints which must be balanced and is presented to illustrate the moment distribution procedure when several joints are involved.

At (*a*) and (*b*) in the figure are shown the loaded beam, the calculation of relative stiffnesses and distribution factors, and the fixed-end moments which result when joints *B* and *C* are temporarily restrained against rotation.

If joint *B* is now allowed to rotate, i.e., if the unbalanced moment of 678 ft.-kips at that point is distributed among connecting members, the result of that distribution will be as shown at (*c*). Similarly the distribution of the unbalanced moment of 586 ft.-kips at joint *C* gives the results shown at (*d*). The single distribution of the unbalanced moments at joints *B* and *C* is not sufficient for the reason that balancing joint *B* produces a moment of +226 ft.-kips at *C*, and balancing joint *C* produces a moment of +176 ft.-kips at joint *B*. These "carry-over moments" unbalance the joints after the initial balancing, thus making another balancing necessary. The second balancing or distribution results in another but much smaller unbalancing as a result of "carry-over" moments. The disturbing carry-over moments show a marked decrease after each distribution in normal structures, and in this problem become negligible after the fourth distribution. It should be noted that if the process had been stopped after the third distribution the result would have differed from that after the fourth distribution by only a little over 1 per cent at *C* and less than 0.5 per cent at *A*, *B*, and *D*.

The systematic arrangement of distributions and carry-overs is very important in order to reduce the possibility of error. At (*e*) in the figure there is indicated the procedure which seems most easily followed. First, the fixed-end moments are written as shown (or as noted in the previous article when vertical members are involved). Second, the unbalanced moments are distributed at successive joints, preferably from left to right along or around the structure; as soon as an unbalanced moment is distributed a line should be drawn under the balancing moments to indicate the balanced status of that joint. Third, the effect of the distributed moments on the far ends of the members concerned should be written down, i.e., the "carry-over" moments should be written at the affected ends. These three steps complete a cycle, and the procedure is then repeated for as many cycles as are necessary for adequate precision. The last step should always be to balance joints which can rotate and carry over to joints which cannot. The latter point is illustrated at (*f*) in the figure, where the last

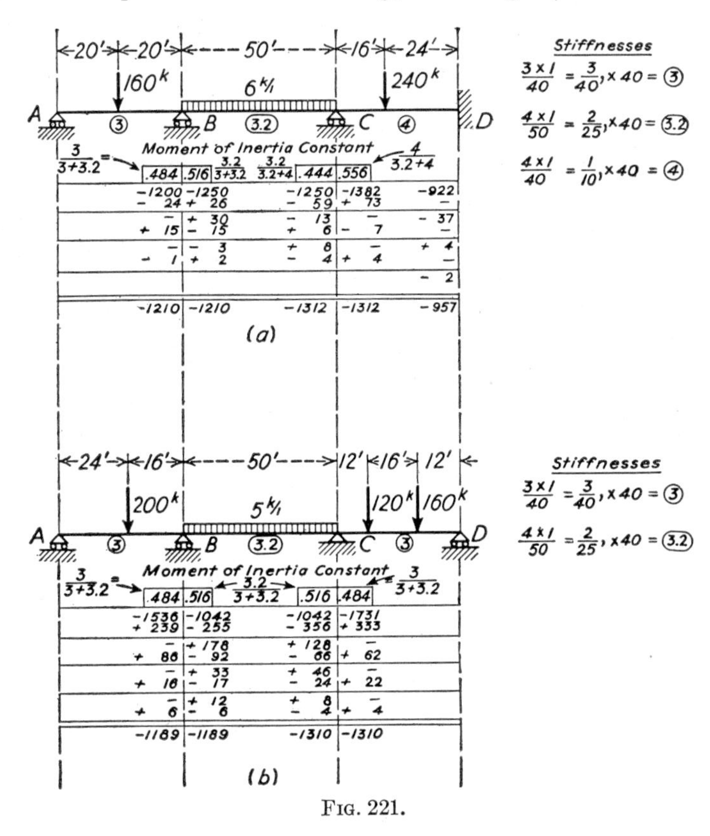

FIG. 221.

step was to balance joints *B* and *C* [Distribution (4)], which can rotate and carry over to joints *A* and *D* which cannot.

180. Two three-span beams are shown in Fig. 221 and analyzed by moment distribution. It should be noted that the last step in the analysis of the beam at (*a*) was to balance joints *B* and *C* and carry over to joint *D* which cannot rotate. The last step in the analysis of the beam at (*b*) was to balance joints *B* and *C*. Obviously there should be no carry-over thereafter since there are no joints which cannot rotate.

The beam shown at (*b*) in the figure was analyzed in Fig. 200 by making the structure determinate and calculating the moments required to restore continuity. It should be noted that, although the calculations of fixed-end moments, distributions, and carry-overs were made only to the nearest whole unit in the solution by

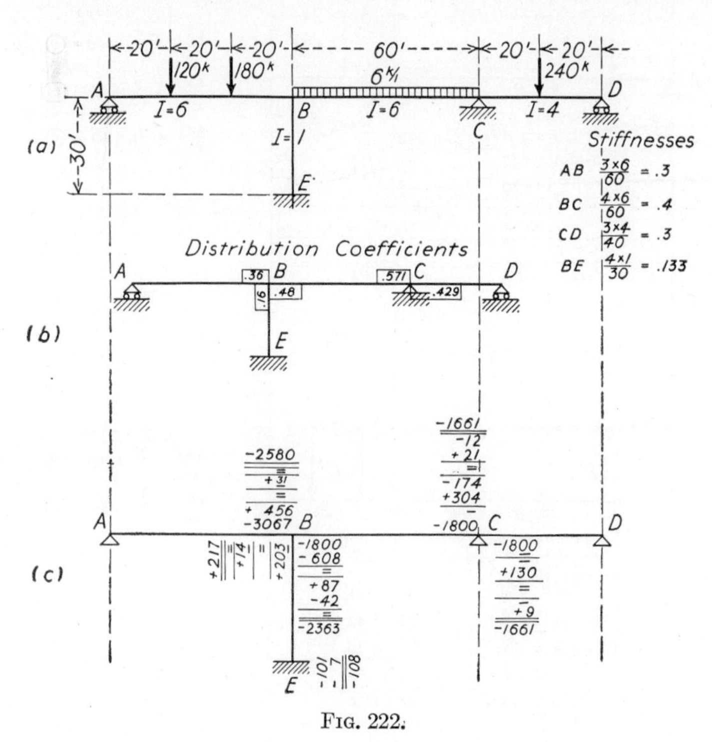

FIG. 222.

moment distribution, the results agree with those previously obtained within less than 0.25 per cent after four distributions.

It is very important for the student to recognize that moment distribution is an *exact* method of analysis in so far as any method is exact. The precision of the results obtained depends only on the precision of the calculations and the number of distributions. One of the great advantages of moment distribution is that an answer sufficiently accurate for design purposes may be obtained very quickly, and that answer later carried to any desired precision by further distributions. One of the great disadvantages of other methods is that, in general, a solution must be complete to get any answer at all.

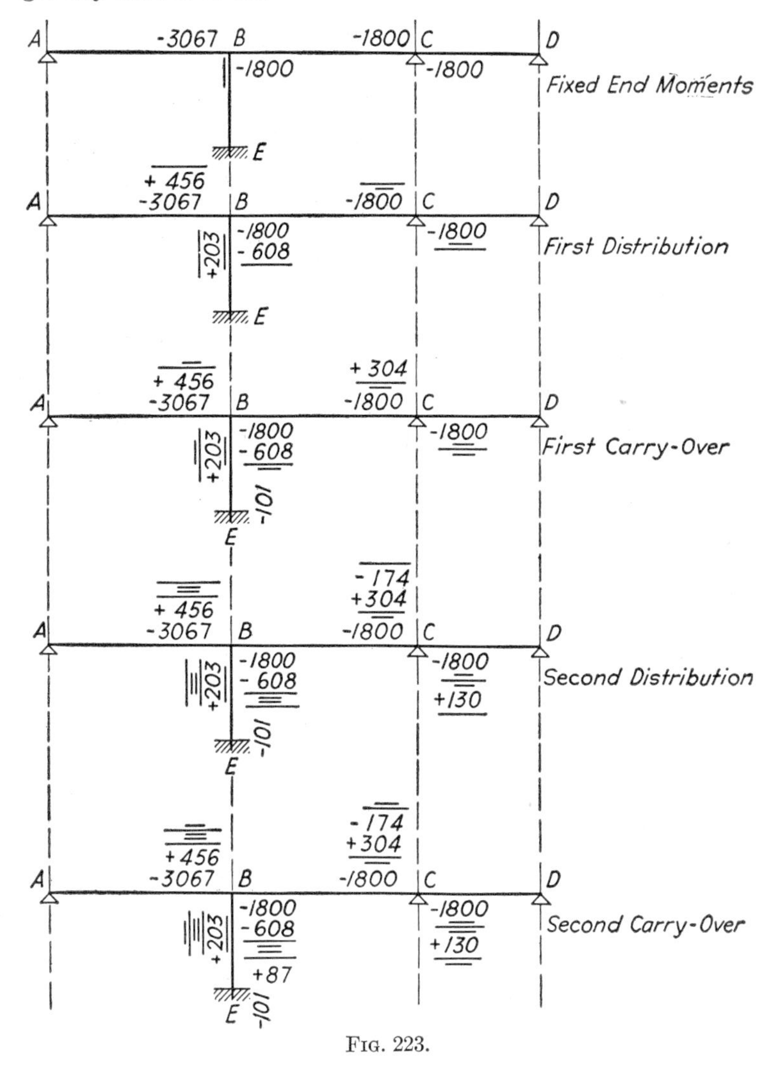

FIG. 223.

181. A further illustration of analysis by moment distribution is given in Fig. 222. The loaded structure is shown at (*a*); the calculation of stiffnesses and the distribution factors are shown at (*b*); and the fixed-end moments, distributions, and final results at (*c*).

For the benefit of the beginner the arrangement of the work at (*c*) in the figure has been shown in detail in Fig. 223. Since there is no unbalanced moment at joint *C* at the first distribution this fact is indicated by short dashes parallel to the fixed-end moments, and the balanced status of that joint is then indicated by lines parallel to the ends of the members concerned. The only ends affected by the first carry-over are the *C* end of *BC*, which has the moment +304 carried over from joint *B*, and the *E* end of *BE*. The fact that the other ends receive no carry-over moments is indicated by the short dashes parallel to the ends concerned.

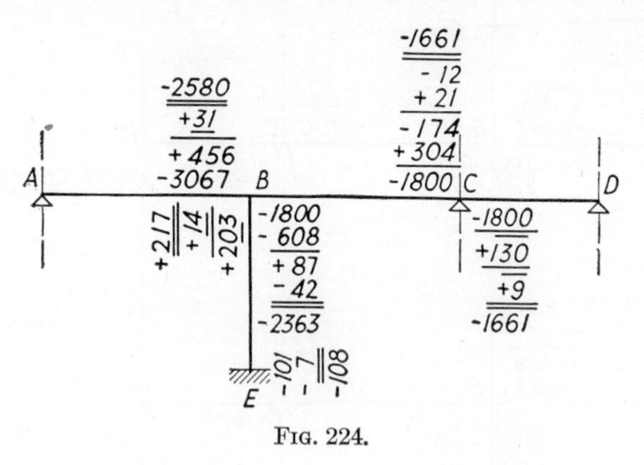

FIG. 224.

Similarly, at the second distribution joint *B* has no unbalanced moment, and this fact, and its continued balanced status, are indicated as in the figure marked "Second Distribution." The same procedure is then followed through the second carry-over, third distribution, third carry-over, and finally the fourth distribution to the result shown at (*c*) in Fig. 222. The experienced computer might omit some of the steps shown in Fig. 222, his work appearing as in Fig. 224.

182. Joint Translation.—It is sometimes necessary to deal with structures in which there may be relative movement of the joints, and in such cases it is necessary to correct the moments found by normal moment distribution which assumes no relative translation of joints.

Before proceeding with illustrations of the necessary corrections attention should be called to the relations shown in Fig. 225. In Fig. 225 (*a*) is shown a fixed-end prismatic beam AB. It is assumed that the end B is moved to B' *without rotation*. Applying

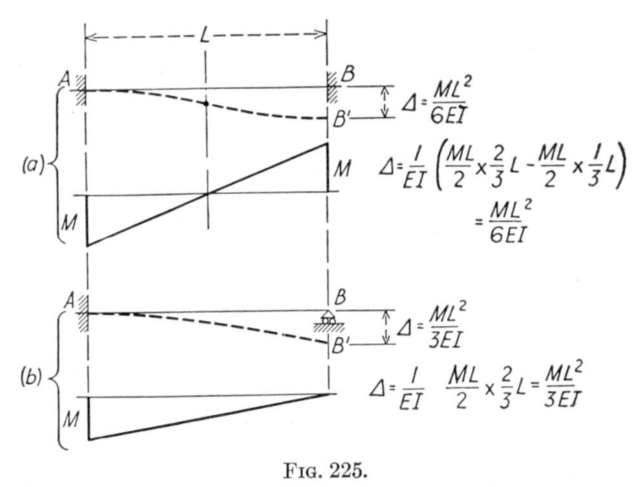

Fig. 225.

the principle relating deflection of B to the tangent at A leads to the statement shown in the figure:

$$\Delta = \frac{ML^2}{6EI}$$

from which we may write at once

$$M = \frac{6EI\Delta}{L^2}$$

From the figure and relation shown at (*b*) it is also clear that we may write

$$M = \frac{3EI\Delta}{L^2}$$

when one end is fixed and the other freely supported.

183. Referring now to the beam analyzed in Fig. 221 (*a*), assume that the support at C settles 1 in. It seems clear that, if the support C were pulled down 1 in. without permitting rotation of the beam at B or C (it could not rotate at D since that is a fixed end), the shape of the beam would be as shown at (b), Fig.

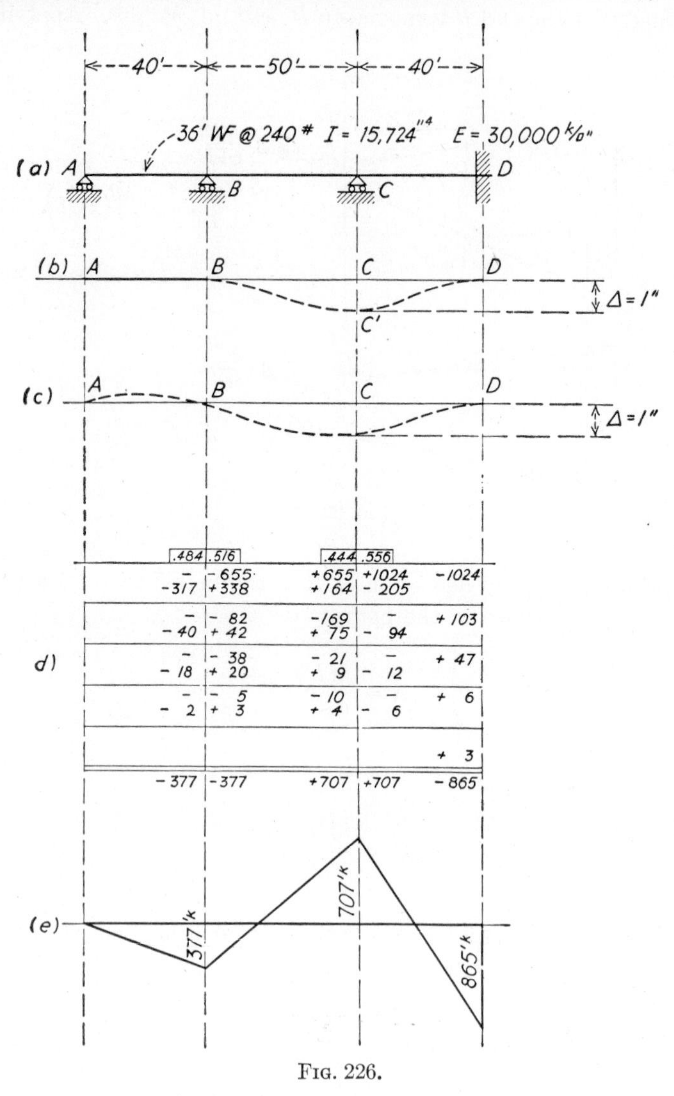

FIG. 226.

226. From the relations noted in the preceding article we may calculate the moments which would result at the ends of spans BC and CD, using the values of I and E shown at (a) in Fig. 226.

$$M_{CB} = \frac{6 \times 30{,}000 \times 15{,}724 \times 1}{600 \times 600} = 7{,}862''^{k} = +655'^{k}$$

$$M_{BC} = -655'^{k}$$

$$M_{CD} = \frac{6 \times 30{,}000 \times 15{,}724 \times 1}{480 \times 480} = 12{,}284''^{k} = +1024'^{k}$$

$$M_{DC} = -1024'^{k}$$

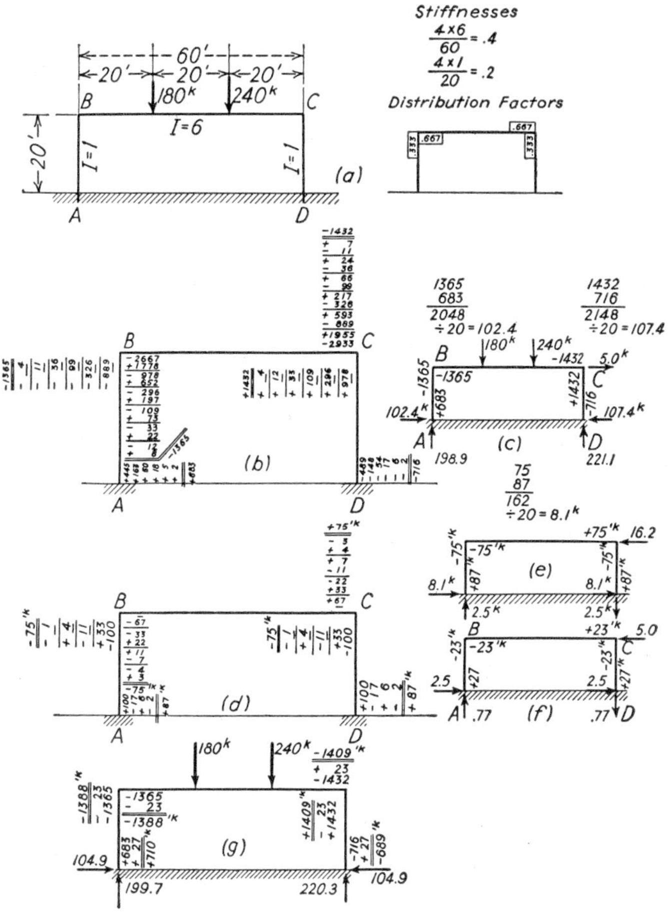

Stiffnesses
4×6/60 = .4
4×1/20 = .2
Distribution Factors
.333 .667 .667 .333

60'
20' 20' 20'
180k 240k
B C
I=6
I=1 I=1
20'
(a)
A D

-1432
+7
-11
+24
-36
+66
-99
+217
-326
+593
-889
+1955
-2933
C

B
-2667
+1778
-978
+652
-296
+197
-109
+73
-33
+22
-12
+8
-1365

-1365 +4 -11 +36 -99 -326 -889

+1432 -4 +12 -35 +109 -296 +978

+445 +148 +80 +18 +5 +2 +683

(b)

-489 -148 -54 -17 -6 -2 -716

A D

1365
683
2048
÷20 = 102.4

1432
716
2148
÷20 = 107.4

B 180k 240k -1432 5.0k
-1365
-1365
+683
+1432
-716
C
102.4k
107.4k
A (c) D
198.9 221.1

75
87
162
÷20 = 8.1k

+75'k
-3
+4
+7
-11
-22
+33
+67
C

B
-67
-33
+22
+11
-7
-4
+3
-75'k

-75'k -1 +4 -11 +33 -100

-75'k -1 +4 -11 +33 -100

+100 +17 +6 +2 +87

(d)

+100 +17 +6 +2 +87'k

A D

+75'k 16.2
-75'k
-75'k
+87'k
(e)
-75'k
+87'k
8.1k 8.1k
2.5k 2.5k

B +23'k 5.0
-23'k
-23'k
+27
-23'k
+27'k
C
2.5 2.5
A .77 (f) .77 D

180k 240k -1409'k
+23
-1432

-1388'k -23 -1365

-1365
-23
-1388'k

+1409'k -23 +1432

+683
+27
+710'k

(g)

-716
+27
-689'k

104.9 104.9
199.7 220.3

FIG. 227.

There will now be unbalanced moments at B and C, and when these joints are allowed to rotate the unloaded structure will take the shape shown at (*c*) in the figure. It seems clear that the moments accompanying this shape can be determined by distribution as shown in the figure at (*d*). The moments shown at (*d*) and (*e*) are those which would result only from a settlement of 1 in. at support *C*, and if these are combined with those found in Fig. 221 (*a*) we will have, of course, the moments in the loaded structure after settlement has taken place.

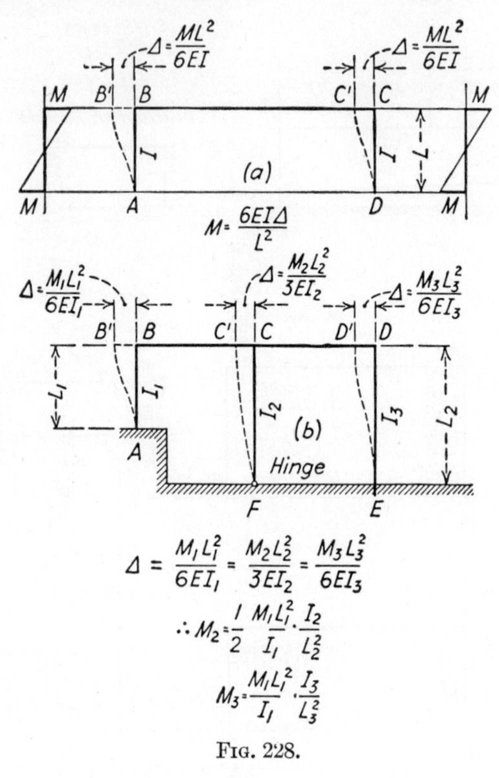

FIG. 228.

184. Sidesway.—The joints of unsymmetrical bents, of symmetrical bents with unsymmetrical loading, or of any bent subject to lateral loads have a tendency to translation.[5] Unless that tendency is restrained by the conditions of support, or adjacent portions of the structure, translation will take place and necessitate a correction in analyses made by moment distribution. The method

[5] Lateral translation of joints in bents is generally called **sidesway.**

of making the necessary correction is similar to that presented in the preceding article, differing in that the amount of translation of the joints is not known and generally need not be found.

As an illustration the bent analyzed in Fig. 209 is reanalyzed by moment distribution in Fig. 227. The loaded frame, relative

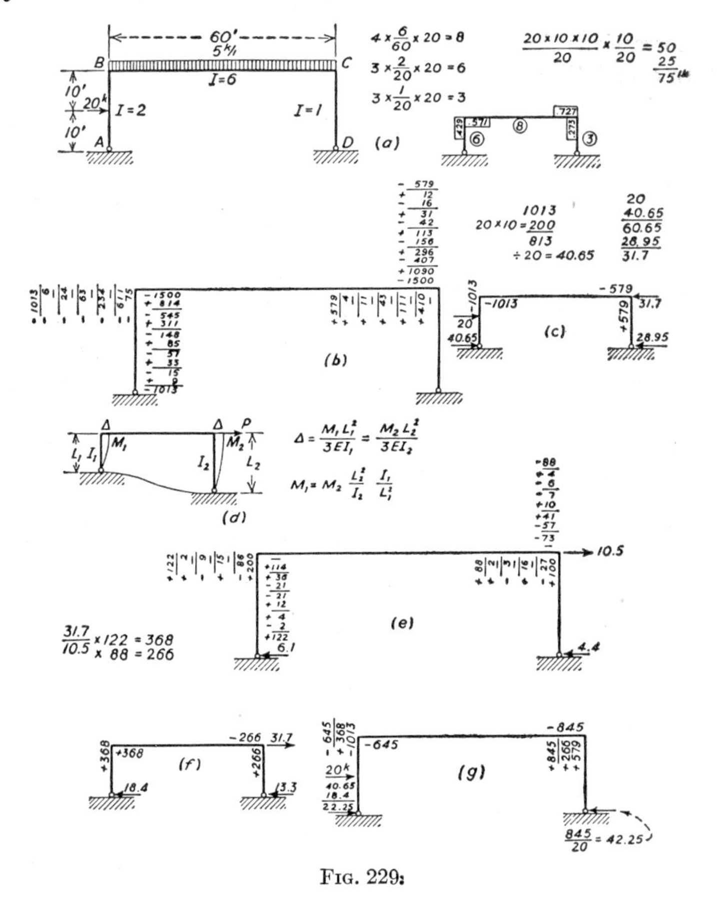

FIG. 229.

moments of inertia, calculation of stiffnesses, and distribution factors are shown at (*a*) in the figure. The distribution of fixed-end moments is shown at (*b*). Study of the moments found in (*b*) will show that they do not satisfy statics unless there is a force of 5.0 kips acting to the right at the top of the bent as shown at (*c*). The force of 5.0 kips is that necessary to prevent joints *B* and *C* from moving to the left, i.e., to prevent "sidesway." If the nature of the framing, of which the bent is a part, is such that this resistance is not present, it is necessary to correct the moments found in (*b*) for the effect of removing the holding force of 5.0 kips. It seems clear that if we add the corrections of (*f*) in the figure to (*c*) the result will be as shown at (*g*). The problem is to determine the corrections shown at (*f*).

In calculating corrections due to sidesway we may make use of the discussion in Art. 182. Assume that joints B and C are drawn to the left, without permitting any rotation, through some distance Δ, as shown in Fig. 228 (*a*). Since the relative translation of the ends is required to take place without permitting rotation of the joints there will be equal moments at the ends of the columns, but opposite in sign, as shown in the figure. Also since the joints are held against rotation no moments will be produced in the girder by the translation. The moments produced are dependent on the distance the joints are moved, and by proper adjustment we may produce any *convenient* moments. If we then hold the joints in the translated position but allow them to rotate we may determine by distribution the moments resulting from translation and by statics the force necessary to produce this translation. This procedure was followed in Fig. 227. As shown at (*d*) the joints B and C were translated without rotation producing *convenient* fixed-end moments of 100 ft.-kips; the bent was then held in this position, the joints allowed to rotate, and the resulting moments determined by distribution. The force necessary to hold the bent in the translated position was determined by statics at (*e*) in the figure. It seems clear that if any force other than 16.2 kips were applied to the bent as at (*e*) in the figure the resulting moments would be in proportion to that force; thus at (*f*) are shown forces and moments $\frac{5.0}{16.2}$ times those shown at (*e*), and these are the corrections to be added to the results shown in (*c*) to give the final solution at (*g*).

The bent shown in Fig. 227 (*a*) is symmetrical, but the same method of attack may be followed in any one story bent. When the bent is unsymmetrical as in Fig. 228 (*b*) one may produce translation without rotation of the joints (B, C, and D) to produce any convenient *consistent* set of fixed-end moments. Any moment may be chosen as the standard and moments consistent therewith determined as in the figure.

185. Additional illustrations of analysis by moment distribution of bents in which sidesway corrections are necessary are given in the problems solved in Figs. 229, 230, and 231. The method of analysis is precisely that presented in Art. 184, and the student should be able to follow the solutions without further com-

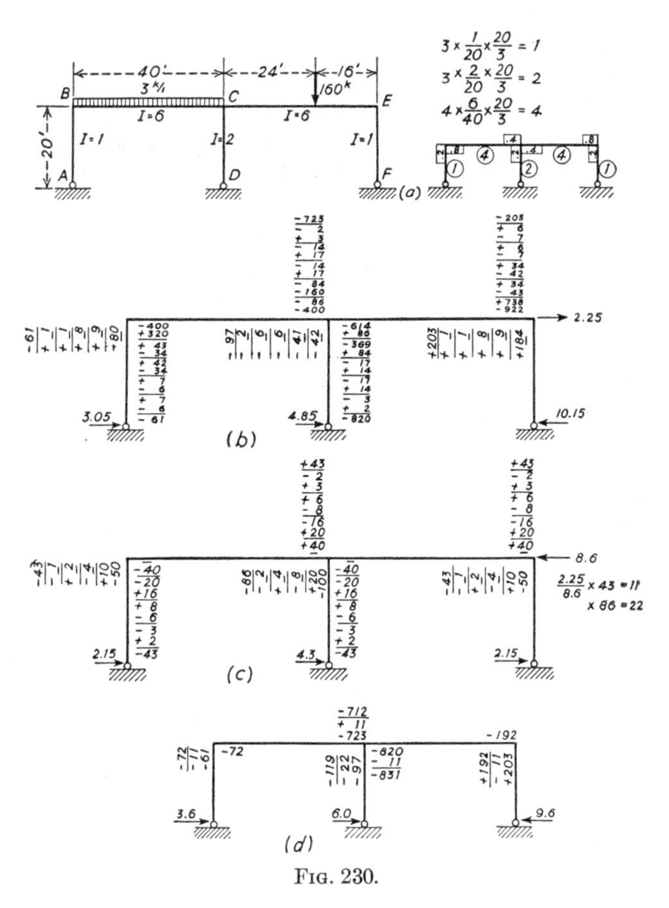

FIG. 230.

ment. It may be worth while, however, to remind the reader that moment distribution will give results as precise as may be needed provided that the necessary number of distributions is carried out with proper accuracy. For the most part the solutions presented as illustrations were carried out with a limited number of distributions (generally made to the nearest whole unit) and in all cases by slide-rule calculations. As will be noted the accuracy obtained by this procedure is quite adequate for design purposes.

186. Movable Uniform Loads.—In dealing with continuous beams and frames subject to movable uniform loads it is necessary to determine maximum shears, moments, and reactions. Maxi-

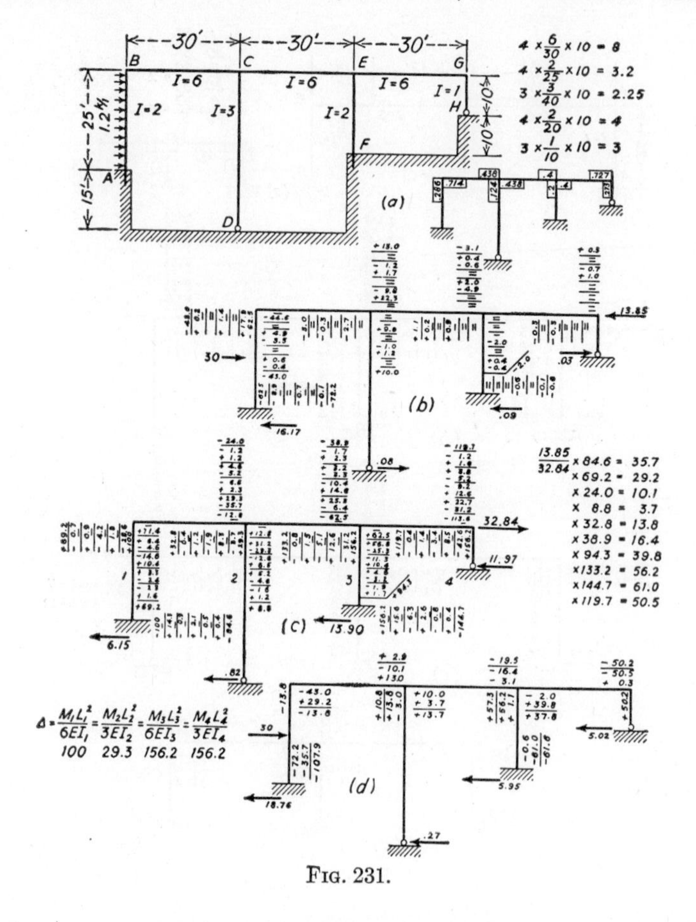

FIG. 231.

mum values occur at different sections for different positions of the load, and it is necessary to make analyses for a great variety of positions of the load or to calculate data from which values for any reasonable arrangement of loading can be quickly determined.

The latter method is preferable, and in Fig. 232 (*a*) and (*b*) are shown calculations of data which will permit rapid determination of shears, moments, or reactions due to any combination of *full span* loading of any intensity.[6] Since the spans are symmetrical it is necessary to calculate only the data for spans 1 and 2. It seems clear that when span 4 is loaded the moments are the same

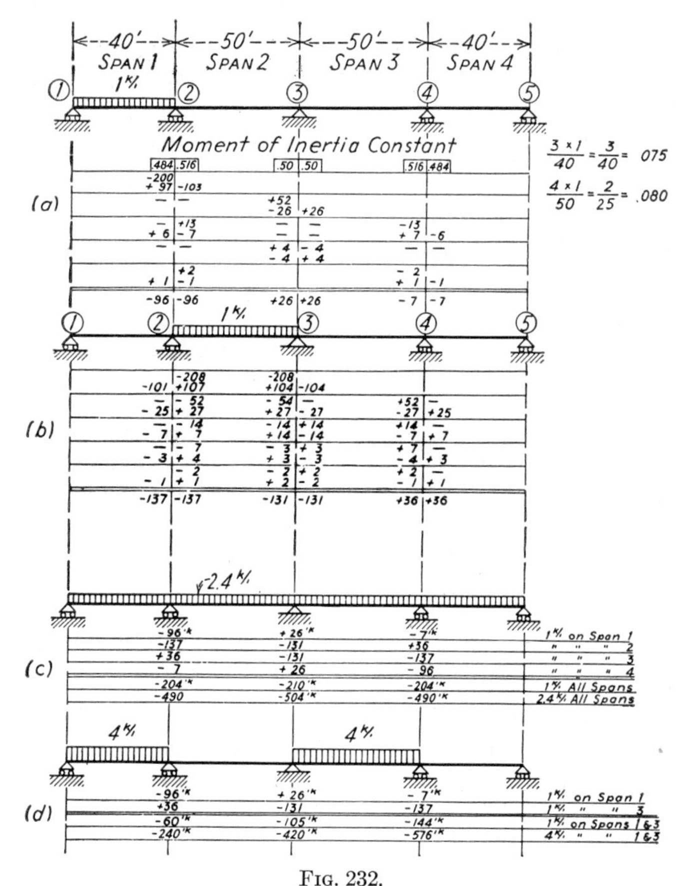

FIG. 232.

as for span 1 loaded but in reverse order, and of course the same relation exists for spans 3 and 2.

The use of the data shown in (*a*) and (*b*), Fig. 232, is illustrated in (*c*) and (*d*). In (*c*) the moments due to a uniform load of 2.4 kips

[6] This method was developed by Professor Hardy Cross. See Chapter VI, "Continuous Frames of Reinforced Concrete," by Cross and Morgan, John Wiley & Sons, New York.

per foot over all spans are determined, and in (*d*) the moments due to a uniform load of 4 kips per foot over spans 1 and 3. It seems clear that the moments at the supports accompanying any combination of full span loadings can be obtained by the procedure illustrated.

187. Qualitative Influence Lines.—In determining where to place full span loadings to produce maximum shears, moments, or reactions it is convenient to have qualitative influence lines, i.e., influence lines which are correct as to general shape without regard to the magnitude of the ordinates. Such influence lines can be drawn freehand by application of what is known as Müller-Breslau's principle. This principle is stated below without proof:[7]

> **If any deforming function—stress, shear, moment, or reaction—is allowed to act through a very small unit displacement the resulting shape of the deflected structure will be an influence line for that function.**

Thus if we wish to draw a qualitative influence line for positive moment at the center of span 1 in the structure shown in Fig. 233 we may assume a hinge introduced at that point, and by imagination picture the shape the elastic line will take if a couple acts on each side of the hinge to produce a unit angular displacement as indicated at (*a*) in the figure. The freehand sketch of the deformed structure shown at (*a*) is then a qualitative influence line for bending moment at the center of span 1. The influence line shows that to produce maximum positive moment at the section the first and third spans should be fully loaded as at (*d*) in Fig. 232. By the same procedure freehand qualitative influence lines have been drawn for bending moment over support ② at (*b*), bending moment near the center of span 2 at (*c*), and reaction at support ② at (*d*) in Fig. 233.

The same method may be applied in sketching influence lines for shear as shown at (*e*) in Fig. 233. It should be noted in applying a shearing displacement that the displaced ends must remain

[7] The proof depends on another principle which has not been discussed as yet—Maxwell's law of reciprocal relations. A complete discussion of the principle is beyond the scope of this book, but the advanced student may refer to "Continuous Frames of Reinforced Concrete" by Cross and Morgan, John Wiley & Sons, New York, which contains a straightforward proof and discussion.

parallel, the sheared section may rotate but the two surfaces must rotate the same.

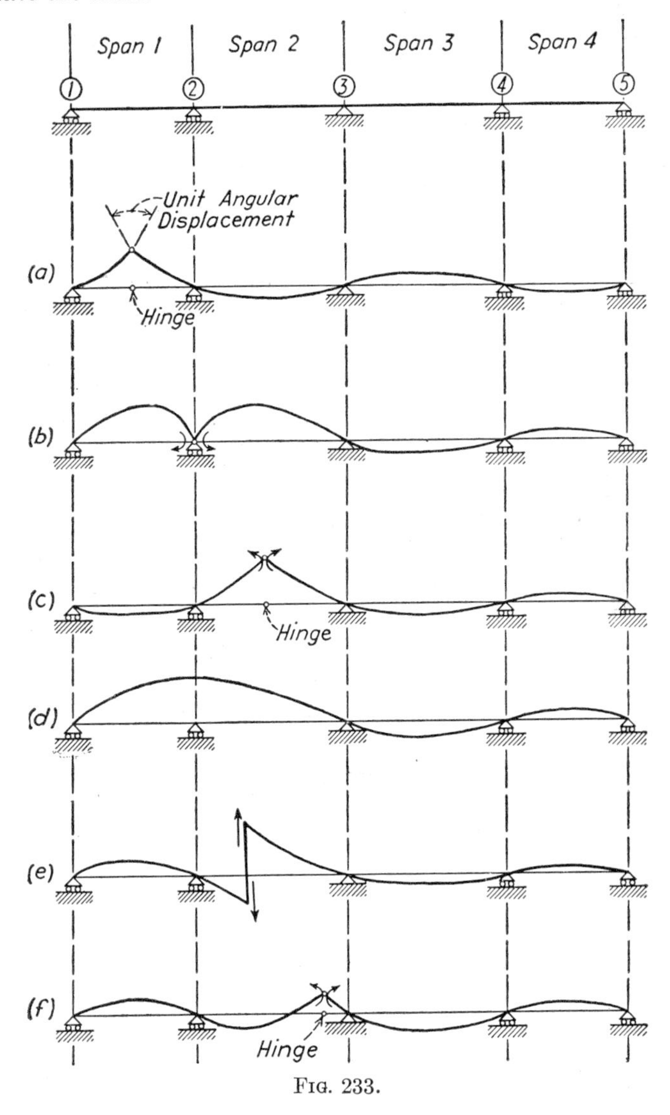

FIG. 233.

The student should be cautioned not to apply this procedure to a section near a support. Between a certain point (sometimes called the "fixed point") and the nearer support an influence line takes the shape shown at (*f*) in Fig. 233 rather than the shape shown at (*a*) or (*c*). In general the "fixed points"[8] are not far from the quarter points, and if, when dealing with moments, the method is confined to sketching influence lines for bend-

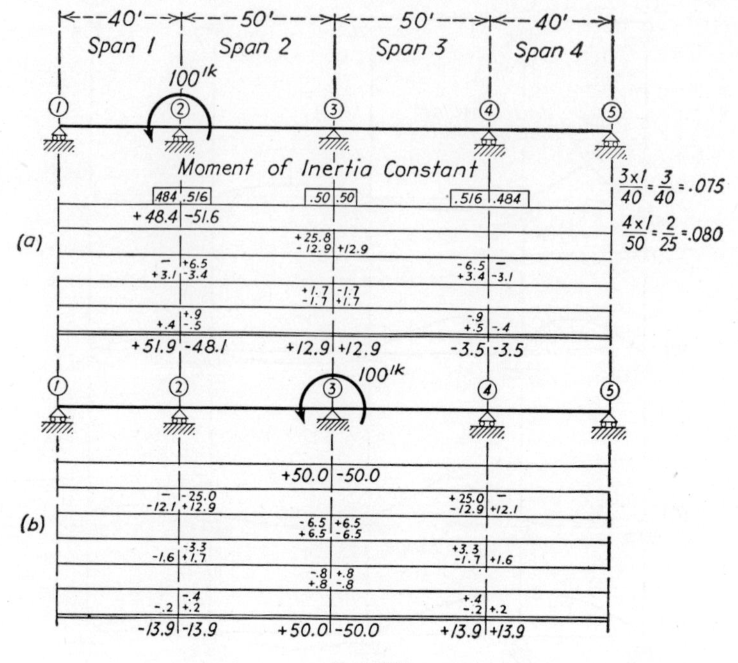

Fig. 234.

ing moment at a support or near the middle of spans the diagrams will always be similar to those in (*a*), (*b*), and (*c*) of the figure.

The purpose of qualitative influence lines is to show what spans should be covered with uniform load to produce the maximum values of reactions, shears, or moments.

[8] A general discussion of fixed points, their location, properties, and physical significance, is beyond the scope of this book. The advanced student may refer to "Continuous Frames of Reinforced Concrete" by Cross and Morgan, John Wiley & Sons, New York, for a brief general discussion. A paper entitled "Moments in Restrained and Continuous Beams by the Method of Conjugate Points" by L. H. Nishkian and D. B. Steinman in the *Trans. Am. Soc. C. E.*, Vol. 90, page 1, makes use of points which are in reality the fixed points, and several of the discussions treat fixed points at length.

188. Quantitative Influence Lines.—When concentrated loads are to be dealt with it may be convenient to draw quantitative influence lines, i.e., influence lines which are correct in both shape and magnitude of ordinates. The moment distribution procedure offers a very convenient way of calculating the data for such influence lines.

Taking the same series of spans considered in Fig. 232, the data shown in Fig. 234 have been calculated. The information shown evidently makes it possible for one to write down immediately the moments at the supports due to an unbalanced moment of any magnitude at any joint. For example, the data at (*a*) in the figure may be used to write down at once the results obtained at (*a*) in Fig. 232. The fixed-end moment of 200 ft.-kips on the right end of span 1 is an unbalanced moment acting counterclockwise on that joint, and this produces moments of 48.1 per cent at ②, 12.9 per cent at ③, and 3.5 per cent at ④.

Therefore

$$M_2 = -\,0.481 \times 200 = -\,96'^k$$

$$M_3 = +\,0.129 \times 200 = 26'^k$$

$$M_4 = -\,0.035 \times 200 = -\,7'^k$$

Obviously if two or more joints are affected the algebraic sum of the individual effects will give the final result.

In using the data of Fig. 234 to determine ordinates for influence lines the most direct procedure is to place a unit load at a series of points, calculate the fixed-end moment or moments due to the load in the various positions, determine the moments at the supports from the data of the figure, and finally calculate by statics the shear, moment, or reaction for which the influence line is being drawn.

This procedure has been followed in Fig. 235. Moments at the supports have been calculated for ten positions of a unit load as indicated, and the reactions calculated by statics. The information in Fig. 235 will make possible the calculation of ordinates (located as in the figure) for an influence line for any function at any section. The data of the figure have been used to calculate influence lines for bending moment shown to scale in Fig. 236, and influence lines for shear shown to scale in Fig. 237. The influence line for shear in span 1 is evidently also an influence line for reaction at ①.

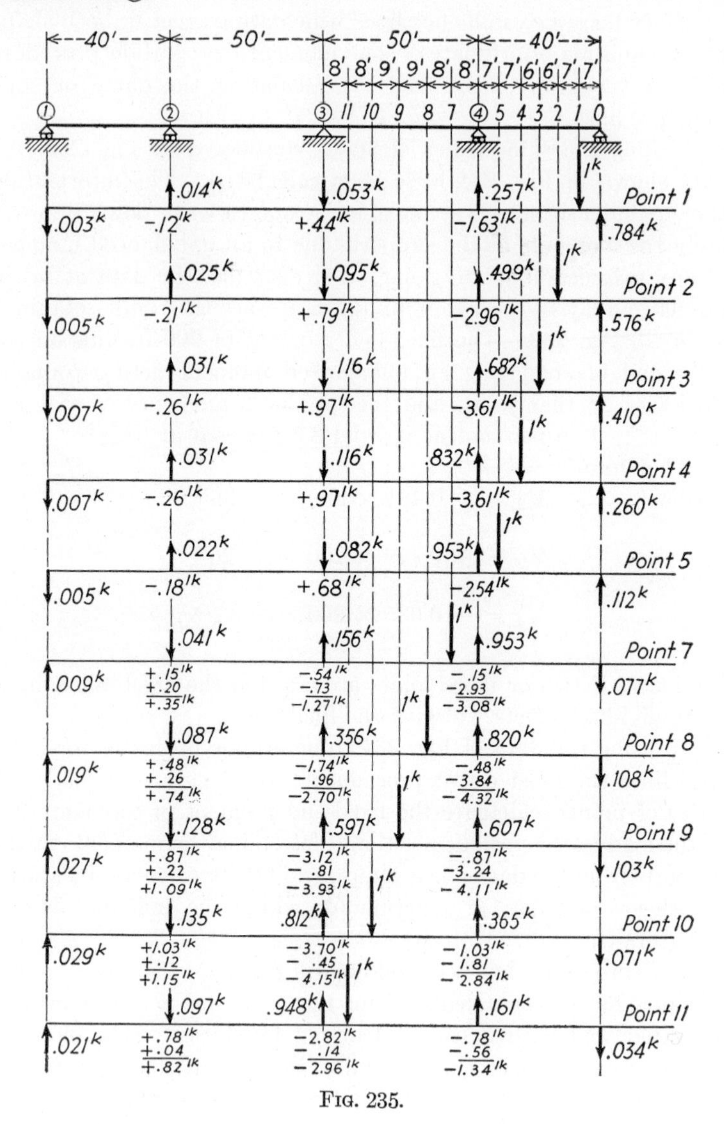

FIG. 235.

189. Non-prismatic Beams.—The method of moment distribution is applicable without change to frames composed of non-prismatic members, i.e., members in which the moment of inertia varies within the span. More labor is required to calculate fixed-

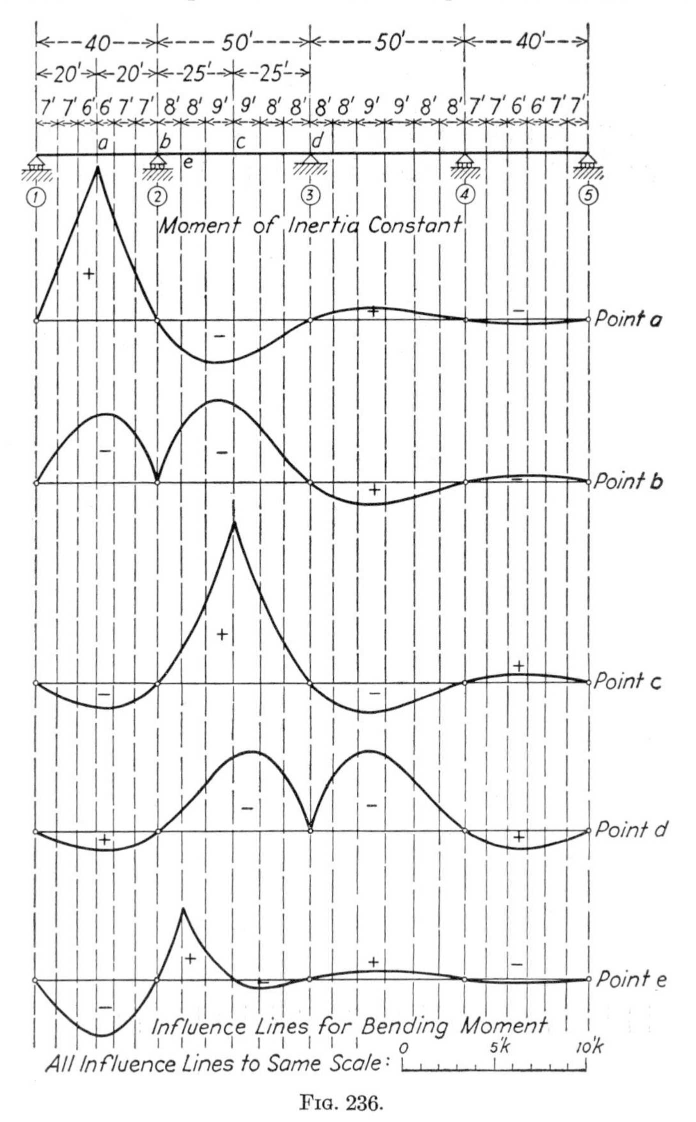

FIG. 236.

end moments, stiffnesses, and carry-over factors, but the definitions of these physical constants are the same, and when they have been calculated the procedure is exactly the same as for frames composed of prismatic members.

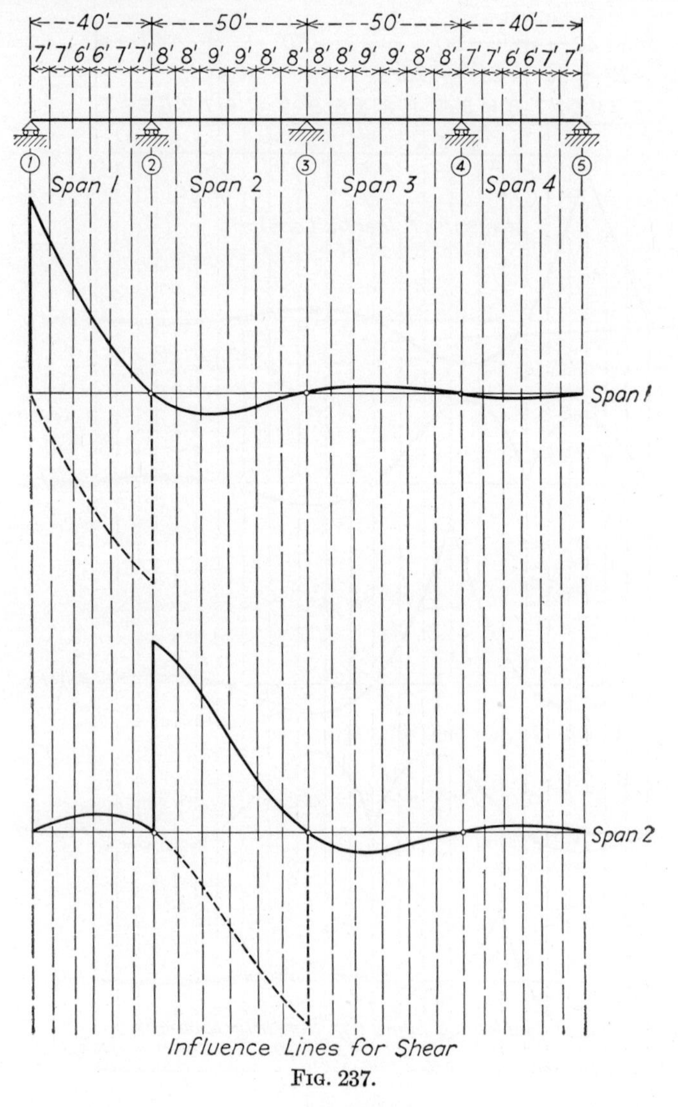

Influence Lines for Shear

FIG. 237.

The principles already discussed are adequate for the calculation of the physical constants mentioned in the preceding paragraph, and as illustrations Figs. 238, 239, and 240 are presented.

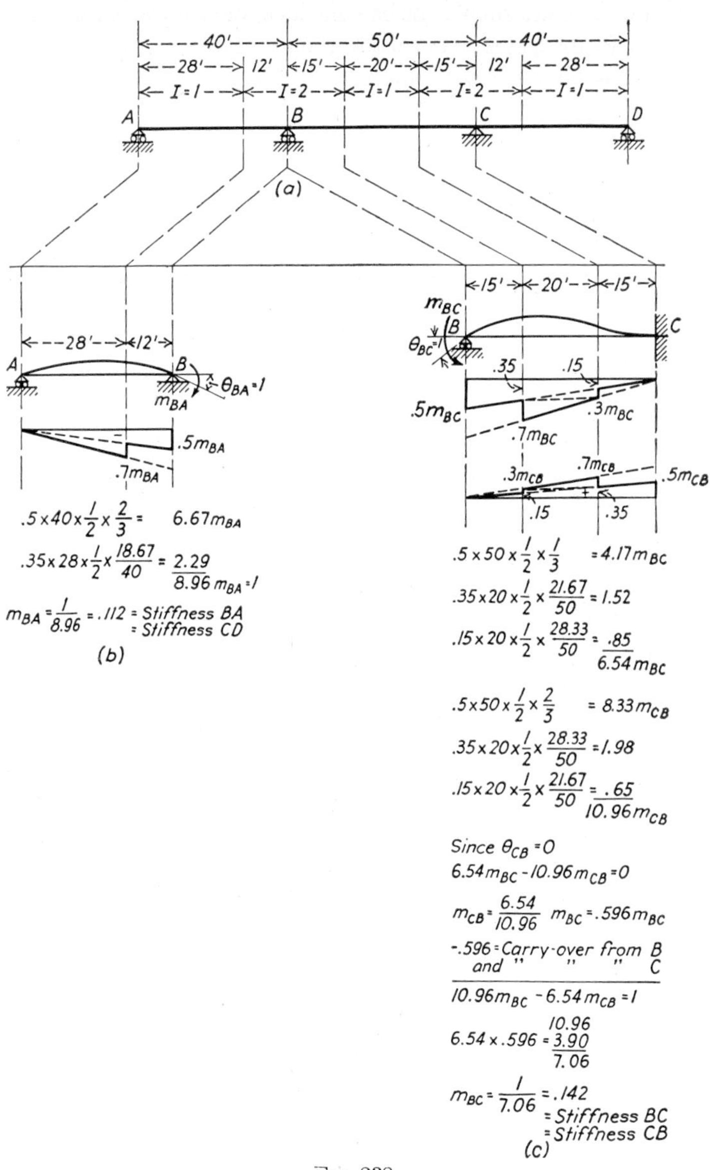
40'
50'
40'
28'
12'
15'
20'
15'
12'
28'
I=1
I=2
I=1
I=2
I=1
A
B
C
D
(a)
28'
12'
A
B
θBA=1
mBA
.5mBA
.7mBA
.5 x 40 x 1/2 x 2/3 = 6.67mBA
.35 x 28 x 1/2 x 18.67/40 = 2.29
8.96 mBA = 1
mBA = 1/8.96 = .112 = Stiffness BA
= Stiffness CD
(b)
15'
20'
15'
mBC
B
θBC=1
C
.35
.15
.5mBC
.3mBC
.7mBC
.7mCB
.3mCB
.5mCB
.15
.35
.5 x 50 x 1/2 x 1/3 = 4.17mBC
.35 x 20 x 1/2 x 21.67/50 = 1.52
.15 x 20 x 1/2 x 28.33/50 = .85
6.54 mBC
.5 x 50 x 1/2 x 2/3 = 8.33mCB
.35 x 20 x 1/2 x 28.33/50 = 1.98
.15 x 20 x 1/2 x 21.67/50 = .65
10.96mCB
Since θCB = 0
6.54mBC - 10.96mCB = 0
mCB = 6.54/10.96 mBC = .596mBC
-.596 = Carry-over from B
and " " " C
10.96mBC - 6.54mCB = 1
10.96
6.54 x .596 = 3.90
7.06
mBC = 1/7.06 = .142
= Stiffness BC
= Stiffness CB
(c)

FIG. 238.

In Fig. 238 are shown the calculations for stiffnesses and carry-over factors for a symmetrical three-span beam: at (*a*) the dimensions and assumed *relative* moments of inertia; at (*b*) the calcula-

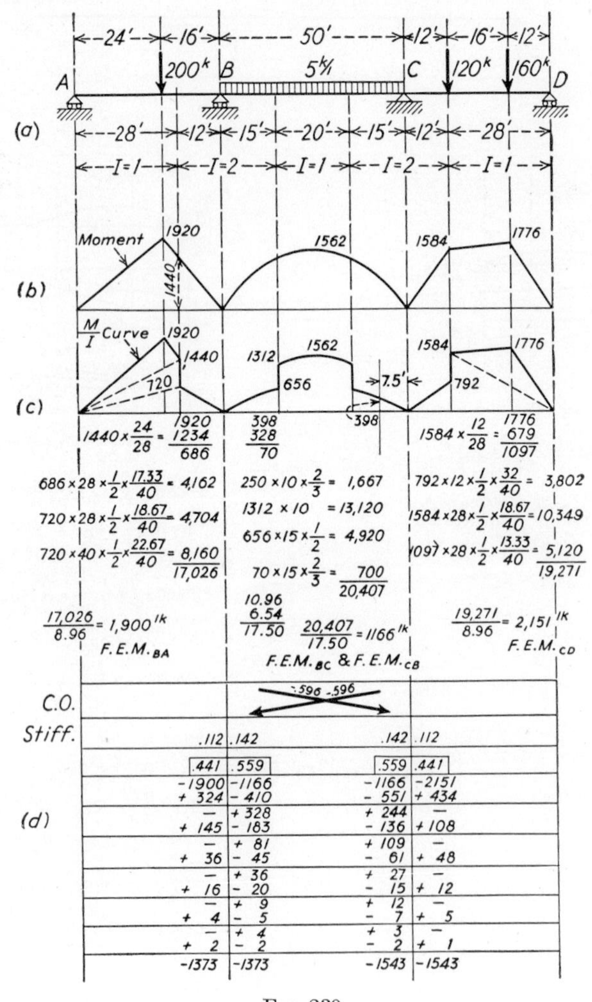

Fig. 239.

tion of stiffness for span AB; and at (*c*) the calculations for stiffness and carry-over factors for span BC.

In Fig. 239 are shown calculations of fixed-end moments due

to the loading shown, and the moment distribution carried out using the physical constants calculated in Fig. 238.

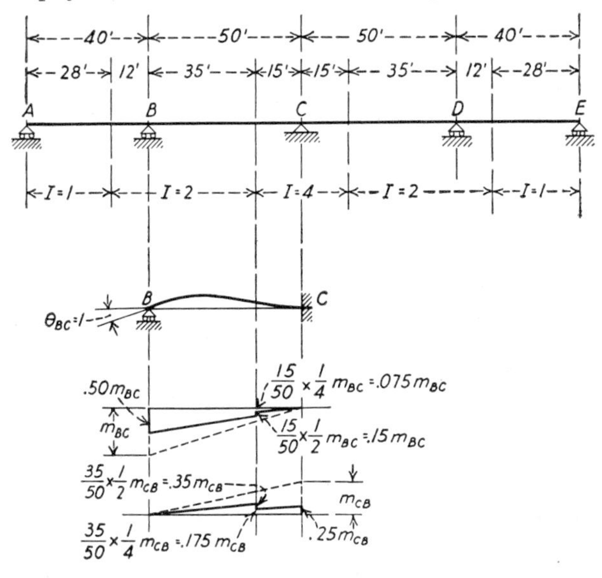

$\frac{M}{I}$ Diagrams as Loads

Reactions at B	Reactions at C
$.50 \times \frac{35}{2} \times \frac{38.33}{50} = 6.71$	$.50 \times \frac{35}{2} \times \frac{11.67}{50} = 2.04$
$.15 \times \frac{35}{2} \times \frac{26.67}{50} = 1.41$	$.15 \times \frac{35}{2} \times \frac{23.33}{50} = 1.23$
$.075 \times \frac{15}{2} \times \frac{10}{50} = .11$	$.075 \times \frac{15}{2} \times \frac{40}{50} = .45$
$8.23 m_{BC}$	$3.72 m_{BC}$
$.35 \times \frac{35}{2} \times \frac{26.67}{50} = 3.27$	$.35 \times \frac{35}{2} \times \frac{23.33}{50} = 2.86$
$.25 \times \frac{15}{2} \times \frac{5}{50} = .19$	$.25 \times \frac{15}{2} \times \frac{45}{50} = 1.69$
$.175 \times \frac{15}{2} \times \frac{10}{50} = .26$	$.175 \times \frac{15}{2} \times \frac{40}{50} = 1.05$
$3.72 m_{CB}$	$5.60 m_{CB}$

Stiffness at B and Carry-over Factor from B

$$8.23 m_{BC} - 3.72 m_{CB} = 1$$
$$3.72 m_{BC} - 5.60 m_{CB} = 0$$

$\frac{m_{CB}}{m_{BC}} = \frac{3.72}{5.60} = .665$ Carry-over factor from B (—)

$m_{BC} = .174$ Stiffness at B

Stiffness at C and Carry-over Factor from C

$$5.60 m_{CB}' - 3.72 m_{BC}' = 1$$
$$3.72 m_{CB}' - 8.23 m_{BC}' = 0$$

$\frac{m_{BC}'}{m_{CB}'} = \frac{3.72}{8.23} = .453$ Carry-over factor from C (—)

$m_{CB}' = .255$ Stiffness at C

FIG. 240.

Figure 240 shows calculations of the stiffnesses and carry-over factors for an unsymmetrical span.

The student will note that the factor $8.96 m_{BA}$ in Fig. 238 (*b*) is the rotation at the B end of the span AB. Therefore

$$8.96 m_{BA} = \theta_{BA}$$

and since, by definition, the stiffness is the moment required to produce a *unit* rotation, $\theta_{BA} = 1$ and

$$m_{BA} = \frac{1}{8.96} = 0.112 = \text{stiffness of } BA$$

Also, if $m_{BA} = 1$,

$$\theta_{BA} = 8.96$$

i.e., a unit couple at B will rotate that end through an angle 8.96, a fact which explains the calculation of fixed-end moments for spans AB and CD in Fig. 239 (*c*). Similarly the factors $6.54m_{BC}$ and $10.96m_{CB}$ show that 6.54 is the rotation at the C end of span BC produced by a unit couple at B and 10.96 is the rotation at the C end produced by a unit couple at C. Therefore, if

$$M_{BC} = \text{the fixed-end moment at } B$$

$$M_{CB} = \text{" \quad " \quad " \quad " \quad "} \ C$$

we have the relation

$$6.54M_{BC} + 10.96M_{CB} = \theta_{BC} = 20{,}407$$

Since the beam is symmetrical both with respect to load and moment of inertia

$$M_{BC} = M_{CB}$$

and

$$(6.54 + 10.96)M_{CB} = 20{,}407$$

$$M_{CB} = M_{BC} = \frac{20{,}407}{17.50} = 1166'^{k}$$

When a beam is unsymmetrical with respect to loads and moment of inertia the fixed-end moments will not in general be equal. For example, suppose that span BC of the four-span beam in Fig. 240 is loaded as in Fig. 241. If hinges are introduced at B and C the rotation of the tangent to the elastic line at $B = 21{,}177$ and at $C = 23{,}448$.

Then if

$$M_{BC} = \text{the fixed-end moment at } B$$

and

$$M_{CB} = \text{" \quad " \quad " \quad " \quad "} \ C$$

we may use the data calculated in Fig. 240 and write

$$8.23M_{BC} + 3.72M_{CB} = 21{,}177$$

$$3.72M_{BC} + 5.60M_{CB} = 23{,}448$$

$$M_{BC} = 973'^{k}$$

$$M_{CB} = 3541'^{k}$$

Stiffnesses, carry-over factors, and fixed-end moments for non-prismatic beams may be calculated somewhat more directly by the

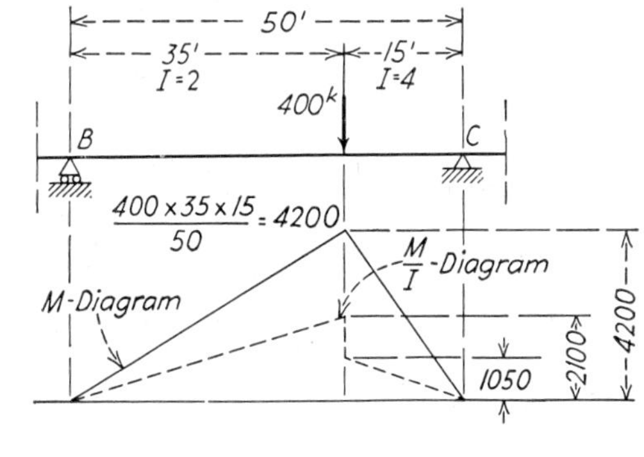

Slope at B

$$\frac{2100 \times 35}{2} = 36{,}750, \times \frac{26.67}{50} = 19{,}602$$

$$\frac{1050 \times 15}{2} = 7875, \times \frac{10}{50} = \underline{1{,}575}$$

$$21{,}177$$

Slope at C

$$36{,}750 \times \frac{23.33}{50} = 17{,}148$$

$$7875 \times \frac{40}{50} = \underline{6300}$$

$$23{,}448$$

FIG. 241.

"column analogy" [9] and the advanced student will find it worth while to familiarize himself with that tool.

[9] "Continuous Frames of Reinforced Concrete" by Cross and Morgan, John Wiley & Sons, New York. This book also contains charts giving fixed-end moments, stiffnesses, and carry-over factors for common forms of haunched beams.

PROBLEMS

In the following problems, where the value of E is required, it should be assumed as 30,000 kips per sq. in. unless otherwise stated.

262. (*a*) Calculate the deflection at the center of the beam shown.

(*b*) Calculate the deflection under the load.

(*c*) Where is the deflection greatest? How much is it?

(*d*) Calculate the slope of the tangent to the elastic line at each end, in radians and in degrees.

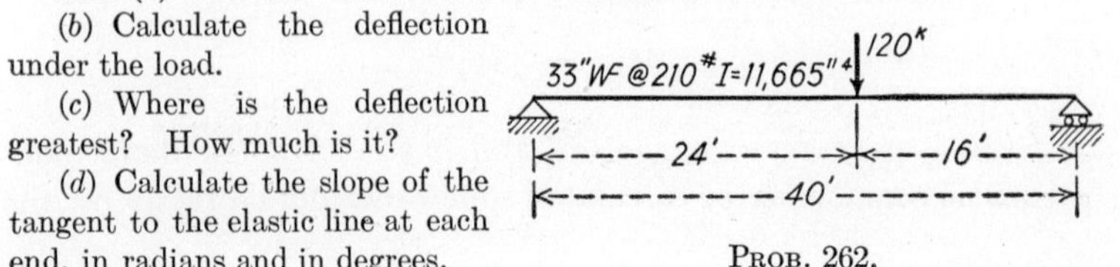

PROB. 262.

263. (*a*) Calculate the deflection at the center of the main span and at the end of the cantilever.

(*b*) Calculate the slope of the elastic line at A, B, and C.

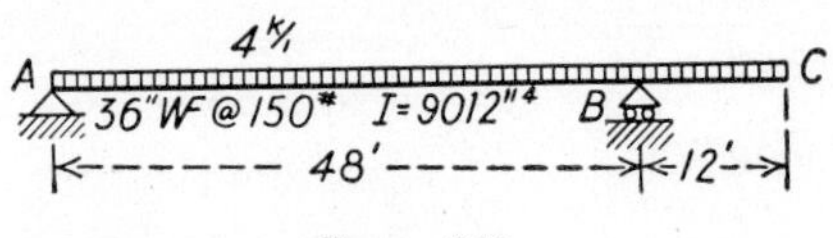

PROB. 263.

264. Calculate the deflection of the beam in Problem 41: (*a*) at the left end of the uniform load; (*b*) at the cantilever end. Assume E and $I = 1$.

265. Calculate the slope of the left end of the beam supporting the uniform load in Problem 48. Assume $E = 1$; $I = 2$ for the lower beam; $I = 1$ for the upper beam.

266. Calculate the deflection at B and at D for the beam shown.

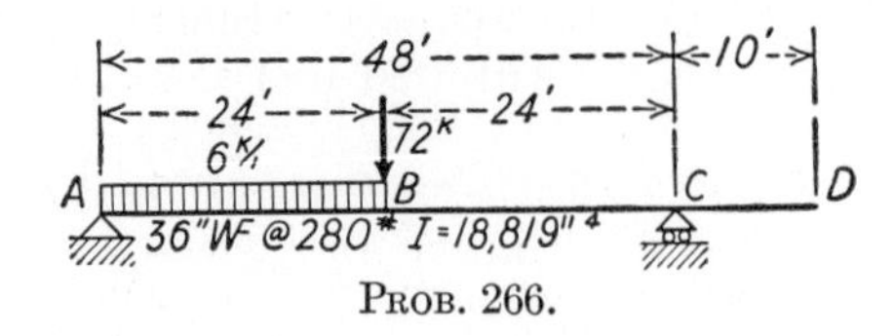

PROB. 266.

267. What force acting down at D on the beam shown in Problem 266 would keep the end D from rising above the horizontal line $ABCD$?

268. How much would the force found in Problem 267 reduce the deflection at B in the beam of Problem 266?

269. Are the reactions given in Problem 74 correct if the moment of inertia is constant throughout? Use angle changes.

270. (*a*) Draw the shear and moment diagrams for the beam shown.

(*b*) The support at *B* settles 3.75 in. Draw the shear and moment diagrams.

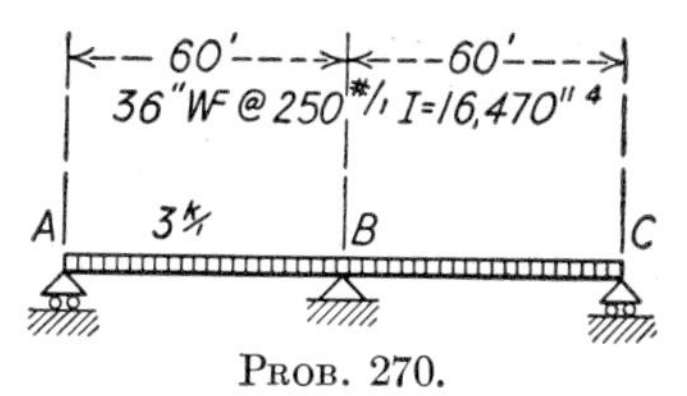

PROB. 270.

271. The member *B–B′* in the structure shown was fabricated 0.48 in. short owing to an error in the shop. Assuming rigid connections at *B* and *B′*, what moments will result from forcing *B–B′* into place during erection?

(*a*) Assume no stress elongation in *B–B′*.

(*b*) The area of *B–B′* is 44 sq. in. gross. What will be the effect on the moments if the elongation of *B–B′* due to stress is included in the calculations?

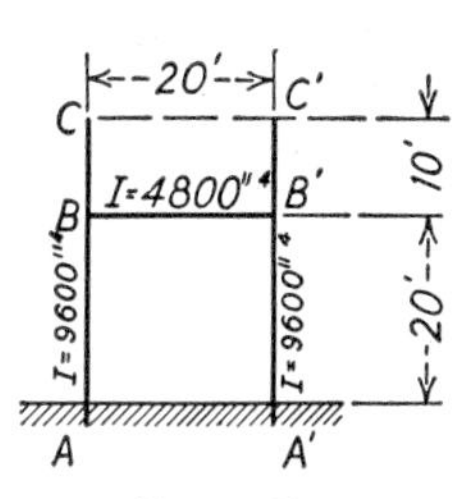

PROB. 271.

272. The member *A–B* in the structure shown is composed of wire rope having a modulus of elasticity of 20,000 kips per sq. in. and an area of 2 sq. in. The steel member *DBC* has a modulus of elasticity of 30,000 kips per sq. in. Calculate the horizontal deflection of point *C*.

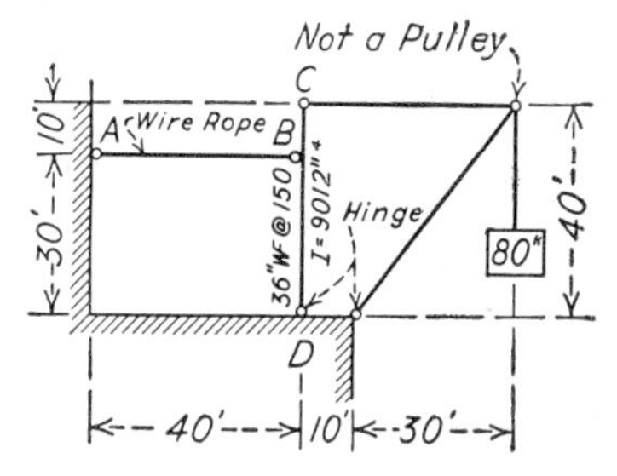

PROB. 272.

273. Draw the shear and moment diagrams for the structure shown. Neglect the change in length of member *BC*.

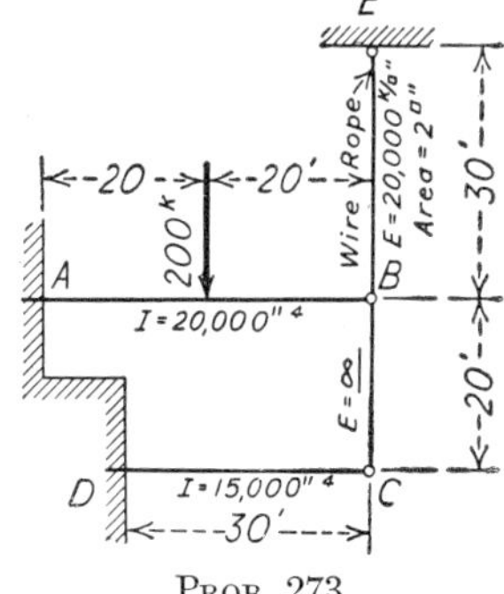

PROB. 273.

274. Draw the shear and moment diagrams for the structure shown.

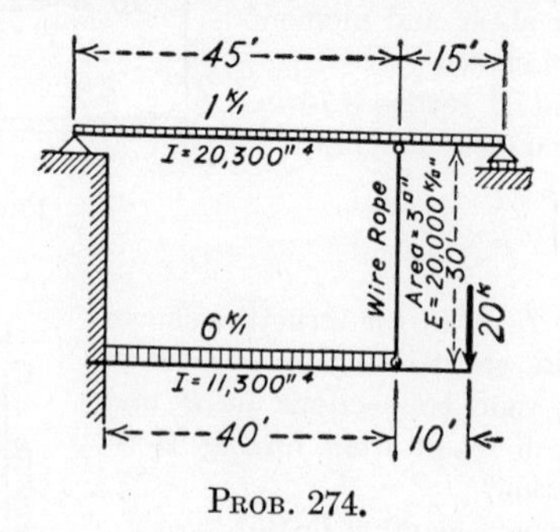

Prob. 274.

275. Draw the shear and moment diagrams for the structure shown. *I* is constant throughout.

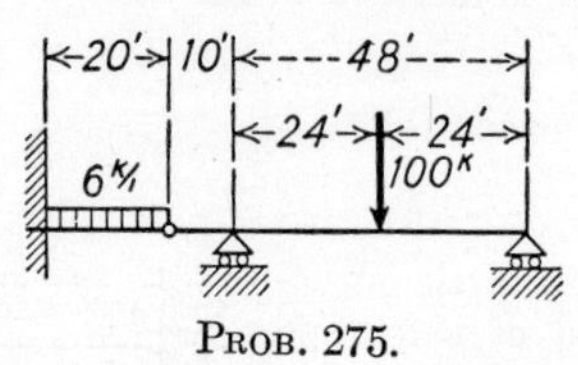

Prob. 275.

276. Draw the shear and moment diagrams for the structure shown. *I* is constant throughout.

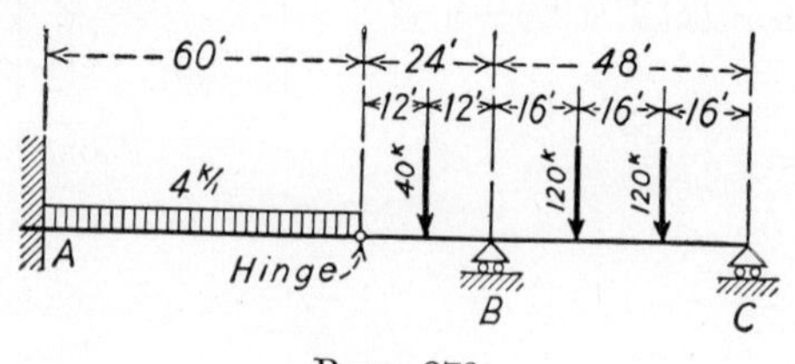

Prob. 276.

277. Pier *B* for the structure in Problem 276 has settled 2 in. Assume $I = 29{,}660$ in.^{4} and draw the shear and moment diagrams.

278. Pier *C* for the structure in Problem 276 has settled 2 in. Assume $I = 29{,}660$ in.^{4} and draw the shear and moment diagrams.

279. Assume that the beam of Problem 73 has a constant *I* throughout, and determine by means of angle changes whether the bending moment at *A* and the reaction at *C* are correct as given.

280. Calculate the horizontal movement of D in the structure shown if there is an angle change of 0.015 radian at B and 0.020 radian at C.

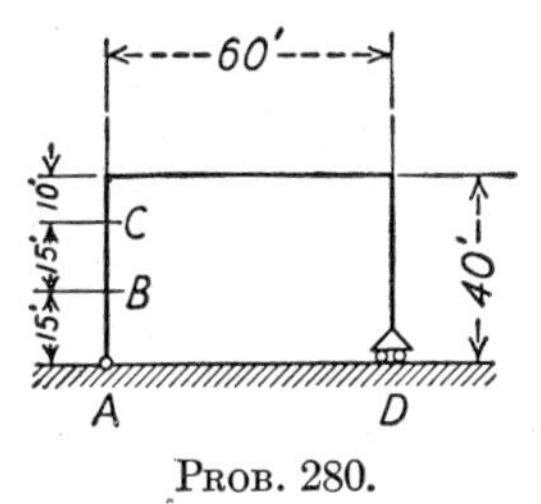

PROB. 280.

281. Each of the vertical members in the structure shown, U_0L_0, U_1L_1, and U_2L_2, is a 36-in. WF @ 300 lb. per ft. Assume that the ties U_0U_1 and U_1U_2 are inextensible, and calculate the maximum moment in each of the vertical members.

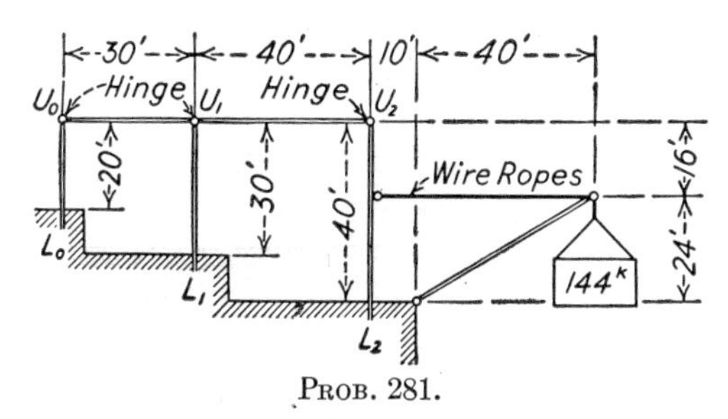

PROB. 281.

The following problems may be conveniently solved by means of moment distribution.

282. Assume that the beam of Problem 74 has a constant I throughout, and determine whether the bending moment at B is correct as given. Draw the shear and moment diagrams.

283. Assume that the beam of Problem 74 has a constant I and that the end reactions are fixed supports. Calculate the indeterminate moments, and draw the shear and moment diagrams.

284. Calculate the indeterminate moments for the structure shown, and draw the shear and moment diagrams.

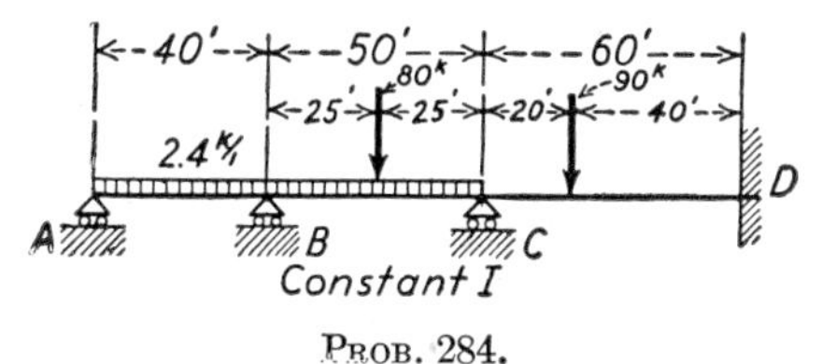

PROB. 284.

285. Calculate the indeterminate moments for the structure shown, and draw the shear and moment diagrams.

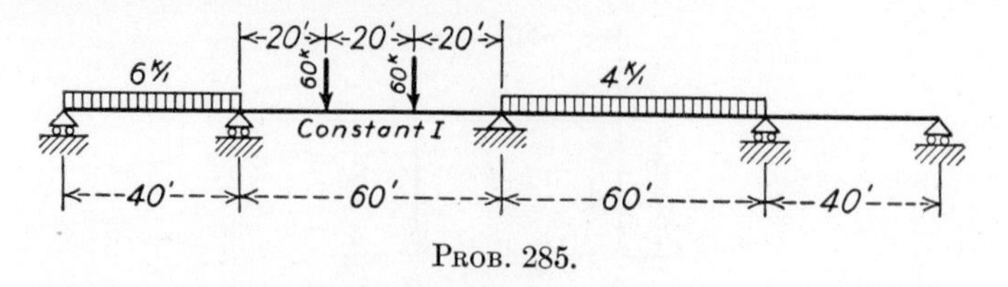

PROB. 285.

286. Draw the shear and moment diagrams for the structure shown.

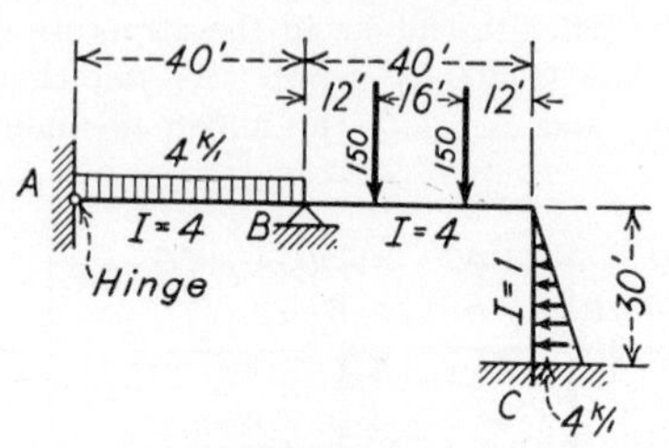

PROB. 286.

287. Draw the shear and moment diagrams for the structure shown.

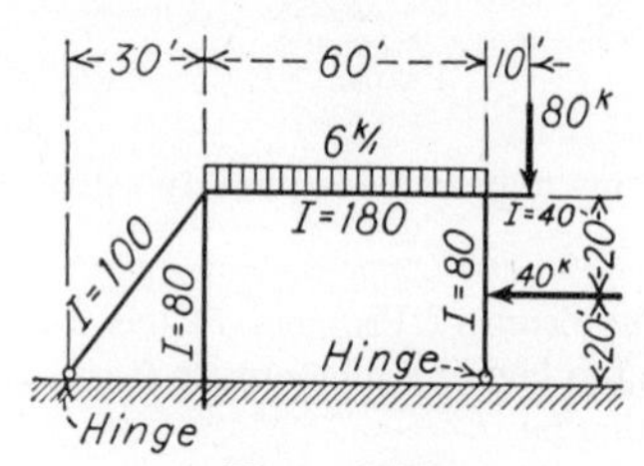

PROB. 287.

288. Draw the shear and moment diagrams which would result if the support at C in the structure shown were moved down 2 in. and 3 in. to the right but without rotation.

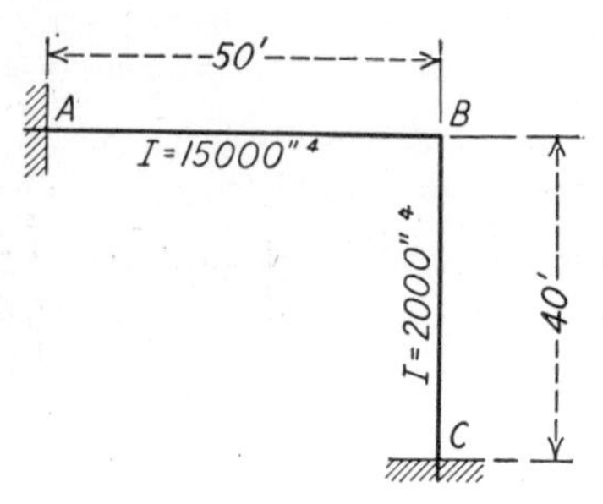

PROB. 288.

289. Draw the shear and moment diagrams for the frame $ABCD$ in the structure shown. Note that the end at A is fixed and that at D is hinged.

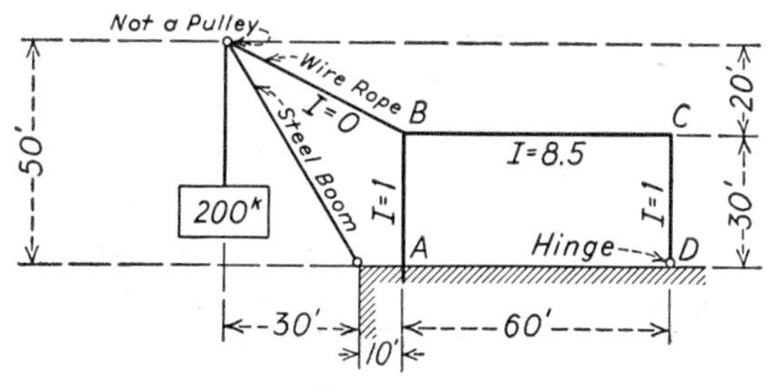

PROB. 289.

290. Draw the shear and moment diagrams for the structure shown.

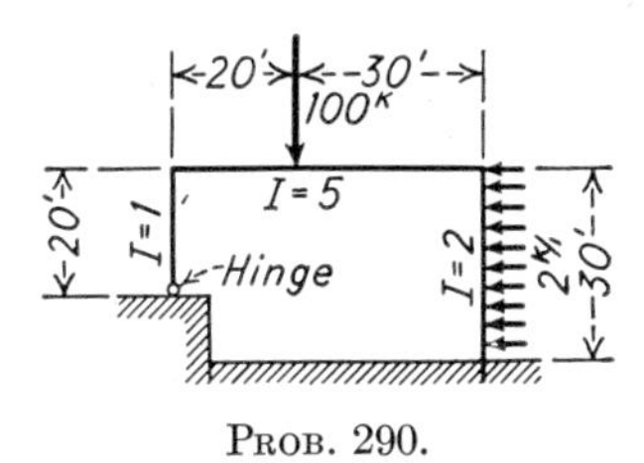

PROB. 290.

291. Assume that the structure shown in Problem 286 is supported at A and B by rollers on horizontal planes, and redraw the shear and moment diagrams.

292. Draw the shear and moment diagrams for the structure shown.

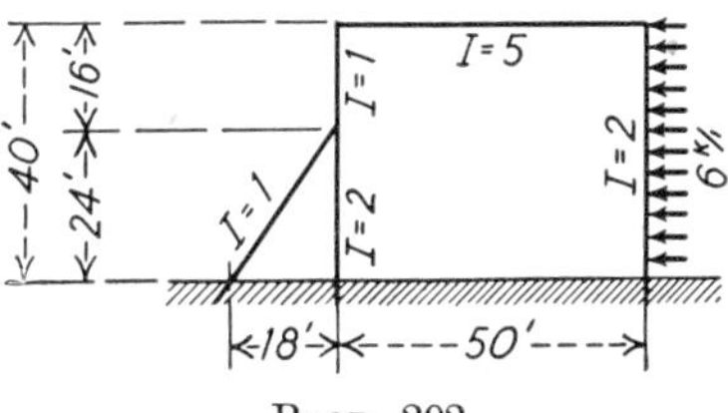

PROB. 292.

293. Sketch the influence line for bending moment at P in the structure shown, and calculate the ordinates thereto at the quarter and center points of each span.

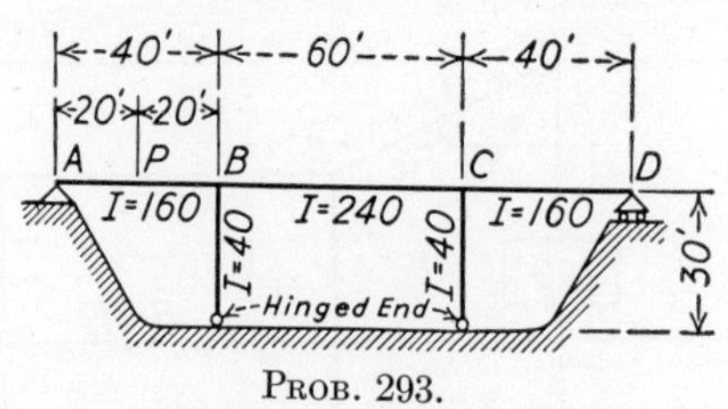

PROB. 293.

294. Calculate the maximum shear, the maximum positive moment, and the maximum negative moment for the structure shown.

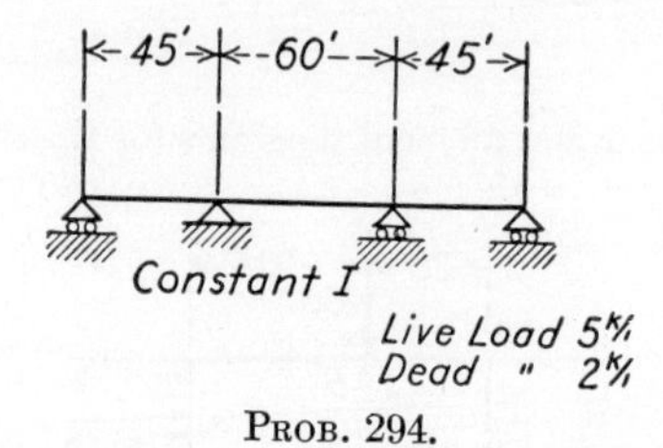

PROB. 294.

295. Draw the shear and moment diagrams for the beam shown, and compare them with those for a prismatic beam with the same lengths and loads.

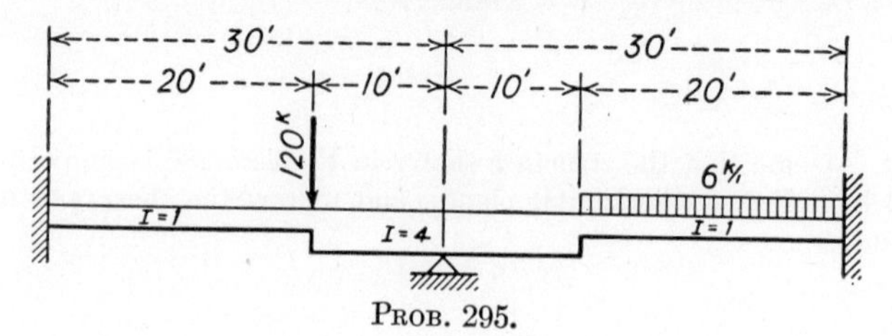

PROB. 295.

296. Draw the shear and moment diagrams for the structure shown.

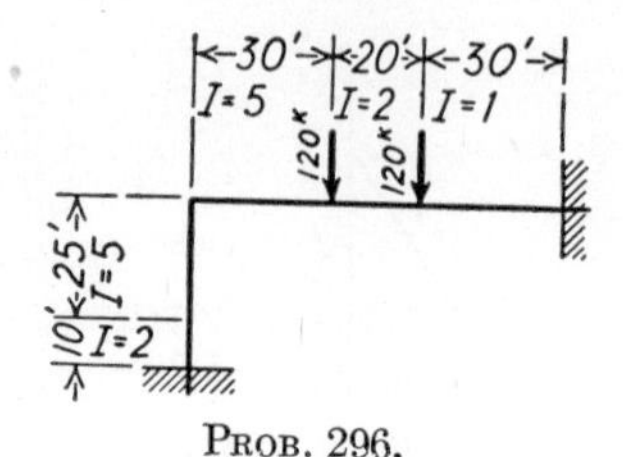

PROB. 296.

297. Draw the shear and moment diagrams for the structure shown.

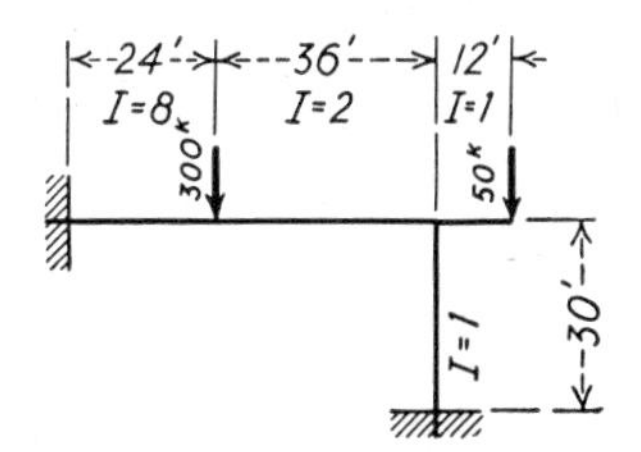

PROB. 297.

298. Draw the shear and moment diagrams for the structure shcwn.

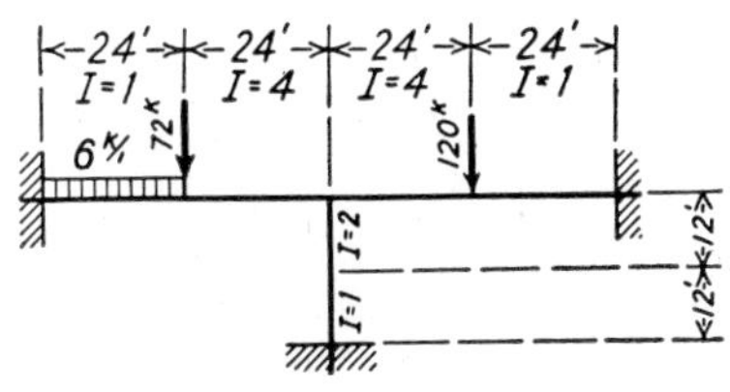

PROB. 298.

CHAPTER XI

TRUSSED STRUCTURES

190. The remarks in the preceding chapter regarding the importance of facility in calculating deformations of beams apply with equal force to trussed structures. Also, as in beams, calculations of deformations in trussed structures perhaps are made more often as a step in analysis of indeterminate structures than simply to determine deformations as such.

The principles already presented have frequent application in dealing with trussed structures, but extensions of those principles and additional procedures are often convenient. As in dealing with beams the authors have a preference for purely geometrical methods.

The limitations previously stated apply also in dealing with trussed structures; i.e., angle changes are so small that the sine, the tangent, and the angle are equal. Also the changes in the shape of the structure are so small that calculations of primary stress are not affected.

191. Angle Changes in Truss Deflections.—As stated in Chapter V the triangle is the basic geometric figure in trusses because it is the only geometric figure which cannot be changed in shape without changing the length of one or more of its sides. Conversely it must be true that if the length of a side of a triangle is changed the angles in the triangle will change.

In the truss shown in Fig. 244 (*a*) a change in any side of the various triangles of which the truss is composed would change the angles in those triangles. There would be, then, angle changes in the line of the bottom chord at the panel points, that at panel point L_1 being the algebraic sum of the changes in the angles marked ① and ②; that at panel point L_2 the algebraic sum of the changes in the angles marked ③, ④, and ⑤, and so on. If these angle changes were known we could compute the deflection of any point on the bottom chord of the truss by application of the general statement (**1**) in Art. 153. A simple method of calculating the changes in the angles of a triangle, resulting from changes in the lengths of the sides, evidently would give a direct solution of the deflection of trusses.

192. Angle Changes in a Triangle.—Figure 242 (*a*) indicates the nomenclature to be used in discussing angle changes in a triangle. In addition let δ_a, δ_b, δ_c represent changes in length of the sides a, b, and c, respectively. The student should keep in mind that these *changes* in length will be very small in comparison with the lengths of the sides, and that the *changes* in angles resulting

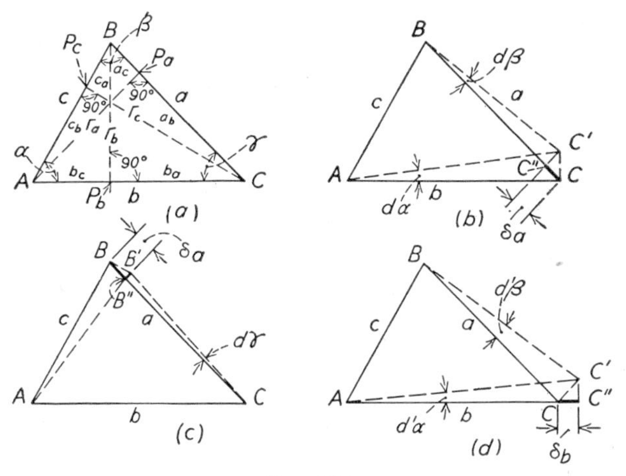

FIG. 242.

therefrom will be so small that the angle changes, their sines, and tangents will be identical. For clarity, diagrams showing changes in sides and angles will be greatly exaggerated in scale.

Assume now that side a of the triangle shown in Fig. 242 (*a*) is shortened by the amount δ_a. The apex C will move to C', and the triangle will take the shape ABC' shown in (*b*) of the figure. It should be noted that CC' is a line perpendicular to AC, and $C''C'$ a line perpendicular to BC. The change in length δ_a and the resulting angle changes $d\alpha$ and $d\beta$ are so small that these perpendicular lines may be considered as arcs drawn from A and B as centers; i.e., the angle changes are so small that the arc, sine, and tangent are identical.

Examination of the figure will show at once the following relations:

$$d\alpha = \frac{CC'}{b} \quad \text{and} \quad d\beta = \frac{C'C''}{a}$$

Also it is clear that triangles AP_aC, $CC''C'$, and BP_bC are similar and we may write

$$\frac{CC'}{\delta_a} = \frac{b}{r_a} \quad \text{and} \quad \frac{C'C''}{\delta_a} = \frac{b_a}{r_b}$$

Therefore

$$CC' = \delta_a \frac{b}{r_a} \quad \text{and} \quad C'C'' = \delta_a \frac{b_a}{r_b}$$

Putting these values in the relations for $d\alpha$ and $d\beta$,

$$d\alpha = \frac{\delta_a}{r_a} \quad \text{and} \quad d\beta = \delta_a \frac{b_a}{a} \times \frac{1}{r_b}$$

We now have expressions giving the change in angles α and β resulting from a change in the length of side a. To obtain an expression for the change in the angle γ it will be more convenient to draw a sketch showing the change in the length of the side a introduced at the other end, as has been done in Fig. 242 (c). We may write by inspection of the figure:

$$d\gamma = \frac{B'B''}{a}$$

Since triangles $B'B''B$ and BP_cC are similar

$$\frac{B'B''}{\delta_a} = \frac{c_a}{r_c}$$

$$B'B'' = \frac{\delta_a c_a}{r_c}$$

From this

$$d\gamma = \delta_a \frac{c_a}{a} \times \frac{1}{r_c}$$

Summarizing these results we may say the changes in the angles of a triangle due to the change of the side a are:

$$d\alpha = \frac{\delta_a}{r_a}$$

$$d\beta = \delta_a \frac{b_a}{a} \times \frac{1}{r_b}$$

$$d\gamma = \delta_a \frac{c_a}{a} \times \frac{1}{r_c}$$

Similar relations can be written for angle changes resulting from changes in the other sides. The relations can be written directly by analogy, but the student will do well to draw separate sketches for each side. A sketch is shown in Fig. 242 (d) of the changed shape resulting from an increase in side b. A change in each side affects each angle in the triangle, and combining all the changes we will obtain:

$$\Delta\alpha = \frac{\delta_a}{r_a} + \frac{\delta_b\left(\dfrac{a_b}{b}\right)}{r_a} + \frac{\delta_c\left(\dfrac{a_c}{c}\right)}{r_a}$$

$$\Delta\beta = \frac{\delta_a\left(\dfrac{b_a}{a}\right)}{r_b} + \frac{\delta_b}{r_b} + \frac{\delta_c\left(\dfrac{b_c}{c}\right)}{r_b}$$

$$\Delta\gamma = \frac{\delta_a\left(\dfrac{c_a}{a}\right)}{r_c} + \frac{\delta_b\left(\dfrac{c_b}{b}\right)}{r_c} + \frac{\delta_c}{r_c}$$

The student will find these easy to remember if he keeps in mind that the change in an angle due to the change in any side is always some portion of the change in side divided by the perpendicular distance from the angle to the side opposite the angle; i.e., the numerator is always some portion of the change in side and the denominator is always the perpendicular distance from the angle to the side opposite the angle. When the side in question is opposite the angle the numerator is the *whole* change; when the side in question is adjacent to the angle the numerator is the change times the projection of the side adjacent on the side opposite the angle, over the side adjacent.

193. Signs in Angle Changes.—It is necessary to adopt a sign convention for angle changes, and it seems most convenient to call an *increase* in angle positive and a *decrease* in angle negative. It is easy to see by a sketch, such as those in Fig. 242, whether an angle change is an increase or a decrease, and in case of doubt the student should make such a sketch. However, in routine calculations it is desirable to have an automatic procedure, and the following rules applied to the relations on page 443 will determine the sign of the angle change automatically.

1. The length of a side and the perpendicular distance from an angle to the side opposite are always positive.

2. The *change* in length of a side is positive when it is an increase and negative when it is a decrease.

3. The projection of one side on another is positive if it lies entirely on an extension of the side projected on; it is negative if it is entirely or in part coincident with the side projected on.

The third rule may be illustrated by reference to Figs. 242 and 243. In Fig. 243 the projection of side a on side b is positive, the projection of side b on side a is positive, the projection of either a or b on c is negative, and the projection of c on either a or b is negative. Generally the projection of one side on another is negative: a projection can never be positive except in an obtuse triangle.

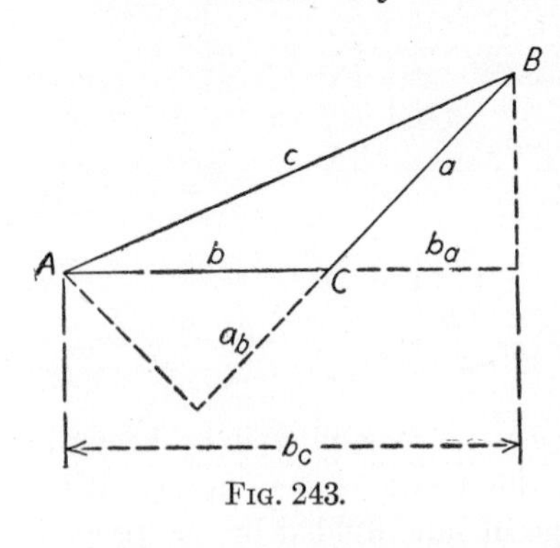

Fig. 243.

One obvious fact which should be kept in mind is that the sum of all the angle changes in a triangle must be zero.

194. Illustration of Truss Deflections Determined by Angle Changes.—The calculation of truss deflections by applying angle changes as loads at the bottom chord panel points is illustrated in Fig. 244. The changes in length of the various members are marked on the truss diagram in (a) and are symmetrical about the center line as noted; consequently, the angle changes will also be symmetrical and need be calculated for one side only. The angle changes needed are calculated in the table and are applied as loads,

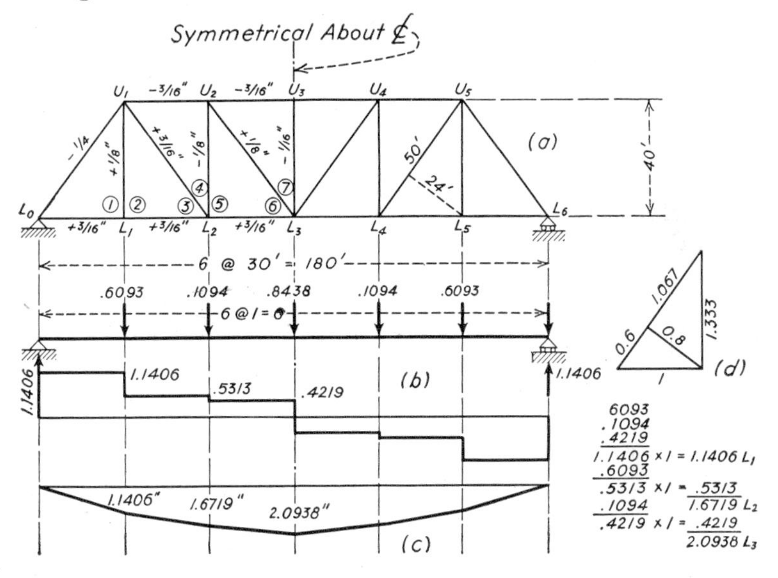

Member	δ"	Joint L_1		Joint L_2		Joint L_3	
L_0L_1	$+3/16$	① $\frac{+3/16(-0.6)}{1\times 0.8}=$	−.1406				
U_1L_0	$-1/4$	① $\frac{-1/4}{0.8}=$	−.3125				
U_1L_1	$+1/8$	① $\frac{+1/8(-1.067)}{1.333\times 0.8}=$	−.1250				
U_1L_1	$+1/8$	② do	−.1250	③ $\frac{+1/8}{1}=$	+.1250		
L_1L_2	$+3/16$	② $\frac{+3/16(-0.6)}{1\times 0.8}=$	−.1406	③ $\frac{+3/16\times 0}{1\times 1}=$	0		
U_1L_2	$+3/16$	② $\frac{+3/16}{0.8}=$	+.2344	③ $\frac{+3/16(-1.333)}{1.667\times 1}=$	−.1500		
U_1L_2	$+3/16$			④ $\frac{+3/16(-1)}{1.667\times 1.333}=$	−.0844		
U_1U_2	$-3/16$			④ $\frac{-3/16}{1.333}=$	−.1406		
U_2L_2	$-1/8$			④ $\frac{-1/8\times 0}{1.333\times 1.333}=$	0		
U_2L_2	$-1/8$			⑤ $\frac{-1/8(-1.067)}{1.333\times 0.8}=$	+.1250	⑥ $\frac{-1/8}{1}=$	−.1250
L_2L_3	$+3/16$			⑤ $\frac{+3/16(-0.6)}{1\times 0.8}=$	−.1406	⑥ $\frac{+3/16\times 0}{1\times 1}=$	0
U_2L_3	$+1/8$			⑤ $\frac{+1/8}{0.8}$	+.1562	⑥ $\frac{+1/8(-1.333)}{1.667\times 1}=$	−.1000
U_2L_3	$+1/8$					⑦ $\frac{+1/8(-1)}{1.667\times 1.333}=$	−.0563
U_2U_3	$-3/16$					⑦ $\frac{-3/16}{1.333}=$	−.1406
U_3L_3	$-1/16$					⑦ $\frac{-1/16\times 0}{1.333\times 1.333}=$	0
			−.6093		−.1094		−.4219

FIG. 244.

and the shear and moment diagrams due to those loads are shown at (b) and (c).

The only comment that seems necessary is to call attention to the fact that the angle changes calculated are *relative* and not actual, since the dimensions were reduced to the panel length as unity, as shown at (*d*) in the figure. The deflections shown at (*c*), however, are the actual deflections in inches, since the length of a panel was also taken as unity in calculating the shear and moment diagrams in (*c*). If the actual angle changes (in radians) are wanted the values shown should be divided by 360, the length of one panel in inches. Study of the relations on page 443 will show that if the changes in the sides are given in inches the deflection

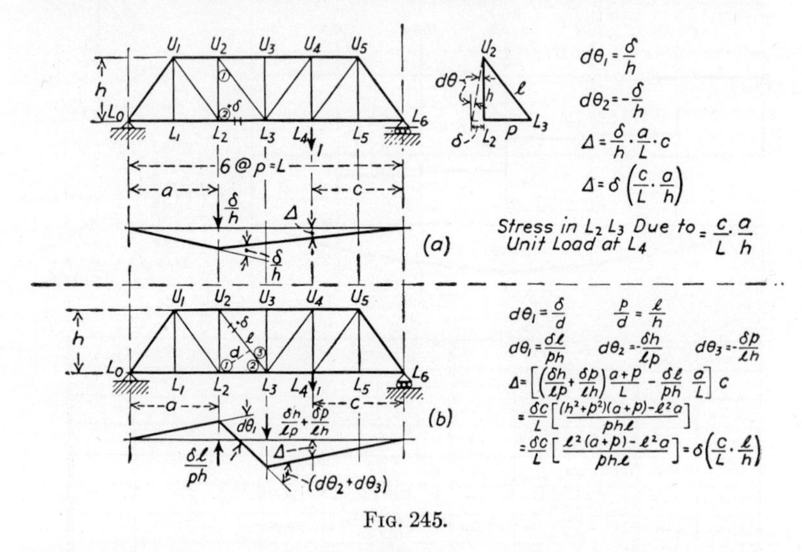

FIG. 245.

of the truss will be in inches whether the other factors are in inches, feet, or any other convenient unit.

195. Geometry of Truss Deflection.—Although the method of calculating truss deflections by angle changes described in the preceding articles is perfectly general it seems worth while to examine the geometry of the deflection caused by a change in length of a single bar, in a few simple cases.

The bottom chord L_2L_3 in the truss shown in Fig. 245 (*a*) is elongated by the amount δ. The angle $U_2L_2L_3$, marked ② in the figure, is the only angle along the bottom chord which is changed by the increase in length of L_2L_3, as may be seen from the diagram of the triangle $U_2L_3L_2$ shown at the right in the figure. Since the angle $U_2L_3L_2$ does not change it is clear that the change in the angle $U_2L_2L_3$ must be equal in magnitude and opposite in sign to the change in $L_2U_2L_3$. The deflection at any point along the bottom chord is then the bending moment at that point due to the angle change $\frac{\delta}{h}$ applied as a load at L_2 on the chord line L_0L_6 as a simply supported beam. The student should note that whether the deflection is found at L_4, as in the figure, or at any other point along the chord it is equal to the change in length of L_2L_3 times the stress in L_2L_3 due to a unit load applied at the point for which the deflection is being calculated.

In Fig. 245 (*b*) the diagonal U_2L_3 is assumed to have an increase in length δ. The angles $U_2L_2L_3$, $U_2L_3L_2$, and $U_2L_3U_3$, marked ①, ②, and ③, respectively, are affected in that case, and the deflected shape of the bottom chord line is as shown below the

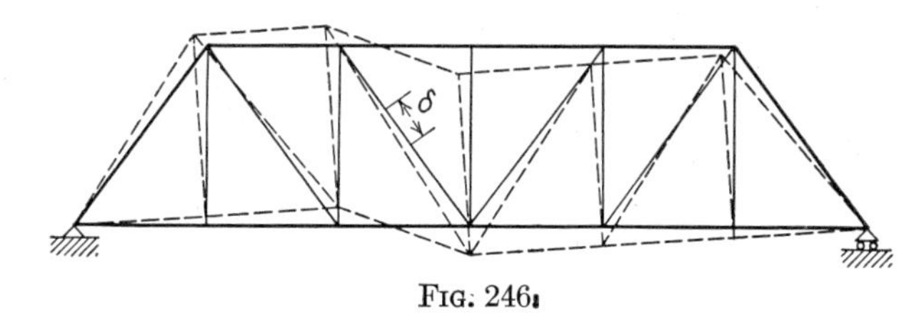

FIG. 246

truss. The angle changes are computed in the figure at the right, and the deflection of L_4 computed as the bending moment at that point due to the angle changes applied as loads as shown. The student will note again that the deflection is also equal to the change in length of U_2L_3 times the stress in U_2L_3 due to a unit load applied at L_4, and that the same relation holds no matter what point along the chord is considered.

Figure 246 shows to an exaggerated scale the shape which the entire truss assumes as a result of the elongation of U_2L_3. The extent of the exaggeration of the deformation should be kept in mind—if drawn to scale the change in shape could not be detected by eye. The student should cultivate the ability to visualize the deformations of structures; making numerous sketches such as Fig. 246, for other bars, will help in that respect.

The deflection of the bottom chord of the truss shown in Fig. 247, due to changes in length of U_2U_3 and U_2L_2, are shown at (*a*) and (*b*), respectively. The method of attack is the same as in Fig. 245.

In all cases studied in Figs. 245 and 247 it will be noted that a purely geometric procedure led to the same general result; that the deflection at any point on the bottom chord due to the change in length of a particular bar is equal to the change in length times the stress in the bar due to a unit load applied at the point for which deflection is being studied. In the next article this general

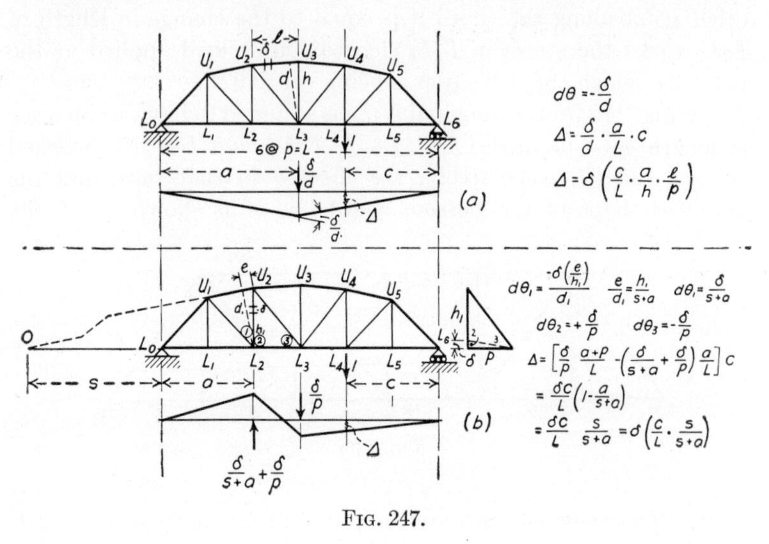

FIG. 247.

result will be established for movement of any point in any direction.

196. The Principle of Virtual Work.—The principle of virtual work is one of the most powerful tools of structural analysis. It is often called by other names and has been credited to different authorities, but most American writers agree that it was first introduced in the United States by the late George Fillmore Swain.[1]

It is sometimes presented in a highly mathematical form, but the brief statement following is adequate for the present purpose.

Consider any body supported at A and B, as shown in Fig. 248, and assume that we wish to determine the movement of the point

[1] "On the Application of the Principle of Virtual Velocities to the Determination of the Deflection and Stresses of Frames," by George Fillmore Swain, *Journal of the Franklin Institute*, Vol. 115, page 102, 1883.

p along the line X–X due to a change in length, δ, of the fiber f. Imagine a unit load applied at p acting in the direction of the movement to be determined. Use the following notation:

δ = change in length of the fiber f.
δ_F = the movement of the point p along the line X–X due to the change in length, δ, of the fiber f.
u = the stress in the fiber f due to the unit load acting at p.

It is assumed that the unit load is acting at p, and the resulting stress, u, is acting on the fiber f. Now change the length of the fiber f by the amount δ. Evidently the stress u acts through the distance δ and does work, $u \times \delta$. The change in length of f causes p to move through the distance δ_F and the unit load moving through that distance does work, $1 \times \delta_F$. If we have not created or dissipated energy, i.e., if we accept the principle of the conservation of energy, we have the relation:

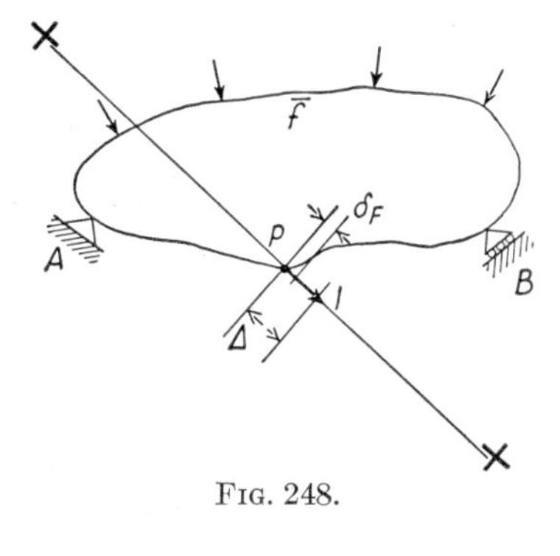

Fig. 248.

$$1 \times \delta_F = u \times \delta$$

or

$$\delta_F = u \times \delta$$

It should be emphasized that δ_F is due only to the change in length of the fiber f. Presumably other fibers in the body also change in length, and each contributes its share to the total movement, Δ, of the point p, which of course must be equal to the sum of the movements contributed by all fibers which change in length. Therefore:

$$\Delta = \Sigma\delta_F = \Sigma\delta u$$

If we wish to study the rotation of point p due to a change in length of the fiber f we may apply a unit couple at p instead of the unit load, and a little study will show that the argument is not changed by so doing. It will still be true that the stress, u (now caused by a unit couple at p), does work, $u \times \delta$ in moving through the distance δ, and the unit couple also does work $1 \times \theta_F$ in which θ_F is the angle through which p (and therefore the unit couple) rotates owing to the change in length of the fiber f. As before

$$1 \times \theta_F = u \times \delta$$

and

$$\theta_F = u \times \delta$$

Further, if other fibers change in length they will contribute to rotation and we may say that the total rotation of p due to all changes in length will be:

$$\theta = \Sigma\theta_F = \Sigma\delta u$$

The student should note that no restriction has been placed on the cause or nature of the change in length of the fiber f. It may be caused by stress due to the application of external loads, by change in temperature, or by errors in the manufacture, and may be either plastic or elastic. Whatever the cause or nature of the change in length of the fiber, if it is known, the movement of p may be calculated, whether that movement is linear or angular.

If the structure is an articulated truss instead of a solid body the bars of the truss replace the fibers of the body and the general principle leads to exactly the same result as found in particular cases in the preceding article by purely geometric methods.

197. Applications of Virtual Work.—As an illustration of the application of the principle of virtual work Fig. 249 is presented. This is the same truss for which deflections were calculated by angle changes in Fig. 244, and in Fig. 249 the deflection of panel point L_3 is found by virtual work. Since the truss and the changes in length are symmetrical about the center line the quantities u and δu are also symmetrical and need be calculated for one side only as has been done in the figure. Of course the result for one side must be doubled to obtain the effect of both sides.

As noted previously the movement of *a particular point* in any direction may be calculated by application of the principle of virtual work. A disadvantage in its use is that calculations must be made for each point to be studied.

As another illustration consider the structure shown in Fig. 250. It is obvious by inspection that any movement of panel point B_4

must be horizontal, and the amount of that movement may be obtained as:

$$\Delta_H = \Sigma \delta u$$

in which δ is the change in length of a particular bar due to the applied loads and u is the stress in that bar due to a unit load

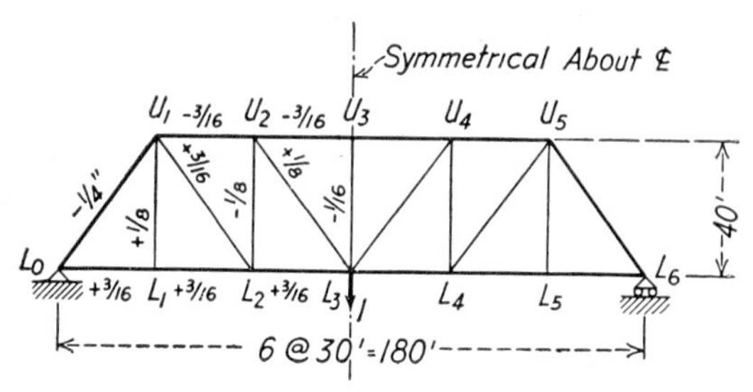

Member	δ	u	δu
$L_0 U_1$	$-1/4''$	$-.625$	$+.1563''$
$U_1 U_2$	$-3/16$	$-.750$	$+.1406$
$U_2 U_3$	$-3/16$	-1.125	$+.2109$
$L_0 L_1$	$+3/16$	$+.375$	$+.0703$
$L_1 L_2$	$+3/16$	$+.375$	$+.0703$
$L_2 L_3$	$+3/16$	$+.750$	$+.1406$
$U_1 L_1$	$+1/8$	0	0
$U_2 L_2$	$-1/8$	$-.500$	$+.0625$
$U_3 L_3$	$-1/16$	0	0
$U_1 L_2$	$+3/16$	$+.625$	$+.1172$
$U_2 L_3$	$+1/8$	$+.625$	$+.0781$
$\Sigma \delta u$			$+1.0468$

$\times 2 = +2.0936''$ Vertical Deflection at L_3

FIG. 249.

acting at B_4, in the direction of the movement being studied, as shown in the figure.

The student should note that, though it is obvious that B_4 must move horizontally, it is not obvious, because of the horizontal load P_3, whether that movement will be to the left or the right, and a sign convention is necessary. The most convenient sign convention is that which calls an increase in length of a member positive and a decrease in length negative. The sign of the stress u is that used throughout the text, tension positive and compression negative. If these signs are used the quantity $\Sigma \delta u$ will be positive when the movement is in the direction of the unit load, and negative if the movement is in the opposite direction. Thus in Fig. 250 if the quantity $\Sigma \delta u$ is positive the point B_4 moves to the right in the direction of the unit load, if it is negative B_4 moves to the left.

198. Absolute Movement.—In the great majority of cases one is interested in the vertical or horizontal movement of a particular point, but, as stated, by the application of the principle of virtual work the calculation of movement in any direction is possible. Furthermore, it should be clear that although the true movement of a point must be along some particular line that movement may

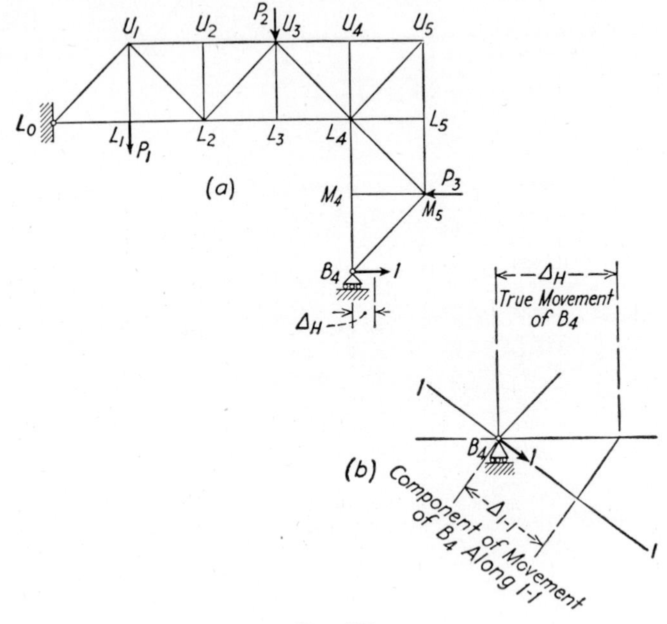

FIG. 250.

be projected on a line in any other direction. The projection on any other line may be thought of as a component of movement along that line. Thus in Fig. 250 (*b*) the true movement of B_4 is horizontal and equal to Δ_H; it may be projected on line 1–1, and Δ_{1-1} is that projection, or it may be called the component of movement along 1–1. If the unit load at B_4 is applied along 1–1, as shown at (*b*) in the figure, the quantity $\Sigma \delta u$ will give the component Δ_{1-1}, the factors δ being the same as before, but the factors u being the stresses due to the unit load acting along the line 1–1.

As a further illustration refer again to Fig. 249. The calculated deflection of L_3, 2.0936 in., is only the vertical movement of that point. Applying a unit load at L_3 acting horizontally, and to the right, we have:

	δ	u	δu
L_0L_1	$+\frac{3}{16}$	+1	+0.1875
L_1L_2	$+\frac{3}{16}$	+1	+0.1875
L_2L_3	$+\frac{3}{16}$	+1	+0.1875
		$\Sigma\delta u =$	+0.5625 in.

That is, panel point L_3 not only moves 2.0936 in. vertically down; it also moves 0.5625 in. to the right, and the true movement is

$$\sqrt{2.0936^2 + 0.5625^2} = 2.1678 \text{ in.}$$

downward to the right along a line having a slope of 0.269 horizontal to 1 vertical.

When the true movement of a point is wanted it is necessary to calculate two components. It is generally more convenient to calculate rectangular components, although a little reflection will show that any two components fix the magnitude and direction of movement of a point in a plane.

199. Causes of Change in Length.—In the preceding discussion the causes of change in length of the bars of a structure or fiber of a body have merely been stated as stress, change in temperature, and error or deliberate change in manufacture.

Stress is probably the most frequent cause of change in length with which the engineer deals, and the student is already familiar with the calculation of such changes. It may be well to summarize the necessary data. Let:

s = intensity of stress in any bar of a frame or any fiber of a flexural member.
l = the length of the bar in question.
ds = the length of the fiber in question.
δ = the change in length of the bar or fiber.
E = the modulus of elasticity.

Then

$$\delta = \frac{sl}{E} \text{ for the bar}$$

and

$$\delta = \frac{sds}{E} \text{ for the fiber}$$

Also, if:

S = the total stress in the bar in question,
A = the gross area of the bar in question,
M = the bending moment at the section being considered in a flexural member,
y = the distance from the neutral axis of the flexural member to the fiber considered,
I = the moment of inertia of the flexural member about its neutral axis,

then

$$s = \frac{S}{A} \text{ for the bar}$$

$$s = \frac{My}{I} \text{ for the fiber}$$

These results are frequently combined in stating the deflection of a truss and given as

$$\Delta = \sum \frac{Sl}{AE} \cdot u$$

200. Calculation of Beam Deflection and Change in Slope by Virtual Work.—The general relations for deflection and change in slope at any section in a flexural member developed from geometric relations in the preceding chapter may be established by the principle of virtual work.[2]

Refer to Fig. 251 and assume that we wish to study the deflection and change in slope at the point p due to the applied loads. The moment diagram shown at (*b*) in the figure is produced by the applied loads, and any ordinate in that diagram is designated by M.

Considering first the deflection, apply a unit load at p in accordance with the general principle; the moment diagram shown at (*c*) in the figure is produced by the unit load, and any ordinate in that diagram is designated by m.

[2] In all that follows regarding deflection of beams it is to be understood that shearing distortions are neglected. The remarks in the footnote on page 344 apply here with equal force.

In accordance with the fundamental statement the deflection of p due to any fiber, such as f in section 1–1, is

$$\delta_F = \delta u = \frac{My}{IE} ds \cdot \frac{my}{I} dA = \frac{Mds}{EI^2} \cdot my^2 dA$$

All terms in this relation have been defined except dA, which is the area of the fiber f. Since u is the total stress on fiber f produced by the unit load at p, and since $\frac{my}{I}$ is the *intensity* of stress, the latter must be multiplied by the area to obtain the total stress u. If all the

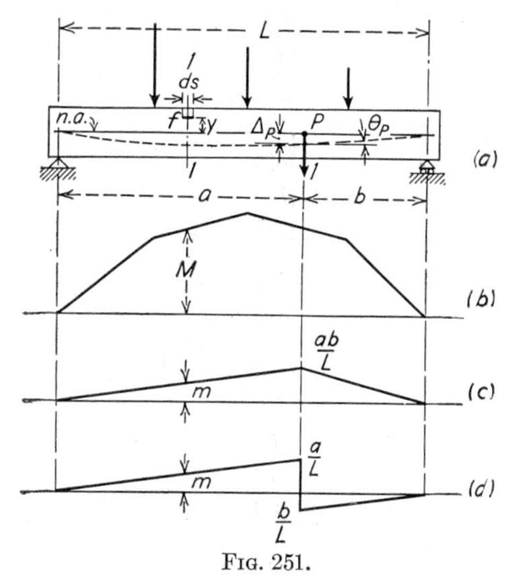

Fig. 251.

fibers in the section 1–1 are taken together we will have the deflection at p due to stresses on all the fibers at section 1–1. Calling that deflection Δ_F we will have

$$\Delta_F = \int \frac{Mds}{EI^2} \cdot my^2 dA = \frac{Mmds}{EI^2} \int y^2 dA = \frac{Mds}{EI} m$$

in which the integration covers the entire area of the section.

To obtain the total deflection at p it is necessary to include the effect of every section along the beam, i.e.,

$$\Delta = \int \frac{Mds}{EI} \cdot m \quad \text{or} \quad \sum \frac{Mds}{EI} \cdot m$$

Study of these expressions will show that they lead to the same results as obtained by purely geometric methods in Chapter X. The quantity $\left(\frac{Mds}{EI}\right)$ will be recognized as the angle change at section 1–1. The moment diagram for a unit load at p is also an *influence line* for bending moment at p. Consequently the product $\left(\frac{Mds}{EI}\right)m$ is the bending moment at p due to the angle change $\left(\frac{Mds}{EI}\right)$ applied as a load at section 1–1.

The same method may be used in studying rotation, and the moment diagram produced by a unit couple at p is shown at (*d*) in the figure. The student will recognize that the moment diagram due to a unit couple at p is identical in shape and ordinates to an influence line for shear at p.

Consequently the statement

$$\theta_p = \sum\left(\frac{Mds}{EI}\right)m$$

means that the change in slope at p is equal to the shear at p due to the angle changes $\left(\frac{Mds}{EI}\right)$ applied to the beam as loads.

201. Williot Diagram.—In some cases a graphical method [3] of determining truss deflections has certain advantages over arithmetical solutions in that one diagram defines completely the movement of all points.

A four-panel truss is shown in Fig. 252 with assumed changes in length shown on the left half; the deformations are symmetrical about the center line.

The Williot diagram is drawn assuming some point fixed in position and some bar fixed in direction. For the present case assume L_2 fixed in position and U_2L_2 fixed in direction. If L_2 is fixed in position and U_2L_2 in direction it is obvious that the only movement possible for U_2 is vertically downward $\frac{1}{8}$ in. to U_2' as indicated in (*b*) of the figure. Imagine the members disconnected

[3] The method is generally attributed to Williot, said to have been a French engineer, and some authors state that it was developed about 1877. Later a German engineer, Otto Mohr, extended the method to unsymmetrical trusses and loads, and it is frequently referred to as the Williot-Mohr diagram.

at U_1, and U_1U_2 moved parallel to its original position to the position $U_2'a$. Now shorten $U_2'a$ (U_1U_2) $\frac{1}{4}$ in. so that a moves to b, and lengthen U_1L_2 so that U_1 (in U_1L_2) moves to c. Actually

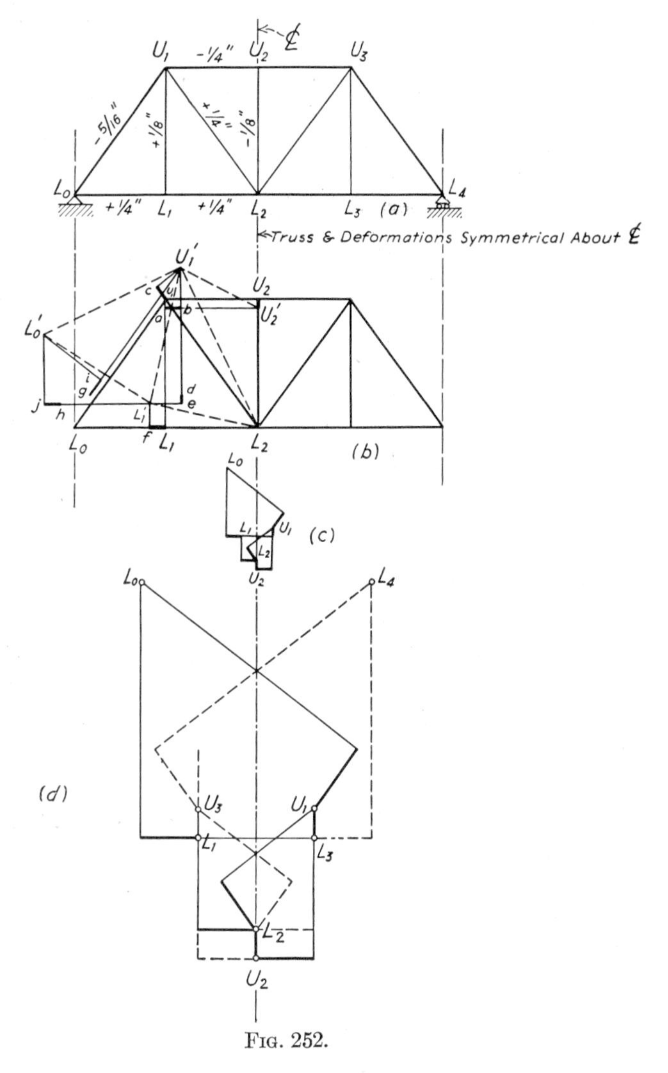

Fig. 252.

the ends of U_1U_2 and U_1L_2, b and c after the changes in length, must be together in a new position consistent with the deformations. This position can be found by drawing an arc using U_2'

as a center and $U_2'b$ as a radius, and an arc using L_2 as a center and L_2c as a radius; the intersection of these arcs at U_1' determines the new position. The actual changes in length are so extremely small compared with the lengths of the members themselves (less than 0.1 per cent in the most extreme cases with present materials) that we may substitute tangents, i.e., normals to the members, for the arcs without detectable inaccuracy, and that substitution is always made. Now imagine that the members at L_1 are disconnected and U_1L_1 allowed to move parallel to its original position so that U_1 (in U_1L_1) moves to U_1'; L_1 (in U_1L_1) then moves to d. Now lengthen U_1L_1 $\frac{1}{8}$ in. so that d moves down to e, and lengthen L_2L_1 so that L_1 (in L_1L_2) moves to f: e and f may then be brought together at the new position of L_1, L_1', by striking arcs from U_1' and L_2 as centers and with $U_1'e$ and L_2f as radii. Follow the same procedure with members connecting at L_0 and find the new position at L_0'. Then the dotted lines in (*b*) of the figure show, enormously exaggerated, the deformed left half of the truss. Since the truss is symmetrical the right half would be in a corresponding position on the right-hand side if it were shown.

To construct such a diagram with the distortions drawn to a convenient scale in the case of a large truss is entirely impracticable. Williot's discovery was that only the distortions and the arcs need be drawn, and that they may be drawn to any convenient scale. This has been done at (*c*) in the figure. Thus starting from L_2 the distortion of U_2L_2 has been laid off, $\frac{1}{8}$ in. downward to U_2, and the distance from L_2 to U_2 is clearly the actual movement of U_2 when L_2 is fixed in position and U_2L_2 in direction. Then from U_2 the distortion of U_1U_2 has been laid off, $\frac{1}{4}$ in. to the right parallel to U_1U_2, and the distortion of U_1L_2 laid off, $\frac{1}{4}$ in. along a line parallel to the member. From the ends of these distortions, arcs (i.e., normals to the directions of the members) are drawn, and the intersection of these establishes the new position of U_1. The actual movement of U_1, under the assumed conditions, is determined in magnitude and direction by the distance from L_2 to U_1. The same procedure may be followed to determine the new position of L_1: from the new position of U_1 lay off the distortion of U_1L_1, $\frac{1}{8}$ in. downward; from L_2 lay off the distortion of L_1L_2, $\frac{1}{4}$ in. to the left; from the ends of these distortions draw arcs intersecting at L_1, the new position of that panel point. As before, the distance from L_2 to L_1 gives in direction and magnitude the actual movement of L_1, under the assumed conditions. The process may now be continued to find the new position of L_0 and its actual movement, under the assumed conditions. The diagram shown at (*c*) in the figure is the Williot diagram, drawn in this case with the changes in length of the various members shown to the same scale as in (*b*) of the figure. A little study will show that, if L_2 in the Williot diagram at (*c*) is placed on the *original position* of any panel point in the distorted truss diagram at (*b*), that panel point in the Williot diagram will coincide exactly with the *new* position of the panel point in the distorted truss. Thus, if L_2 in the Williot diagram is placed on U_1 in the truss diagram of (*b*), U_1 in the Williot diagram will coincide with U_1' in the distorted truss of (*b*), showing that the distance from U_1 to L_2 in the Williot diagram gives in magnitude and direction the actual movement of U_1 under the assumed conditions. The student should show that the same situation exists with reference to other panel points.

In the actual truss the point L_2 is not fixed, but since the truss and the assumed changes in length are symmetrical about the center line it is clear that the bar U_2L_2 will remain fixed in direction, i.e., it will not rotate even though it does move. In the actual truss the panel point L_0 is fixed in position. Since the right half of the distorted structure must correspond to the left half, evidently a horizontal line drawn through L_0' in the distorted truss at (*b*) would pass through L_4', and all vertical deflections should be measured from this line since in the actual structure L_0 and L_4 remain at their original levels. Similarly in the Williot diagram (*c*) all vertical deflections should be measured from a horizontal line through L_0, and since L_0 does not move horizontally all horizontal movements should be measured from L_0 in the Williot diagram. The student will note then that the distance from L_0 in the Williot diagram (*c*) to L_2, for example, is the true movement of L_2 in the actual truss, and the vertical and horizontal projections of this distance are the vertical and horizontal movements of L_2.

As stated before, the Williot diagram may be drawn to any convenient scale, and as an illustration the Williot diagram of Fig. 252 (*c*) is redrawn at (*d*) to a much larger scale. In the diagram at (*d*) the right-hand half has been added in dotted lines.

Parts of the right and left sides coincide, but the student will notice that all the full lines in the diagram at (*d*) are exactly parallel and proportional to the corresponding lines in (*c*). In both diagrams the changes in length are indicated by heavy lines as a help in following the construction.

As further illustrations, Figs. 253, 254, and 255 are presented. The Williot diagram shown in Fig. 253 is for the truss for which

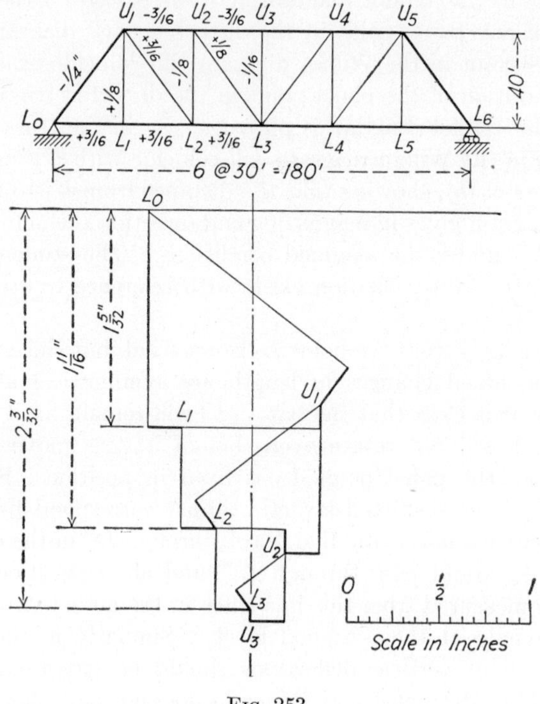

FIG. 253.

deflections were calculated by angle changes in Fig. 244, and for which the center deflection was calculated by virtual work in Fig. 249. The student will note that the calculations by angle changes give directly only the vertical movements of the bottom chord panel points; the calculations by virtual work give only the vertical movement of panel point L_3; but the Williot diagram gives the complete movement of every panel point. This does not necessarily indicate universal superiority for the Williot diagram; frequently, if not usually, the vertical or horizontal movement of a single point or the vertical movements of the panel points on one chord may be all that is required.

Attention is called to the fact that in drawing the Williot diagrams of Fig. 254 and 255 lines are drawn past intersections. This practice is usually followed since it leads to greater accuracy.

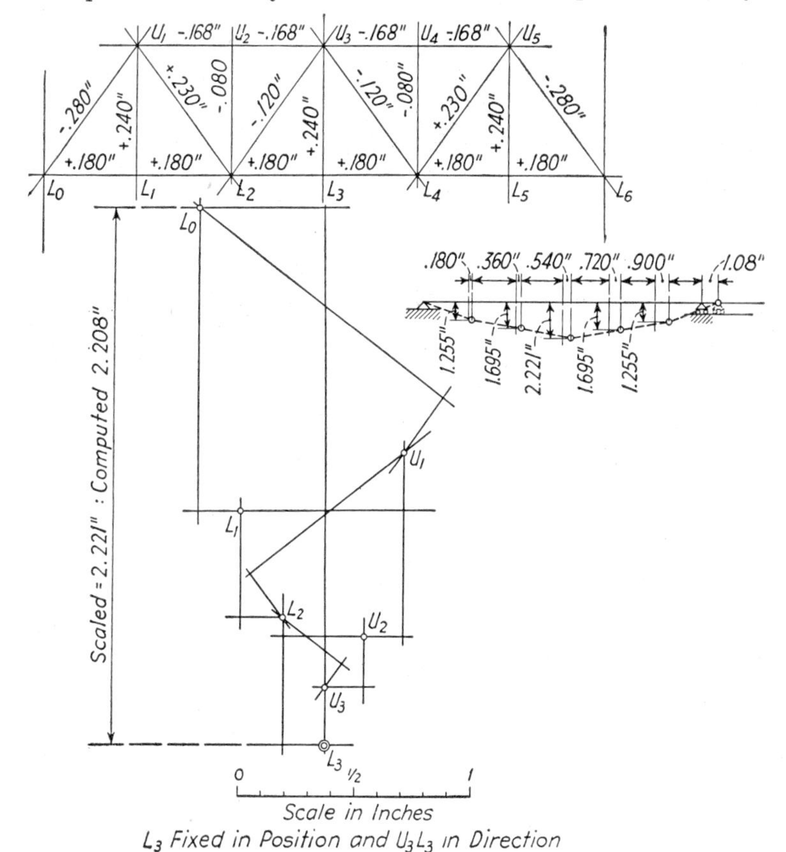

Fig. 254.

The student will notice, of course, that the structure in Fig. 255 is unsymmetrical with respect to both truss and distortions shown thereon. However, the Williot diagram was drawn with respect to L_0 as the fixed point and U_0L_0 as the fixed direction. Since the point L_0 is in fact fixed in position, and U_0L_0 fixed in direction, the diagram is correct in spite of the dissymmetry.

202. Williot Diagram for Unsymmetrical Cases.—In the majority of practical applications of the Williot diagram symmetrical trusses symmetrically loaded are dealt with. In such cases there will always be some bar or line which does not rotate,

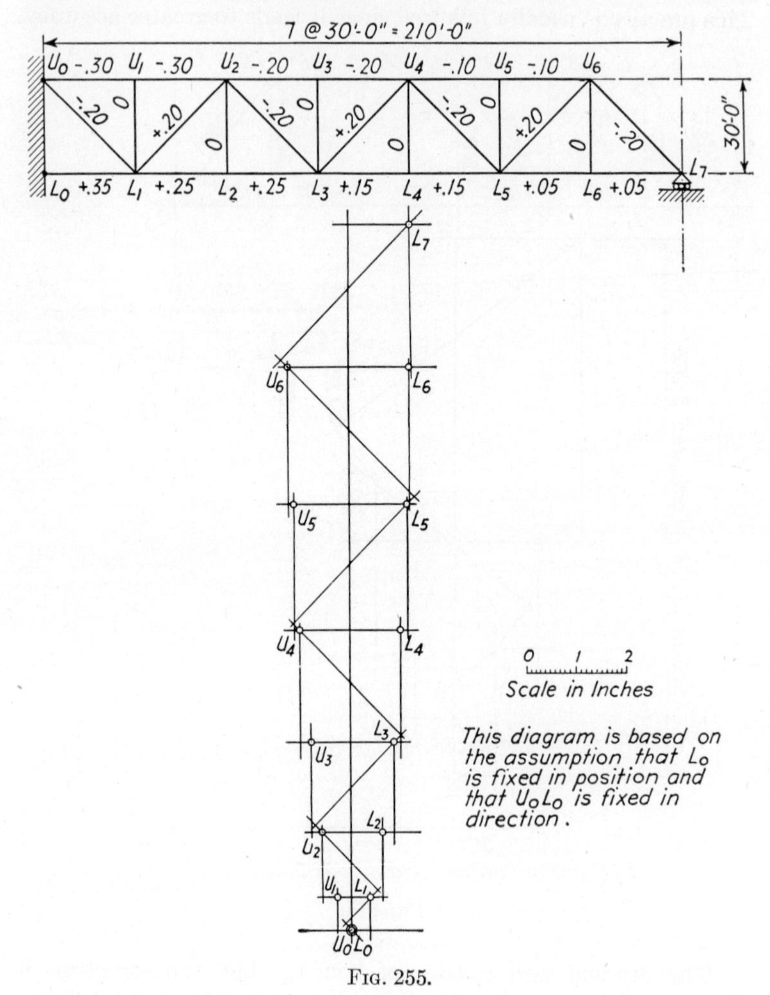

FIG. 255.

and the Williot diagram should always be referred to such a bar or line whenever it is possible. However, because of dissymmetry of either truss or loading, there are cases in which there is no known line or bar that has no rotation. When that is so it is necessary to correct the Williot diagram to include the effect of rotation of the reference line. As stated in the footnote on page 456, the corrected diagram is frequently called the Williot-Mohr diagram.

The construction of the Williot diagram for an unsymmetrical truss or unsymmetrical distortion does not differ in any respect from that for a symmetrical truss except that the entire diagram must be drawn, as was illustrated by Fig. 255.

The four-panel truss for which Williot diagrams were drawn in Fig. 252 (*c*) and (*d*) will be used to illustrate the Mohr rotation or correction diagram. In Fig. 256 (*b*) a Williot diagram is drawn based on the assumption that L_0 is fixed in position and L_0L_1 fixed in direction. The Williot diagram is shown in full lines with the changes in bar lengths made heavier. The scale of the diagram Fig. 256 (*b*) is the same as that of the diagram Fig. 252 (*c*)

The shape which the truss would take if L_0 is fixed in position and L_0L_1 fixed in direction is shown greatly exaggerated at (*a*) in Fig. 256. The scale of the deformations used in drawing the sketch at (*a*) is one-half that used in drawing the Williot diagram at (*b*).

The Williot diagram in Fig. 256 (*b*) gives the movements of all points when L_0 is fixed in position and L_0L_1 fixed in direction. The diagram indicates a movement of L_4 up and to the right, and since the conditions of support are such that L_4 obviously can move only in a horizontal direction it is clear that the reference line L_0L_1 must be rotated until L_4 is brought down to the same level as L_0. It is necessary, therefore, to add graphically, to the movements shown by the Williot diagram in Fig. 256 (*b*), the movements which will result from rotating the truss about L_0 until L_4 moves vertically down through the vertical projection of the distance L_0L_4 in the diagram at (*b*). This is shown as $0–L_4'$ in the distorted truss in (*a*) of the figure. The student is reminded that although $0–L_4'$ is shown as a large distance in the figure, because of the greatly exaggerated scale, it is in fact a very small distance compared with the size of the truss, and the arc drawn in rotating the truss about L_0 until L_4' is brought down to 0 in the diagram at (*a*) cannot be distinguished from a normal to L_0L_4 at 0. All members of the truss rotate through the same angle when L_4' is brought down to the horizontal line L_0L_4, and each panel point then must move normal to a line connecting it to L_0 (the center of rotation) and through a distance that is to $0–L_4'$ as the distance from L_0 to the panel point in question is to L_0L_4. Thus panel point U_2 must move normal to U_2L_0 and through a distance equal to $\frac{U_2L_0}{L_0L_4} \times 0\text{–}L_4'$, using the scale of the sketch in (*a*), Fig. 256. This movement in magnitude and direction added graphically, and to the proper scale, to L_0U_2 in the Williot diagram, Fig. 256 (*b*), evidently will give the true movement of panel point U_2. Similar relations will give the true movements

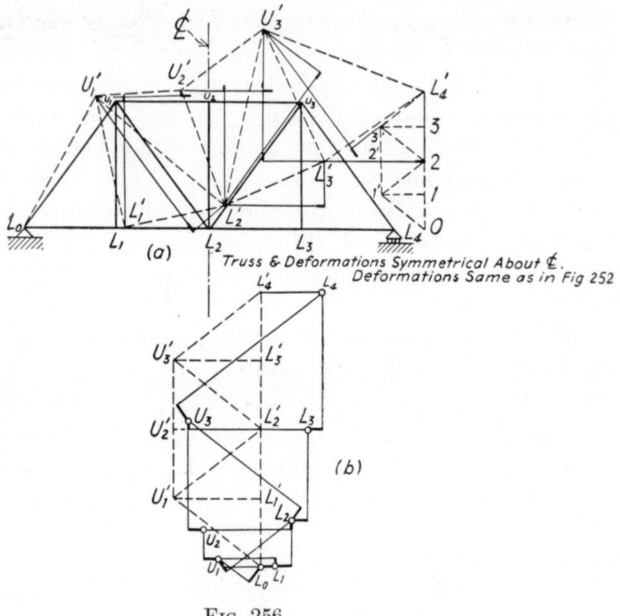

FIG. 256.

of all panel points. Study of the diagram at (*a*), Fig. 256, will show that the distance from any panel point to *0* of the small dotted truss drawn on $0\text{–}L_4'$ as a base is the true movement of that panel point due to the rotation necessary to bring L_4' down to *0*; i.e., considering panel point U_2, it is clear that

$$\frac{0\text{–}2'}{0\text{–}L_4'} = \frac{L_0U_2}{L_0L_4}$$

It follows that the distance from any panel point to L_0 of the dotted truss shown in the Williot diagram, Fig. 256 (*b*), is the movement of that point, due to rotation of the truss, to the scale of the Williot diagram. Of course that movement combined with the movement shown in the Williot diagram proper gives the true

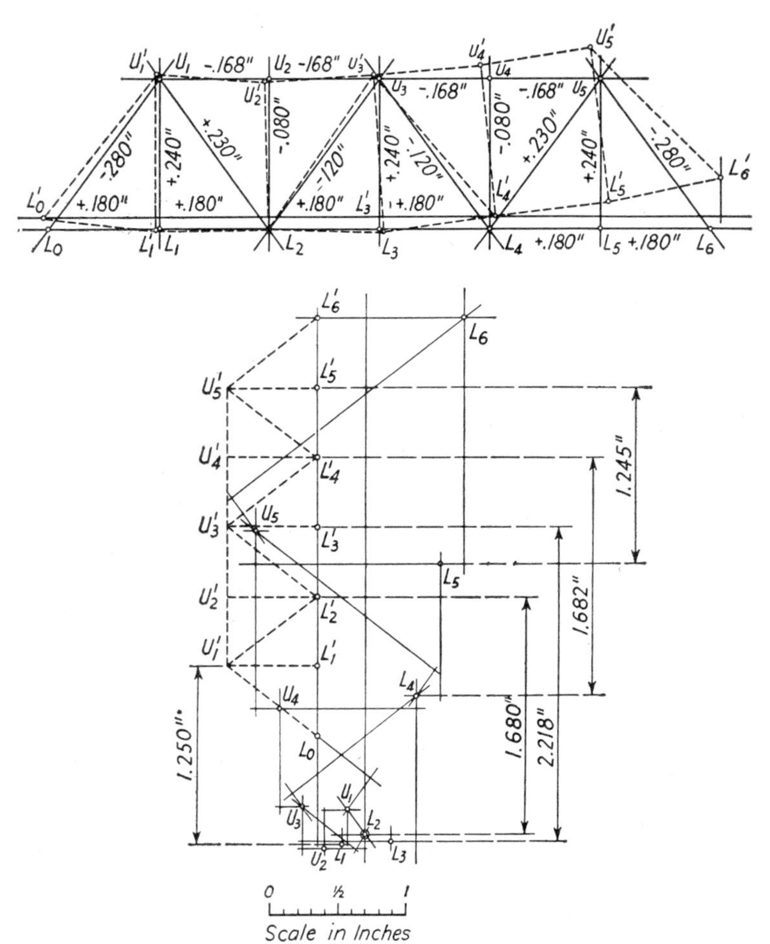

FIG. 257.

movement of the panel point in question. Considering again panel point U_2, its true movement is given in the diagram of (b), Fig. 256, as L_0U_2 plus (graphically) $U_2'L_0$. A sketch plus a little study will show the student that the resultant movement is equal to the distance from U_2' to U_2. Since the same procedure will give the true movement of any panel point it follows that the distances from the panel points of the dotted truss in (*b*), Fig. 256, to the corresponding panel points in the Williot diagram are the true movements of those points.

As a further illustration, Fig. 257 shows a Williot diagram with the rotation correction, for the truss shown in Fig. 254, using panel point L_2 as the fixed point, and U_1L_2 as the bar fixed in direction. In that solution it is clear that both L_0 and L_6 move with respect to the reference point, and the rotation diagram must be constructed to rotate the truss about L_0 until L_6 is brought to the level of a horizontal line through L_0. It will be clear upon reflection that here also the distances from the panel points of the dotted truss to the corresponding points of the Williot diagram give the true movements of those points.

203. Deflections from Influence Lines for Stress.—When influence lines for stress in the various bars of a truss are available they may be used to obtain deflections by a very simple procedure. It will be recalled that the principle of virtual work gives the movement of any point due to the change in length of any fiber in a solid body, or the change in length of a bar in a frame as δu, in which δ is the change in length of the fiber or bar, and u the stress in that fiber or bar due to a unit load applied at the point and in the direction of the movement to be calculated. Referring now to the truss and influence lines on page 285, assume that we wish to calculate the vertical deflection of all bottom chord panel points due to an increase in length of, say, $\frac{2}{10}$ in. in the bar U_2L_3. The influence line for stress in U_2L_3 gives the stress in that bar for a unit load at each panel point, consequently the ordinates to the influence line times $\frac{2}{10}$ in. will be the deflections sought. Thus:

L_0	L_1	L_2	L_3	L_4
0×0.2	-0.197×0.2	-0.394×0.2	$+0.644 \times 0.2$	$+0.515 \times 0.2$
0	-0.0394 in.	-0.0788 in.	$+0.1288$ in.	$+0.1030$ in.

L_5	L_6	L_7	L_8
$+0.386 \times 0.2$	$+0.258 \times 0.2$	$+0.129 \times 0.2$	0×0.2
$+0.0772$ in.	$+0.0516$ in.	$+0.0258$ in.	0

Obviously the same procedure may be followed for other bars and the total deflection obtained by summing the results for all members of the truss.

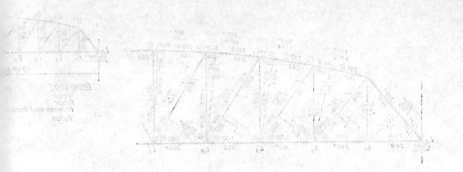

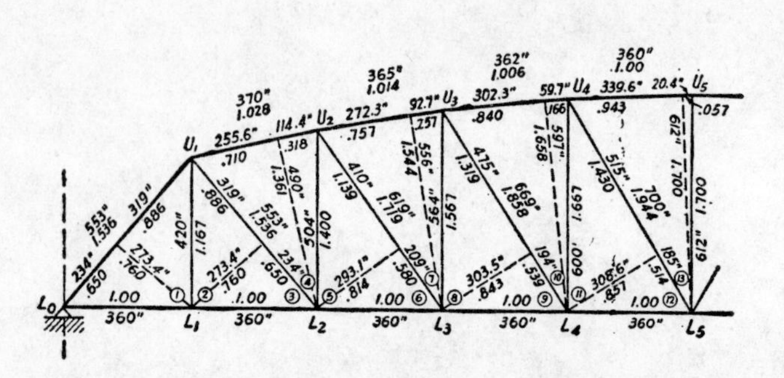

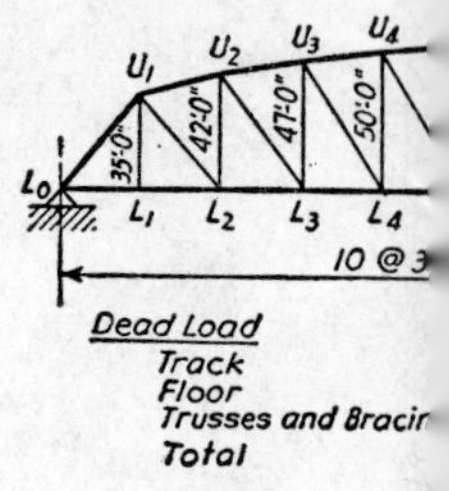

Member	Stress[k]	Length"	Area[□"]	$\frac{SL}{AE}=\delta$	Panel Point L_1		Panel Point L_2		Panel Point L_3		Panel Point L_4		Panel
L_0L_1	+1359	360"	105.62	+.154"	① $\overset{+}{.154}\times\frac{.650}{1.00}\times\frac{1}{.760}=$	−.132							
U_1L_0	−2087	553	161.19	−.239"	① $\bar{.239}\times\frac{1}{.760}=$	−.314							
U_1L_1	+314	420	37.37	+.118"	① $\overset{+}{.118}\times\frac{.886}{1.167}\times\frac{1}{.760}=$	−.118							
U_1L_1	do.	do.	do.	+.118"	② do. $=$	−.118	③ $\overset{+}{.118}\times\frac{1}{1.00}=$	+.118					
L_1L_2	+1359	360	105.62	+.154"	② $\overset{+}{.154}\times\frac{.650}{1.00}\times\frac{1}{.760}=$	−.132	③ $\overset{+}{.154}\times\frac{0}{1.00}\times\frac{1}{1.00}=$	0					
U_1L_2	+1005	553	81.99	+.226"	② $\overset{+}{.226}\times\frac{1}{.760}=$	+.297	③ $\overset{+}{.226}\times\frac{1.167}{1.536}\times\frac{1}{1.00}=$	−.172					
U_1L_2	do.	do.	do.	+.226"			④ $\overset{+}{.226}\times\frac{.710}{1.536}\times\frac{1}{1.361}=$	−.0768					
U_1U_2	−2067	370	147.31	−.173"			④ $\bar{.173}\times\frac{1}{1.361}=$	−.127					
U_2L_2	−449	504	54.88	−.137"			④ $\bar{.137}\times\frac{.318}{1.40}\times\frac{1}{1.361}=$	+.0229					
U_2L_2	do.	do.	do.	−.137"			⑤ $\bar{.137}\times\frac{1.139}{1.40}\times\frac{1}{.814}=$	+.137	⑥ $\bar{.137}\times\frac{1}{1.00}=$	−.137			
L_2L_3	+2012	360	152.32	+.159"			⑤ $\overset{+}{.159}\times\frac{.580}{1.00}\times\frac{1}{.814}=$	−.113	⑥ $\overset{+}{.159}\times\frac{0}{1.00}\times\frac{1}{1.00}=$	0			
U_2L_3	+598	619	60.24	+.205			⑤ $\overset{+}{.205}\times\frac{1}{.814}=$	+.252	⑥ $\overset{+}{.205}\times\frac{1.400}{1.719}\times\frac{1}{1.00}$	−.167			
U_2L_3	do.	do.	do.	+.205"					⑦ $\overset{+}{.205}\times\frac{.757}{1.719}\times\frac{1}{1.544}=$	−.0585			
U_2U_3	−2393	365	170.43	−.171"					⑦ $\bar{.171}\times\frac{1}{1.544}=$	−.111			
U_3L_3	−173	564	49.72	−.065"					⑦ $\bar{.065}\times\frac{.257}{1.567}\times\frac{1}{1.544}=$	+.0069			
U_3L_3	do.	do.	do.	−.065"					⑧ $\bar{.065}\times\frac{1.319}{1.567}\times\frac{1}{.843}=$	+.0649	⑨ $\bar{.065}\times\frac{1}{1.00}=$	−.065	
L_3L_4	+2360	360	177.32	+.160"					⑧ $\overset{+}{.160}\times\frac{.539}{1.00}\times\frac{1}{.843}=$	−.102	⑨ $\overset{+}{.160}\times\frac{0}{1.00}\times\frac{1}{1.00}=$	0	
U_3L_4	+326	669	57.24	+.127"					⑧ $\overset{+}{.127}\times\frac{1}{.843}=$	+.151	⑨ $\overset{+}{.127}\times\frac{1.567}{1.858}\times\frac{1}{1.00}=$	−.107	
U_3L_4	do.	do.	do.	+.127"							⑩ $\overset{+}{.127}\times\frac{.840}{1.858}\times\frac{1}{1.658}=$	−.0350	
U_3U_4	−2549	362	179.69	−.171"							⑩ $\bar{.171}\times\frac{1}{1.658}=$	−.103	
U_4L_4	+39	600	45.25	+.017"							⑩ $\overset{+}{.017}\times\frac{.166}{1.667}\times\frac{1}{1.658}=$	−.0010	
U_4L_4	do.	do.	do.	+.017"							⑪ $\overset{+}{.017}\times\frac{1.430}{1.667}\times\frac{1}{.857}=$	−.0170	⑫ $\overset{+}{.017}\times\frac{1}{1.00}$
L_4L_5	+2536	360	188.57	+.161"							⑪ $\overset{+}{.161}\times\frac{.514}{1.00}\times\frac{1}{.857}=$	−.0966	⑫ $.161\times\frac{0}{1.00}\times$
U_4L_5	+105	700	49.99	+.049"							⑪ $\overset{+}{.049}\times\frac{1}{.857}=$	+.0572	⑫ $\overset{+}{.049}\times\frac{1.667}{1.944}$
U_4L_5	do.	do.	do.	+.049"									⑬ $\overset{+}{.049}\times\frac{.943}{1.944}$
U_4U_5	−2591	360	179.69	−.173"									⑬ $\bar{.173}\times\frac{1}{1.700}$
U_5L_5	+135	612	23.72	+.116"									⑬ $\overset{+}{.116}\times\frac{.057}{1.700}\times$
						−.517		+.0411		−.3527		−.3674	

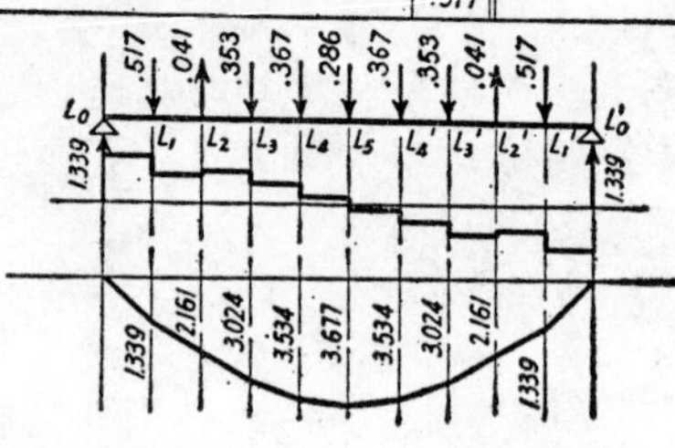

Williot Diagram Based on L_5 Fixed in Position and U_5L_5 Fixed in Direction

Truss Deflections by Angle

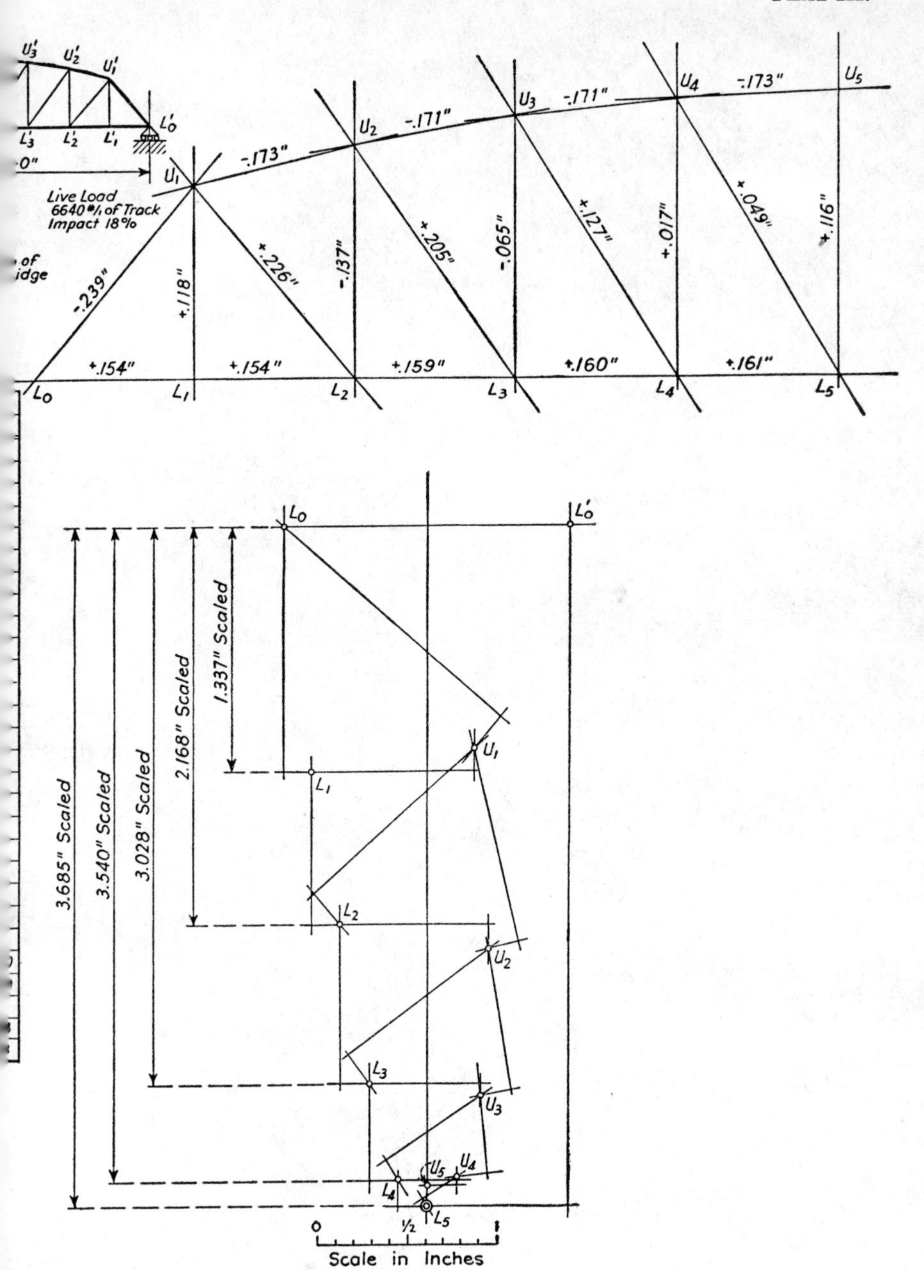

ges and Williot Diagram.

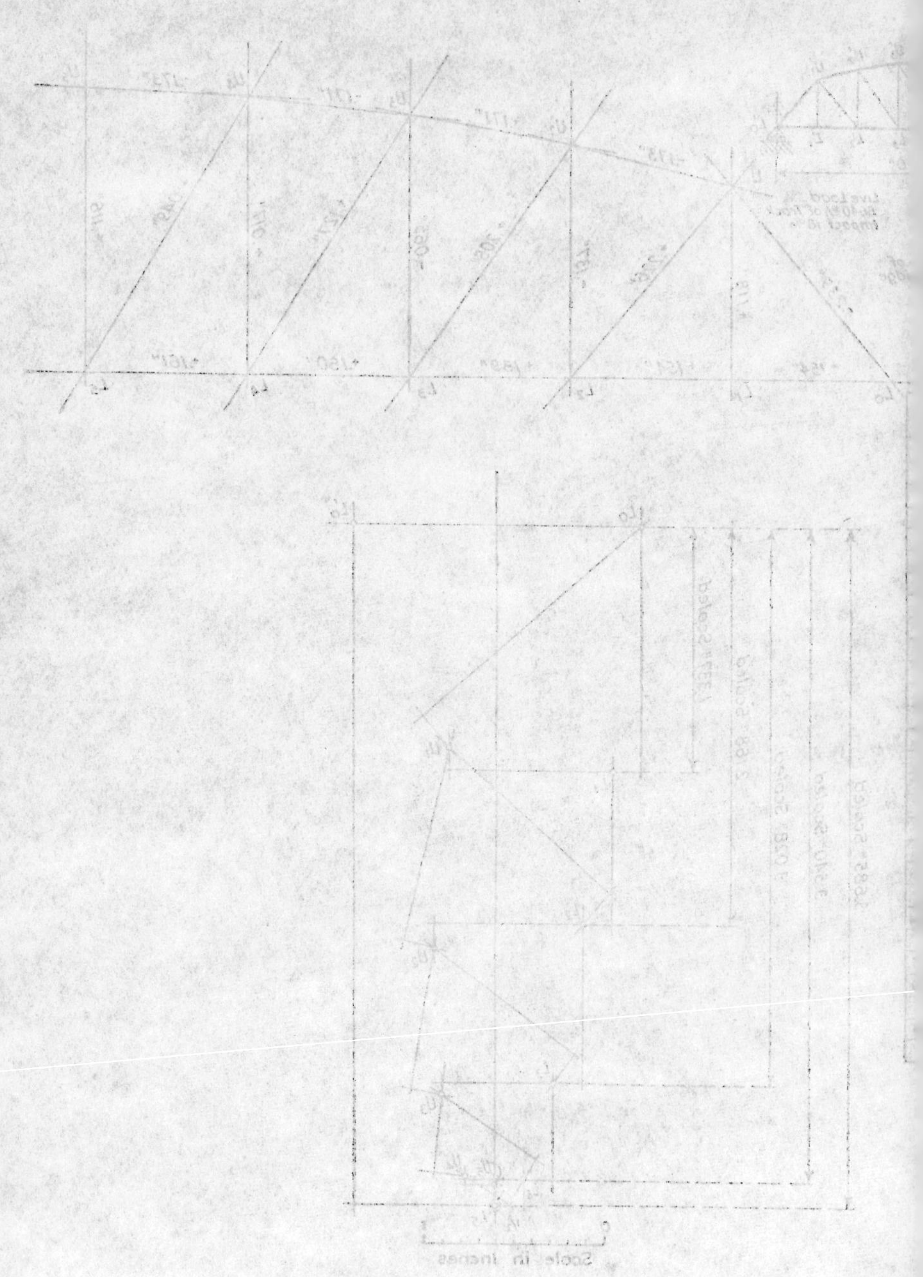

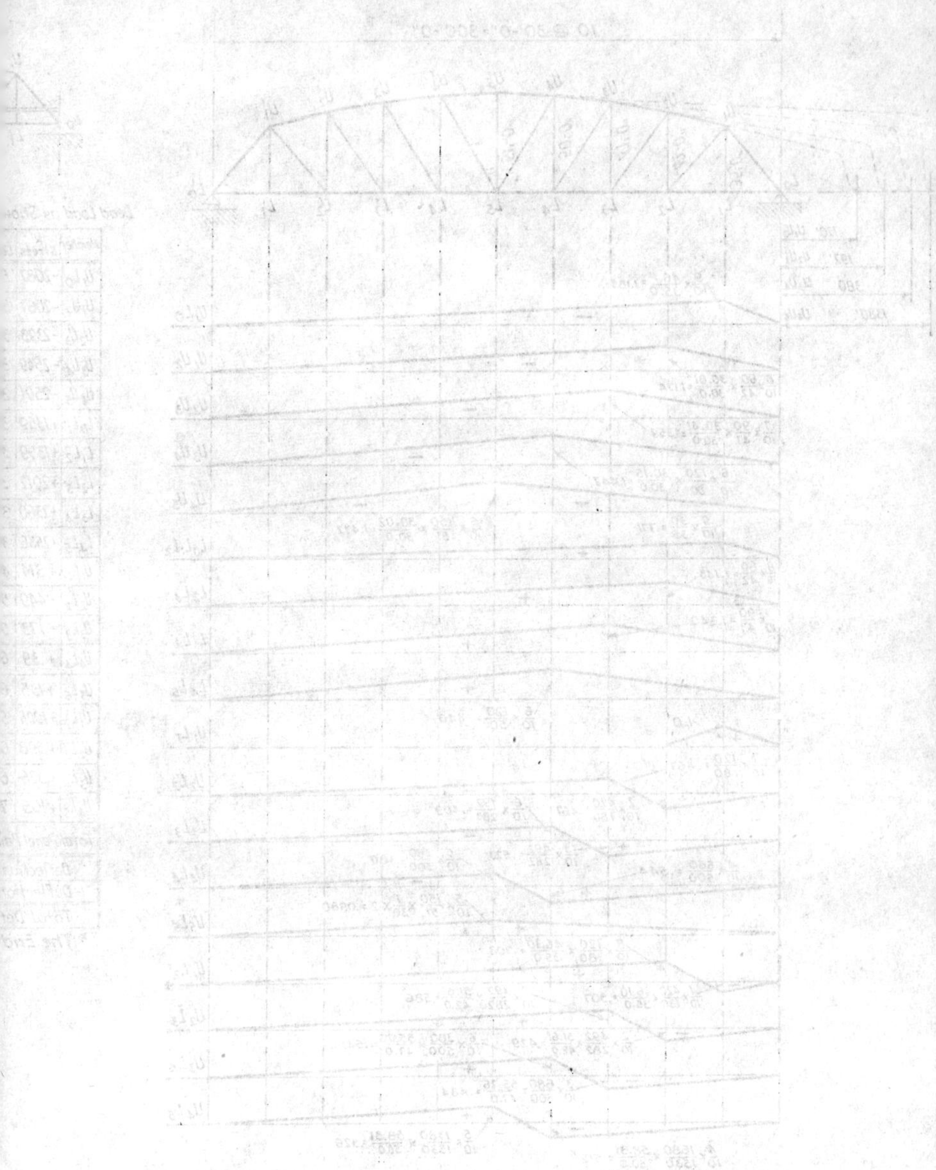

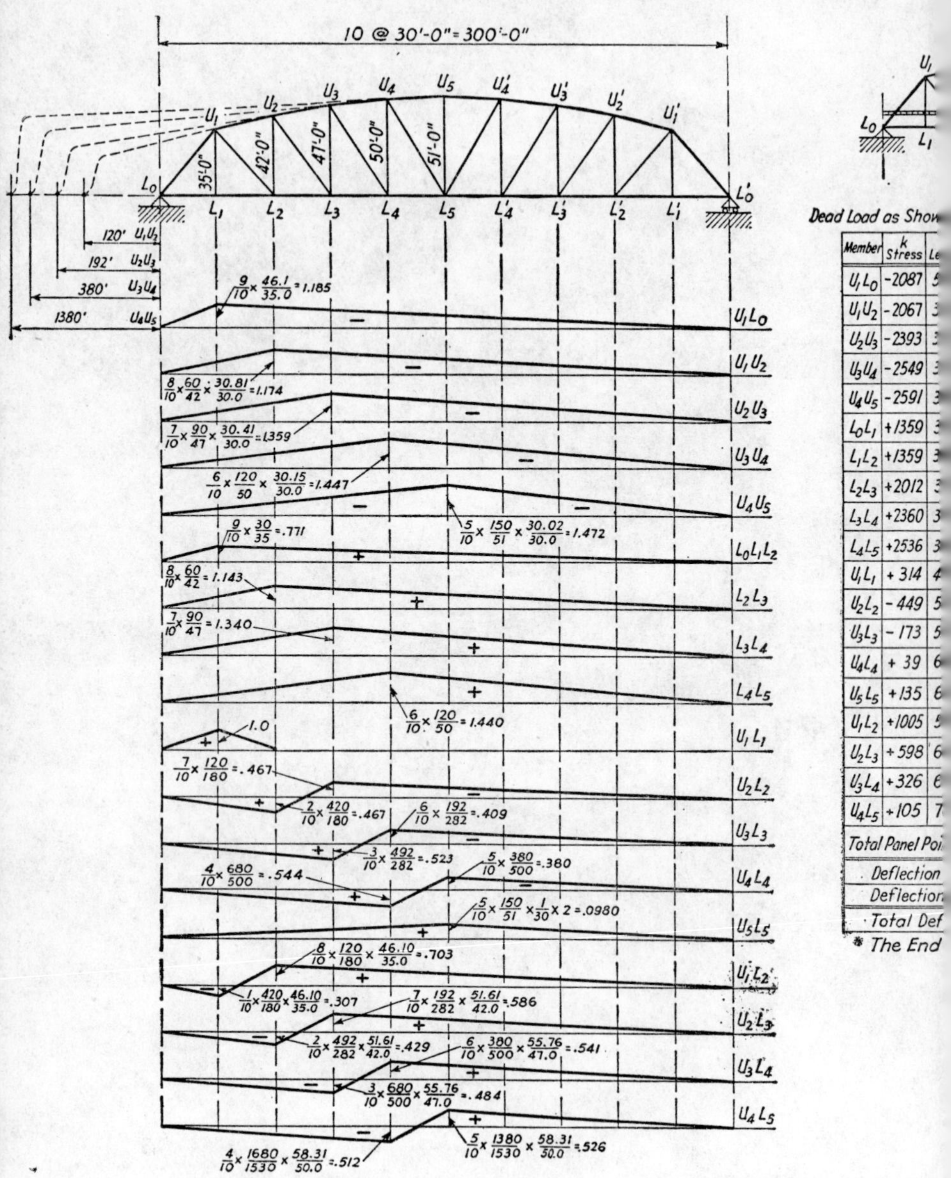

Member	k Stress	Le
U_1L_0	-2087	5
U_1U_2	-2067	3
U_2U_3	-2393	3
U_3U_4	-2549	3
U_4U_5	-2591	3
L_0L_1	+1359	3
L_1L_2	+1359	3
L_2L_3	+2012	3
L_3L_4	+2360	3
L_4L_5	+2536	3
U_1L_1	+ 314	4
U_2L_2	- 449	5
U_3L_3	- 173	5
U_4L_4	+ 39	6
U_5L_5	+ 135	6
U_1L_2	+1005	5
U_2L_3	+ 598	6
U_3L_4	+ 326	6
U_4L_5	+ 105	7
Total Panel Poi		
Deflection		
Deflection		
Total Def		

* The End

Truss Deflections Calcu

PLATE IV.

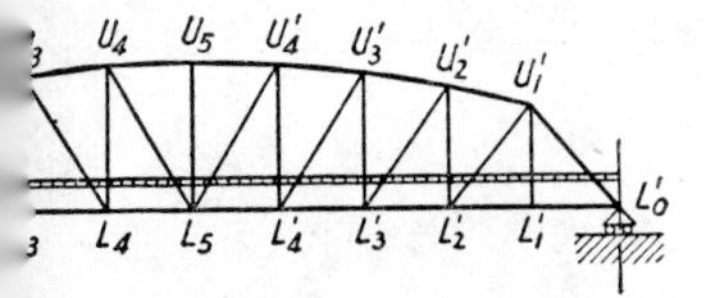

III. Live Load 6640 #/1 on Each Track +18% Impact

$\frac{SL}{AE}$" $=\delta$	L_1	L_2	L_3	L_4	L_5
-.239"	+.283" +.0315	+.252 +.0629	+.220 +.0944	+.189 +.126	+.157 +.157
-.173	+.1016 +.0254	+.203 +.0508	+.178 +.0762	+.152 +.1016	+.127 +.127
-.171	+.0775 +.0332	+.155 +.0664	+.232 +.0996	+.199 +.133	+.166 +.166
-.171	+.0619 +.0412	+.124 +.0825	+.186 +.124	+.247 +.165	+.206 +.206
-.173	+.0509 +.0509	+.1019 +.1019	+.153 +.153	+.204 +.204	+.255 +.255
+.154	+.119 +.0132	+.1055 +.0264	+.0923 +.0396	+.0792 +.0528	+.0660 +.0660
+.154	+.119 +.0132	+.1055 +.0264	+.0923 +.0396	+.0792 +.0528	+.0660 +.0660
+.159	+.0909 +.0227	+.182 +.0454	+.159 +.0682	+.136 +.0909	+.114 +.114
+.160	+.0715 +.0306	+.143 +.0613	+.214 +.0919	+.184 +.123	+.153 +.153
+.161	+.0580 +.0386	+.116 +.0773	+.174 +.116	+.232 +.155	+.193 +.193
+.118	+.118 —	— —	— —	— —	— —
-.137	-.0320 +.0091	-.0640 +.0183	+.0640 +.0274	+.0548 +.0366	+.0457 +.0457
-.065	-.0113 +.0044	-.0227 +.0089	-.0340 +.0133	+.0266 +.0177	+.0222 +.0222
+.017	+.0023 -.0013	+.0046 -.0026	+.0069 -.0039	+.0092 -.0052	-.0065 -.0065
+.116	+.0023 —	+.0045 —	+.0068 —	+.0091 —	+.0114 —
+.226	-.0694 +.0199	+.159 +.0397	+.139 +.0596	+.119 +.0794	+.0993 +.0993
+.205	-.0440 +.0172	-.0879 +.0343	+.120 +.0515	+.103 +.0686	+.0858 + 0858
+.127	-.0205 +.0115	-.0410 +.0229	-.0615 +.0344	+.0687 +.0458	+.0573 +.0573
+.049	-.0063 +.0052	-.0125 +.0103	-.0188 +.0155	-.0251 +.0206	+.0258 +.0258
ons =	1.3389	2.1610	3.0233	3.5343	3.6766
hords*	1.3338	2.0892	2.6031	2.9055	3.0060
Veb	.0051	.0718	.4202	.6288	.6706
	1.3389	2.1610	3.0233	3.5343	3.6766

have been included with the chords

Dead Load as Shown on Plate III. Live Load E-60 on Each Track, Wheel 3 at Panel Point L_3 Train Headed Left. Impact, 24%, Added to Live Load Stress

Member	k Stress	" Length	□" Gross Area	$\frac{SL}{AE}$" $=\delta$	L_1	L_2	L_3	L_4	L_5	L_4'	L_3'	L_2'	L_1'
U_1L_0	-1708	553	161.19	-.195"	+.231	+.205	+.180	+.154	+.128	+.103	+.0770	+.0513	+.0257
U_1U_2	-1812	370	147.31	-.152	+.0892	+.178	+.156	+.134	+.112	+.0892	+.0669	+.0446	+.0223
U_2U_3	-2260	365	170.43	-.162	+.0733	+.147	+.220	+.189	+.157	+.126	+.0944	+.0629	+.0314
U_3U_4	-2475	362	179.69	-.166	+.0600	+.120	+.180	+.240	+.200	+.160	+.120	+.0801	+.0400
U_4U_5	-2570	360	179.69	-.172	+.0506	+.1013	+.152	+.203	+.253	+.203	+.152	+.1013	+.0506
U_5U_4'	-2570	360	179.69	-.172	+.0506	+.1013	+.152	+.203	+.253	+.203	+.152	+.1013	+.0506
$U_4'U_3'$	-2516	362	179.69	-.169	+.0408	+.0815	+.122	+.163	+.204	+.245	+.183	+.122	+.0611
$U_3'U_2'$	-2355	365	170.43	-.169	+.0328	+.0656	+.0984	+.131	+.164	+.197	+.230	+.153	+.0766
$U_2'U_1'$	-2034	370	147.31	-.170	+.0249	+.0499	+.0748	+.0998	+.125	+.150	+.175	+.200	+.0998
$U_1'L_0'$	-2051	553	161.19	-.235	+.0309	+.0619	+.0928	+.124	+.155	+.186	+.217	+.248	+.278
L_0L_1	+1108	360	105.62	+.126	+.0971	+.0864	+.0756	+.0648	+.0540	+.0432	+.0324	+.0216	+.0108
L_1L_2	+1108	360	105.62	+.126	+.0971	+.0864	+.0756	+.0648	+.0540	+.0432	+.0324	+.0216	+.0108
L_2L_3	+1761	360	152.32	+.139	+.0794	+.159	+.139	+.119	+.0993	+.0794	+.0596	+.0397	+.0199
L_3L_4	+2228	360	177.32	+.150	+.0670	+.134	+.201	+.172	+.144	+.115	+.0861	+.0574	+.0287
L_4L_5	+2462	360	188.57	+.156	+.0562	+.112	+.168	+.225	+.187	+.150	+.112	+.0749	+.0374
L_5L_4'	+2505	360	188.57	+.159	+.0382	+.0763	+.114	+.153	+.191	+.229	+.172	+.114	+.0572
$L_4'L_3'$	+2324	360	177.32	+.157	+.0301	+.0601	+.0902	+.120	+.150	+.180	+.210	+.140	+.0701
$L_3'L_2'$	+1981	360	152.32	+.156	+.0223	+.0446	+.0669	+.0892	+.111	+.134	+.156	+.178	+.0892
$L_2'L_1'$	+1332	360	105.62	+.151	+.0129	+.0259	+.0388	+.0517	+.0647	+.0776	+.0905	+.1035	+.116
$L_1'L_0'$	+1332	360	105.62	+.151	+.0129	+.0259	+.0388	+.0517	+.0647	+.0776	+.0905	+.1035	+.116
U_1L_1	+ 79	420	37.37	+.030	+.0300	—	—	—	—	—	—	—	—
U_2L_2	- 652	504	54.84	-.199	-.0465	-.0929	+.0929	+.0797	+.0664	+.0531	+.0398	+.0266	+.0133
U_3L_3	- 277	564	49.72	-.104	-.0181	-.0363	-.0544	+.0425	+.0354	+.0284	+.0213	+.0142	+.0071
U_4L_4	- 46	600	45.25	-.020	-.0027	-.0054	-.0082	-.0109	+.0076	+.0061	+.0046	+.0030	+.0015
U_5L_5	+ 134	612	23.72	+.115	+.0023	+.0045	+.0068	+.0090	+.0113	+.0090	+.0068	+.0045	+.0023
$U_4'L_4'$	+ 26	600	45.25	+.012	-.0009	-.0018	-.0027	-.0036	-.0046	+.0065	+.0049	+.0033	+.0016
$U_3'L_3'$	- 187	564	49.72	-.071	+.0048	+.0097	+.0145	+.0194	+.0242	+.0290	-.0371	-.0248	-.0124
$U_2'L_2'$	- 454	504	54.84	-.139	+.0093	+.0185	+.0278	+.0371	+.0464	+.0556	+.0649	-.0649	-.0325
$U_1'L_1'$	+ 302	420	37.37	+.113	—	—	—	—	—	—	—	—	+.113
U_1L_2	+ 1003	553	81.99	+.225	-.0691	+.158	+.138	+.119	+.0989	+.0791	+.0593	+.0395	+.0198
U_2L_3	+ 804	619	60.24	+.276	-.0592	-.118	+.162	+.139	+.116	+.0924	+.0693	+.0462	+.0231
U_3L_4	+ 439	669	57.24	+.171	-.0276	-.0552	-.0828	+.0925	+.0771	+.0617	+.0463	+.0308	+.0154
U_4L_5	+ 192	700	49.99	+.090	-.0115	-.0230	-.0346	-.0461	+.0473	+.0379	+.0284	+.0189	+.0094
$U_4'L_5$	+ 117	700	49.99	+.055	+.0058	+.0116	+.0174	+.0231	+.0289	-.0282	-.0211	-.0141	-.0070
$U_3'L_4'$	+ 342	669	57.24	+.133	+.0120	+.0240	+.0360	+.0480	+.0600	+.0720	-.0644	-.0429	-.0215
$U_2'L_3'$	+ 591	619	60.24	+.203	+.0170	+.0340	+.0510	+.0680	+.0850	+.102	+.119	-.0871	-.0435
$U_1'L_2'$	+ 993	553	81.99	+.223	+.0196	+.0392	+.0588	+.0784	+.0980	+.118	+.137	+.157	-.0685
Deflection Due to Chords*					+1.1973	+1.9221	+2.4359	+2.7520	+2.8707	+2.7912	+2.5088	+2.0187	+1.2922
Deflection Due to Web					-.1348	-.0331	+.4225	+.6951	+.7979	+.7226	+.4790	+.1102	+.0211
Total Deflection					+1.0625	+1.8890	+2.8584	+3.4471	+3.6686	+3.5138	+2.9878	+2.1289	+1.3133

* The End Posts have been included with the chords

from Influence Lines.

So far as the authors know this method has not been published before. By a slight extension it leads to the so-called method of "elastic weights," but that extension seems an unnecessary obfuscation of a very simple relation.

204. Illustrative Examples.—The methods of calculating deflections of trusses by angle changes, Williot diagram, and influence lines are illustrated in Plates III and IV. The truss shown is a double-track railroad bridge designed for Cooper's E–60 under the "Specifications for Design and Construction of Steel Railway Bridge Superstructure," published by the American Society of Civil Engineers [4] in 1923.

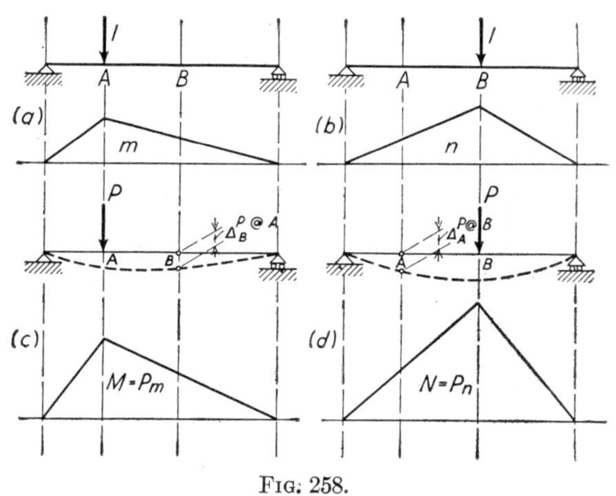

FIG. 258.

No particular comment on the calculations seems necessary. Obviously all three methods should give identical results if all were carried out with perfect precision. In general, however, the Williot diagram is likely to be somewhat less precise than the method of angle changes or influence lines owing to the normal imperfections of drafting equipment and technique.

205. Maxwell's Law of Reciprocal Relations.—A very useful relation which the student may have observed in some of the problems previously studied is illustrated in Fig. 258. Assume that we wish to calculate the deflection at B due to a load P acting at A, and the deflection at A when the load P is at B. At (a) in the figure is shown the moment diagram due to a unit

[4] *Transactions Am. Soc. C. E.*, Vol. 86, 1923, page 471.

load acting at A, at (b) that due to a unit load acting at B, at (c) the moment diagram due to the load P acting at A, and at (d) that due to the load P at B.

In accordance with the general statement on page 455 we may write at once:

$$\Delta_B^{P \text{ at } A} = \int \frac{Mds}{EI} \cdot n = P \int \frac{mds}{EI} \cdot n$$

and

$$\Delta_A^{P \text{ at } B} = \int \frac{Nds}{EI} \cdot m = P \int \frac{nds}{EI} \cdot m$$

These two quantities are identical, and since there was no restriction on the location of the points we may make the general statement: **the deflection at B due to a load P acting at A is equal to the deflection at A due to the load P acting at B.** This is a somewhat restricted statement of the law of reciprocal relations discovered by the English scientist, James Clerk Maxwell, and announced by him in 1864. It need not be restricted to vertical displacements, and may be extended to include rotations. It is just as applicable to trusses as to beams, and it is the basis of Müller-Breslau's principle stated in the preceding chapter. The law of reciprocal relations is very useful in dealing with indeterminate structures. It is advisable for the beginner to prove carefully each use of Maxwell's law. Although it is very simple, it is easy to make statements which sound plausible but are erroneous.

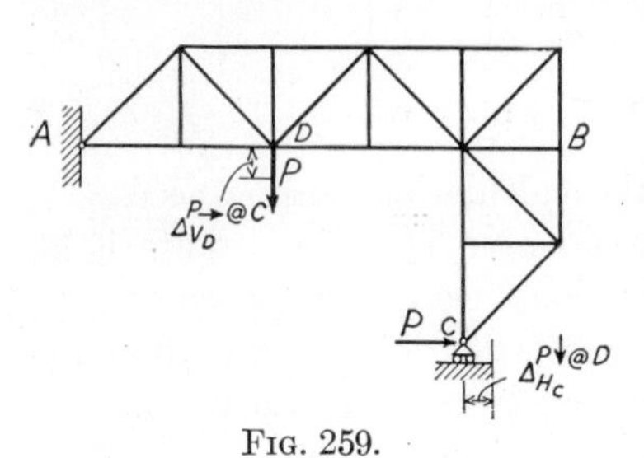

FIG. 259.

A further illustration is given in Fig. 259. Maxwell's law states that the horizontal movement of point C due to a load P acting vertically at point D is equal to the vertical movement of point D due to the load P acting horizontally at point C. This may be shown as follows:

Let u = the stress in any bar due to a unit load acting down at point D.

v = the stress in any bar due to a unit load acting horizontally at point C.

Then

Pu = the stress in any bar due to the load P acting down at point D.

Pv = the stress in any bar due to the load P acting horizontally at point C.

Applying the principle of virtual work we may write:

$$\Delta_{H_C}{}^{P\downarrow \text{ at } D} = \sum \frac{Pul}{AE} \cdot v = P\sum \frac{ul}{AE} \cdot v$$

$$\Delta_{V_D}{}^{P\rightarrow \text{ at } C} = \sum \frac{Pvl}{AE} \cdot u = P\sum \frac{vl}{AE} \cdot u$$

Since these quantities are identical the relation is proved in this case.

206. Applications.—The principles discussed so far in this chapter are fundamental tools in structural analysis and design. They have no virtue in themselves and become of value only so far as they contribute to the design, fabrication, and erection of engineering structures. They have occasional utility in dealing with ordinary determinate structures, but perhaps their greatest application is as an aid in the analysis of statically indeterminate structures. In both fields, but particularly in the latter, it is sometimes convenient to extend and elaborate them, but such extension and elaboration are for the most part only a convenience, not a necessity. The majority of problems that the engineer meets can be dealt with by direct application of the principles presented.

Lack of space prevents an extended discussion of applications but a few simple illustrations will be presented.

207. Camber.—Most specifications governing the design of bridge trusses require that the trusses be "cambered," i.e., that they be so fabricated that when erected on the falsework the bottom chord panel points will be above the design position and will come down to that position only under a specified loading, frequently called the camber loading. Various ways of accomplishing the specified result are used, but the most direct and effective is to shorten tension members by the amount they would lengthen under the camber loading, and lengthen compression members by the amount they would shorten. The "camber diagram," a diagram showing the position taken by the bottom chord panel points as a result of these changes in length, can then be obtained by drawing a Williot diagram, or by calculating the movements by angle changes or from influence lines. It should be noted that the latter methods will give only the vertical movements. However, the horizontal movements can be determined directly from the changes in length of the bottom chord, when that is horizontal, which it usually is. Of course the Williot diagram gives both movements directly.

As an example assume that the truss shown on Plates III and IV is to be cambered for the load given: dead load, plus 6640 lb. per ft. on each track and 18 per cent impact (ordinarily impact is not included in computing camber). The changes in length under this loading are shown in the tables on each plate. Now if these

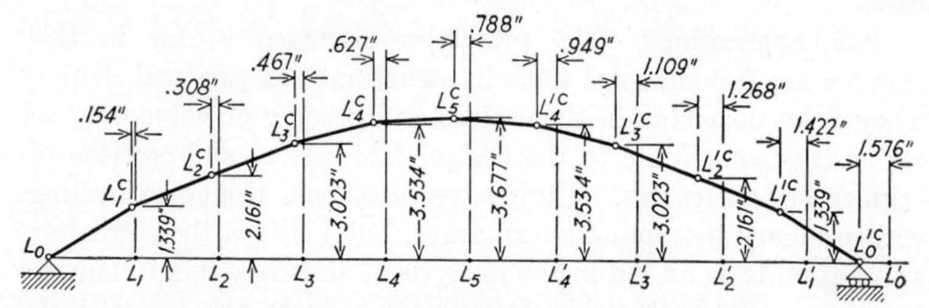

Camber Diagram Based on Data from Plate IV

FIG. 260.

changes are made in reverse in fabrication, i.e., if U_1L_0 is made 0.239 in. longer, L_0L_1 is made 0.154 in. shorter, and so on for other bars, the bottom chord panel points will lie above the horizontal by amounts equal to the downward deflection shown in the lower left corner on Plate III. In other words, the deflection diagram shown on Plate III turned upside down would be a camber diagram except for the horizontal movements which can be determined directly from the changes in length. Thus if the changes shown in the table were reversed L_1 would move 0.154 in. *toward* L_0; L_2 would move 0.308 in. toward L_0; L_3, 0.467 in. toward L_0, and so on. The resulting camber diagram would be as shown in Fig. 260. Actually, however, the true camber diagram would not agree exactly with the inverted deflection diagram for the reason that the fabricating shop could not make exactly the changes in length shown. Shops can work only in multiples of $\frac{1}{32}$ in.; consequently the camber change for U_1L_0 would have to be $+0.250$ in. ($\frac{1}{4}$ in.) instead of $+0.239$ in.; the camber change for L_0L_1, -0.156 in. ($\frac{5}{32}$ in.) instead of -0.154 in.; and so on. The true camber diagram would then be computed from the actual changes in length which the shop made. It would differ very little from the illustrated diagram of Fig. 260.

208. Redundant Members.—Occasionally trusses are built in which more members are provided than are necessary for stability. As an example the truss in Fig. 261 (*a*) has two diagonals in the panel 1–2. All bars are capable of resisting either tension or compression, and the truss is therefore statically indeterminate in panel 1–2; i.e., the stress in bars in that panel cannot be calculated from statics alone. An analysis can be made, however, applying the principles discussed in this chapter. Any one of the six bars in panel 1–2 may be considered as the extra or redundant member, and if that bar is removed the stresses in the remaining bars can be calculated by statics. It will then be possible to calculate the relative movement between the points to which the redundant bar is connected, and having this movement to calculate the force necessary to restore these points to the positions they would occupy with the bar in place. That is the usual method of analysis.

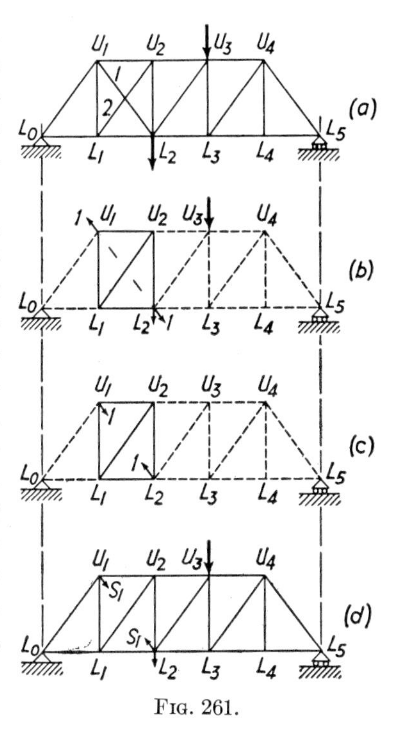

Fig. 261.

In Fig. 261 (*b*) the diagonal U_1L_2 has been called the redundant member and removed. The panel points U_1 and L_2 will then separate by an amount $\Delta = \sum \frac{Sl}{AE} u$. Unit loads acting on the panel points as shown in Fig. 261 (*c*) will draw the points together by an amount $\delta = \sum \frac{ul}{AE} u$. If the stress in the bar is S_1, that stress acting as in (*d*) will draw the points together $S_1\delta$, and we may write

$$S_1\delta + \frac{S_1 l_1}{A_1 E} = \Delta$$

in which S_1, l_1, and A_1 refer specifically to U_1L_2. It should be clear that E could be omitted from the calculations since it is the same for all members. The same method may be followed adopting any other bar as the redundant.

If there is more than one redundant bar, of course it is necessary to obtain as many relations as there are redundants.

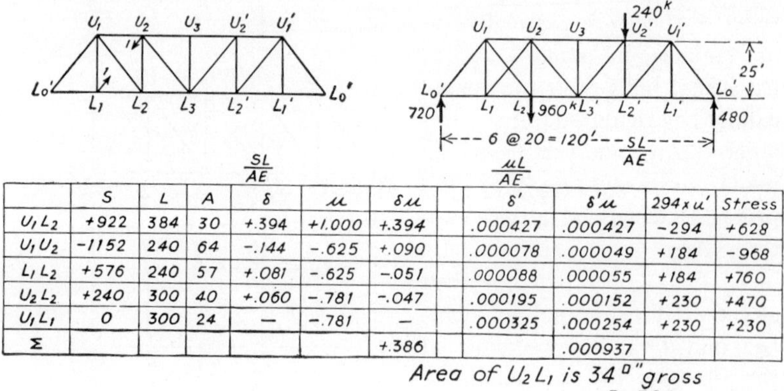

	S	L	A	δ (SL/AE)	u	δu		δ' (uL/AE)	δ'u	294×u'	Stress
U_1L_2	+922	384	30	+.394	+1.000	+.394		.000427	.000427	−294	+628
U_1U_2	−1152	240	64	−.144	−.625	+.090		.000078	.000049	+184	−968
L_1L_2	+576	240	57	+.081	−.625	−.051		.000088	.000055	+184	+760
U_2L_2	+240	300	40	+.060	−.781	−.047		.000195	.000152	+230	+470
U_1L_1	0	300	24	—	−.781	—		.000325	.000254	+230	+230
Σ						+.386			.000937		

Area of U_2L_1 is 34 □" gross

$$.000937\,P + \frac{P \times 384}{30{,}000 \times 34} = .386''$$

$P = 294^k$ comp

FIG. 262.

Illustrations of the analysis of trusses containing redundant members are given in Figs. 262 and 263. As indicated in the truss diagrams above the calculations, the truss dealt with in Fig. 262 contains one redundant member, and that in Fig. 263, two redundant members. The calculations follow exactly the procedure outlined at the beginning of the article, and no comments are necessary except to call attention to some terms the meaning of which may not be clear. In Fig. 262 the column headed u contains stresses due to unit loads acting at U_2 and L_1, as shown in the diagram above the table. In the column headed $294u'$ the factor u' is the same as u but with the directions of the unit loads reversed. Similarly in Fig. 263 the column headed u_1 contains stresses due to unit loads acting at U_2 and L_1, and the column headed u_2 stresses due to unit loads acting at U_3 and L_2 as shown in the diagram above the table. As in Fig. 262 factors u_1' and u_2' are the same as u_1 and u_2 but with the directions of the unit load reversed. In each figure the right-hand column headed "Stress" contains the stresses in the members of the panels containing a redundant member.

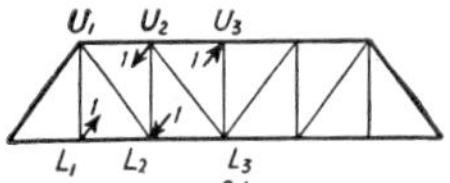

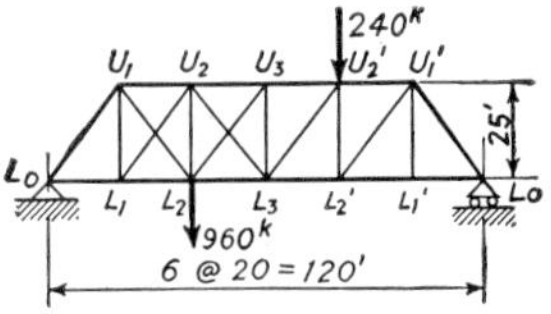

	S	L	A	δ ($\frac{SL}{AE}$)	u_1	δu_1	u_2	δu_2	$\frac{u_1^2 L}{AE}$	$\frac{u_1' u_2' L}{AE}$	$\frac{u_2^2 L}{AE}$	$P_1 u_1'$	$P_2 u_2'$	Stress
U_1L_2	+922	384	30	+.394	+1.000	+.394	0	—	.000427	—	—	−312	—	+610
U_1U_2	−1152	240	64	−.144	−.625	+.090	0	—	.000049	—	—	+195	—	−957
L_1L_2	+576	240	57	+.081	−.625	−.051	0	—	.000055	—	—	+195	—	+771
U_1L_1	0	300	24	0	−.781	0	0	—	.000254	—	—	+244	—	+244
U_2L_2	+240	300	40	+.060	−.781	−.047	+.781	+.047	.000152	−.000152	.000152	+244	−121	+363
U_2L_3	−307	384	11	−.357	0	—	−1.000	+.357	—	—	.001164	—	+155	−152
U_2U_3	−960	240	78	−.0985	0	—	+.625	−.062	—	—	.000040	—	−97	−1057
L_2L_3	+1152	240	69	+.134	0	—	+.625	+.084	—	—	.000045	—	−97	+1055
U_3L_3	0	300	16	0	0	—	+.781	0	—	—	.000381	—	−121	−121
U_2L_1	—	384	34											−312
U_3L_2	—	384	10											+155
Σ						+.386		+.426	.000937	−.000152	.001782			

$$311.9 \times .000152 = .047$$
$$\frac{.426}{.473}$$

$$\frac{P_1 \times 384}{34 \times 30{,}000} + .000937\,P_1 - .000152\,P_2 = .386$$

$$\frac{P_2 \times 384}{10 \times 30{,}000} + .001782\,P_2 - .000152\,P_1 = .426$$

$$\begin{aligned} .001313\,P_1 - .000152\,P_2 &= .386 \\ -.000152\,P_1 + .003062\,P_2 &= .426 \\ .026450\,P_1 - .003062\,P_2 &= 7.776 \\ .026298\,P_1 \qquad\qquad &= 8.202 \\ .003062\,P_2 &= .473 \end{aligned}$$

$P_1 = 311.9$ Comp

$P_2 = 154.5$ Tens

FIG. 263.

209. Use of Maxwell's Law in Obtaining Influence Lines.—In Art. 187 Müller-Breslau's principle was stated without proof. A general proof is perhaps beyond the scope of a textbook for beginners, but we may make use of Maxwell's law of reciprocal relations to establish the principle in two simple cases.

Figure 264 shows an unsymmetrical two-span beam. Assume that a unit load is placed at any point such as P. We may calculate the reaction at B by removing the support and calculating the force necessary to restore B to the proper level. We may say then, using the data from the figure:

$$R_B^{1\downarrow \text{ at } P} = \frac{\delta_B^{1\downarrow \text{ at } P}}{\delta_B^{1\uparrow \text{ at } B}}$$

However, Maxwell's theorem says that

$$\delta_B^{1\downarrow \text{ at } P} = \delta_P^{1\uparrow \text{ at } B}$$

Therefore

$$R_B^{1\downarrow \text{ at } P} = \frac{\delta_P^{1\uparrow \text{ at } B}}{\delta_B^{1\uparrow \text{ at } B}}$$

That is, the deflection curve resulting from a unit force (or any other convenient value) acting upward at B is an influence line for B, and the numerical values of the ordinates to the influence line may be obtained by dividing each ordinate of the deflection curve by the deflection at B.

As a second example refer again to Fig. 259 and assume that the right-hand support is hinged but not free to move horizontally. The structure is then statically indeterminate, but we may determine the horizontal reaction at C due to a unit load at any panel point between A and B by imagining the end at C on rollers, calculating the horizontal movement due to the load at any panel point, and then finding the force necessary to restore C to its original position.

Let H_c = horizontal reaction at C due to unit load at any panel point.

$\delta_{H_C}^{1\downarrow \text{ at } P.P.}$ = the horizontal movement of C (when C is on rollers) due to a unit load at any panel point.

$\delta_{H_C}^{1\leftarrow \text{ at } C}$ = the horizontal movement of C due to a unit horizontal reaction at C.

$\delta_{V_{P.P.}}^{1\leftarrow \text{ at } C}$ = the vertical movement of any panel point between A and B due to a unit horizontal reaction at C.

Then we may write

$$H_c = \frac{\delta_{H_C}^{1\downarrow \text{ at } P.P.}}{\delta_{H_C}^{1\leftarrow \text{ at } C}}$$

But from Maxwell's theorem

$$\delta_{H_C}^{1\downarrow \text{ at } P.P.} = \delta_{V_{P.P.}}^{1\leftarrow \text{ at } C}$$

Therefore

$$H_c = \frac{\delta_{V_{P.P.}}^{1\leftarrow \text{ at } C}}{\delta_{H_C}^{1\leftarrow \text{ at } C}}$$

Since there was no restriction on the panel point between A and B to be loaded, we may conclude that the deflected shape of the bottom chord between A and B, due to a unit horizontal reaction at C, is an influence line for horizontal reaction at C, and the numerical values of the ordinates to that influence line may be obtained by dividing the deflections of the various panel points between A and B by the horizontal deflection at C.

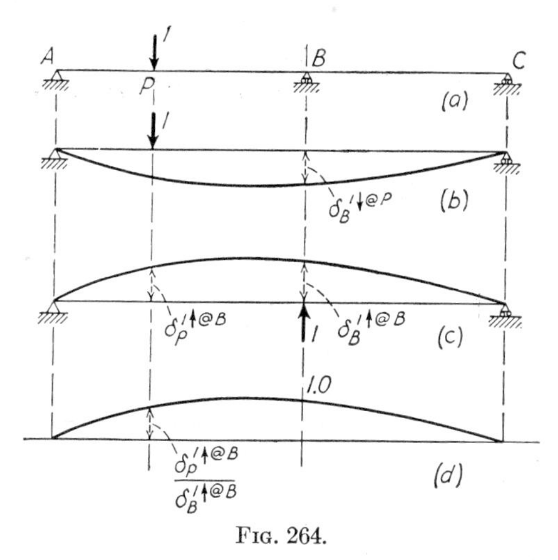

FIG. 264.

The relations just established will be applied in connection with a continuous truss and a two-hinged arch in succeeding articles.

210. Two-span Continuous Truss.—The preceding article described the use of Maxwell's reciprocal theorem in determining the influence line for center reaction in an unsymmetrical two-span beam. The same method may be followed in dealing with a truss continuous over two spans.

The major difficulty in dealing with indeterminate structures is the necessity for having known proportions before an analysis can be made. The real problem then is to assume a structure near enough to the right proportions so that repeated corrections will not have to be made. The problem of analysis is relatively easy, but the problem of design may be rather difficult. The matter cannot be treated adequately in an elementary book, and procedures which experience has shown to be satisfactory will be used without explanation.

Consider the two-span continuous truss shown in Fig. 265 (a). According to the principle established in Art. 209, we may allow

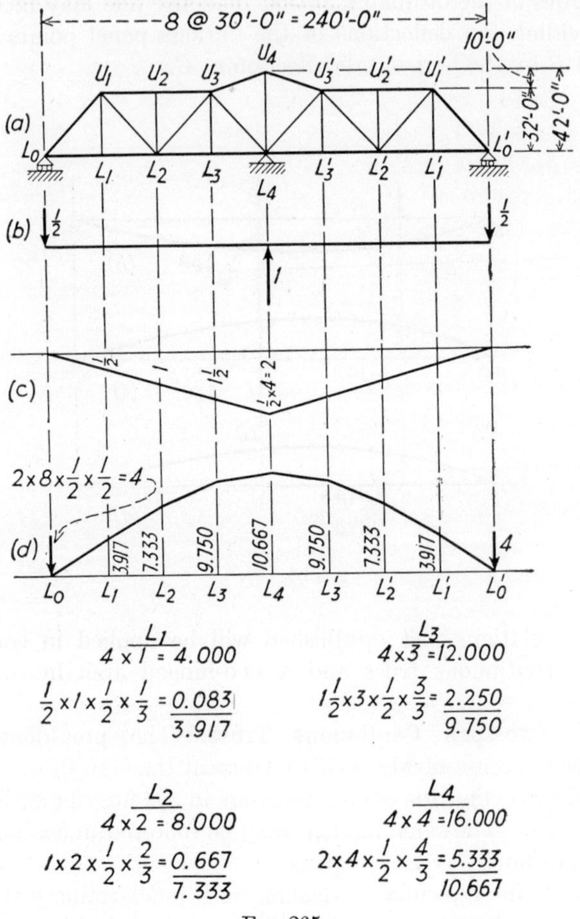

Fig. 265.

a unit reaction to act at the center support as shown at (b) in the figure, and the resultant deflected structure will be the influence line for the center reaction. The difficulty is that to determine the deflected position of the bottom chord we must know the areas of the bars of the truss. We will *assume*, for a preliminary design, that the deflections may be found as those of a continuous beam having constant moment of inertia. This has been done in Fig. 265. At (*c*) is shown the moment diagram due to the unit reaction at the center support (using the panel length as unity), and at (*d*) the bending moment diagram due to the moment diagram of (*c*) applied as a load. The moment diagram at (*d*) is also the deflection diagram, and as shown in Art. 209 the ordinates to the influence line may be found by dividing the ordinates of the deflection curve by the center ordinate, i.e., by 10.667.

The influence line for center reaction determined by the procedure described in the preceding paragraph is shown at (*b*), Fig. 266. With an influence line for center reaction, the structure may be analyzed by statics, and influence lines for the various bars in the truss may be determined by the simple device of placing a unit load at successive panel points and calculating the resulting stress in the bars. The resulting influence lines are shown in Fig. 266 designated by the usual bar notation.

There are various short cuts and semi-automatic devices for obtaining influence lines for stress from the influence line for center reaction. However, these methods are not essential, and the beginner will do well to confine his first studies to fundamental procedures which are easily understood and less subject to error.

The influence lines for stress having been obtained, the next step is the determination of the live-load stresses. Two procedures are open to the engineer. He may deal with the actual wheel loads, placed on the influence line in the most unfavorable position, as stated in Art. 56, or he may make use of equivalent uniform loads as described in Art. 124. The exercise of judgment will be necessary in either case.

When dealing with the actual wheel loads the most unfavorable position cannot be determined exactly by the criteria developed for simple structures as the influence lines do not have linear variation. The student will generally find, however, that wheels located in accordance with the criteria for simple structures will be in the proper position within one wheel on either side. Thus, in considering U_1L_0, the criterion for position at panel point 1 in a simple span of 4 panels of 30′–0″ each would require placing wheel 5 (Cooper's E loadings) at the panel point. If the student does not find that position to be correct for this case he will probably find that either wheel 4 or wheel 6 at the panel point is the correct position. One should always try first the position of the wheel which would satisfy the criterion for the most nearly comparable influence line for a simple structure.

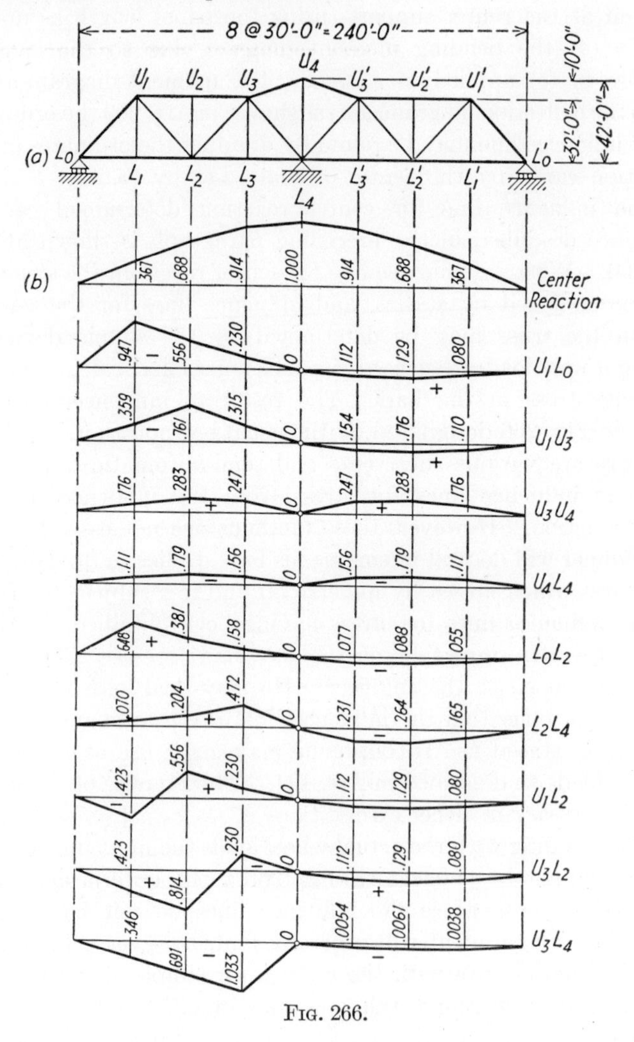

Fig. 266.

The use of the equivalent loads given on Plates I and II will usually lead to results sufficiently accurate for design purposes. It is obvious that such loads are not exactly equivalent for indeterminate structures since they were developed for influence lines having linear variation, and influence lines for indeterminate structures do not have linear variation. The student will do well to compare the results obtained from equivalent uniform loads with those obtained from the actual wheel loads. He will find that the differences are not very significant from a design point of view in most cases, but he should guard against sweeping general conclusions based on a few comparisons.

The calculation of dead-load stresses is clearly a matter of statics. With an influence line for center reaction, all reactions from dead load are obtainable from statics and the calculation of stresses may be carried out in any convenient way, arithmetical or graphical.

Member	l ft.	A □"	u	$\delta = \frac{ul}{AE}$ *	δu
U_1L_0	43.86	40.71	+.685	+.738	+.506
U_1U_2	30.0	30.36	+.9375	+.926	+.868
U_2U_3	30.0	30.36	+.9375	+.926	+.868
U_3U_4	31.62	24.96	+1.506	+1.908	+2.873
L_0L_1	30.0	23.40	-.469	-.601	+.282
L_1L_2	30.0	23.40	-.469	-.601	+.282
L_2L_3	30.0	20.46	-1.406	-2.062	+2.899
L_3L_4	30.0	20.46	-1.406	-2.062	+2.899
U_1L_2	43.86	12.06	-.685	-2.491	+1.706
U_3L_2	43.86	23.40	+.685	+1.284	+ .880
U_3L_4	43.86	45.21	-.0326	-.0316	+.001
U_1L_1	32.0	23.44	0	–	–
U_2L_2	32.0	19.80	0	–	–
U_3L_3	32.0	23.44	0	–	–
U_4L_4	42.0	19.80	-.952	-2.019	+1.922
					15.986

* In these Computations $E=1$

×2 = 31.972
1.922
30.050

FIG. 267.

The live-load, impact, and dead-load stresses, and the wind stresses, if significant, having been determined, a tentative design may be made. The next step is then the determination of a more accurate influence line for center reaction. The revised influence line may be found again as the deflected shape of the bottom chord, except that now having tentative areas the deflected positions of the panel points may be found by one of the methods discussed in preceding articles.

For the structure shown in Fig. 266 a tentative design led to the areas given in the table in Fig. 267. By using the relative changes in length in the members given in the same table, the Williot diagram shown in Fig. 268 was drawn. This leads at once to the revised influence line for center reaction shown in Fig. 269. Corrected influence lines are shown for U_1U_3, U_3L_2, and L_2L_4. The student should compare these with the tentative influence lines in Fig. 266, and compute the corrected influence lines for other bars for comparison with the originals.

A thorough study of the influence lines based on the areas

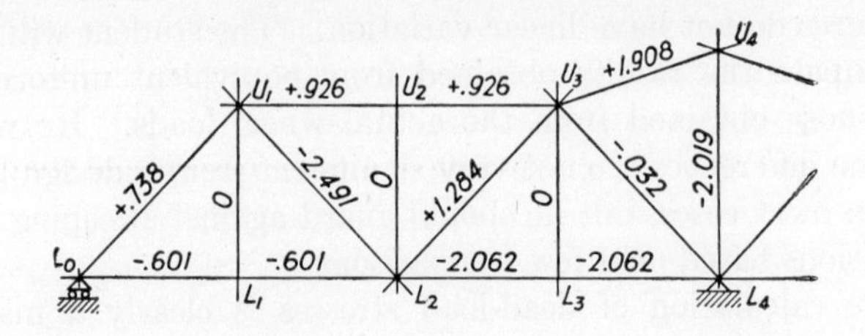

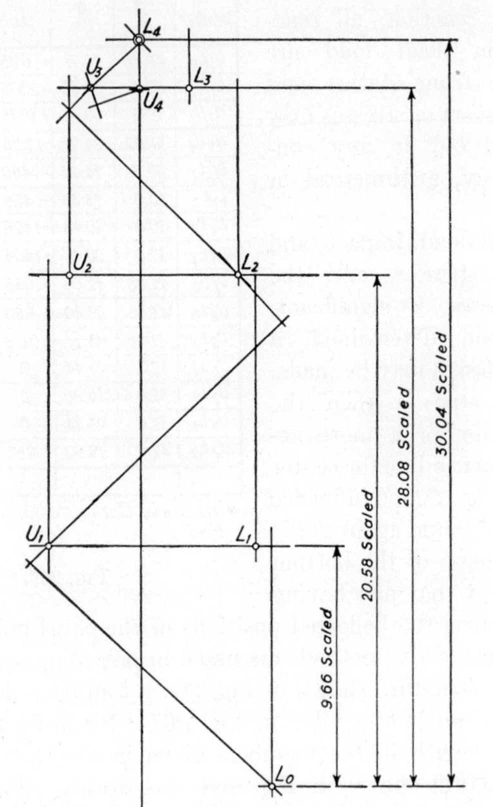

Based on L_4 Fixed in Position and U_4L_4 Fixed in Direction

FIG. 268.

given in the table in Fig. 267 will show that only a few minor changes are necessary for final design, and those changes are so small that a recalculation of the influence line for center reaction would not alter the result. It will be noted that some small ordinates of the influence lines have a large percentage change, but

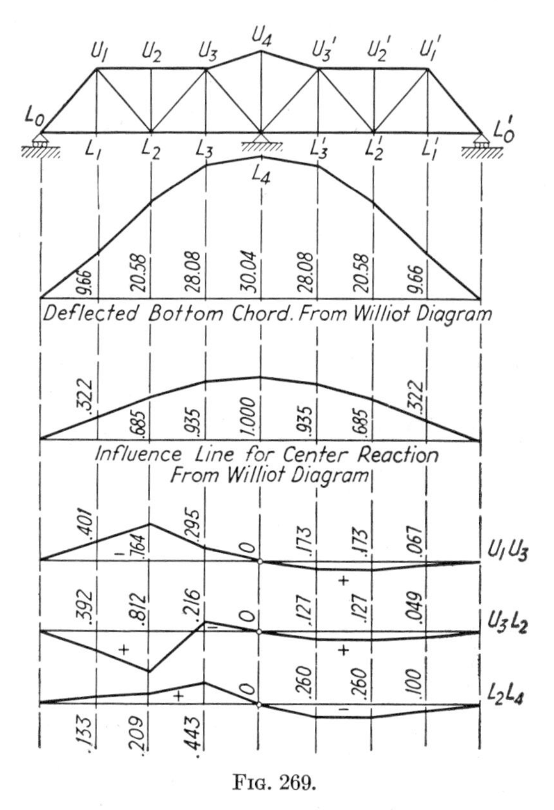

FIG. 269.

that those ordinates which have large relative changes have little or no significance in the determination of design stresses.

Other redundants may be used for analysis instead of the center reaction, such as one of the end reactions or some bar in the truss. Each possible procedure has its advocates, as well as its advantages and disadvantages, but they need not concern the beginner.

211. Two-hinged Arch.—The two-hinged arch is similar to the two-span truss in that it is indeterminate to the first degree. The

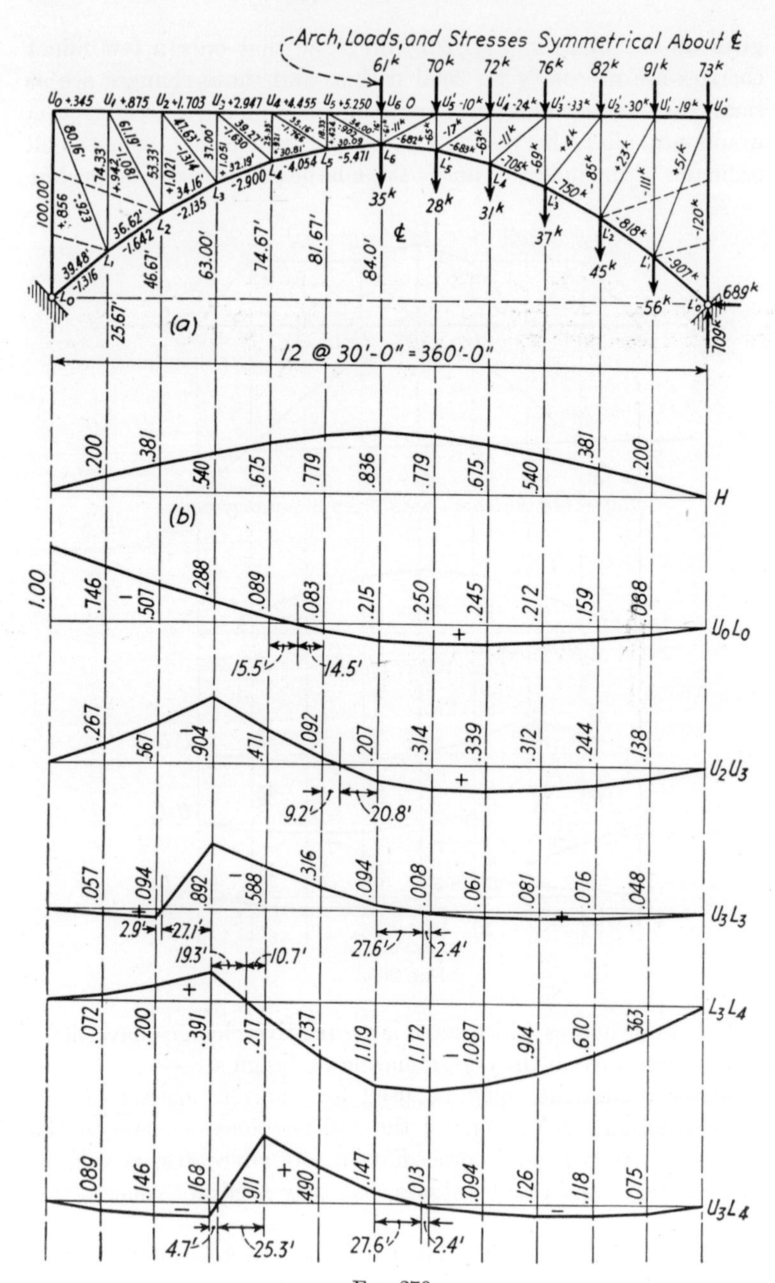
Arch, Loads, and Stresses Symmetrical About ℄
(a)
12 @ 30'-0" = 360'-0"
(b)
H
U_0L_0
U_2U_3
U_3L_3
L_3L_4
U_3L_4

FIG. 270.

problem of analysis is similar, but the problem of preliminary design is somewhat less obvious and beyond the scope of this book. Nevertheless the two-hinged arch affords an interesting application of the principles discussed in this chapter, and certain parts of the problem can be presented without discussing the background.

Member	Length Feet	Stress in Kips					Area Sq. In.
		D.L.	L.L.	Imp.	Temp.	Total	
U_0U_1	30	− 19	−190 +132	− 80 + 42	− 20 + 13	− 309 + 168	43.50
U_1U_2	30	− 30	−404 +272	−171 + 86	− 51 + 32	− 656 + 360	43.50
U_2U_3	30	− 33	−636 +408	−244 +142	−100 + 62	−1013 + 579	69.76
U_3U_4	30	− 24	−832 +468	−318 + 90	−172 +108	−1346 + 642	89.88
U_4U_5	30	− 10	−854 +344	−296 +132	−261 +163	−1421 + 629	93.92
U_5U_6	30	0	−776 + 98	−296 + 46	−307 +192	−1379 + 336	91.92
L_0L_1	39.48	−907	−1880	−390	− 48	−3225	214.86
L_1L_2	36.62	−818	−1760	−406	− 60	−3044	203.61
L_2L_3	34.16	−750	−1674	−428	− 78	−2930	196.11
L_3L_4	32.19	−705	−1600	−454	−106	−2865	192.36
L_4L_5	30.81	−683	−1466	−460	−148	−2757	184.86
L_5L_6	30.09	−682	−1128	−392	−200	−2402	162.36
U_0L_1	80.16	+ 51	+508 −350	+215 −110	+ 54 − 34	+ 828 − 443	56.44
U_1L_2	61.19	+ 23	+468 −294	+198 −102	+ 63 − 40	+ 752 − 413	51.24
U_2L_3	47.63	+ 4	+434 −125	+204 − 78	+ 77 − 48	+ 719 − 247	48.74
U_3L_4	39.27	− 11	+442 −118	+208 − 45	+ 95 − 60	+ 734 − 234	48.74
U_4L_5	35.16	− 17	+524 −336	+201 −142	+103 − 65	+ 811 − 560	54.24
U_5L_6	34.0	− 11	+790 −700	+274 −268	+ 53 − 33	+1106 −1012	73.44
U_0L_0	100.0	−120	−670 +326	−284 +102	− 50 + 31	−1124 + 339	76.24
U_1L_1	74.33	−111	−684 +258	−262 + 89	− 55 + 34	−1112 + 270	81.74
U_2L_2	53.33	− 85	−614 +174	−259 + 60	− 60 + 37	−1018 + 186	83.94
U_3L_3	37.0	− 69	−538 + 76	−228 + 29	− 61 + 38	− 896 + 74	59.19
U_4L_4	25.33	− 63	−494 +114	−171 + 54	− 54 + 34	− 782 + 139	51.24
U_5L_5	18.33	− 65	−536 +228	−168 + 48	− 25 + 16	− 794 + 227	53.44
U_6L_6	16.0	− 61	− 326	−186	0	− 573	40.00

Live Load Stresses from Cooper's E-75

FIG. 271.

It seems clear that, if an influence line for horizontal reaction is available, influence lines can be drawn step by step by moving a unit load from panel point to panel point and computing the stress in the various bars. That in general is the common procedure. Various devices are used to obtain a preliminary influence line for the horizontal reaction.

Figure 270 shows a twelve-panel, two-hinged, double-track railroad arch to be designed for Cooper's E–75. The preliminary influence line assumed for H is shown at (*b*) in the figure. Below the influence line for H are shown influence lines for stress in five typical bars, calculated by the fundamental method of placing a unit load at successive panel points. The student should check the influence lines shown and draw additional influence lines by the same procedure. The problem is evidently one in statics since the horizontal reaction can be taken from the influence line. For example, assume that the unit load is at U_3'; the horizontal reaction is then 0.540, and the vertical reaction at the left end is $\frac{3}{12}$ (=.25). The reactions being known, of course the stress in any bar may be calculated.

The live-load stresses may be calculated from the influence lines by the same methods suggested in the preceding article for the two-span truss. The dead-load stresses may be calculated either graphically or arithmetically. Two-hinged arches are frequently erected as three-hinged, and the dead-load stresses are then statically determined. Temperature stresses may be important in two-hinged arches, and it is necessary to estimate the probable reaction due to temperature change, but the methods of doing so cannot be discussed here.

The stresses determined for the arch in Fig. 270 are shown in the table in Fig. 271. The estimated dead-load panel concentrations are shown on the right-hand side of the arch in Fig. 270 (*a*), and the dead-load stresses were found assuming erection as a three-hinged arch. The areas based on the stresses in the table are shown in the last column of the table.

A tentative design, as shown in the last column of the table, having been prepared, the next step is to calculate the influence line for H based on that design. The influence line may be found from the deflected top chord due to a unit horizontal reaction when one end is on rollers as in the angle frame of Fig. 259, described in Art. 209. The stresses due to a unit horizontal reaction are shown on the left half of the arch in Fig. 270 (*a*), and the *relative* changes in length due to these stresses are shown on the half arch in Fig. 272 (*a*). The Williot diagram based on these relative changes in length is also shown in the figure.

The influence line for H, determined from the Williot diagram, is shown in Fig. 272 (*b*). The ordinates from the preliminary influence line, Fig. 270, are shown below in parentheses for comparison. The student should note in calculating the ordinates to

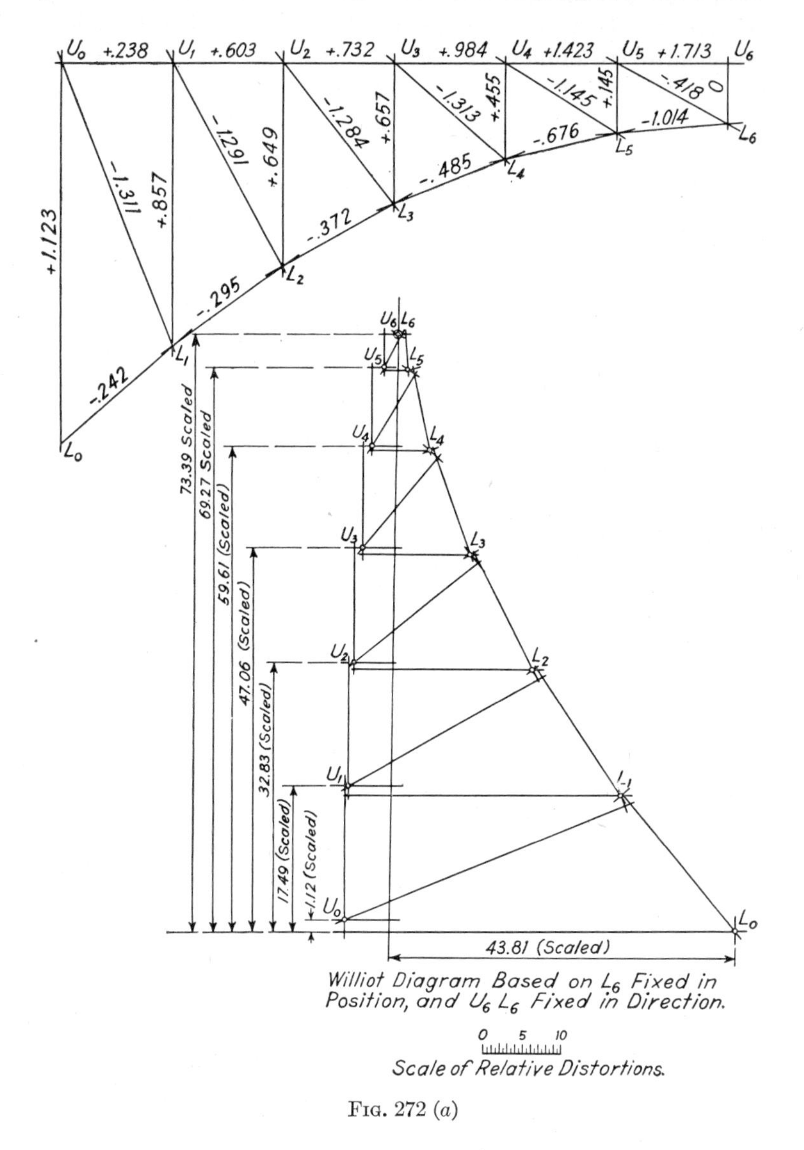

FIG. 272 (a)

the influence line that the distance 43.81 shown as the movement of L_0 is in fact only half the movement, since only half of the

Williot diagram is drawn. Since the other half of the diagram would be the same in magnitude of movements as that shown, the true horizontal movement of L_0 relative to L_0' is $2 \times 43.81 = 87.62$. Consequently the ordinate to the influence line at, say, U_2 is:

$$\frac{32.83}{87.62} = 0.375$$

The other ordinates are calculated in the same manner.

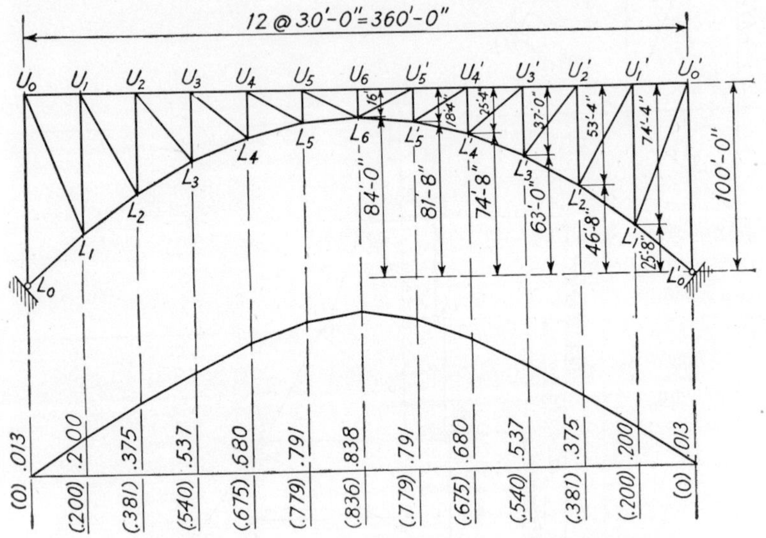

Influence Line for H Based on Areas Shown in Fig. 271

FIG. 272 (*b*)

It is obvious by inspection that there cannot be very serious changes in the design stresses shown in the table, Fig. 271, but the student should recalculate one or two influence lines for stress and compare the design stresses obtained therefrom with those shown in the table.

212. Secondary Stresses.—The problem of secondary stresses is so broad that it is only possible, or justifiable, in this book to give some indication of what the problem is and show by a very brief and elementary example the application of moment distribution in calculating secondary moments.

The secondary moments under consideration here are those in

the plane of the truss resulting from restraints which prevent changes in angles between the bars of the truss. These restraints may result from gusset plates or from friction between members and pins in the connections. The two-panel truss shown by heavy full lines in Fig. 273, when loaded at L_1, would deflect, and if the

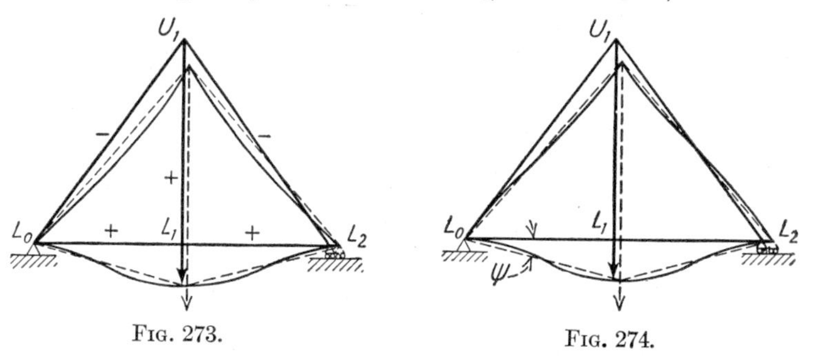

FIG. 273. FIG. 274.

connections were in fact frictionless pins would take the position shown to greatly exaggerated scale by the dotted lines. The angles $U_1L_0L_1$ and $L_0U_1L_1$ would increase, and the angle $U_1L_1L_0$ decrease, with corresponding changes in the other triangle. However, the members are actually connected by gusset plates which resist any tendency for the angles between the bars to change. Since the changes in length, and consequently the deflection, must take place, the bars of the truss will be forced to bend into the shape shown by light full lines in the figure. The moments accompanying the bending of the bars are the secondary moments in the plane of the truss, and flexural stresses resulting from these secondary moments are the so-called secondary stresses under consideration.

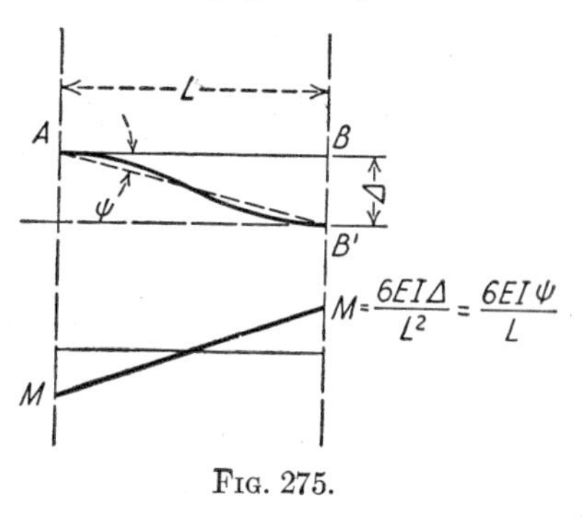

FIG. 275.

During the deflection of a truss the various bars and joints rotate even though the gusset plates prevent changes in angles between the bars. If we imagine the deflection and bar rotations to take place, but hold all joints parallel to their original positions, it is clear that the various bars will be bent into shapes as shown by

Fig. 274. Since all joints are presumed held parallel to their original positions the moments caused by deflection and rotation may be calculated from the relation previously developed and shown in Fig. 275. Having computed the moments at the ends of all members we may sum up those at each joint. In general we will find unbalanced moments at the joints, and if the joints are successively released the unbalanced moments will be distributed among the connecting members in proportion to their stiffnesses. Moments may then be "carried over" in accordance

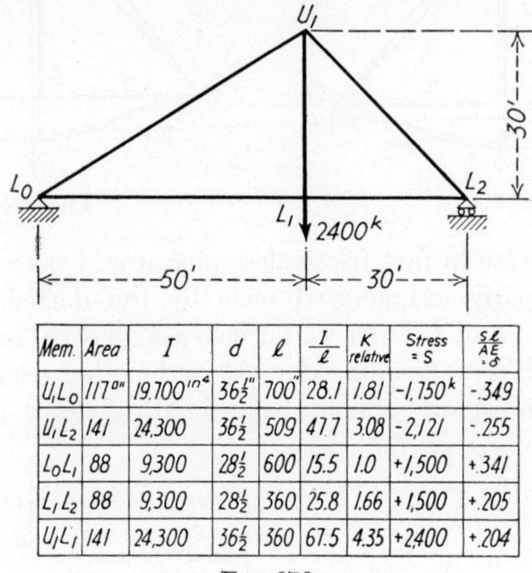

Mem.	Area	I	d	ℓ	$\frac{I}{\ell}$	K relative	Stress = S	$\frac{S\ell}{AE} = \delta$
U_1L_0	117□"	19,700 in⁴	$36\frac{1}{2}$"	700"	28.1	1.81	-1,750k	-.349
U_1L_2	141	24,300	$36\frac{1}{2}$	509	47.7	3.08	-2,121	-.255
L_0L_1	88	9,300	$28\frac{1}{2}$	600	15.5	1.0	+1,500	+.341
L_1L_2	88	9,300	$28\frac{1}{2}$	360	25.8	1.66	+1,500	+.205
U_1L_1	141	24,300	$36\frac{1}{2}$	360	67.5	4.35	+2400	+.204

Fig. 276.

with the usual moment distribution procedure and the process repeated to satisfactory convergence.

The procedure is illustrated by Figs. 276, 277, and 278. Figure 276 shows the truss and essential data concerning its members. In Fig. 277 the calculations of the angle changes are shown. The sketch at the top of the table in Fig. 278 shows the bar rotations based on the assumption that L_0L_1 is fixed in direction.[5] As will be noted, bar rotations have been called positive when clockwise and negative when counter-clockwise.

[5] It seems clear that any other bar could have been chosen as a reference line and the rotations calculated with reference thereto. For example, if U_1L_1 had been assumed fixed in direction the bar rotations would have been:

U_1L_0.....	+0.001778	L_0L_1.....	+0.002417
U_1L_2.....	−0.001070	L_1L_2.....	−0.002138

The moments due to bar rotations with joints held against rotation are computed from the relation shown in Fig. 275, and are recorded in the table. The quantity $6\frac{EI}{l}\psi$ would give the moment in inch-kips, since E was used as 30,000 kips per sq. in., and that factor has been divided by 12 to secure moments in foot-kips.

The distribution is carried out in tabular form, and the only comment necessary is to call attention to the sign convention.

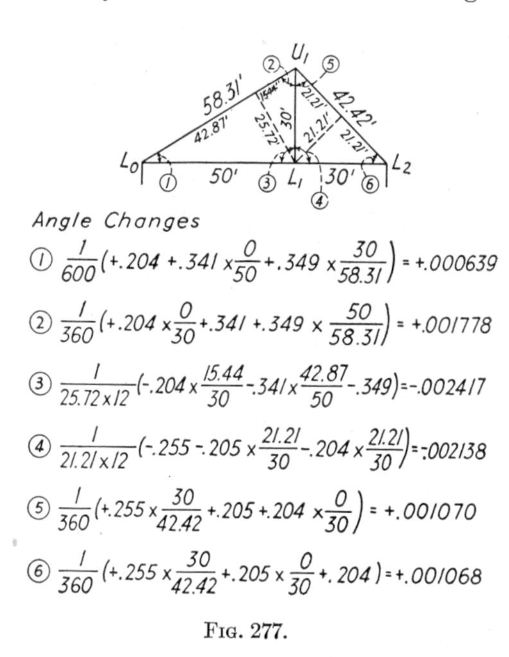

Fig. 277.

In calculations of this type a convention based on direction of joint rotation has some advantages. A moment which tends to rotate the joint clockwise is called positive and the reverse negative. This change in sign convention makes no difference in the moment distribution procedure, but the student should note that the carry-over moment has the same sign as the distributed moment.

Although the problem shown here is very simple the same method of attack will be adequate for any case. It should be noted, however, that when dealing with a symmetrical truss symmetrically loaded the center vertical or center line will not rotate; use of this member or line as the reference line will make it possible to limit the calculations to one half the truss.

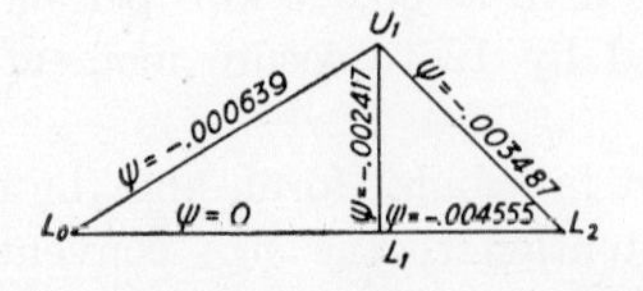

	Joint L_0			Joint U_1				Joint L_1				Joint L_2		
Member→	L_0U_1	L_0L_1		U_1L_0	U_1L_2	U_1L_1		L_1L_0	L_1U_1	L_1L_2		L_2L_1	L_2U_1	
$\frac{I}{l}$	28.1	15.5		28.1	47.7	67.5		15.5	67.5	25.8		25.8	47.7	
K (relative)	1.81	1.0	2.81	1.81	3.08	4.35	9.24	1.0	4.35	1.66	7.01	1.66	3.08	4.74
$\frac{K}{\Sigma K}$	.644	.356		.196	.333	.471		.143	.620	.237		.350	.650	
ψ	-.000639	0		-.000639	-.003487	-.002417		0	-.002417	-.004555		-.004555	-.003487	
$6E\frac{I}{l}\psi \div 12$	-269	—	-269	-269	-2495	-2447	-5211	—	-2447	-1763	-4210	-1763	-2495	-4258
1st Dist.	+173	+96	✓	+1021	+1736	+2454	✓	+602	+2610	+998	✓	+1490	+2768	✓
C. O.	+511	+301	+812	+87	+1384	+1305	+2776	+48	+1227	+745	+2020	+499	+868	+1367
2nd Dist.	-523	-289	✓	-544	-924	-1308	✓	-289	-1252	-479	✓	-478	-889	✓
C.O.	-272	-145	-417	-262	-445	-626	-1333	-145	-654	-239	-1038	-240	-462	-702
3rd Dist.	+269	+148	✓	+261	+444	+628	✓	+148	+644	+246	✓	+246	+456	✓
C.O.	+131	+74	+205	+135	+228	+322	+685	+74	+314	+123	+511	+123	+222	+345
4th Dist.	-132	-73	✓	-134	-228	-323	✓	-73	-317	-121	✓	-121	-224	✓
C.O.	-67	-37	-104	-66	-112	-159	-337	-37	-162	-62	-261	-62	-114	-176
5th Dist.	+67	+37	✓	+66	+112	+159	✓	+37	+162	+62	✓	+62	+114	✓
Moments	-112	+112		+295	-300	+5		+365	+125	-490		-244	+244	
Stress = $\frac{Mc}{I}$	1.25 k/□"	2.06		3.28	2.70	.045		6.71	1.13	9.01		4.49	2.20	

FIG. 278.

No attempt should be made to draw conclusions from the secondary stresses found in this case. The problem is presented merely as an exercise in applying moment distribution, and the results have no significance from any other point of view.

PROBLEMS

In the following problems, where the value of E is required, it should be assumed as 30,000 kips per sq. in. unless otherwise stated.

299. Calculate, by means of angle changes, the deflection of point L_1 of the structure shown.

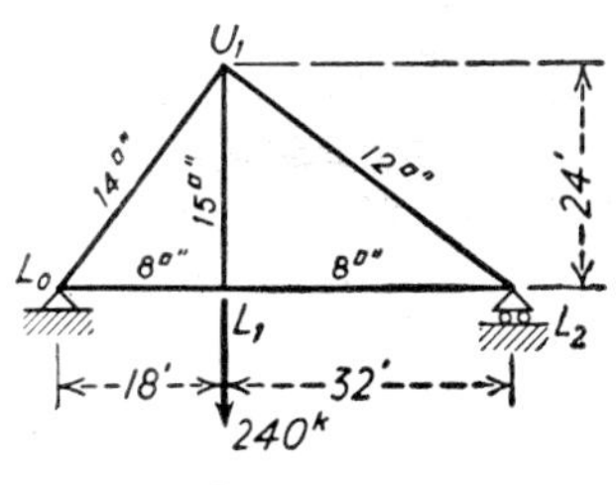

PROB. 299.

300. Assume that the truss in Problem 158 is so designed and loaded that the changes in length of the members are as follows. Each top chord member is shortened $\frac{3}{16}$ in. Each bottom chord member is lengthened $\frac{3}{16}$ in. The end posts U_1L_0 and U_7L_8 are shortened $\frac{1}{4}$ in. The diagonals are lengthened $\frac{3}{16}$ in. The hangers U_1L_1 and U_7L_7 are lengthened $\frac{1}{8}$ in. The vertical U_4L_4 is lengthened $\frac{1}{16}$ in. The other four verticals are shortened $\frac{1}{8}$ in. Calculate the deflection of each bottom chord panel point by means of angle changes.

301. Solve Problem 280 by means of virtual work.

302. Calculate the reactions for the structure shown, assuming equal areas for all bars.

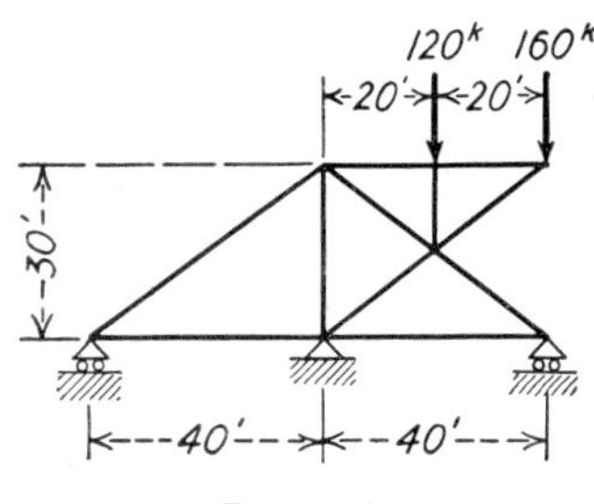

PROB. 302.

303. Solve Problem 299 by means of virtual work.

304. Determine the movement of each panel point in the truss of Problem 300 by means of a Williot diagram.

305. Calculate the stresses in all the bars of the truss shown.

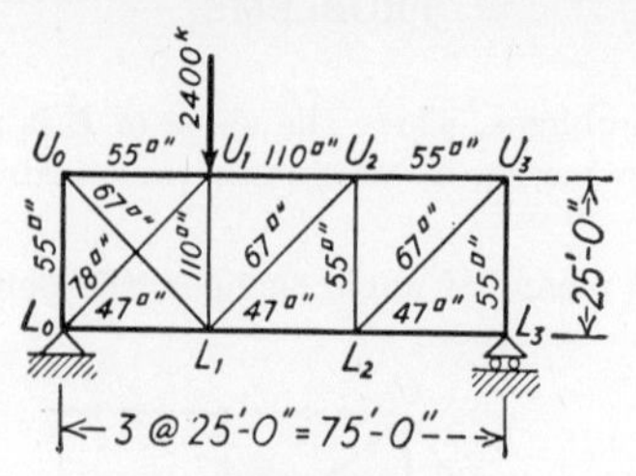

PROB. 305.

306. Calculate the deflection of panel points L_1 and L_2, in the truss of Problem 305, by means of angle changes.

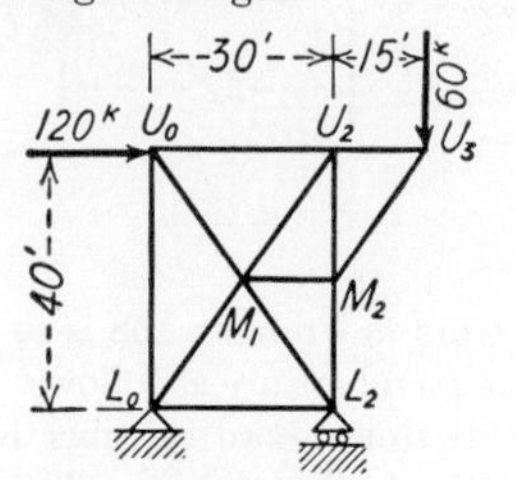

PROB. 307.

307. Assume all bars to have equal areas: 10.0 sq. in. each.

(*a*) Calculate the stress in L_0L_2 of the structure shown.

(*b*) The member L_0L_2 has been fabricated 0.25 in. short owing to an error in the shop. What stresses will be produced in the bars of the structure if L_0L_2 is forced into place in the erection?

308. Calculate the stresses in all the members of the structure shown with the load in the position shown.

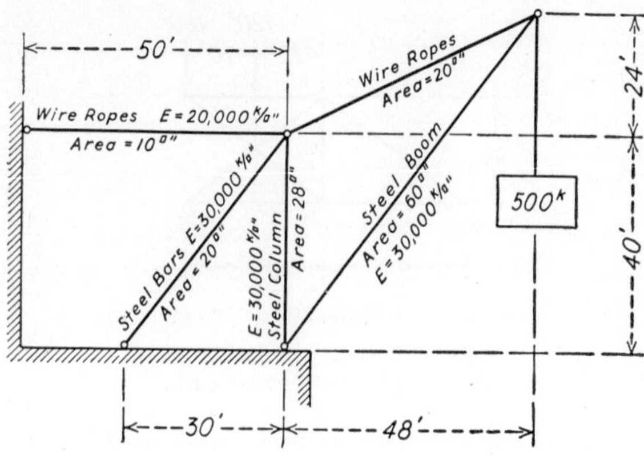

PROB. 308.

309. Determine the angle through which the boom, in Problem 308, rotates as the result of changes in length of the sides of the triangle of which it is a part.

310. Calculate the stress in the tie rods of the structure shown.

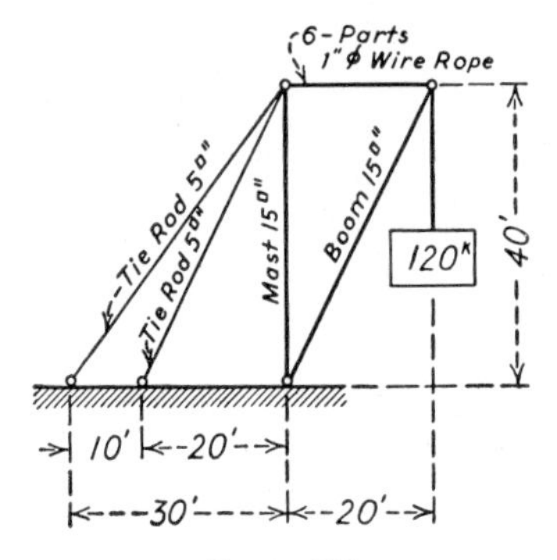

PROB. 310.

311. Calculate the stresses in the ties W_3U_3 and W_2U_2 of the structure shown. The gross areas of the bars of the truss are shown in the figure. The tie W_3U_3 is a wire cable having an area of 3.0 sq. in. and a modulus of elasticity of 20,000 kips per sq. in. The tie W_2U_2 is a steel bar having an area of 4.0 sq. in. and a modulus of elasticity of 30,000 kips per sq. in.

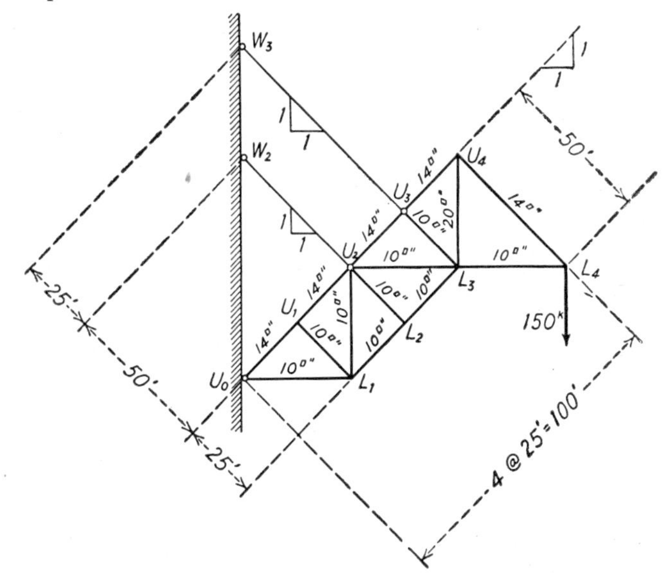

PROB. 311.

312. Calculate the reactions for the structure shown, assuming equal areas for all bars.

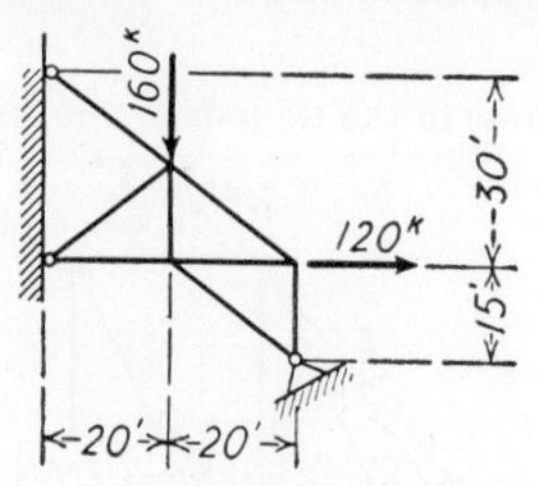

PROB. 312.

313. Calculate the stress in L_3R_2 and $L_1L_2L_3$ of the structure shown.

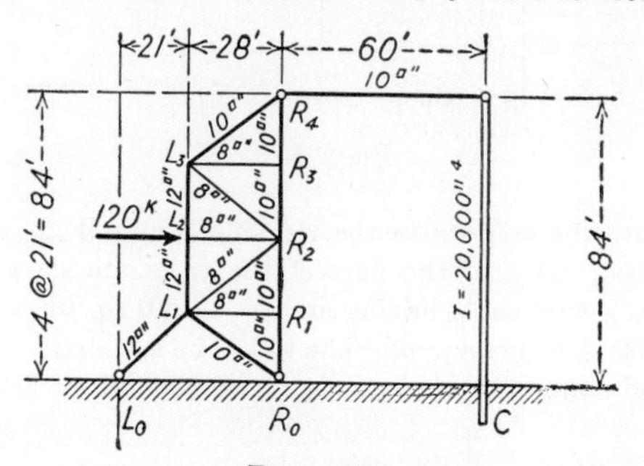

PROB. 313.

314. Calculate the angle changes in triangle $L_0L_1R_0$ of the structure in Problem 313.

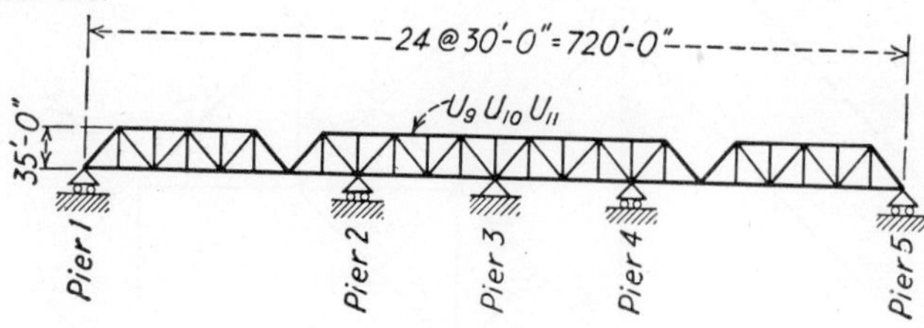

PROB. 315.

315. Assume that deflections of the structure shown are the same as for a beam having constant moment of inertia.

(*a*) Draw the influence line for reaction at Pier 3.

(*b*) Draw the influence line for stress in $U_9U_{10}U_{11}$.

(*c*) From the influence line for stress in $U_9U_{10}U_{11}$ calculate the maximum tension and the maximum compression in the bar due to a moving uniform load of 2,000 lb. per ft. plus a roving concentration of 60 kips.

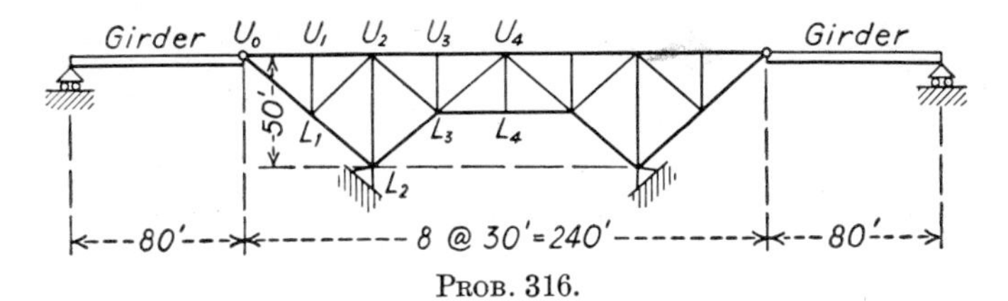

PROB. 316.

316. Assume equal areas in all the bars of the structure shown, and draw an influence line for H, giving all ordinates. Use a Williot diagram to obtain the panel-point movements needed to calculate the ordinates.

317. Calculate the stress in U_2L_3 of the arch shown in Fig. 272 (b) due to a load of 160 kips acting horizontally and to the right at L_1. Obtain the necessary information from the Williot diagram in Fig. 272 (a).

318. The two hinged arch shown in Fig. 272 (b) is loaded at U_3 with a vertical downward load of 240 kips, and at L_2 with a horizontal load acting to the right of 160 kips. Calculate the stress in U_3U_4 and U_4L_4. Obtain the necessary information from the influence line for H in Fig. 272 (b) and the Williot diagram in Fig. 272 (a).

319. If the arch of Problem 318 is supported by rollers on a horizontal plane at L_{12} and has a horizontal tie of 54 sq. in. gross area between L_0 and L_{12}, recalculate the stresses in the members asked for in Problem 318.

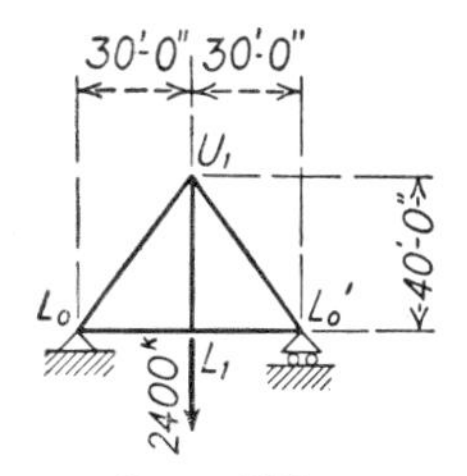

PROB. 320.

320. Calculate the secondary stresses in the structure shown. The members have the following properties, with the gravity axes at the centers of the members.

	$L_0L_1L'_0$	U_1L_0 and $U_1L'_0$	U_1L_1
Gross area....................	60.0 sq. in.	101.9 sq. in.	141.0 sq. in.
Moment of inertia.............	6370 in.^{4}	17,400 in.^{4}	24,300 in.^{4}
Distance b. to b. angles........	$30\frac{1}{2}$ in.	$36\frac{1}{2}$ in.	$36\frac{1}{2}$ in.

321. Add the secondary members M_1L_1 and M'_1L_1 to the structure in Problem 320, and recalculate the secondary stresses. Secondary members, two 15 in. channels @ 40 lb. $I = 693$ in.^{4}

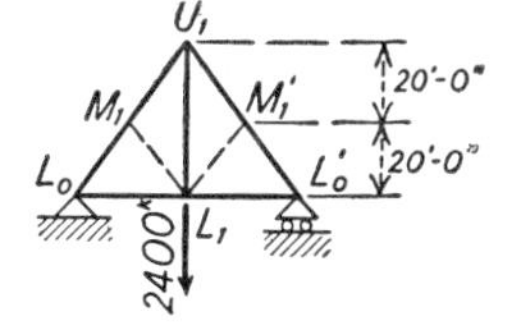

PROB. 321.

PROPERTIES OF TRIANGLES AND QUADRATIC PARABOLAS

The figure on page 497 gives simple relations for the areas into which moment diagrams may often be divided for convenience in calculation, and also the location in a horizontal direction of the centroids of such areas. The data shown will be helpful in calculating deflections and changes in slope of beams subjected to combinations of uniform and concentrated loading.

Most students remember the properties of a right triangle, and the data regarding a parabola shown in the lower right-hand corner of the figure. Many, however, do not recall the less frequently used relations.

The reader is cautioned against the common error of assuming that the relations between a rectangle and a parabola shown in the lower right-hand corner hold for any rectangle in which the ends of a diagonal lie on the parabola. It is not necessary to restrict the relations to a rectangle at the apex of the parabola, but one side of the rectangle must be tangent to the parabola and the parallel side a chord or semi-chord of the parabola. When the side parallel to the tangent is a semi-chord, of course, one diagonal of the rectangle is a chord of the parabola.

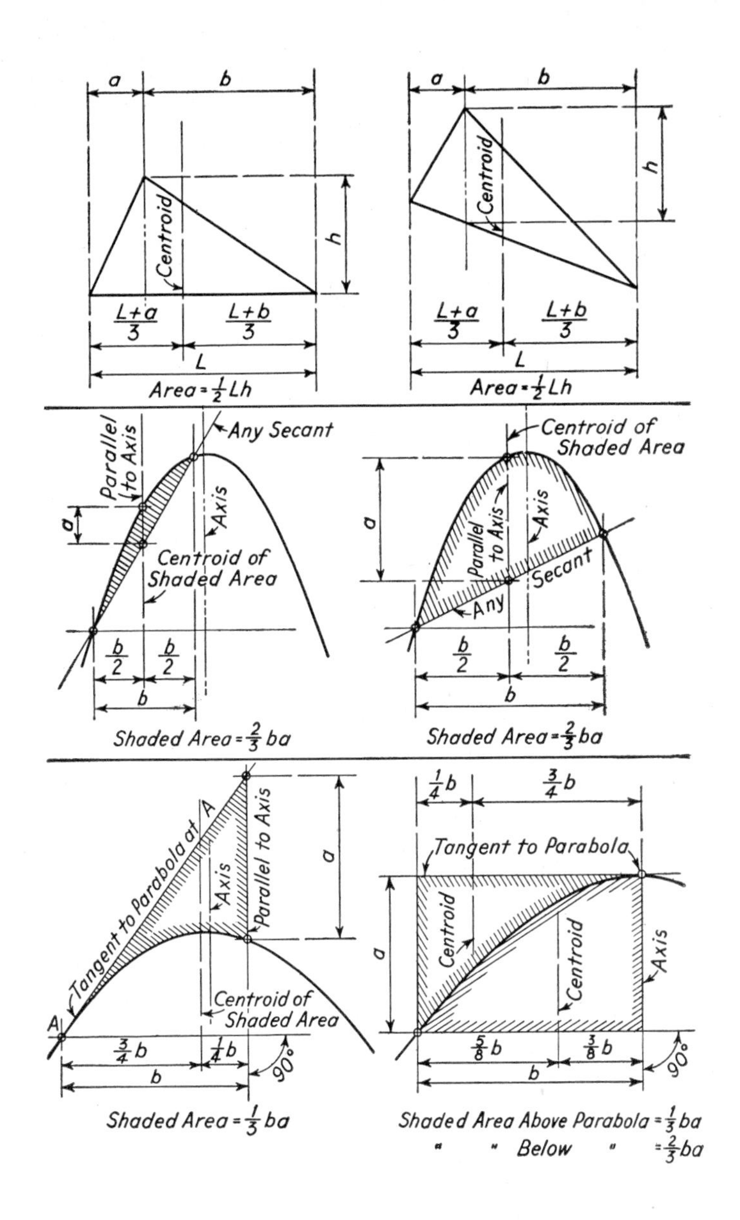
a
b
Centroid
h
$\frac{L+a}{3}$
$\frac{L+b}{3}$
L
Area = $\frac{1}{2}Lh$
a
b
Centroid
h
$\frac{L+a}{3}$
$\frac{L+b}{3}$
L
Area = $\frac{1}{2}Lh$
Parallel to Axis
Any Secant
Axis
a
Centroid of Shaded Area
$\frac{b}{2}$
$\frac{b}{2}$
b
Shaded Area = $\frac{2}{3}ba$
Centroid of Shaded Area
a
Parallel to Axis
Axis
Any Secant
$\frac{b}{2}$
$\frac{b}{2}$
b
Shaded Area = $\frac{2}{3}ba$
Tangent to Parabola at A
Axis
Parallel to Axis
a
Centroid of Shaded Area
A
$\frac{3}{4}b$
$\frac{1}{4}b$
b
90°
Shaded Area = $\frac{1}{3}ba$
$\frac{1}{4}b$
$\frac{3}{4}b$
Tangent to Parabola
a
Centroid
Centroid
Axis
$\frac{5}{8}b$
$\frac{3}{8}b$
b
90°
Shaded Area Above Parabola = $\frac{1}{3}ba$
" " Below " = $\frac{2}{3}ba$

INDEX

A

B